Solutions and Study Guide for

Algebra and Trigonometry
Fourth Edition

by
Lial/Miller

Eldon L. Miller
University of Mississippi

Scott, Foresman and Co.   •   Glenview, Illinois   •   London, England

ISBN 0-673-18297-5

1 2 3 4 5 6 - BKC - 90 89 88 87 86 85

CONTENTS

How to Use This Book

This Solutions and Study Guide is keyed to the chapters and sections of the text ALGEBRA AND TRIGONOMETRY, Fourth Edition, by Margaret L. Lial and Charles D. Miller.

The procedure for studying given below has proven beneficial for many students of differing backgrounds and abilities.

1. Read the textbook and go to class. Participate actively in class discussions. Feel free to ask questions.

2. Use the appropriate section or sections of this Solutions and Study Guide. The sections begin with additional examples. These examples have been chosen to complement the examples given in the text itself. Some of these examples also explore the theory in more detail. Study these additional examples as necessary.

3. Start working on the homework problems. Be sure to check your answers with those given in the back of the textbook. Be careful with these answers: sometimes the answer in the back is really the same as the one you have, but merely in a different form. For example, if you are asked to factor $-xy + 8x$, there are two possible answers: $x(-y + 8)$ and $-x(y - 8)$. The text will give only one of these, but both are equally correct.

4. If you have difficulty with the homework assignments, refer to the solutions given in this book. (The solutions come immediately after the additional examples for a given section.) We could not give solutions to all exercises, but we have tried to give solutions to all different types of exercises in a particular exercise set. Also, we have tried to give proofs to most of the exercises that require proofs.

5. At the end of a chapter, use the Chapter Review Exercises provided in the textbook. These exercises provide an excellent summary of the topics in the chapter.

6. If you feel that you need additional help, see your instructor or other people provided to help you.

7. Take the Chapter Test given at the end of each chapter in this book. These tests have been designed not for a time limit, but rather to test all the ideas in the chapter. The answers to the tests are given at the end of the book.

8. Take any tests required by your instructor.

CHAPTER 1   Fundamentals of Algebra

Section 1.1   The Real Numbers

Additional Examples

Example 1 Simplify the following expression.

$$\frac{-4(2 - 3) + (-3)(-12) \div 4 - (-3)}{15 \cdot 3 \div 9 \div 2 + 5 - 6 \div 3}$$

Solution We must treat the numerator and denominator separately. Care must be taken in the order of the operations. For the numerator we have,

$$-4(2 - 3) + (-3)(-12) \div 4 - (-3)$$
$$= [-4(-1)] + [(36) \div 4] + 3$$
$$= 4 + 9 + 3 = 16.$$

In the denominator,

$$15 \cdot 3 \div 9 \div 2 + 5 - 6 \div 3$$
$$= [(\frac{15 \cdot 3}{9}) \div 2] + 5 - (\frac{6}{3})$$
$$= [5 \div 2] + 5 - 2$$
$$= \frac{5}{2} + 5 - 2 = \frac{11}{2}$$

The numerator divided by the denominator gives

$$\frac{16}{11/2} = 16 \times \frac{2}{11} = \frac{16}{1} \times \frac{2}{11} = \frac{32}{11}.$$

Hence,

$$\frac{-4(2 - 3) + (-3)(-12 \div 4 - (-3)}{15 \cdot 3 \div 9 \div 2 + 5 - 6 \div 3} = \frac{32}{11}.$$

Example 2 Prove that $(ab)^{-1} = a^{-1}b^{-1}$ and then use this to show that $(x/y)^{-1} = y/x.$

Solution Using the definition that $u^{-1} = 1/u$, we have

$$(ab)^{-1} = \frac{1}{ab}, \quad a^{-1} = \frac{1}{a}, \quad \text{and } b^{-1} = \frac{1}{b}.$$

Hence,

$$a^{-1}b^{-1} = \frac{1}{a} \cdot \frac{1}{b} = \frac{1}{ab},$$

which equals $(ab)^{-1}$. This justifies that $(ab)^{-1} = a^{-1}b^{-1}$.

To show that $(x/y)^{-1} = y/x$, we observe that

$$\frac{x}{y} = x(\frac{1}{y}).$$

Then,

$$(\frac{x}{y})^{-1} = [x(\frac{1}{y})]^{-1}$$
$$= x^{-1}(\frac{1}{y})^{-1}$$
$$= \frac{1}{x} \cdot y = \frac{y}{x}.$$

Selected Solutions

1. $8 \cdot 9 = 9 \cdot 8$ is the commutative property of multiplication.

5. $-7 + 0 = -7$ is the identity property of addition.

9. This is a statement of the closure property of addition of two real numbers.

13. False, $8 \cdot 0 = 0$ is the multiplication property of zero.

17. False, 1 and 0 are both rational numbers but the quotient 1/0 is undefined.

21. The set $\{1, - 1\}$ is closed with respect to division since the quotients are $1 \div 1 = 1$, $1 \div (-1) = -1$, $(-1) \div 1 = -1$, and $(-1) \div (-1) = 1.$

25. The irrationals are not closed with respect to addition. Add $\sqrt{2}$ and $-\sqrt{2}$: $\sqrt{2} + (-\sqrt{2}) = 0.$ Zero is not an irrational number.

29. $\{0\}$ is closed for addition: $0 + 0 = 0.$

33. $9 \div 3 \cdot 4 \cdot 2 = 3 \cdot 4 \cdot 2$ multiply and
        $= 12 \cdot 2$ divided in order
        $= 24$ from left to right

37. $(-9 + 4 \cdot 3)(-7)$

$= (-9 + 12)(-7)$ work in parentheses
first

$= (3)(-7)$

$= -21$

41. $\dfrac{17 \div (3 \cdot 5 + 2) \div 8}{-6 \cdot 5 - 3 - 3(-11)}$

$= \dfrac{17 \div (15 + 2) \div 8}{-30 - 3 + 33}$ work numerator
and denominator
separately

$= \dfrac{17 \div 17 \div 8}{-33 + 33}$

$= \dfrac{1 \div 8}{0}$ This is not a real number

since division by zero is not
possible.

45.   12 satisfies a, b, c, d, and f;
natural, whole, integer, rational,
and real.

49. $-\dfrac{5}{9}$ satisfies d and f; rational and

real.

53. $-\sqrt{36}$ satisfies c, d, and f; integer,
rational, and real since $-\sqrt{36} = -6$.

57.   If $p = -2$ and $q = 4$, then
$7p - 4q + 10 = 7(-2) - 4(4) + 10 =$
$-14 - 16 + 10 = -20$.

61.   If $p = -2$, $q = 4$, and $r = -5$, then
$\dfrac{q + r}{q + p} = \dfrac{4 + (-5)}{4 + (-2)} = \dfrac{-1}{2}$.

65.   If $p = -2$, $q = 4$, and $r = -5$, then
$\dfrac{\frac{q}{4} - \frac{r}{5}}{\frac{p}{2} + \frac{q}{2}} = \dfrac{\frac{4}{4} - \frac{(-5)}{5}}{\frac{(-2)}{2} + \frac{4}{2}} = \dfrac{1 + 1}{-1 + 2} = \dfrac{2}{1} = 2$.

68.   If $p = -2$, $q = 4$, and $r = -5$, then
$\dfrac{\frac{2}{p + 1} + \frac{1}{q - 2}}{\frac{1}{r + 2} - \frac{1}{q + 2}} = \dfrac{\frac{2}{-2 + 1} + \frac{1}{4 - 2}}{\frac{1}{-5 + 2} - \frac{1}{4 + 2}}$

$= \dfrac{-2 + \frac{1}{2}}{-\frac{1}{3} - \frac{1}{6}}$

$= \dfrac{-\frac{3}{2}}{-\frac{3}{6}} = \dfrac{-3}{2} \cdot \dfrac{-6}{3} = 3$.

69. $a + (b \cdot c) = (a + b)(a + c)$ is
false. Take $a = 1$, $b = 2$, $c = 3$.
The left hand side is $a + (b \cdot c) =$
$1 + (2 \cdot 3) = 1 + 6 = 7$.
The right hand side is
$(a + b)(a + c) = (1 + 2)(1 + 3)$
$= 3 \cdot 4 = 12$.

73. $-a(b) = -(ab)$
Proof:
$-a(b) + ab = (-a + a)b$ distributive
property

$(-a + a)b = 0 \cdot b$ since $-a + a = 0$
(inverse property)

$0 \cdot b = 0$ multiplication
property of 0

Thus, $-a(b) + ab = 0$ and so $-a(b)$
is the additive inverse of ab. But
$-(ab)$ is also the additive inverse
of ab. By the uniqueness of the
additive inverse, it must be true
that $-a(b) = -(ab)$.

74. $(-a)(-b) = ab$
Proof:
$b + (-b) = 0$ by inverse property
of addition

$-a(b + (-b)) = a \cdot 0$

$= 0$, since $x \cdot 0 = 0$
for any x

$-a(b + (-b)) = -a \cdot b + (-a)(-b)$ by
the distributive property.
Thus, $-a \cdot b + (-a)(-b) = 0$.
   But, $a \cdot b + (-a \cdot b) = 0$.
   Hence, $(-a)(-b) = a \cdot b$ from
the uniqueness of the additive
inverse.

75. $a \cdot 0 = 0$

Proof:

$a(0 + 0) = a \cdot 0$, since $0 + 0 = 0$.

By the distributive law,

$$a(0 + 0) = a \cdot 0 + a \cdot 0$$

Thus, $a \cdot 0 + a \cdot 0 = a \cdot 0$

Add $-(a \cdot 0)$ to both sides to get

$$a \cdot 0 + a \cdot 0 + (-(a \cdot 0)) = a \cdot 0 + (-(a \cdot 0)).$$

Hence $a \cdot 0 = 0$,   since

$$a \cdot 0 + (-(a \cdot 0)) = 0.$$

76. If $a = b$ then $a + c = b + c$.

Proof:

$a = b$	is given
$a + c = a + c$	since a quantity equals itself
$a + c = b + c$	substitution property

77. If $a = b$ then $ac = bc$.

Proof:

$a = b$	is given
$ac = ac$	since a quantity equals itself
$ac = bc$	substitution property

78. If $ab = 0$ then either

$a = 0$ or $b = 0$.

Proof:

Suppose $a \neq 0$.

There is some number $1/a$ such that $a \cdot (1/a) = 1$, by inverse property of multiplication.

$ab = 0$	given
$\frac{1}{a}(ab) = \frac{1}{a} \cdot 0$	from Exercise 77
$(\frac{1}{a} \cdot a) \cdot b = 0$	since $1/a \cdot 0 = 0$ and

by the associative property of multiplication

$1 \cdot b = 0$	since $1/a \cdot a = 1$
$b = 0$	identity property

79. $ab(a^{-1} + b^{-1})$

$= (ab)a^{-1} + (ab)b^{-1}$ distributive law

$= a^{-1}(ab) + a(bb^{-1})$ distributive law

$= a^{-1}(ab) + a(bb^{-1})$ commutative law and associative law

$= (a^{-1}a)b + a$ associative law and definition of identity

$= b + a$

80. $(a + b)(a^{-1} + b^{-1})$

$= (a + b)a^{-1} + (a + b)b^{-1}$ distributive law

$= aa^{-1} + ba^{-1} + ab^{-1} + bb^{-1}$ distributive law

$= 1 + ba^{-1} + ab^{-1} + 1$ definition of identity

$= 2 + ba^{-1} + ab^{-1}$

81. The product of two irrational numbers can be rational since $\sqrt{2} \cdot \sqrt{2} = 2$. Also, the product of two irrational numbers can be irrational since $\sqrt{2} \cdot \sqrt{3} = \sqrt{6}$, and $\sqrt{6}$ is an irrational number.

82. Let r_1 and r_2 be two rational numbers. The average of r_1 and r_2 is $\frac{r_1 + r_2}{2} = \frac{1}{2}r_1 + \frac{1}{2}r_2$.

$\frac{1}{2}r_1$ and $\frac{1}{2}r_2$ are both rational and the sum of two rationals is rational.

Thus, the average $\frac{r_1 + r_2}{2}$ is rational.

The average of the irrational numbers $-\sqrt{2}$ and $\sqrt{2}$ is $\frac{-\sqrt{2} + \sqrt{2}}{2}$

$= \frac{0}{2} = 0$, which is rational. However the average of the two irrational numbers $\frac{1}{\sqrt{2}}$ and $\sqrt{2}$ is

$$\frac{\frac{1}{\sqrt{2}} + \sqrt{2}}{2} \cdot \frac{\sqrt{2}}{\sqrt{2}} = \frac{1 + 2}{2\sqrt{2}} = (\frac{3}{2\sqrt{2}}) \cdot \frac{\sqrt{2}}{\sqrt{2}}$$

$$= \frac{3\sqrt{2}}{4} = \frac{3}{4}\sqrt{2}, \text{ which is irrational.}$$

Section 1.2   The Number Line and Absolute Value

Additional Examples

Example 1   If $A = 3 - \pi$, $B = \sqrt{11} - 3$,
and $C = \sqrt{11} - \pi$, find   (a) $d(A, B)$,
(b) $d(A, C)$,   (c) $d(B, C)$

Solution   We have,

(a) $d(A, B) = |A - B|$
$= |(3 - \pi) - (\sqrt{11} - 3)|$
$= |3 - \pi - \sqrt{11} + 3|$
$= |6 - \pi - \sqrt{11}|$
$= |6 - (\pi + \sqrt{11})|$
$= \pi + \sqrt{11} - 6,$

since $\pi > 3$ and $\sqrt{11} > 3$ implies
that $\pi + \sqrt{11} > 6.$

Example 1

(b) $d(A, C) = |A - C|$
$= |(3 - \pi) - (\sqrt{11} - \pi)|$
$= |3 - \pi - \sqrt{11} + \pi|$
$= |3 - \sqrt{11}|$
$= \sqrt{11} - 3,$

since $\sqrt{11} > 3.$

(c) $d(B, C) = |B - C|$
$= |(\sqrt{11} - 3) - (\sqrt{11} - \pi)|$
$= |\sqrt{11} - 3 - \sqrt{11} + \pi|$
$= |-3 + \pi|$
$= |\pi - 3|$
$= \pi - 3, \text{ since } \pi > 3.$

Example 2   If $|a| > |b|$, what can be
said about the numbers a and b?
Show that if $|a| < b$, then
$-b < a < b.$

Solution   For any real number r, $|r|$
denotes the distance r lies from
zero. Hence, $|a| > |b|$ implies
that a is further away from the
number 0 than b.

In considering the inequality
$|a| < b$, b cannot be negative or
zero since $|a|$ is a nonnegative
number. Therefore, b is positive.
The inequality $|a| < b$ implies
that a is closer to zero than b.
a can be to the left of zero or to
the right, but closer to zero than
b. Since -b is the same distance
from 0 as b, then a can lie any-
where between -b and b. That is,
$-b < a < b.$ This shows that $|a| <$
b implies that $-b < a < b.$

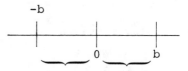

Selected Solutions

1.   -9, -4, -2, 3, 8

5.   -5, -4, -2, $-\sqrt{3}$, $\sqrt{6}$, $\sqrt{8}$, 3

9.   Since $|-8 + 2| = |-6| = 6$,
$-|3| = -3$, $- |-2| + (-3) = -5$,
$- |-2| = -2$, and $- |-8| - |-6| =$
$-8 - 6 = -14$, the numerical order
is $- |-8| - |-6|$, $- |-2| + (-3)$,
$-|3|$, $- |-2|$, $|-8 + 2|$.

13.   If $y = -4$ and $y = 2$, then
$|x - y| = |(-4) - 2| = |-6| = 6.$

17.   If $x = -4$ and $y = 2$, then
$|-4x + y| - |y| = |-4(-4) + 2| -$
$|2| = |16 + 2| -2 = 18 - 2 = 16.$

21. If $x = -4$ and $y = 2$, then

$$\frac{x\big|-2 + y + |x|\big|}{|x + 3|} = \frac{(-4)\big|-2 + 2 + |-4|\big|}{|(-4 + 3|}$$

$$= \frac{(-4)\big|-2 + 2 + 4\big|}{|-1|} = \frac{(-4)(4)}{1} = -16.$$

23. $|-6| = 6$

25. $-|-8| + |-2| = -8 + 2 = -6$

27. Since $\sqrt{64} = 8$ we have $8 > \sqrt{50}$, or $8 - \sqrt{50} > 0$. Hence, $|8 - \sqrt{50}| = 8 - \sqrt{50}.$

31. Since $\pi > 3$, we have $\pi - 3 > 0$. Hence, $|\pi - 3| = \pi - 3$.

35. If $k < 4$, then $2k < 8$ so that $2k - 8 < 0$ and $8 - 2k > 0$. Therefore, $|2k - 8| = 8 - 2k$, when $k < 4$.

39. If $m > -2$, then $m + 2 > 0$ and hence, $-4(m + 2) = -4m - 8 < 0$. Therefore $|-8 - 4m| = -(-8 - 4m) = 8 + 4m.$

41. If $x < y$, then $x - y < 0$ and $y - x > 0$. Therefore, $|x - y| = y - x.$

43. For all real numbers x we have $x^2 \geq 0$, so that $3 + x^2 > 0$. Therefore, $|3 + x^2| = 3 + x^2$ for all real x.

45. For all real p we have $p^2 \geq 0$, so that $-p^2 \leq 0$ and $-1 - p^2 < 0$. Therefore, $|-1 - p^2| = -(-1 - p^2) = 1 + p^2.$

49. Since $\sqrt{7} > 2$, we have $|\sqrt{7} - 2| = \sqrt{7} - 2$. Therefore, $|\sqrt{7} - 2| + 1 = \sqrt{7} - 2 + 1 = \sqrt{7} - 1.$

51. If $3 < m < 4$, then $m - 3 > 0$ and $4 - m > 0$. Therefore $|m - 3| + |m - 4| = (m - 3) + (4 - m) = 1.$

55. If $A = -3$; $B = -5$; $C = -12$; $D = -3$, then
    (a) $d(A, B) = |-3 - (-5)|$
    $$= |-3 + 5|$$
    $$= |2| = 2$$
    (b) $d(B, C) = |-5 - (-12)|$
    $$= |-5 + 12|$$
    $$= |7| = 7$$
    (c) $d(B, D) = |-5 - (-3)|$
    $$= |-5 + 3|$$
    $$= |-2| = 2$$
    (d) $d(D, A) = |-3 - (-3)|$
    $$= |-3 + 3|$$
    $$= |0| = 0$$
    (e) $d(A, B) + d(B, C)$
    $$= 2 + d(B, C) \quad \text{(see part (a))}$$
    $$= 2 + 7 = 9 \quad \text{(see part (b))}$$

57. If $2k < 8$, then $k < 4$ by using the Multiplicative Property of Order and multiplying by $\frac{1}{2}$.

59. If $-4x < 24$, then $x > -6$ by using the Multiplicative Property of Order and multiplying by $-\frac{1}{4}$.

63. $|8 + m| \leq |8| + |m|$ is valid using the triangle inequality.

67. $\left|\frac{-12}{5}\right| = \frac{|-12|}{|5|}$ is valid using the division property of absolute values.

69. The statement that if p is a real number, then $p < 5$, $p > 5$, or $p = 5$ is valid since for all p we must have $|p - 5| \geq 0$. If $|p - 5| = 0$, then $p = 5$. If $|p - 5| > 0$, then either $p > 5$ or $p < 5$.

73. $|x + y| = |x| = |y|$

This will be true if $y = 0$, for then $|x + y| = |x + 0| = |x|$ and $|x| - |y| = |x| - |0| = |x| - 0 = |x|$.

This will also be true if $x + y = 0$. Then $|x + y| = 0$; $x = -y$ (since $x + y = 0$), so that $|x| = |-y| = |y|$.

Therefore $|x| - |y| = 0$ and $x + y = |x| - |y|$.

Finally, it will be true if $x > 0 > y$ and $|x| > |y|$, for then $x + y > 0$ so that $|x + y| = x + y$ and $|x| - |y| = x - (-y) = x + y$.

77. Evaluate $\dfrac{|x|}{x}$ if $x \neq 0$.

Case I: If $x < 0$, then $|x| = -x$, so that $\dfrac{|x|}{x} = \dfrac{-x}{x} = 1$.

Case II: If $x > 0$, then $|x| = x$, so that $\dfrac{|x|}{x} = \dfrac{x}{x} = 1$.

79. Evaluate $\left|\dfrac{x - y}{y - x}\right|$ if $y - x \neq 0$ [i.e. $y \neq x$]. Since $y - x = -(x - y)$, we have

$$\left|\frac{x - y}{y - x}\right| = \left|-\frac{x - y}{x - y}\right| = |-1| = 1.$$

81. $|-a| = |a|$

Proof: By definition,

$$|x| = \begin{cases} x \text{ if } x \geq 0 \\ -x \text{ if } x < 0. \end{cases}$$

If $x = a \neq 0$, then

$$|a| = \begin{cases} a \text{ if } a > 0 \\ -a \text{ if } a < 0. \end{cases}$$

If $x = -a \neq 0$, then

$$|a| = \begin{cases} (-a) \text{ if } -a > 0 \\ -(-a) \text{ if } -a < 0 \end{cases} = \begin{cases} -a \text{ if } a < 0 \\ a \text{ if } a > 0 \end{cases}$$

But then $|a| = |-a|$ for $a \neq 0$.
If $a = 0$ then $|a| = |-a| = 0$.

82. $|a - b| = |b - a|$

Proof: $|a - b| = |-(b - a)| = |b - a|$ from Exercise 81.

83. $|a| \cdot |b| = |ab|$

Proof: Case 1: If $a > 0$, $b > 0$, then $|a| = a$ and $|b| = b$, so that $|a| \cdot |b| = a \cdot b = ab$. Since $a > 0$ and $b > 0$, $a\,b > 0$. Therefore, $|ab| = ab$ and $|a| \cdot |b|$ $|ab|$.

Case 2: If $a > 0$, $b < 0$, then $|a| = a$, $|b| = -b$. Therefore, $|a||b| = a(-b) = -(ab)$. Since $a > 0$ and $b < 0$, $ab < 0$. Therefore, $|ab| = -(ab)$ and $|a| \cdot |b| = |ab|$.

Case 3: If $a < 0$, $b < 0$, then $|a| = -a$, $|b| = -b$.
So $|a| \cdot |b| = (-a)(-b) = ab$. Since $a < 0$, $b < 0$, $ab > 0$ so that $|ab| = ab$. Hence, $|a| \cdot |b| = |ab|$.

Case 4: If $a < 0$ and $b < 0$, then $|a| = -a$ and $|b| = -b$. Also $ab > 0$ so that $|ab| = ab$, then $|a||b| = (-a)(-b) = ab = |ab|$.

Case 5: If either $a = 0$ or $b = 0$, equality holds.

85. $-|a| \leq a \leq |a|$

Proof: Case 1: If $a = 0$, then $|a| = 0$ and $-|a| = 0$, so $0 \leq 0 \leq 0$ is true.

Case 2: If $a > 0$, then $|a| = a$ and $-|a| < 0 < a$. Since $-|a| < a = |a|$, it is certainly true that $-|a| \leq a \leq |a|$ for the case $a > 0$.

Case 3: If $a < 0$, then $|a| = -a$ and so, $a = -|a|$. Therefore $-|a| = a < |a|$. Again, it follows that $-|a| \leq a \leq |a|$.

86. $|a + b| \leq |a| + |b|$

    Proof: Using the right hand inequality in exercise 85, $a \leq |a|$ and $b \leq |b|$ so that $2ab \leq 2|a||b|$. Since $a^2 = |a|^2$ and $b^2 = |b|^2$, add each of these to both sides of the inequality and arrive at $a^2 + 2ab + b^2 \leq |a|^2 + 2|a||b| + |b|^2$, $(a + b)^2 \leq (|a| + |b|)^2$. Take square roots: $|a + b| \leq |a| + |b|$ (We use the fact that $\sqrt{x^2} = |x|$.)

87. $d(A, B) = d(B, A)$

    Proof:

    $d(A, B) = |a - b|$ (definition)
    $\qquad = |b - a|$ (problem 48)
    $\qquad = d(B, A)$ (definition of $d(B, A)$).

88. $d(A, B) \geq 0$

    Proof:

    $d(A, B) = |a - b| \geq 0$ by definition of absolute value.

89. $d(A, 0) = |a - 0| = |a|$

90. $d(A, A) = |a - a| = |0| = 0$

91. Suppose $x^2 \leq 81$. Then it must be true that $x \leq 9$ since letting $x > 9$ means that $x^2 > 81$.

92. Suppose $x^2 \geq 81$. In this case we cannot conclude that $x \geq 9$ because letting $x = -10$ gives $x^2 = 100 > 81$.

93. Consider $\frac{1}{x} < x$ for $x \neq 0$.

    Case 1: If $x < 0$, then multiplying by x gives $1 > x^2$. Thus $\sqrt{x^2} = |x| < 1$. If $x < 0$ and $|x| < 1$, then we must have $-1 < x < 0$.

    Case 2: If $x > 0$, then multiplying by x gives $1 < x^2$. Thus, $\sqrt{x^2} = |x| > 1$. If $x > 0$ and $|x| > 1$, then we must have $x > 1$.

    Hence, the inequality $\frac{1}{x} < x$ holds for all real numbers x such that either $-1 < x < 0$ or $x > 1$.

94. Consider $x < x^2$ for $x \neq 0$.

    Case 1: If $x < 0$, then $\frac{1}{x} < 0$ and multiplying both sides by $\frac{1}{x}$ gives $1 > x$ or $x < 1$. Hence, every real number x with $x < 0$ satisfies $x < x^2$.

    Case 2: If $x > 0$, then $\frac{1}{x} > 0$ and multiplying both sides by $\frac{1}{x}$ gives $1 < x$ or $x > 1$. Thus, every real number x with $x > 1$ satisfies $x < x^2$.

    We conclude that the inequality $x < x^2$ holds for all real numbers x such that either $x < 0$ or $x > 1$.

Section 1.3 Integer Exponents

Additional Examples

Example 1   Simplify the fraction

$$\left[\frac{(2c^{-3}t^4)^2 z^{-7}}{(ct^2)^{-3} 4z^{-2}} \right]^{-3}$$

by expressing it with only positive exponents.

Solution   Using the properties of exponents, we have

$$\left[\frac{(2c^{-3}t^4)^2 z^{-7}}{(ct^2)^{-3} 4z^{-2}} \right]^{-3}$$

$$= \left[\frac{4c^{-6}t^8 z^{-7}}{4c^{-3}t^{-6} z^{-2}} \right]^{-3}$$

$$= [c^{-6+3} t^{8+6} z^{-7+2}]^{-3}$$

$$= [c^{-3} t^{14} z^{-5}]^{-3}$$

$$= c^9 t^{-42} z^{15}$$

$$= \frac{c^9 z^{15}}{t^{42}}.$$

This is the desired simplification.

Example 2   Simplify

$$\left(\frac{2a}{3}\right)^{-2} - \left[\frac{3b^{-3}}{2b^{-1}}\right]^2$$

as a single fraction having only positive exponents.

Solution   We can see that

$$\left(\frac{2a}{3}\right)^{-2} = \left[\left(\frac{2a}{3}\right)^{-1}\right]^2 = \left(\frac{3}{2a}\right)^2 = \frac{9}{4a^2},$$

since $(n/d)^{-1} = d/n$.   Also,

$$\left(\frac{3b^{-3}}{2b^{-1}}\right)^2 = \left(\frac{3}{2b^{3-1}}\right)^2 = \left(\frac{3}{2b^2}\right)^2 = \frac{9}{4b^4}.$$

Hence, we have

$$\left(\frac{2a}{3}\right)^{-2} - \left(\frac{3b^{-3}}{2b^{-1}}\right)^2 = \left(\frac{3}{2a}\right)^2 - \left(\frac{3}{2b^2}\right)^2$$

$$= \frac{9}{4a^2} - \frac{9}{4b^4}.$$

A common denominator of the two fractions is $4a^2b^4$ so that

$$\left(\frac{2a}{3}\right)^{-2} - \left(\frac{3b^{-3}}{2b^{-1}}\right)^2 = \frac{9}{4a^2} \cdot \frac{b^4}{b^4} - \frac{9}{4b^4} \cdot \frac{a^2}{a^2}$$

$$= \frac{9b^4}{4a^2 b^4} - \frac{9a^2}{4a^2 b^4}$$

$$= \frac{9b^4 - 9a^2}{4a^2 b^4}.$$

Example 3   Simplify the expression

$$\frac{(x+2)^k (2+x)^{3-2k}}{(x+2)^{-3k} (-2-x)^2},$$

where k is a positive integer.

Solution   Since $(-2-x) = -(2+x)$
$= -(x+2)$, then $(-2-x)^2 = [-(2+x)]^2$
$= (x+2)^2$.   Then we have,

$$\frac{(x+2)^k (2+x)^{3-2k}}{(x+2)^{-3k} (-2-x)^2}$$

$$= (x+2)^k (x+2)^{3-2k} (x+2)^{3k} (x+2)^{-2}$$

$$= (x+2)^{k+(3-2k)+3k-2}$$

$$= (x+2)^{2k+1}$$

Example 4   Assume that m and n are positive integers and simplify the expression

$$\frac{(3x^{2m})(2x^{2-m})^2 (y^n)^{-2}}{(2y^{2-3n})(y^{n-2})^2 (x^{-m})^{-1}}$$

Solution   Using the properties of exponents we have

$$\frac{(3x^{2m})(2x^{2-m})^2 (y^n)^{-2}}{(2y^{2-3n})(y^{n-2})^2 (x^{-m})^{-1}}$$

$$= \frac{3x^{2m} \cdot 4x^{2(2-m)} y^{-2n}}{2y^{2-3n} \cdot y^{2(n-2)} x^m}$$

$$= \frac{12x^{2m+4-2m} y^{-2n}}{2y^{2-3n+2n-4} x^m}$$

$$= \frac{6x^4 y^{-2n}}{y^{-n-2} x^m}$$

$$= \frac{6x^{4-m}}{y^{-n-2+2n}}$$

$$= \frac{6x^{4-m}}{y^{n-2}}.$$

This is a simplification of the given expression, but there are two cases to consider if we want our answers to have nonnegative exponents.   If m = 1, 2, 3, or 4, the answer above is correct.   However, if m > 4, we simplify to arrive at

$$\frac{6}{x^{m-4} y^{n-2}}.$$

How would we write this result if n < 2?

Selected Solutions

1. $15^3 = 15 \cdot 15 \cdot 15 = 3375$

5. $4^{-1} + {}^{-3} = \frac{1}{4} + \frac{1}{3^3}$

$$= \frac{1}{4} + \frac{1}{27}$$

$$= \frac{27}{108} + \frac{4}{108}$$

$$= \frac{31}{108}$$

9. $\left(\frac{1}{2}\right)^{-3} = \frac{1}{\left(\frac{1}{2}\right)^3}$ or $\left(\frac{1}{2}\right)^{-3} = \left(\frac{2}{1}\right)^3$

$$= \frac{1}{\frac{1}{8}} \qquad\qquad = 2^3$$

$$\qquad\qquad\qquad = 8$$

$$= 8$$

13. $\frac{12}{10^{-2}} = \frac{12}{\frac{1}{10^2}} = \frac{12}{1} \cdot \frac{10^2}{1} = 1200$

17. $(3m)^2(-2m)^3 = 3^2 m^2 \cdot (-2)^3 m^3$

$$= 9(-8)m^5$$

$$= -72m^5$$

21. $5^3(5^{-5})(5^{-2}) = 5^{3+(-5)+(-2)}$

$$= 5^{-4}$$

$$= \frac{1}{5^4}$$

$$= \frac{1}{625}$$

25. $\frac{(d^{-1})(d^{-2})}{(d^8)(d^{-3})} = \frac{d^{-1+(-2)}}{d^{8+(-3)}}$

$$= \frac{d^{-3}}{d^5}$$

$$= d^{-3-5}$$

$$= d^{-8}$$

$$= \frac{1}{d^8}$$

29. $\frac{(4+s)^3(4+s)^{-2}}{(4+s)^{-5}}$

$$= (4+s)^{3+(-2)-(-5)} = (4+s)^6$$

33. $\left(\frac{a^{-1}}{b^2}\right)^{-3} = \frac{(a^{-1})^{-3}}{(b^2)^{-3}} = \frac{a^{(-1)(-3)}}{b^{2(-3)}}$

$$= \frac{a^3}{b^{-6}} = a^3 b^6$$

37. $\frac{(3^{-1}m^{-2}n^2)^{-2}}{(mn)^{-1}} = \frac{(3^{-1})^{-2}(m^{-2})^{-2}(n^2)^{-2}}{m^{-1}n^{-1}}$

$$= \frac{3^2 m^4 n^{-4}}{m^{-1}n^{-1}} = \frac{9m^5}{n^3}$$

41. $\frac{[k^2(p+q)^4]^{-1}}{k^{-4}(p+q)^3} = \frac{k^{-2}(p+q)^{-4}}{k^{-4}(p+q)^7}$

$$= \frac{k^{-2+4}}{(p+q)^{7+4}} = \frac{k^2}{(p+q)^{11}}$$

45. If $b = -3$ and $c = 0$, then

$$-b^2 + 3(c + \cdot 5) = -(-3)^2 + 3(0+5)$$
$$= -9 + 3(5) = -9 + 15 = 6.$$

49. If $a = 2$ and $b = -3$, then

$$a^b + b^a = 2^{-3} + (-3)^2 = \frac{1}{2^3} + 9$$

$$= \frac{1}{8} + 9 = \frac{1}{8} + \frac{9}{1} = \frac{1+72}{8} = \frac{73}{8}.$$

51. If $a = 2$, $b = -3$, and $c = 0$, then

$$b^a a^b a^c = (-3)^2 2^{-3} 2^0$$

$$= 9 \cdot \frac{1}{8} \cdot 1 = \frac{9}{8}.$$

53. If $c = 0$, then

$$(3a^3 + 5b^2)^c = (3a^3 + 5b^2)^0 = 1$$

for any real numbers a and b.

57. If $a = 2$ and $b = -3$, then

$$\frac{2b^{-1} - 3a^{-1}}{a + b^2} = \frac{\frac{2}{b} - \frac{3}{a}}{a + b^2}$$

$$= \frac{\frac{2}{-3} - \frac{3}{2}}{2 + (-3)^2}$$

$$= \frac{\frac{-4 - 9}{6}}{2 + 9}$$

$$= -\frac{\frac{13}{6}}{11}$$

$$= -\frac{13}{66}$$

59. $69,300 = 6.93 \times 10^4$

63. $.00792 = 7.92 \times 10^{-3}$

67. $.009 \times 10^{-5} = 9 \times 10^{-8}$

71. $8.2 \times 10^5 = 820,000$

75. $6.15 \times 10^{-3} = .00615$

79. $809 \times 10^{-4} = .0809$

83. $(4600)(.00092)$

$= (4.6 \times 10^3)(9.2 \times 10^{-4})$

$= 42.32 \times 10^{-1}$

$= 4.232$

87. $\frac{.000034}{.017} = \frac{3.4 \times 10^{-5}}{1.7 \times 10^{-2}}$

$= 2 \times 10^{-3}$

$= .002$

91. $(1.66 \times 10^4)(2.93 \times 10^3)$

$= 4.86 \times 10^7$

95. $\frac{(-4.389 \times 10^4)(2.421 \times 10^{-2})}{1.76 \times 10^{-9}}$

$= \frac{(-4.389)(2.421)}{1.76} \times 10^{4-2-(-9)}$

$= -6.04 \times 10^{11}$

97. $\frac{-3.9801 \times 10^{-6}}{(7.4993 \times 10^{-8})(2.117 \times 10^{-4})} =$

$\frac{-3.9801}{(7.4993)(2.117)} \times 10^{-6-(-8)-(-4)}$

$= 0.2506989 \times 10^6$

$= -2.51 \times 10^5$, rounded off.

99. Using time $= \frac{distance}{rate}$ we have

$t = \frac{9.3 \times 10^7}{2.9 \times 10^3} = 3.207 \times 10^4$ hours.

This is 32,070 hours $\approx$ 3.66 years
or $\approx$ 3 years, 8 months.

100. If light travels 1.86×10^5 miles
per second, and 1 year = (365 days)·
$(24 \frac{hours}{day})(60 \frac{min}{hour})(60 \frac{sec}{min})$, then
using distance = rate x time, we
have the number of miles in a light
year is

$d = (1.86 \times 10^5)(365)(24)(60)(60)$

$d = (1.86 \times 10^5)(3.2536 \times 10^7)$

$d = 5.865696 \times 10^{12}$ miles.

101. Using time $= \frac{distance}{rate}$ and converting
time into minutes we have

$t = \frac{9.3 \times 10^7 \text{ mi}}{1.86 \times 10^5 \text{ mi/sec}} = \frac{9.3}{1.86} \times 10^2$ sec

$= (\frac{9.3}{1.86} \times 10^2)$ sec $(\frac{1 \text{ min}}{60 \text{ sec}}) =$

$\frac{9.3}{(1.86)(60)} \times 10^2$ min

$= .083333 \times 10^2 = 8.33...$ min.

103. In engineering notation we would
write $80,000 = 80 \times 10^3$.

105. In engineering notation

$.000047 = 47 \times 10^{-6}$

109. In engineering notation
$$9.05 \times 10^{-8} = 90.5 \times 10^{-9}.$$

111. $(2k^m)(k^{1-m}) = 2 \, k^{m+1-m} = 2k$

115. $(5x^p)(3x^2) = 15 \, x^{p+2}$

119. $\dfrac{(b^2)^y}{(2 \, b^y)^3} = \dfrac{b^{2y}}{8 \, b^{3y}} = \dfrac{1}{8 \, b^y}$

121. $\dfrac{(2m^n)^2(-4m^{2+n})}{8m^{4n}} = \dfrac{(4m^{2n})(-4m^{2+n})}{8m^{4n}} =$

$\dfrac{-16m^{2+3n}}{8m^{4n}} = -2m^{2-n}$

123. $(1 + 2^3)^{-1} + (1 + 2^{-3})^{-1} =$

$9^{-1} + (1 + \frac{1}{8})^{-1} = \frac{1}{9} + (\frac{9}{8})^{-1} =$

$\frac{1}{9} + \frac{8}{9} = 1.$

Using the same style we have
$\left(1 + x^{a-b}\right)^{-1} + \left(1 + x^{b-a}\right)^{-1} =$

$= \dfrac{1}{1 + x^{a-b}} + \left(1 + \dfrac{1}{x^{a-b}}\right)^{-1}$

$= \dfrac{1}{1 + x^{a-b}} + \left(\dfrac{x^{a-b} + 1}{x^{a-b}}\right)^{-1}$

$= \dfrac{1}{1 + x^{a-b}} + \dfrac{x^{a-b}}{1 + x^{a-b}}$

$= \dfrac{1 + x^{a-b}}{1 + x^{a-b}} = 1.$

Section 1.4 Polynomials

Additional Examples
Example 1   Find the following products:

(a) $(3m - 2n)^3$, and

(b) $(2x - y + 3z)^2$.

Solution   (a) We can use the formula
$$(a - b)^3 = a^3 - 3a^2b + 3ab^2 - b^3,$$
with $a = 3m$ and $b = 2n$ to arrive at
$$(3m - 2n)^3 = (3m)^3 - 3(3m)^2(2n)$$
$$+ 3(3m)(2n)^2 - (2n)^3$$
$$(3m - 2n)^3 = 27m^3 - 54m^2n + 36mn^2$$
$$- 8n^3, \quad (I)$$
or we could calculate
$$(3m - 2n)(3m - 2n)(3m - 2n)$$
$$= (3m - 2n)(9m^2 - 12mn + 4n^2)$$
and continue with term by term multiplication to arrive at (I).

(b) To calculate $(2x - y + 3z)^2$ it is best to multiply term by term as follows:

$(2x - y + 3z)^2 = (2x - y + 3z) \cdot$
$(2x - y + 3z)$
$= 2x(2x-y+3z) -$
$y(2x-y+3z) +$
$3z(2x-y+3z)$

$= 4x^2 - 2xy + 6xz -$
$2xy + y^2 - 3yz +$
$6xz - 3yz + 9z^2$

$= 4x^2 - 4xy + 12xz +$
$y^2 - 6yz + 9z^2.$

Since all like terms have been combined, this is the final result.

Example 2   Find each of the following:

(a) $-4(2q + 1)(3q + 2) +$
$5(2 - q)(4 - 3q)$, and

(b) $(2x - 1)(4x + 2x + 1).$

Solution   Using the rules of multiplication and combination of like terms gives the following:

(a) $-4(2q + 1)(3q + 2) +$
$5(2 - q)(4 - 3q)$

$= -4[6q^2 + 7q + 2] +$
$5[8 - 10q + 3q^2]$

$$= -24q^2 - 28q - 8 + 40 - 50q + 15q^2$$

$$= -9q^2 - 78q + 32.$$

(b) $(2x - 1)(4x^2 + 2x + 1)$

$$= 2x(4x^2 + 2x + 1) - 1(4x^2 + 2x + 1)$$

$$= 8x^3 + 4x^2 + 2x - 4x^2 - 2x - 1$$

$$= 8x^3 - 1.$$

Example 3   Express the product
$(4m^{-1} + 3n^{-1})(2m^{-1} + 5n^{-1})$
as a fraction with only positive exponents.

Solution   Using the properties of exponents and rules of multiplication, we have

$(4m^{-1} + 3n^{-1})(2m^{-1} + 5n^{-1})$

$$= (\frac{4}{m} + \frac{3}{n})(\frac{2}{m} + \frac{5}{n})$$

$$= (\frac{4n + 3m}{mn})(\frac{2n + 5m}{mn}), \text{ since}$$

$$\frac{a}{b} + \frac{c}{d} = \frac{ad + bc}{bd},$$

$$= \frac{(4n + 3m)(2n + 5m)}{(mn)(mn)}, \text{ since}$$

$$\frac{a}{b} \cdot \frac{c}{d} = \frac{ac}{bd},$$

$$= \frac{8n^2 + 20\ mn + 6mn + 15m^2}{m^2n^2}$$

$$= \frac{8n^2 + 26mn + 15m^2}{m^2n^2}.$$

The same answer can be obtained by first multiplying and then simplifying to arrive at an expression with positive exponents. Observe that

$(4m^{-1} + 3n^{-1})(2m^{-1} + 5n^{-1})$

$$= 8m^{-2} + 26m^{-1}n^{-1} + 15n^{-2}$$

$$= \frac{8}{m^2} + \frac{26}{mn} + \frac{15}{n^2}$$

$$= \frac{8}{m^2} \cdot \frac{n^2}{n^2} + \frac{26}{mn} \cdot \frac{mn}{mn} + \frac{15}{n^2} \cdot \frac{m^2}{m^2},$$

to obtain a common denominator of m^2n^2

$$= \frac{8n^2 + 26mn + 15m^2}{m^2n^2}$$

Selected Solutions

1. $(3x^2 - 4x + 5) + (-2x^2 + 3x - 2)$

$$= x^2 - x + 3$$

5. $(12y^2 - 8y + 6) - (3y^2 - 4y + 2)$

$$= 12y^2 - 8y + 6 - 3y^2 + 4y - 2$$
                         remove parentheses

$$= 9y^2 - 4y + 4 \quad \text{combine like terms}$$

9. $(3a^2 - 2a) + (4a^2 + 3a + 1) - (a^2 + 2)$

$$= 3a^2 - 2a + 4a^2 + 3a + 1 - a^2 - 2$$
                         remove parentheses

$$= 6a^2 + a - 1 \quad \text{combine like terms}$$

13. $-3(4q^2 - 3a + 2) + 2(-q^2 + q - 4)$

$$= -12q^2 + 9q - 6 - 2q^2 + 2q - 8$$
                         remove parentheses

$$= -14q^2 + 11q - 14$$
                         combine like terms

17. $(6p + 5q)(3p - 7q)$

$$= 18p^2 - 42pg + 15pq - 35q^2$$

$$= 18p^2 - 27pq - 35q^2$$

21. $(\frac{2}{5}y + \frac{1}{8}z)(\frac{3}{5}y + \frac{1}{2}z)$

$$= \frac{6}{25}y^2 + \frac{1}{5}yz + \frac{3}{40}yz + \frac{1}{16}z^2$$

$$= \frac{6}{26}y^2 + \frac{11}{40}yz + \frac{1}{16}z^2$$

25. $(4x + 3y)(4x - 3y) = 16x^2 - 9y^2$,

    using $(a + b)(a - b) = a^2 - b^2$.

29. $(4m + 2n)^2$

    $$= (4m)^2 + 2(4m)(2n) + (2n)^2$$

    $$= 16m^2 + 16m + 4n^2,$$

    using

    $(a + b)^2 = a^2 + 2ab + b^2$.

33. $4x^2(3x^3 + 2x^2 - 5x + 1)$

    $= 4x^2 \cdot 3x^3 + 4x^2 \cdot 2x^2 - 4x^2 \cdot 5x +$

    $4x^2 \cdot 1$ distributive law

    $= 12x^5 + 8x^4 - 20x^3 + 4x^2$

37. $(2z - 1)(-z^2 + 3z - 4)$

    $= (2z - 1)(-z^2) + (2z - 1)(3z) -$

    $(2z - 1)(4)$ distributive law

    $= (-2z^3 + z^2) + (6z^2 - 3z) - (8z - 4)$

                         distributive law

    $= -2z^3 + 7z^2 - 11z + 4,$

                         combining terms.

41. $(2m + 1)(4m^2 - 2m + 1)$

    $= (2m + 1) 4m^2 + (2m + 1) 2m +$

    $(2m + 1) 1$ distributive law

    $= 8m^3 + 4m^2 - 4m^2 - 2m + 2m + 1$

    $= 8m^3 + 1$

45. $(a - b + 2c)^2 = (a - b + 2c)(a - b + 2c)$

    $= a(a - b + 2c) - b(a - b + 2c) +$

    $2c(a - b + 2c)$ distributive law

    $= a^2 - ab + 2ac - ab + b^2 - 2bc + 2ac -$

    $2bc + 4c^2$

    $= a^2 - 2ab + 4ac + b^2 - 4bc + 4c^2$

49. $(3m^{-1} - 2n^{-1})(4m^{-1} + n^{-1})$

    $= 3m^{-1}(4m^{-1} + n^{-1}) - 2n^{-1}(4m^{-1} + n^{-1})$

$= 12m^{-2} + 3m^{-1}n^{-1} - 8n^{-1}m^{-1} - 2n^{-2}$

$= 12m^{-2} - 5m^{-1}n^{-1} - 2n^{-2}$

51. Using $(a + b)(a - b) = a^2 - b^2$ with
    $a = \sqrt{6} + \sqrt{5}$, $b = \sqrt{3}$ and then expanding, we have

    $(\sqrt{6} + \sqrt{5} + \sqrt{3})(\sqrt{6} + \sqrt{5} - \sqrt{3})$

    $= (\sqrt{6} + \sqrt{5})^2 - 3$

    $= (\sqrt{6})^2 + 2\sqrt{6}\sqrt{5} + \sqrt{5})^2 - 3$

    $= 6 + 2\sqrt{30} + 5 - 3 = 8 + 2\sqrt{30}.$

53. Using the formula for $(a - b)^3$ we have

    $(\sqrt[3]{2} - \sqrt[3]{5})^3 = (\sqrt[3]{2})^3 - 3(\sqrt[3]{2})^2\sqrt[3]{5} +$

    $3\sqrt[3]{2}\ (\sqrt[3]{5})^2 - (\sqrt[3]{5})^3$

    $= 2 - 3\sqrt[3]{4}\sqrt[3]{5} + 3\sqrt[3]{2}\sqrt[3]{25} - 5$

    $= -3\sqrt[3]{20} + 3\sqrt[3]{50} - 3.$

57. $\dfrac{15x^4 + 30x^3 + 12x^2 - 9}{3x}$

    $= \dfrac{15x^4}{3x} + \dfrac{30x^3}{3x} + \dfrac{12x^2}{3x} - \dfrac{9}{3x}$

    $= 5x^3 + 10x^2 + 4x - \dfrac{3}{x}$

61. $(x^2 + 4x)(-3x^2 + 4x - 1)$

    The coefficient of x^3 comes from
    $x^2(4x)$ and $4x(-3x^2)$. The coefficient
    is $4 - 12 = -8$.

65. $x^2(4 - 3x)^2$

    The coefficient of x in $(4 - 3x)^2$
    is $2(4)(-3) = -24$, so the coefficient
    of x^3 is -24.

69. $(b^r + 3)(b^r - 2)$

    $= b^r(b^r - 2) + 3(b^r - 2)$

    $= b^{2r} - 2b^r + 3b^r - 6$

    $= b^{2r} + b^r - 6$

73. $(m^x - 2)^2 = (m^x)^2 - 2(2)m^x + 2^2$

$$= m^{2x} - 4m^x + 4$$

77.   Let $p(x) = a_3x^3 + \ldots + a_0$ and

$q(x) = b_3x^3 + \ldots + b_0$,

with $a_3 \neq 0$ and $b_3 \neq 0$.

(a)   Then $p(x) + q(x) = (a_3 + b_3)x^3 + \ldots + (a_0 + b_0)$. If $a_3 + b_3 = 0$, then $p + q$ has degree less than three, but if $a_3 + b_3 \neq 0$, then $p + q$ has degree 3.

(b) $p(x) - q(x) = (a_3 - b_3)x^3 + \ldots + (a_0 - b_0)$. If $a_3 = b_3$, then $p - q$ has degree less than 3, but if $a_3 \neq b_3$, then $p - q$ has degree 3.

(c) $p(x)\,q(x) = (a_3b_3)x^6 + \ldots + a_0b_0$. Since $a_3 \neq 0$ and $b_3 \neq 0$ we must have the degree of pq equal to 6.

79.   Let $p(x) = a_mx^m + \ldots + a_0$ and

$q(x) = b_nx^n + \ldots + b_0$ with $a_m \neq 0$, $b_n \neq 0$ and $n < m$.

(a) $p(x) + q(x) = a_mx^m + $ (terms of degree $< m$). Hence, $p + q$ has degree m.

(b) $p(x) - q(x) = a_mx^m + $ (terms of degree $< m$). Hence, $p - q$ has degree m.

(c) $p(x) \cdot q(x) = a_mb_nx^{m+n} + \ldots + a_0b_0$. Hence, $p \cdot q$ has degree $m + n$ since $a_mb_n \neq 0$.

80.   Let p be a polynomial with the property that there is a polynomial q such that $pq = 1$.

Let deg $p = n$ and deg $q = m$. It was shown in exercise 79 that we must have deg $pq = m + n$. Since deg $pq = 0$ we must have $m + n = 0$. Since $m \geq 0$ and $n \geq 0$, this implies $m = 0$ and $n = 0$. Hence, p must have degree 0.

81. $(x + y + z)^2 = (x + y)^2 + 2(x + y)z + z^2$

$= x^2 + 2xy + y^2 + 2xz + 2yz + z^2$

$= x^2 + y^2 + z^2 + 2xy + 2xz + 2yz$

82. $(x + y + z)(x + y - z)$

$= (x + y)^2 - z^2$

$= x^2 + 2xy + y^2 - z^2$

Section 1.5 Factoring

Additional Examples

Example 1   Factor the following expressions as completely as possible:

(a) $2(a + b)^2 + 5(a + b)c + 3c^2$

(b) $(x + 2y)^2 - (2x - y)^2$

Solution   We have the following:

(a)   To factor $2(a + b)^2 + 5(a + b)c + 3c^2$, we treat $a + b$ as a single term, say u, and factor $2u^2 + 5uc + 3c^2$. This factors as

$2u^2 + 5uc + 3c^2 = (2u + 3c)(u + c)$.

Hence,

$2(a + b)^2 + 5(a + b)c + 3c^2$

$= [2(a + b) + 3c][(a + b) + c]$

$= (2a + 2b + 3c)(a + b + c)$.

Note that we clear brackets and parenthesis to the greatest extent possible so that the final result is as uncluttered (simple) as possible.

(b) We see that $(x + 2y)^2 - (2x - y)^2$ has the form $a^2 - b^2$, the difference of two squares. Treating $x + 2y = a$ and $2x - y = b$ gives

$(x + 2y)^2 - (2x - y)^2$

$= [(x+2y) + (2x-y)][x+2y) - (2x-y)]$

$= [x + 2y + 2x - y][x + 2y - 2x + y]$

$= (3x + y)(-x + 3y).$

Example 2   Factor as completely as possible: (a) $15x^{2k} + 26x^k + 8$, and (b) $(x)^{4n} - (2y)^{8m}$.

Solution   (a) To factor $15x^{2k} + 26x^k + 8$ we can consider $x^k = u$ and we then wish to factor $15u^2 + 26u + 8$, which factors to $(5u + 2)(3u + 4)$. Hence,

$15x^{2k} + 26x^k + 8 = (5x^k + 2)(3x^k + 4).$

(b) Using the formula for the difference of two square, $a^2 - b^2 = (a + b)(a - b)$, and letting $a = x^{2n}$, $b = (2y)^{4m}$, we have

$x^{4n} - (2y)^{8m}$

$= [x^{2n} + (2y)^{4m}][x^{2n} - (2y)^{4m}].$

A second application gives

$x^{4n} - (2y)^{8m}$

$= [x^{2n} + (2y)^{4m}][x^n + (2y)^{2m}][x^n - (2y)^{2m}].$

Since we have no information as to whether n is odd or even, we consider this as the final result. If n is even, another step is necessary.

Example 3   Factor $(x + h)^3 - x^3$ as completely as possible and then simplify.

Solution   We have the difference of two cubes so that

$(x + h)^3 - x^3$

$= [(x+h) - x][(x+h)^2 + x(x+h) + x^2]$

$= [x+h-x][x^2+2xh+h^2+x^2+xh+x^2]$

$= h(3x^2 + 3xh + h^2).$

Selected Solutions

1. $12mn - 8m = 4m \cdot 3n - 4m \cdot 2$
$= 4m(3n - 2)$

5. $6px^2 - 8px^3 - 12px$
$= 2px \cdot 3x - 2px \cdot 4x^2 - 2px \cdot 6)$
$= 2px(3x - 4x^2 - 6)$

9. $x^2 - 11x + 24 = (x - 3)(x - 8)$

13. $2z^2 + 7z - 30 = (2z - 5)(z + 6)$

17. $18r^2 - 3rs - 10s^2$
$= (6r - 5s)(3r + 2s)$

21. $9x^2 - 6x^3 + x^4 = x^2(9 - 6x + x^2)$
$= x^2(3 - x)^2$ or
$= x^2(x^2 - 6x + 9)$
$= x^2(x - 3)^2$

25. $4m^2 - 25 = (2m)^2 - 5^2$
$= (2m - 5)(2m + 5)$

29. $121p^4 - 9q^4$
$= (11p^2 - 3q^2)(11p^2 + 3q^2)$

33. $p^8 - 1$
$= (p^4 - 1)(p^4 + 1)$
$= (p^2 - 1)(p^2 + 1)(p^4 + 1)$
$= (p - 1)(p + 1)(p^2 + 1)(p^4 + 1)$

64. $64 - x^6 = 8^2 - (x^3)^2$

$\qquad = (8 - x^3)(8 + x^3)$

$\qquad = (2^3 - x^3)(2^3 + x^3)$

$\qquad = (2 - x)(4 + 2x + x^2)(2 + x)$

$\qquad\quad (4 - 2x + x^2)$

41. $q^2 + 6q + 9 - p^2$

$\qquad = (q^2 + 6q + 9) - p^2$

$\qquad = (q + 3)^2 - p^2$

$\qquad = [(q + 3) - p][(q + 3) + p]$

$\qquad = (q + 3 - p)(q + 3 + p).$

45. $x^2 - (x - y)^2$

$\qquad = [x - (x - y)][x + (x - y)]$

$\qquad = (x - x + y)(x + x - y)$

$\qquad = y(2x - y).$

49. Let $u = (x + y)$.

$(x + y)^2 + 2(x + y)z - 15z^2$

$\qquad = u^2 + 2uz - 15z^2$

$\qquad = (u + 5z)(u - 3z)$

$\qquad = (x + y + 5z)(x + y - 3z)$

53. Let $a = p + q$, and $b = p - q$. Then

$(p + q)^2 - (p - q)^2$

$\qquad = a^2 - b^2$

$\qquad = (a - b)(a + b)$

$\qquad = [(p + q) - (p - q)][(p + q) + (p - q)]$

$\qquad = (p + q - p + q)(p + q + p - q)$

$\qquad = 2q \cdot 2p$

$\qquad = 4pq$

57. Using the difference of two cubes

formula $a^3 - b^3 = (a - b)(a^2 + ab + b^2)$

with $b = m + 2n$ gives $27 - (m + 2n)^3$

$\qquad = [3 - (m + 2n)] \cdot$

$\qquad\quad [9 + 3(m + 2n) + (m + 2n)^2]$

$\qquad = (3m - m - 2n)$

$\qquad\quad (9 + 3m + 6n + m^2 + 4mn + 4n^2)$

61. $m^{2n} - 16 = (m^n + 4)(m^n - 4)$

63. Using the difference of two cubes
formula gives

$x^{3n} - y^{6n} = (x^n - y^{2n})(x^{2n} + x^n y^{2n} + y^{4n}).$

65. $2x^{2n} - 23x^n y^n - 39y^{2n}$

$\qquad = (2x^n + 3y^n)(x^n - 13y^n)$

69. $25q^{2r} - 30q^r t^p + 9t^{2p} =$

$\qquad = (5q^r - 3t^p)(5q^r - 3t^p)$

$\qquad = (5q^r - 3t^p)^2.$

73. If we let $x = m + p$, then we have

$6(m + p)^{2k} + (m + p)^k - 15$

$\qquad = 6x^{2k} + x^k - 15$

$\qquad = (2x^k - 3)(3x^k + 5)$

$\qquad = [2(m + p)^k - 3][3(m + p)^k + 5]$

75. $9.44x^3 + 48.144x^2 - 30.208x + 37.76$

$\qquad = 9.44(x^3 + 5.1x^2 - 3.2x + 4)$

79. $p^{-4} - p^{-2} = p^{-4}(1 - p^2)$

83. $100p^{-6} - 50p^{-2} + 75p^2$

$\qquad = 25p^{-6}(4 - 2p^4 + 3p^8)$

85. $(3z - z^2)^2 + (9 - z^2)^2 + (3 - z)^2$

$\qquad = z^2(3 - z)^2 + (3 - z)^2(3 + z)^2 +$

$\qquad\quad (3 - z)^2$

$\qquad = (3 - z)^2[z^2 + (3 + z)^2 + 1]$

$\qquad = (3 - z)^2(2z^2 + 6z + 10)$

$\qquad = 2(3 - z)^2(z^2 + 3z + 5)$

89. $x^4 + 64 = (x^4 + 16x^2 + 64) - 16x^2$

$\qquad\qquad = (x^2 + 8)^2 - 16x^2$

$$= [(x^2 + 8) + 4x]$$

$$[(x^2 + 8) - 4x]$$

$$= (x^2 + 4x + 8)(x^2 - 4x + 8)$$

93. $z^4 - 11z^2 + 25 = (z^4 - 10z^2 + 25) - z^2$

$$= (z^2 - 5)^2 - z^2$$

$$= [(z^2 - 5) + z][z^2 - 5) - z]$$

$$= (z^2 + z - 5)(z^2 - z - 5)$$

95. $(x^3 + 5)^2 (4) (5x - 11)^3 (5) +$

$(5x - 11)^4 (2)(x^3 + 5)(3x^2)$

$= 2(x^3 + 5)(5x - 11)^3$

$\quad \cdot [10(x^3 + 5) + 3x^2 (5x - 11)]$

$= 2(x^3 + 5)(5x - 11)^3$

$\quad \cdot (10x^3 + 50 + 15x^3 - 33x^2)$

$= 2(x^3 + 5)(5x - 11)^3$

$\quad \cdot (25x^3 - 33x^2 + 50)$

97. $(x + 3)^{-2} (-3)(4x + 7)^{-4} (4) +$

$(4x + 7)^{-3} (-2)(x^2 + 3)^{-3} (2x)$

$= 4(x^2 + 3)^{-3} (4x + y)^{-4}$

$\quad \cdot [-3(x^2 + 3) - x(4x + 7)]$

$= 4(x^2 + 3)^{-3} (4x + 7)^{-4}$

$\quad \cdot (-3x^2 - 9 - 4x^2 - 7x)$

$= 4(x^2 + 3)^{-3} (4x + 7)^{-4}$

$\quad \cdot (-7x^2 - yx - 9)$

Section 1.6 Fractional Expressions

Additional Examples

Example 1   Simplify $\dfrac{x^2 y^{-2} - y^2 x^{-2}}{yx^{-1} + xy^{-1}}$.

Solution   In order to simplify this expression we first simplify the numerator and denomintor to single fractions using the properties of exponents and laws of arithmetic. These procedures give

$$\frac{x^2 y^{-2} - y^2 x^{-2}}{yx^{-1} + xy^{-1}}$$

$$= \frac{x^2 \left(\frac{1}{y^2}\right) - y^2 \left(\frac{1}{x^2}\right)}{y \left(\frac{1}{x}\right) + x \left(\frac{1}{y}\right)}, \text{ using } a^{-n} = \frac{1}{a^n},$$

$$= \frac{\frac{x^2}{y^2} - \frac{y^2}{x^2}}{\frac{y}{x} + \frac{x}{y}}, \text{ using } a\left(\frac{1}{b}\right) = \frac{a}{1} \cdot \frac{1}{b} = \frac{a}{b},$$

$$= \frac{\frac{x^4 - y^4}{x^2 y^2}}{\frac{y^2 + x^2}{xy}}, \text{ using } \frac{a}{b} \pm \frac{c}{d} = \frac{ad \pm bc}{bd},$$

$$= \frac{x^4 - y^4}{x^2 y^2} \quad \frac{xy}{y^2 + x^2}, \text{ using } \frac{a/b}{c/d} = \frac{a}{b} \cdot \frac{d}{c},$$

$$= \frac{xy(x^4 - y^4)}{x^2 y^2 (x^2 + y^2)}$$

$$= \frac{xy(x^2 - y^2)(x^2 + y^2)}{x^2 y^2 (x^2 + y^2)}, \text{ since}$$

$$x^4 - y^4 = (x^2 - y^2)(x^2 + y^2)$$

$$\frac{x^2 - y^2}{xy}, \text{ or } = \frac{(x - y)(x + y)}{xy}.$$

Either of these results could be accepted. There are instances when the factored form is preferable.

Example 2   Simplify $\dfrac{\frac{a-3}{a+2} - \frac{a+2}{a-3}}{\frac{a}{(a-3)(a+2)} + 1}$

Solution: We perform the following steps:

$$\frac{\frac{a-3}{a+2} - \frac{a+2}{a-3}}{\frac{a}{(a-3)(a+2)} + 1}$$

$$= \frac{\frac{(a-3)^2 - (a+2)^2}{(a+2)(a-3)}}{\frac{a + (a-3)(a+2)}{(a-3)(a+2)}}, \text{ using}$$

$$\frac{n}{b} \pm \frac{c}{d} = \frac{nd \pm bc}{bd}$$

$$= \frac{(a-3)^2 - (a+2)^2}{(a+2)(a-3)} \cdot \frac{(a-3)(a+2)}{a + (a-3)(a+2)},$$

since $\frac{n/b}{c/d} = \frac{n}{b} \cdot \frac{d}{c}$

$$= \frac{(a-3)^2 - (a+2)^2}{a + (a-3)(a+2)}, \quad \text{after}$$

cancelling like terms if $a \neq 3$ and $a \neq -2$,

$$= \frac{[(a-3) - (a+2)][(a-3) + (a+2)]}{a^2 - 6},$$

since $a + (a-3)(a+2) = a + a^2 - a - 6$,

$$= \frac{-5(2a-1)}{a^2 - 6}.$$

We can consider this simplified. It should be noted that we could write $a^2 - 6 = (a - \sqrt{6})(a + \sqrt{6})$, but this introduces radicals and does not seems to give a more simple appearance.

To interpret the word "simplify," operate on any expression to reduce it to a single fraction in which the numerator and denominator are in a form which most easily allows the determination of the numbers which make them equal to zero.

Example 3   Perform the indicated operations and simplify the following:

(a) $(a+b)^{-2}(a^{-2} - b^{-2})$,

(b) $1 + \dfrac{1 + 1/a}{a - 1/a}$

Solution   Performing the indicated operations gives

(a) $(a+b)^{-2}(a^{-2} - b^{-2})$

$$= \frac{1}{(a+b)^2}\left(\frac{1}{a^2} - \frac{1}{b^2}\right)$$

$$= \frac{1}{(a+b)^2}\left(\frac{b^2 - a^2}{a^2 b^2}\right)$$

$$= \frac{1}{(a+b)^2} \cdot \frac{(b+a)(b-a)}{a^2 b^2}$$

$$= \frac{b-a}{a^2 b^2 (b+a)}, \quad \text{since}$$

$a + b = b + a$.

(b) $1 + \dfrac{1 + \dfrac{1}{a}}{a - \dfrac{1}{a}} = 1 + \dfrac{\dfrac{a+1}{a}}{\dfrac{a^2-1}{a}},$

since

$\dfrac{1}{1} + \dfrac{1}{a} = \dfrac{a+1}{a}$ and $\dfrac{a}{1} - \dfrac{1}{a} = \dfrac{a^2 - 1}{a},$

$$= 1 + [\frac{a+1}{a} \cdot \frac{a}{a^2 - 1}],$$

using $\dfrac{n/b}{c/d} = \dfrac{n}{b} \cdot \dfrac{d}{c},$

$$= 1 + \frac{a+1}{a^2 - 1}$$

$$= 1 + \frac{a+1}{(a+1)(a-1)}$$

$$= 1 + \frac{1}{a-1}$$

$$= \frac{(a-1) + 1}{a-1},$$

using $\dfrac{1}{1} + \dfrac{1}{a-1} = \dfrac{1(a-1) + 1(1)}{(1)(a-1)}$

$$= \frac{a}{a-1}.$$

Selected Solutions

1. The domain of $\dfrac{x-2}{x+6}$ consists of all numbers except the ones that make the denominator zero. The domain is the set $\{x \mid x \neq -6\}$.

5. Since the denominator $x^2 + 1$ is never zero the domain of $\dfrac{-8}{x^2 + 1}$ is the set R, the set of all real numbers.

9. We have
$\dfrac{8k + 16}{9k + 18} = \dfrac{8(k+2)}{9(k+2)} = \dfrac{8}{9}$ provided $k \neq -2$.

13. $\dfrac{8x^2 + 16x}{4x^2} = \dfrac{4x(2x+4)}{4x^2} = \dfrac{2x+4}{x}$ if $x \neq 0$.
This could also be written as
$\dfrac{2x}{x} + \dfrac{4}{x} = 2 + \dfrac{4}{x}$, if so desired.

17. $\dfrac{8m^2 + 6m - 9}{16m^2 - 9} = \dfrac{(2m + 3)(4m - 3)}{(4m + 3)(4m - 3)}$

$= \dfrac{2m + 3}{4m + 3}$, if $m \neq \dfrac{3}{4}$.

21. $\dfrac{15p^3}{9p^2} \div \dfrac{6p}{10p^2} = \dfrac{15p^3}{9p^2} \cdot \dfrac{10p^2}{6p} = \dfrac{5p}{3} \quad \dfrac{5p}{3}$

$= \dfrac{5p}{3} \quad \dfrac{5p}{3} = \dfrac{25p^2}{9}$, if $p \neq 0$.

25. $\dfrac{9y - 18}{6y + 12} \cdot \dfrac{3y + 6}{15y - 30} = \dfrac{9(y - 2)}{6(y + 2)} \cdot$

$\dfrac{3(y + 2)}{15(y - 2)} = \dfrac{3}{10}$, provided $y \neq -2$

and $y \neq 2$.

29. $\dfrac{4a + 12}{2a - 10} \div \dfrac{a^2 - 9}{a^2 - a - 20} = \dfrac{4(a + 3)}{2(a - 5)} \cdot$

$\dfrac{(a - 5)(a + 4)}{(a + 3)(a - 3)} = \dfrac{2(a + 4)}{a - 3}$,

provided $a \neq -3$ and $a \neq 5$.

33. $\dfrac{k^2 - k - 6}{k^2 + k - 12} \cdot \dfrac{k^2 + 3k - 4}{k^2 + 2k - 3}$

$= \dfrac{(k - 3)(k + 2)}{(k - 3)(k + 4)} \cdot \dfrac{(k - 1)(k + 4)}{(k - 1)(k + 3)}$

$= \dfrac{k + 2}{k + 3}$, if $k \neq -4$, 1, 3.

37. $\dfrac{2m^2 - 5m - 12}{m^2 - 10m + 24} \div \dfrac{4m^2 - 9}{m^2 - 9m + 18}$

$= \dfrac{(2m + 3)(m - 4)}{(m - 6)(m - 4)} \cdot \dfrac{(m - 3)(m - 6)}{(2m + 3)(2m - 3)}$

$= \dfrac{m - 3}{2m - 3}$, if $m \neq -\dfrac{3}{2}$, 4, 6.

39. $\left(1 + \dfrac{1}{x}\right)\left(1 - \dfrac{1}{x}\right) = 1 - \dfrac{1}{x^2}$, or $\dfrac{x^2 - 1}{x^2}$

41. $\dfrac{x^3 + y^3}{x^2 - y^2} \cdot \dfrac{x + y}{x^2 - y + y^2}$

$= \dfrac{(x + y)(x^2 - yx + y)}{(x + y)(x - y)} \cdot$

$\dfrac{x + y}{(x - xy + y)} = \dfrac{x + y}{x - y}$,

provided $x \neq -y$.

45. $\dfrac{8}{r} + \dfrac{6}{r} = \dfrac{14}{r}$.

49. $\dfrac{2}{3y} - \dfrac{1}{4y} = \dfrac{2}{3y} \cdot \dfrac{4}{4} - \dfrac{1}{4y} \cdot \dfrac{3}{3}$

$= \dfrac{8}{12y} - \dfrac{3}{12y} = \dfrac{5}{12y}$.

53. $\dfrac{3}{p} + \dfrac{1}{2} = \dfrac{6 + p}{2p}$, using

$\dfrac{a}{b} + \dfrac{c}{d} = \dfrac{ad + bc}{bd}$.

57. $\dfrac{1}{6m} + \dfrac{2}{5m} + \dfrac{4}{m} = \dfrac{5}{30m} + \dfrac{12}{30m} + \dfrac{120}{30m} = \dfrac{137}{30m}$.

61. $\dfrac{2}{a + b} - \dfrac{1}{2(a + b)} = \dfrac{4}{2(a + b)} - \dfrac{1}{2(a + b)}$

$= \dfrac{3}{2(a + b)}$

65. Using $\dfrac{a}{b} + \dfrac{c}{d} = \dfrac{ad + bc}{bd}$, we have

$\dfrac{m + 1}{m - 1} + \dfrac{m - 1}{m + 1} = \dfrac{(m + 1)^2 + (m - 1)^2}{m^2 - 1}$

$= \dfrac{m^2 + 2m + 1 + m^2 - 2m + 1}{m^2 - 1}$

$= \dfrac{2m^2 + 2}{m^2 - 1}$, or $\dfrac{2(m^2 + 1)}{m^2 - 1}$.

67. $\dfrac{3}{a - 2} - \dfrac{1}{2 - a} = \dfrac{3}{a - 2} - \dfrac{1}{-(a - 2)}$

$= \dfrac{3}{a - 2} + \dfrac{1}{a - 2} = \dfrac{4}{a - 2}$.

69. $\dfrac{x + y}{2x - y} - \dfrac{2x}{y - 2x} = \dfrac{x + y}{2x - y} + \dfrac{2x}{2x - y}$

$= \dfrac{3x + y}{2x - y}$.

73. $\dfrac{1}{x^2 + x - 12} - \dfrac{1}{x^2 - 7x + 12} +$

$\dfrac{1}{x^2 - 16} = \dfrac{1}{(x - 3)(x + 4)} -$

$\dfrac{1}{(x - 3)(x - 4)} + \dfrac{1}{(x + 4)(x - 4)}$

[a common denominator is
$(x - 3)(x + 4)(x - 4)$]

$= \dfrac{x - 4}{(x - 3)(x + 4)(x - 4)} -$

$\dfrac{x + 4}{(x - 3)(x + 4)(x - 4)} +$

$\dfrac{x - 3}{(x - 3)(x + 4)(x - 4)}$

$$= \frac{(x - 4) - (x + 4) + (x - 3)}{(x - 3)(x + 4)(x - 4)}$$

$$= \frac{x - 11}{(x - 3)(x + 4)(x - 4)}$$

77. $\dfrac{4x - 1}{x^2 + 3x - 10} + \dfrac{2x + 3}{x^2 + 4x - 5}$

$$= \frac{4x - 1}{(x + 5)(x - 2)} + \frac{2x + 3}{(x + 5)(x - 1)}$$

[a common denominator is

$(x + 5)(x - 2)(x - 1)$]

$$= \frac{(4x - 1)(x - 1)}{(x + 5)(x - 2)(x - 1)} +$$

$$\frac{(2x + 3)(x - 2)}{(x + 5)(x - 2)(x - 1)}$$

$$= \frac{(4x^2 - 5x + 1) + (2x^2 - x - 6)}{(x - 5)(x - 2)(x - 1)}$$

$$= \frac{6x^2 - 6x - 5}{(x - 5)(x - 2)(x - 1)}.$$

81. $\dfrac{\dfrac{1}{x + h} - \dfrac{1}{x}}{h} = \dfrac{\dfrac{x - (x + h)}{x(x + h)}}{h} = \dfrac{\dfrac{-h}{x(x + h)}}{\dfrac{h}{1}}$

$$= \frac{-h}{x(x + h)} \cdot \frac{1}{h} = \frac{-1}{x(x + h)}, \text{ if } h \neq 0.$$

83. $\dfrac{1 + \dfrac{1}{x}}{1 - \dfrac{1}{x}} = \dfrac{\dfrac{x + 1}{x}}{\dfrac{x - 1}{x}} = \dfrac{x + 1}{x} \cdot \dfrac{x}{x - 1}$

$$= \frac{x + 1}{x - 1}, \text{ if } x \neq 0.$$

85. $\dfrac{\dfrac{1}{x + 1} - \dfrac{1}{x}}{\dfrac{1}{x}} = \dfrac{\dfrac{x - (x + 1)}{x(x + 1)}}{\dfrac{1}{x}}$

$$= \frac{-1}{x(x + 1)} \cdot \frac{x}{1} = \frac{-1}{x + 1}, \text{ if } x \neq 0.$$

89. $\dfrac{\dfrac{m}{1} - \dfrac{1}{m^2 - 4}}{\dfrac{1}{m + 2}} = \dfrac{\dfrac{m(m^2 - 4) - 1}{m^2 - 4}}{\dfrac{1}{m + 2}}$

$$= \frac{m^3 - 4m - 1}{(m + 2)(m - 2)} \quad \frac{m + 2}{1}$$

$$= \frac{m^3 - 4m - 1}{m - 2}, \text{ if } m \neq -2.$$

91. $\dfrac{\dfrac{8}{z^2 - 25z} + 3}{\dfrac{5}{z(z + 1)}} = \dfrac{\dfrac{8 + 3(z^2 - 25z)}{z(z - 25)}}{\dfrac{5}{z(z + 1)}}$

$$= \frac{3z^2 - 75z + 8}{z(z - 25)} \quad \frac{z(z + 1)}{5}$$

$$= \frac{(z + 1)(3z^2 - 75z + 8)}{5(z - 25)}, \text{ if } z \neq 10.$$

Note that $3z^2 - 75z + 8$ does not factor.

93. $(2^{-1} - 3^{-1})^{-1} = (\frac{1}{2} - \frac{1}{3})^{-1}$

$$(\frac{1}{2} - \frac{1}{3})^{-1} = (\frac{3 - 2}{6})^{-1}$$

$$= (\frac{1}{6})^{-1} = 6.$$

97. $\dfrac{a^{-1} + b^{-1}}{(ab)^{-1}}$

$$\frac{\dfrac{1}{a} + \dfrac{1}{b}}{\dfrac{1}{ab}} = (\frac{b + a}{ab}) \cdot \frac{ab}{1} = b + a \text{ or } a + b$$

99. $\dfrac{r^{-1} + q^{-1}}{r^{-1} - q^{-1}} \quad \dfrac{r - q}{r + q}$

$$= \frac{\dfrac{1}{r} + \dfrac{1}{q}}{\dfrac{1}{r} - \dfrac{1}{q}} \quad \frac{r - q}{r - q}$$

$$= \frac{\dfrac{q + r}{rq}}{\dfrac{q - r}{rq}} \quad \frac{r - q}{r + q}$$

$$= [\frac{q + r}{rq} \cdot \frac{rq}{q - r}] \quad \frac{r - q}{r + q}$$

$$= \frac{q + r}{q - r} \quad \frac{r - q}{r + q}$$

$$= \frac{r + q}{-(r - q)} \quad \frac{r - q}{r + q}$$

$$= \frac{1}{-1}$$

$$= -1.$$

100. $\dfrac{xy^{-1} + yx^{-1}}{x^2 + y^2} = \dfrac{\dfrac{x}{y} + \dfrac{y}{x}}{x^2 + y^2}$

$$= \frac{\dfrac{x^2 + y^2}{yx}}{\dfrac{x^2 + y^2}{1}}$$

$$= \frac{x^2 + y^2}{xy} \cdot \frac{1}{x^2 + y^2}$$

$$= \frac{1}{xy}.$$

101. $(a + b)^{-1}(a^{-1} + b^{-1})$

$= (\frac{1}{a+b})(\frac{1}{a} + \frac{1}{b}) = (\frac{1}{a+b})(\frac{b+a}{ab}) = \frac{1}{ab}$

103. $(x - 9y^{-1})[(x - 3y^{-1})(x + 3y^{-1})]^{-1}$

$= (x - \frac{9}{y})[(x^2 - 9y^{-2})]^{-1}$

$= (x - \frac{9}{y}) \cdot \frac{1}{(x^2 - 9y^{-2})}$

$= \frac{x - \frac{9}{y}}{x^2 - \frac{9}{y^2}}$

$= \frac{\frac{xy - 9}{y}}{\frac{x^2y^2 - 9}{y^2}}$

$= \frac{xy - 9}{y} \cdot \frac{y^2}{x^2y^2 - 9}$

$= \frac{(xy - 9)y}{x^2y^2 - 9}.$

105. $4(\frac{x^3 + 2}{x - 5})^3 \left[\frac{(x - 5)(3x^2) - (x^3 + 2)}{(x - 5)^2}\right]$

$= 4\frac{(x^3 + 2)^3}{(x - 5)^3} \cdot \frac{3x^3 - 15x^2 - x^3 - 2}{(x - 5)^2}$

$= \frac{4(x^3 + 2)^3(2x^3 - 15x^2 - 2)}{(x - 5)^5}.$

Section 1.7   Radicals

Additional Examples

Example 1   Evaluate the product

$(2\sqrt[3]{9} - 3)(4\sqrt[3]{9^2} + 6\sqrt[3]{9} + 9).$

Solution   We can either multiply term by term or recognize this in the form $(a - b)(a^2 + ab + b^2)$, which multiplies to give $a^3 - b^3$. We will evaluate the product by both methods.

(i)   If we let $a = 2\sqrt[3]{9}$ and $b = 3$, then note that

$(a - b)(a^2 + ab + b^2) = a^3 - b^3.$

Thus, we have

$(2\sqrt[3]{9} - 3)(4\sqrt{9^2} + 6\sqrt[3]{9} + 9) = (2\sqrt[3]{9})^3 - 3^3.$

$= 8(9) - 27$

$= 72 - 27$

$= 45.$

(ii)   Using term by term multiplication gives

$(2\sqrt[3]{9} - 3)(4\sqrt[3]{9^2} + 6\sqrt[3]{9} + 9)$

$= 8\sqrt[3]{9}\sqrt[3]{9^2} + 12\sqrt[3]{9}\sqrt[3]{9} + 18\sqrt[3]{9} - 12\sqrt[3]{9^2} - 18\sqrt[3]{9} - 27$

$= 8\sqrt[3]{9^3} + 12\sqrt[3]{9^2} - 12\sqrt[3]{9^2} - 27$

$= 8 \cdot 9 - 27$

$= 72 - 27 = 45.$

Examples 2   Consider the statements

(1) $\sqrt{3\frac{3}{8}} = 3\sqrt{\frac{3}{8}}$ and

$\sqrt{6\frac{6}{35}} = 6\sqrt{\frac{6}{35}}.$

Are these statements true or false? If false, give a reason for this conclusion, and if true, verify the answer.

Solution   Upon first consideration, the statements seem obviously false. A reason for the conclusion would appear to be the violation of the property $\sqrt{ab} = \sqrt{a}\sqrt{b}$. However, we must consider the statements further. The number 3 3/8 is not the product of 3 and 3/8, but is actually 3 + 3/8. Therefore, $\sqrt{ab} = \sqrt{a}\sqrt{b}$ is not applicable. The number 3 3/8 should be changed to the form

$3\frac{3}{8} = 3 + \frac{3}{8} = \frac{24 + 3}{8} = \frac{27}{8} = \frac{9 \cdot 3}{8}.$

Then $\sqrt{3\frac{3}{8}} = \sqrt{\frac{9 \cdot 3}{8}} = \sqrt{(9)(\frac{3}{8})},$

and this is a product. Using $\sqrt{ab} = \sqrt{a}\sqrt{b}$ we have

$\sqrt{3\frac{3}{8}} = \sqrt{(9)(\frac{3}{8})} = 3\sqrt{\frac{3}{8}}.$

Similarly, statement (2) is true since

$$\sqrt{6\frac{6}{35}} = \sqrt{6 + \frac{6}{35}} = \sqrt{\frac{216}{35}}$$

$$= \sqrt{\frac{36 \cdot 6}{35}} = \sqrt{(36)(\frac{6}{35})}$$

$$= 6\sqrt{\frac{6}{35}}.$$

Example 3   Simplify the expression
$$\frac{\sqrt[3]{16x^4y^5}\,\sqrt[3]{xy^2z}}{\sqrt[3]{2xy^2z^2}}$$

Solution   Using the properties of exponents and radicals, we have

$$\frac{\sqrt[3]{16x^4y^5}\,\sqrt[3]{xy^2z}}{\sqrt[3]{2xy^2z^2}} = \sqrt[3]{\frac{(16x^4y^5)(xy^2z)}{(2xy^2z^2)}}$$

$$= \sqrt[3]{\frac{16x^5y^7z}{2xy^2z^2}}$$

$$= \sqrt[3]{\frac{8x^4y^5}{z}}$$

$$= \sqrt[3]{8x^3y^3\left(\frac{xy^2}{z}\right)}$$

$$= 2xy\sqrt[3]{\frac{xy^2}{z}}$$

$$= 2xy\sqrt[3]{\frac{xy^2}{z}\left(\frac{z^2}{z^2}\right)}$$

$$= 2xy\sqrt[3]{\frac{xy^2z^2}{z^3}}$$

$$= \left(\frac{2xy}{z}\right)\sqrt[3]{xy^2z^2}$$

Example 4   Rationalize the denominator of the expression
$$\frac{\sqrt{x+1} - \sqrt{x-1}}{\sqrt{x+1} + \sqrt{x-1}}$$
and simplify.

Solution   To rationalize the denominator we multiply and divide by the conjugate of denominator. This gives

$$\frac{\sqrt{x+1} - \sqrt{x-1}}{\sqrt{x+1} + \sqrt{x-1}}$$

$$= \frac{\sqrt{x+1} - \sqrt{x-1}}{\sqrt{x+1} + \sqrt{x-1}} \cdot \frac{\sqrt{x+1} - \sqrt{x-1}}{\sqrt{x+1} - \sqrt{x-1}}$$

$$= \frac{(x+1) - 2\sqrt{x+1}\,\sqrt{x-1} + (x-1)}{(x+1) - (x-1)}$$

$$= \frac{2x - 2\sqrt{(x+1)(x-1)}}{2}$$

$$= x - \sqrt{x^2 - 1}.$$

Example 5   Show that
$$\sqrt{8 + 2\sqrt{15}} = \sqrt{3} + \sqrt{5}.$$

Solution   By definition $a = b$ if and only if $b^2 = a$. Hence, the statement is true if $(\sqrt{3} + \sqrt{5})^2 = 8 + 2\sqrt{15}$. To show this, consider

$$(\sqrt{3} + \sqrt{5})^2 = (\sqrt{3})^2 + 2\sqrt{3}\sqrt{5} + (\sqrt{5})^2$$

$$= 3 + 2\sqrt{15} + 5$$

$$= 8 + 2\sqrt{15}.$$

This shows that $\sqrt{8 + 2\sqrt{15}} = \sqrt{3} + \sqrt{5}.$

Selected Solutions

1. $\sqrt{50} = \sqrt{25 \cdot 2}$
$$= \sqrt{25} \cdot \sqrt{2}$$
$$= 5\sqrt{2}$$

3. $\sqrt[3]{250} = \sqrt[3]{125 \cdot 2}$
$$= \sqrt[3]{125} \cdot \sqrt[3]{2}$$
$$= 5\sqrt[3]{2}$$

5. $-\sqrt{\frac{9}{5}} = -\frac{\sqrt{9}}{\sqrt{5}} = -\frac{3}{\sqrt{5}} \cdot \frac{\sqrt{5}}{\sqrt{5}}$
$$= \frac{-3\sqrt{5}}{5}$$

9. $4\sqrt{3} - 5\sqrt{12} + 3\sqrt{75}$
$$= 4\sqrt{3} - 5 \cdot 2\sqrt{3} + 3 \cdot 5\sqrt{3}$$
$$= 4\sqrt{3} - 10\sqrt{3} + 15\sqrt{3}$$
$$= 9\sqrt{3}$$

13. $-\sqrt[3]{\frac{3}{2}} \cdot \frac{\sqrt[3]{4}}{\sqrt[3]{4}} = -\frac{\sqrt[3]{12}}{\sqrt[3]{8}} = \frac{-\sqrt[3]{12}}{2}$

15. $\sqrt[4]{\frac{3}{2}} = \frac{\sqrt[4]{3}}{\sqrt[4]{2}} \cdot \frac{\sqrt[4]{2^3}}{\sqrt[4]{2^3}} = \frac{\sqrt[4]{24}}{2}$

17. $3\sqrt[3]{16} - 4\sqrt[3]{2} = 3\sqrt[3]{8 \cdot 2} - 4\sqrt[3]{2}$
$$= 3(2)\sqrt[3]{2} - 4\sqrt[3]{2}$$
$$= 6\sqrt[3]{2} - 4\sqrt[3]{2}$$
$$= 2\sqrt[3]{2}$$

21. $\frac{1}{\sqrt{3}} - \frac{2}{\sqrt{12}} + 2\sqrt{3} = \frac{1}{\sqrt{3}} - \frac{2}{2\sqrt{3}} + 2\sqrt{3}$

$$= \frac{1}{\sqrt{3}} - \frac{1}{\sqrt{3}} + 2\sqrt{3}$$

$$= 2\sqrt{3}$$

25. $\sqrt{2x^3y^2z^4} = \sqrt{x^2y^2z^4(2x)}$

$\qquad = xyz^2\sqrt{2x}$

29. $\sqrt{a^3b^5} - 2\sqrt{a^7b^3} + \sqrt{a^3b^9}$

$\qquad = ab^2\sqrt{ab} - 2a^3b\sqrt{ab} + ab^4\sqrt{ab}$

$\qquad = (ab^2 - 2a^3b + ab^4)\sqrt{ab}$

$\qquad = ab\sqrt{ab}(b - 2a^2 + b^3)$

33. $(\sqrt[3]{11} - 1)(\sqrt[3]{11^2} + \sqrt[3]{11} + 1)$

$\qquad = \sqrt[3]{11^3} + \sqrt[3]{11^2} + \sqrt[3]{11} - \sqrt[3]{11^2} - \sqrt[3]{11} - 1$

$\qquad = 11 - 1 = 10$

37. $(3\sqrt{2} + \sqrt{3})(2\sqrt{3} - \sqrt{2})$

$\qquad = 6\sqrt{6} - 6 + 6 - \sqrt{6}$

$\qquad = 5\sqrt{6}$

45. $\sqrt{\dfrac{2}{3x}} \cdot \dfrac{\sqrt{3x}}{\sqrt{3x}} = \dfrac{\sqrt{6x}}{3x}$

49. $\sqrt[4]{\dfrac{g^3h^5}{9r^6}} \cdot \dfrac{\sqrt[4]{9r^2}}{\sqrt[4]{9r^2}} = \dfrac{h\sqrt[4]{9r^2g^3h}}{3r^2}$

53. $\dfrac{\sqrt[4]{32x^5y} \cdot \sqrt[4]{2xy^4}}{\sqrt[4]{4x^3y^2}} = \sqrt[4]{\dfrac{64x^6y^5}{4x^3y^2}} = \sqrt[4]{16x^3y^3}$

$\qquad\qquad\qquad\qquad = 2\sqrt[4]{x^3y^3}$

57. $\sqrt[6]{\sqrt[3]{x}} = (\sqrt[3]{x})^{1/6} = (x^{1/3})^{1/6} = x^{1/18}$

$\qquad = \sqrt[18]{x}$

59. $\sqrt{\dfrac{2m - 3p}{2m + 3p}} \cdot \sqrt{\dfrac{4m^2 + 12mp + 9p^2}{4m^2 - 9p^2}}$

$\qquad\qquad = \dfrac{\sqrt{2m - 3p}}{\sqrt{2m + 3p}} \cdot$

$\qquad\qquad\qquad \dfrac{\sqrt{(2m + 3p)^2}}{\sqrt{(2m + 3p)(2m - 3p)}}$

$\qquad\qquad = \dfrac{\sqrt{2m - 3p}}{(2m + 3p)} \dfrac{(2m + 3p)}{\sqrt{2m - 3p}}$

$\qquad\qquad = 1$, if $m \neq \pm \dfrac{3}{2}p$

61. $\dfrac{3}{1 - \sqrt{2}} \cdot \dfrac{1 + \sqrt{2}}{1 + \sqrt{2}} = \dfrac{3(1 + \sqrt{2})}{1 - 2}$

$\qquad\qquad = \dfrac{3(1 + \sqrt{2})}{1 - 2}$

$\qquad\qquad = -3(1 + \sqrt{2})$

63. $\dfrac{\sqrt{3}}{4 + \sqrt{3}} \cdot \dfrac{4 - \sqrt{3}}{4 - \sqrt{3}} = \dfrac{4\sqrt{3} - 3}{16 - 3} = \dfrac{4\sqrt{3} - 3}{13}$

65. $\dfrac{4}{2 - \sqrt{y}} \cdot \dfrac{2 + \sqrt{y}}{2 + \sqrt{y}} = \dfrac{4(2 + \sqrt{y})}{4 - y}$

69. $\dfrac{2}{\sqrt{5} - \sqrt{3} + 1} = \dfrac{2}{(\sqrt{5} + 1) - \sqrt{3}} \cdot$

$\qquad \dfrac{(\sqrt{5} + 1) + \sqrt{3}}{(\sqrt{5} + 1) + \sqrt{3}} = \dfrac{2(\sqrt{5} + 1 + \sqrt{3})}{5 + 2\sqrt{5} + 1 - 3}$

$\qquad = \dfrac{2(\sqrt{5} + 1 + \sqrt{3})}{3 + 2\sqrt{5}} \cdot \dfrac{3 - 2\sqrt{5}}{3 - 2\sqrt{5}}$

$\qquad = \dfrac{(2\sqrt{5} + 2 + 2\sqrt{3})(3 - 2\sqrt{5})}{9 - 4(5)}$

$\qquad = \dfrac{3(2\sqrt{5} + 2 + 2\sqrt{3}) - 2\sqrt{5}(2\sqrt{5} + 2 + 2\sqrt{3})}{-11}$

$\qquad = \dfrac{6\sqrt{5} + 6 + 6\sqrt{3} - 20 - 4\sqrt{5} - 4\sqrt{15}}{-11}$

$\qquad = \dfrac{14 + 4\sqrt{15} - 2\sqrt{5} - 6\sqrt{3}}{11}$

71. $\dfrac{12}{\sqrt[3]{4}} \cdot \dfrac{\sqrt[3]{2}}{\sqrt[3]{2}} = \dfrac{12\sqrt[3]{2}}{\sqrt[3]{8}} = \dfrac{12\sqrt[3]{2}}{2} = 6\sqrt[3]{2}$

75. $\dfrac{y}{\sqrt{x} + (y + z)} \cdot \dfrac{\sqrt{x} - (y + z)}{\sqrt{x} - (y + z)}$

$\qquad = \dfrac{y(\sqrt{x} - y - z)}{x - (y + z)^2}$

77. $\dfrac{2}{3 + \sqrt{1 + k}} \cdot \dfrac{3 - \sqrt{1 + k}}{3 - \sqrt{1 + k}}$

$\qquad = \dfrac{6 - 2\sqrt{1 + k}}{9 - (1 + k)} = \dfrac{6 - 2\sqrt{1 + k}}{8 - k}$

79. $\dfrac{m}{\sqrt{p}} + \dfrac{p}{\sqrt{m}} = \dfrac{m}{\sqrt{p}} \cdot \dfrac{\sqrt{p}}{\sqrt{p}} + \dfrac{p}{\sqrt{m}} \cdot \dfrac{\sqrt{m}}{\sqrt{m}}$

$\qquad = \dfrac{m\sqrt{p}}{p} + \dfrac{p\sqrt{m}}{m} = \dfrac{m^2\sqrt{p} + p^2\sqrt{m}}{mp}$

81. $\dfrac{\sqrt{x} + \sqrt{x+1}}{\sqrt{x} - \sqrt{x+1}} \cdot \dfrac{\sqrt{x} + \sqrt{x+1}}{\sqrt{x} + \sqrt{x+1}} = \dfrac{(\sqrt{x} + \sqrt{x+1})^2}{x - (x+1)}$

$= \dfrac{x + 2\sqrt{x}\,\sqrt{x+1} + (x+1)}{-1}$

$= -(2x + 1 + 2\sqrt{x(x+1)})$

83. $\dfrac{5}{\sqrt[3]{a} + \sqrt[3]{b}} \cdot \dfrac{\sqrt[3]{a^2} - \sqrt[3]{ab} + \sqrt[3]{b^2}}{\sqrt[3]{a^2} - \sqrt[3]{ab} + \sqrt[3]{b^2}}$

$= \dfrac{5(\sqrt[3]{a^2} - \sqrt[3]{ab} + \sqrt[3]{b^2})}{a + b}$

by using $(x + y)(x^2 - xy + y^2) = x^3 + y^3$

with $x = \sqrt[3]{a}$ and $y = \sqrt[3]{b}$.

85. $\dfrac{5}{(2 - \sqrt{3})(1 + \sqrt{2})} \cdot$

$\dfrac{(2 + \sqrt{3})(1 - \sqrt{2})}{(2 + \sqrt{3})(1 - \sqrt{2}}$

$= \dfrac{5(2 + \sqrt{3})(1 - \sqrt{2})}{(4 - 3)(1 - 2)}$

$= -5(2 + \sqrt{3})(1 - \sqrt{2})$

89. We have

$\dfrac{1}{\sqrt{3} - \sqrt{2}} \cdot \dfrac{\sqrt{3} + \sqrt{2}}{\sqrt{3} + \sqrt{2}} = \dfrac{\sqrt{3} + \sqrt{2}}{3 - 2}$

$= \sqrt{3} + \sqrt{2}.$

Thus, the smaller of $\dfrac{1}{\sqrt{3} - \sqrt{2}}$ and

$\dfrac{\sqrt{3} + \sqrt{2}}{2}$ is $\dfrac{\sqrt{3} + \sqrt{2}}{2}.$

91. We have

$\dfrac{1}{\sqrt{7} - \sqrt{2}} \quad \dfrac{\sqrt{7} + \sqrt{2}}{\sqrt{7} + \sqrt{2}} = \dfrac{\sqrt{7} + \sqrt{2}}{7 - 2} = \dfrac{\sqrt{7} + \sqrt{2}}{5}.$

Thus, the smaller of $\dfrac{\sqrt{7} + \sqrt{2}}{7}$ and

$\dfrac{1}{\sqrt{7} - \sqrt{2}}$ is $\dfrac{\sqrt{7} + \sqrt{2}}{7}.$

93. $\dfrac{\sqrt{3}}{2} \cdot \dfrac{\sqrt{3}}{\sqrt{3}} = \dfrac{3}{2\sqrt{3}}$

95. $\dfrac{1 + \sqrt{2}}{2} \cdot \dfrac{1 - \sqrt{2}}{1 - \sqrt{2}} = \dfrac{1 - 2}{2 - 2\sqrt{2}} = \dfrac{-1}{2 - 2\sqrt{2}}$

$= \dfrac{1}{2\sqrt{2} - 2}$

99. $\dfrac{\sqrt{x} + \sqrt{x+1}}{\sqrt{x} - \sqrt{x+1}} \cdot \dfrac{\sqrt{x} - \sqrt{x+1}}{\sqrt{x} - \sqrt{x+1}}$

$= \dfrac{x - (x+1)}{(\sqrt{x} - \sqrt{x+1})^2}$

$= \dfrac{-1}{x - 2\sqrt{x}\sqrt{x+1} + x + 1}$

$= \dfrac{-1}{2x + 1 - 2\sqrt{x(x+1)}}$

103. $\sqrt[4]{3.87 \times 10^{-4}} = \sqrt[4]{3.87} \cdot \sqrt[4]{10^{-4}}$

$= \sqrt[4]{3.87} \times 10^{-1}$

$\approx 1.40258 \times 10^{-1}$

$\approx 1.40 \times 10^{-1}$ in 3 significant
digits

107. $\sqrt{(4.721)^2 + (8.963)^2 - 2(4.721)(8.963)(.0468)}$

$= \sqrt{(22.287841) + (80.335369) - 3.9606206}$

$= \sqrt{98.662589} = 9.9329044,$ or

9.93 with three significant digits

111. $(3\sqrt{z^2 - 2} - 2\sqrt{z^2 + 2}) \cdot$

$(3\sqrt{z^2 - 2} + 2\sqrt{z^2 + 2})(\sqrt{5}z + \sqrt{26})^{-1}$

$= \dfrac{9(z^2 - 2) - 4(z^2 + 2)}{\sqrt{5}z + \sqrt{26}} = \dfrac{5z^2 - 26}{\sqrt{5}z + \sqrt{26}}$

$= \dfrac{(\sqrt{5}z + \sqrt{26})(\sqrt{5}z - \sqrt{26})}{\sqrt{5}z + \sqrt{26}} = \sqrt{5}z - \sqrt{26},$

provided $\sqrt{5}z + \sqrt{26} \neq 0$

113. Prove $\dfrac{\sqrt[n]{a}}{\sqrt[n]{b}} = \sqrt[n]{\dfrac{a}{b}}$ $(b \neq 0)$

Proof: $\left(\dfrac{\sqrt[n]{a}}{\sqrt[n]{b}}\right)^n = \dfrac{(\sqrt[n]{a})^n}{(\sqrt[n]{b})^n} = \dfrac{a}{b}$

Also, $\left(\sqrt[n]{\dfrac{a}{b}}\right)^n = \dfrac{a}{b}$

Thus, $\dfrac{\sqrt[n]{a}}{\sqrt[n]{b}} = \sqrt[n]{\dfrac{a}{b}}\;.$

114.
$$\sqrt[m]{\sqrt[n]{a}} = (\sqrt[n]{a})^{1/m}$$
$$= (a^{1/n})^{1/m}$$
$$= a^{\frac{1}{mn}}$$
$$= \sqrt[mn]{a}$$

116. Show $\sqrt{5 + 2\sqrt{6}} = \sqrt{2} + \sqrt{3}$

$$(\sqrt{5 + 2\sqrt{6}})^2 = 5 + 2\sqrt{6}$$
$$(\sqrt{2} + \sqrt{3})^2 = 2 + 2\sqrt{2}\sqrt{3} + 3$$
$$= 5 + 2\sqrt{6}$$

Hence, $\sqrt{5 + 2\sqrt{6}} = \sqrt{2} + \sqrt{3}.$

Section 1.8   Rational Exponents

Additional Examples

Example 1   Rewrite

$$\left[(2x - x^{-1/2})^2 + 8x^{1/2}\right]^{1/2}$$

using only positive exponents and rationalize the denominator.

Solution   Consider the following steps:

$$\left[(2x - x^{-1/2})^2 + 8x^{1/2}\right]^{1/2}$$
$$= \left[(4x^2 - 4x^{1/2} + x^{-1}) + 8x^{1/2}\right]^{1/2}$$
$$= [4x^2 + 4x^{1/2} + x^{-1}]^{1/2}$$
$$= [(2x + x^{-1/2})^2]^{1/2}$$
$$= 2x + x^{-1/2}$$
$$= 2x + \frac{1}{x^{1/2}}$$
$$= \frac{2x}{1} + \frac{1}{x^{1/2}}$$
$$= \frac{2x^{3/2} + 1}{x^{1/2}}, \text{ using } \frac{a}{b} + \frac{c}{d} = \frac{ad + bc}{bd},$$
$$= \frac{2x^{3/2} + 1}{x^{1/2}} \cdot \frac{x^{1/2}}{x^{1/2}}, \quad \text{rationalizing the denominator,}$$
$$= \frac{2x^2 + x^{1/2}}{x}.$$

Example 2   Simplify the expression

$$\frac{(3x+2)^{\frac{1}{2}}[\frac{1}{2}(2x+1)^{-\frac{1}{2}}(2)] - (2x+1)^{\frac{1}{2}}[\frac{1}{3}(3x+2)^{-\frac{1}{2}}(3)]}{3x + 2}$$

and express an answer with the numerator free of radicals.

Solution   Consider the following steps:

$$\frac{(3x+2)^{\frac{1}{2}}[\frac{1}{2}(2x+1)^{-\frac{1}{2}}(2)] - (2x+1)^{\frac{1}{2}}[\frac{1}{3}(3x+2)^{-\frac{1}{2}}(3)]}{3x + 2}$$

$$= \frac{\dfrac{2(3x + 2)^{1/2}}{2(2x + 1)^{1/2}} - \dfrac{3(2x + 1)^{1/2}}{3(3x + 2)^{1/2}}}{(3x + 2)}$$

$$= \frac{\dfrac{(3x + 2)^{1/2}}{(2x + 1)^{1/2}} - \dfrac{(2x + 1)^{1/2}}{(3x + 2)^{1/2}}}{(3x + 2)}$$

use $\frac{a}{b} + \frac{c}{d} = \frac{ad + bc}{bd}$,

$$= \frac{\dfrac{(3x+2)^{1/2}(3x+2)^{1/2} - (2x+1)^{1/2}(2x+1)^{1/2}}{(2x+1)^{1/2}(3x+2)^{1/2}}}{\dfrac{(3x + 2)}{1}}$$

$$= \frac{(3x + 2) - (2x + 1)}{(2x + 1)^{1/2}(3x + 2)^{1/2}} \cdot \frac{1}{(3x + 2)}$$

$$= \frac{x + 1}{(2x + 1)^{1/2}(3x + 2)^{3/2}}.$$

The numerator is free of radicals, so this is the desired result.

Selected Solutions

1. $4^{1/2} = \sqrt{4} = 2$

2. $27^{-2/3} = \dfrac{1}{27^{2/3}} = 1/(27^{1/3})^2$, so

   that $27^{-2/3} = \dfrac{1}{3^2} = \dfrac{1}{9}$

7. $(\frac{4}{9})^{-3/2} = (\frac{9}{4})^{3/2} = (\sqrt{\frac{9}{4}})^3 = (\frac{3}{2})^3 = \frac{27}{8}$

9. $(243)^{-3/5} = (\sqrt[5]{243})^{-3} = (3)^{-3}$
   $$= (\frac{1}{3})^3 = \frac{1}{27}$$

13. $(16p^4)^{1/2} = 16^{1/2}(p^4)^{1/2} = 4p^2$

17. $\sqrt[3]{x^2} = (x^2)^{1/3} = x^{2/3}$

21. $y^3 \sqrt[4]{y^6} = y^3(y^6)^{1/4} = y^3(y^{3/2})$
$$= y^{3+3/2} = y^{9/2}$$

25. $(m^{2/3})(m^{5/3}) = m^{2/3 + 5/3} = m^{7/3}$

29. $(2y^{3/4}z)(3y^{1/4}z^{-1/3})$
$$= 6y^{3/4 + 1/4}z^{1 - 1/3}$$
$$= 6yz^{2/3}$$

33. $\dfrac{a^{4/3}b^{1/2}}{a^{2/3}b^{-3/2}} = a^{4/3 - 2/3}\ b^{1/2 - (-3/2)}$
$$= a^{2/3}b^2$$

37. $\dfrac{(5x)^{-2}(x^{-3})^{-4}}{(25^{-1}x^{-3})^{-1}} = \dfrac{5^{-2}x^{-2}x^{12}}{25x^3}$
$$= \dfrac{x^{10}}{5^2(25)x^3}$$
$$= \dfrac{x^7}{625}$$

41. $\dfrac{6m^{-2}p - 5m^{-2}}{36m^{-3}p^2 - 25m^{-3}} = \dfrac{m^{-2}(6p - 5)}{m^{-3}(36p^2 - 25)}$
$$= \dfrac{m^{-2 - (-3)}(6p - 5)}{(6p + 5)(6p - 5)} = \dfrac{m}{6p + 5},$$
$$\text{if } p \neq \frac{5}{6}$$

45. $(r^{3/p})^{2p}(r^{1/p})p^2 = r^{\frac{3}{p} \cdot 2p} \cdot r^{\frac{1}{p} \cdot p^2}$
$$= r^6 \cdot r^p$$
$$= r^{p + 6}$$

49. $\dfrac{p^{\frac{1}{n}} \cdot p^{\frac{1}{m}}}{p^{-\frac{m}{n}}} = p^{\frac{1}{n} + \frac{1}{m} - (-\frac{m}{n})}$
$$= p^{\frac{1}{n} + \frac{1}{m} + \frac{m}{n}}$$
$$= p^{\frac{m + n + m^2}{nm}}$$

53. $-4k(k^{7/3} - 6k^{1/3}) = -4k^{1 + 7/3} +$
$$24k^{1 + 1/3}$$
$$= -4k^{10/3} + 24k^{4/3}$$

57. $(r^{1/2} - r^{-1/2})^2$
$$= (r^{1/2})^2 - 2r^{1/2}r^{-1/2} + (r^{-1/2})^2$$
$$= r - 2 + r^{-1} \quad \text{or}$$
$$= r - 2 + \frac{1}{r} \quad \text{or}$$
$$= \frac{r^2}{r} - \frac{2r}{r} + \frac{1}{r}$$
$$= \frac{r^2 - 2r + 1}{r}$$

59. $[(x^{1/2} - x^{-1/2})^2 + 4)]^{1/2}$
$$= [(x^{1/2} - \frac{1}{x^{1/2}})^2 + 4]^{1/2}$$
$$= \left[\left(\frac{x - 1}{x^{1/2}}\right)^2 + 4\right]^{1/2}$$
$$= [\frac{(x - 1)^2}{x} + 4]^{1/2}$$
$$= [\frac{x^2 - 2x + 1}{x} + 4]^{1/2}$$
$$= [\frac{x^2 - 2x + 1 + 4x}{x}]^{1/2}$$
$$= [\frac{x^2 + 2x + 1}{x}]^{1/2}$$
$$= [\frac{(x + 1)^2}{x}]^{1/2} = \frac{x + 1}{x^{1/2}}$$

63. $\sqrt[10]{p^8} \cdot \sqrt{p} = (p^8)^{1/10} \cdot p^{1/2}$
$$= p^{4/5} \cdot p^{1/2}$$
$$= p^{4/5 + 1/2} = p^{13/10}$$
$$= \sqrt[10]{p^{13}} = p\sqrt[10]{p^3}$$

65. $\sqrt[4]{p^2q^8} \cdot \sqrt[3]{p^5} = (p^2q^8)^{1/4} \cdot (p^5)^{1/3}$

$= p^{1/2}q^2 \quad p^{5/3}$

$= p^{1/2 + 5/3} \quad q^2$

$= p^{3/6}q^2$

$= p^2q^2\sqrt[6]{p}$

67. $\sqrt{m^2n} \ \sqrt[3]{m^4n^2} = (m^2n)^{1/2}(m^4n^2)^{1/3}$

$= (mn^{1/2})(m^{4/3}n^{2/3})$

$= m^{1 + 4/3}n^{1/2 + 2/3}$

$= m^{7/3}n^{7/6} = m^{14/6}n^{7/6}$

$= (m^{14}n^7)^{1/6} = \sqrt[6]{m^{14}\,n^7}$

$= m^2n\sqrt[6]{m^2n}$

69. $\sqrt[5]{m^3n^6} \cdot \sqrt[3]{m^4n^5} = (m^3n^6)^{1/5}(m^4n^5)^{1/3}$

$= m^{3/5}n^{6/5}m^{4/3}n^{5/3}$

$= m^{3/5 + 4/3}n^{6/5 + 5/3}$

$= m^{\frac{9 + 20}{15}}n^{\frac{18 + 25}{15}}$

$= m^{29/15}n^{43/15}$

$= mn^2 \ \sqrt[15]{m^{14}n^{13}}$

71. $4(p - 3)^{-1/2} + 2(p - 3)^{1/2}$

$= 2(p - 3)^{-1/2}[2 + (p - 3)]$

$= \dfrac{2}{(p - 3)^{1/2}}[p - 1] = \dfrac{2(p - 1)}{(p - 3)^{1/2}}$

75. $\dfrac{\dfrac{m}{\sqrt{m - 1}} - \sqrt{m - 1}}{(m - 1)} \cdot \dfrac{\sqrt{m - 1}}{\sqrt{m - 1}}$

$= \dfrac{m - (m - 1)}{(m - 1)^{3/2}}$

$= \dfrac{1}{(m - 1)^{3/2}}$

77. $4k^{7/4} + k^{3/4} = k^{3/4}(4k + 1)$

81. $p^{-3/4} - 2p^{-1/4} = p^{-1/4}(p^{-1/2} - 2)$

85. $\dfrac{(p + 1)^{1/2} - p(\frac{1}{2})(p + 1)^{-1/2}}{p + 1}$

$= \dfrac{(p + 1)^{1/2} - \dfrac{p}{2(p + 1)^{1/2}}}{(p + 1)}$

$= \dfrac{\dfrac{2(p + 1) - p}{2(p + 1)^{1/2}}}{p + 1} = \dfrac{\dfrac{p + 2}{2(p + 1)^{1/2}}}{(p + 1)}$

$= \dfrac{p + 2}{2(p + 1)^{1/2}} \quad \dfrac{1}{(p + 1)}$

$= \dfrac{p + 2}{2(p + 1)^{1/2}} \cdot$ Alternatively, we have

$\dfrac{(p + 1)^{1/2} - p(\frac{1}{2})(p + 1)^{-1/2}}{p + 1} \cdot$

$\dfrac{2(p + 1)^{1/2}}{2(p + 1)^{1/2}} = \dfrac{2(p + 1) - p}{2(p + 1)^{3/2}}$

$= \dfrac{p + 2}{2(p + 1)^{1/2}}$

87. $\dfrac{3(2x^2 + 5)^{1/3} - x(2x^2 + 5)^{-2/3}(4x)}{(2x^2 + 5)^{2/3}} \cdot$

$\dfrac{(2x^2 + 5)^{2/3}}{(2x^2 + 5)^{2/3}} = \dfrac{3(2x^2 + 5) - 4x^2}{(2x^2 + 5)^{4/3}}$

$= \dfrac{6x^2 + 15 - 4x^2}{(2x^2 + 5)^{4/3}}$

$= \dfrac{2x^2 + 15}{(2x^2 + 5)^{4/3}},$

by multiplying and dividing by the term with the negative exponent in the numerator.

89. $(x^{-1} - 5)^3(2)(2 - x^{-2})(2x^{-3}) +$

$\quad (2 - x^{-2})^2(3)(x^{-1} - 5)^2(-x^{-2})$

$= \dfrac{4}{x^3}(\frac{1}{x} - 5)^3(2 - \frac{1}{x^2}) -$

$\quad \dfrac{3}{x^2}(2 - \frac{1}{x^2})^2(\frac{1}{x} - 5)^2$

$= \dfrac{4}{x^3}(\frac{1 - 5x}{x})^3(\frac{2x^2 - 1}{x^2}) -$

$\quad \dfrac{3}{x^2}(\frac{2x^2 - 1}{x^2})^2(\frac{1 - 5x}{x})^2$

59) $\dfrac{x + 1}{x^{1/2}} = \dfrac{x}{x^{1/2}}\dfrac{x^{1/2}}{x^{1/2}} + \dfrac{1}{x^{1/2}} \quad = \dfrac{x^{1\frac{1}{2}}}{x} + \dfrac{1}{x^{1/2}} = x^{1/2} + \dfrac{1}{x^{1/2}} = x^{1/2} + x^{-1/2}$

$$= \frac{4(1 - 5x)^3(2x^2 - 1)}{x^8} -$$

$$\frac{3(2x^2 - 1)^2(1 - 5x)^2}{x^8}$$

$$= \frac{(1 - 5x)^2(2x^2 - 1)}{x^8} \cdot$$

$$[4(1 - 5x) - 3(2x^2 - 1)]$$

$$= \frac{(1 - 5x)^2(2x^2 - 1)}{x^8} \cdot$$

$$(4 - 20x - 6x^2 + 3)$$

$$= \frac{(1 - 5x)^2(2x^2 - 1)(7 - 20x - 6x^2)}{x^8}$$

91. If $a = 2$ and $b = \frac{1}{2}$, then a is rational, b is rational, but $a^b = \sqrt{2}$, which is irrational.

92. If $a = 1$ and $b = \sqrt{2}$, then a is rational, b is irrational, but $a^b = 1^{\sqrt{2}} = 1$, which is rational.

93. If $p = 2x^{1/2} + 3x^{2/3}$, then
$$p(64) = 2(64)^{1/2} + 3(64)^{2/3}$$
$$= 2(8) + 3(4)^2 = 16 + 3(16) = 64.$$

95. Use
$$(\frac{E_{large}}{E_{small}})^{3/2} \times 1{,}000{,}000$$

$$E_{large} = 48, \ E_{small} = 3$$
$$(\frac{48}{3})^{3/2} \times 10^6 = (16)^{3/2} \times 10^6$$
$$= 4^3 \times 10^6$$
$$= 64 \times 10^6$$

$64{,}000{,}000 should be spent on the large state.

97. $(\frac{28}{6})^{3/2} \times 10^6 = 10.0811522 \times 10^6$
$$= 10{,}081{,}152.2$$
Approximately 10,000,000 should be spent on the large state.

99. $D = 1.22x^{1/2}$
$x = 5000$ gives $D = 1.22(5000)^{1/2}$
$$= 1.22(100 \cdot 50)^{1/2}$$
$$= (1.22)(10)(5\sqrt{2})$$
$$\approx 86.3 \text{ miles}$$

103. $S = 28.6A^{0.32}$
$A = 1$ gives $S = 28.6(1)^{0.32}$
$$S = 28.6$$
or about 29 different species.

105. $S = 28.6(300)^{0.32}$
$$\approx 177.43726$$
$$S \approx 177$$

Section 1.9   Complex Numbers

Additional Examples
Example 1   Evaluate
$$\frac{1 + i}{2 - 1} \div \frac{4 - 3i}{1 - i}$$
and express the result in $a + bi$ form.
Solution   We evaluate by using the following steps:
$$\frac{1 + i}{2 - i} \div \frac{4 - 3i}{1 - i}$$
$$= \frac{1 + 1}{2 - i} \cdot \frac{1 - i}{4 - 3i}$$
$$= \frac{1 - i^2}{8 - 10i + 3i^2}$$
$$= \frac{2}{5 - 10i}$$
$$= \frac{2}{5 - 10i} \cdot \frac{5 + 10i}{5 + 10i},$$
and $(5 - 10i)(5 + 10i) = 25 - 100i^2,$
$$= \frac{10 + 20i}{25 + 100}$$
$$= \frac{10 + 20i}{125}$$
$$= \frac{2}{25} + \frac{4}{25}i$$

Example 2   Evaluate

$$\frac{4 - 3i}{5 + 2i} - \frac{2 + i}{3 - 2i}$$

and express the result in a + bi form.

Solution   We will evaluate by simplifying each fraction first and then performing the subtraction. This gives

$$\frac{4 - 3i}{5 + 2i} - \frac{2 + i}{3 - 2i}$$

$$= \frac{4 - 3i}{5 + 2i} \cdot \frac{5 - 2i}{5 - 2i} - \frac{2 + i}{3 - 2i} \cdot \frac{3 + 2i}{3 + 2i}$$

$$\frac{20 - 6 - 23i}{25 + 4} - \frac{6 - 2 + 7i}{9 + 4},$$

using $i^2 = -1$,

$$= \frac{14 - 23i}{29} - \frac{4 + 7i}{13}$$

$$= \frac{14}{29} - \frac{23}{29}i - \left(\frac{4}{13} + \frac{7}{13}i\right)$$

$$= \left(\frac{14}{29} - \frac{4}{13}\right) - \left(\frac{23}{29} + \frac{7}{13}\right)i$$

$$= \left(\frac{182 - 116}{377}\right) - \left(\frac{299 + 203}{377}\right)i$$

$$= \frac{66}{377} - \frac{502}{377}i$$

Example 3   Show that

$$\frac{\sqrt{2}}{2} + \frac{\sqrt{2}}{2}i$$

is a square root of i.

Solution   By definition $\sqrt{a} = b$ if and only if $a = b^2$. Thus, if we can show that

$$\left(\frac{\sqrt{2}}{2} + \frac{\sqrt{2}}{2}i\right)^2 = i$$

the result is verified. We have

$$\left(\frac{\sqrt{2}}{2} + \frac{\sqrt{2}}{2}i\right)^2 = \left(\frac{\sqrt{2}}{2}\right)^2 + 2\left(\frac{\sqrt{2}}{2}\right)\left(\frac{\sqrt{2}}{2}i\right) +$$

$$\left(\frac{\sqrt{2}}{2}i\right)^2$$

$$= \frac{2}{4} + \frac{4}{4}i + \frac{2}{4}i^2$$

$$= \frac{2}{4} + i - \frac{2}{4},$$

$$= i$$

This verifies the desired conclusion.

Selected Solutions

1.   -9i is imaginary and complex.

7.   2 + 5i is a complex number

9. $\sqrt{-100} = \sqrt{(-1)(100)} = \sqrt{100}\,\sqrt{-1} = 10i$

13. $-\sqrt{-39} = -\sqrt{39}\sqrt{-1} = -\sqrt{39}\,i$

17. $-6 - \sqrt{-196} = -6 - \sqrt{(14)^2\,(-1)}$
$$= -6 - 14i$$

21. $\sqrt{-5}\sqrt{-5} = (\sqrt{5}\,i)(\sqrt{5}\,i) = 5i^2 = -5,$
since $i^2 = -1$. Note that $\sqrt{a} \cdot \sqrt{b}$
$= \sqrt{ab}$ is valid only when $a \geq 0$ and
$b \geq 0$. If we tried to use this
property we would come up with
$\sqrt{-5}\,\sqrt{-5} = \sqrt{(-5)(-5)} = \sqrt{25} = 5,$
which is an incorrect answer.

25. $\dfrac{\sqrt{-40}}{\sqrt{-10}} = \dfrac{2\sqrt{10}i}{\sqrt{10}i} = 2.$ Note that we
could also write $\dfrac{\sqrt{-40}}{\sqrt{-10}} = \dfrac{\sqrt{40}i}{\sqrt{10}i}$
$$= \frac{\sqrt{40}}{\sqrt{10}} = \sqrt{\frac{40}{10}} = \sqrt{4} = 2.$$

29.   (3 + 2i) + (4 - 3i)
$$= (3 + 4) + (2i - 3i) = 7 - i$$

33.   (2 - 5i) - (3 + 4i) - (-2 + i)
$$= (2 - 3 + 2) - 5i - 4i - i$$
$$= 1 - 10i$$

37.   (2 + i)(3 - 2i)
$$= (2 + i)\,3 + (2 + i)(-2i)$$
$$= 6 + 3i - 4i - 2i^2$$
$$= 6 + 3i - 4i - 2(-1) = 8 - i$$

41. $(-3 + 2i)^2 = (-3)^2 + 2(-3)(2i) + (2i)^2$
$$= 9 - 12i + 4(-1)$$
$$= 5 - 12i$$

45. $(2 + 3i)(2 - 3i) = 4 - 9i^2$
$$= 4 + 9$$
$$= 13$$

47. $(\sqrt{6} + i)(\sqrt{6} - i) = 6 - i^2$
$$= 6 + 1$$
$$= 7$$

49. $i(3 - 4i)(3 + 4i) = i(9 - 16i^2)$
$$= i(9 + 16)$$
$$= 25i$$

51. $3i(2 - i)^2 = 3i(4 - 4i + i^2)$
$$= 3i(4 - 4i - 1)$$
$$= 3i(3 - 4i)$$
$$= 9i - 12i^2$$
$$= 9i - 12(-1)$$
$$= 12 + 9i$$

55. $\dfrac{4 - 3i}{4 + 3i} = \dfrac{4 - 3i}{4 + 3i} \cdot \dfrac{4 - 3i}{4 - 3i}$
$$= \dfrac{(4 - 3i)^2}{16 + 9}$$
$$= \dfrac{16 - 24i + 9i^2}{25}$$
$$\dfrac{7 - 24i}{25} \text{ or } \dfrac{7}{25} - \dfrac{24}{25}i$$

59. $\dfrac{-3 + 4i}{2 - i} \cdot \dfrac{2 + i}{2 + i} = \dfrac{-6 + 8i - 3i + 4i^2}{4 - i^2}$
$$= \dfrac{-6 + 5i - 4}{4 + 1}$$
$$= \dfrac{-10 + 5i}{5} = -2 + i$$

63. $\dfrac{1 - \sqrt{-5}}{3 + \sqrt{-4}} = \dfrac{1 - i\sqrt{5}}{3 + i\sqrt{4}} = \dfrac{1 - i\sqrt{5}}{3 + 2i} \cdot \dfrac{3 - 2i}{3 - 2i}$
$$= \dfrac{3 - 3\sqrt{5}i - 2i + 2\sqrt{5}i^2}{9 - 4i^2}$$
$$= \dfrac{3 - 2\sqrt{5} - 2i - 3\sqrt{5}i}{9 + 4}$$
$$= \dfrac{(3 - 2\sqrt{5}) - (2 + 3\sqrt{5})i}{13}$$

67. $i^9 = i^4 \cdot i^4 \cdot i = (1)(1)i = i$

69. $i^{12} = (i^4)^3 = 1^3 = 1$

71. $i^{43} = i^{40} \cdot i^3 = (i^4)^{10} \cdot i^3$
$$= 1^{10} \cdot i^3 = -i$$

75. $i^{-15} = i^{-16} \cdot i = (i^4)^{-4} \cdot i$
$$= (1)^{-4} \cdot i = 1 \cdot i = i$$

79. $\dfrac{6 + 2i}{5 - i} \cdot \dfrac{1 - 3i}{2 + 6i} = \dfrac{6 - 16i - 6i^2}{10 + 28i - 6i^2}$
$$= \dfrac{12 - 16i}{16 + 28i}$$
$$= \dfrac{4(3 - 4i)}{4(4 + 7i)}$$
$$= \dfrac{3 - 4i}{4 + 7i}$$
$$= \dfrac{3 - 4i}{4 + 7i} \cdot \dfrac{4 - 7i}{4 - 7i}$$
$$= \dfrac{12 - 37i + 28i^2}{16 - 49i^2}$$
$$= \dfrac{-16 - 37i}{16 + 49}$$
$$= \dfrac{-16 - 37i}{65}$$
$$\text{or} = \dfrac{-16}{65} - \dfrac{37}{65}i$$

83. $\dfrac{6 + 2i}{1 + 3i} + \dfrac{2 - i}{1 - 3i}$ using $\dfrac{a}{b} + \dfrac{c}{d} = \dfrac{ad + bc}{bd}$
$$= \dfrac{(6 + 2i)(1 - 3i) + (1 + 3i)(2 - i)}{(1 + 3i)(1 - 3i)}$$
$$= \dfrac{(6 - 16i - 6i^2) + (2 + 5i - 3i^2)}{1 - 9i^2}$$
$$= \dfrac{8 - 11i - 9i^2}{1 + 9}$$
$$= \dfrac{17 - 11i}{10} \text{ or } \dfrac{17}{10} - \dfrac{11}{10}i$$

85. $\dfrac{6 + 3i}{1 - i} - \dfrac{2 - i}{4 + i}$ using $\dfrac{a}{b} - \dfrac{c}{d} = \dfrac{ad - bc}{bd}$
$$= \dfrac{(6 + 3i)(4 + i) - (1 - i)(2 - i)}{(1 - i)(4 + i)}$$
$$= \dfrac{(24 + 18i + 3i^2) - (2 - 3i + i^2)}{4 - 3i - i^2}$$

$$= \frac{22 + 21i + 2i^2}{5 - 3i}$$

$$= \frac{20 + 21i}{5 - 3i} \cdot \frac{5 + 3i}{5 + 3i}$$

$$= \frac{100 + 165i + 63i^2}{25 + 9}$$

$$= \frac{37 + 165i}{34} \quad \text{or} \quad \frac{37}{34} + \frac{165}{34}i$$

87. If $a + bi = 23 + 5i$, then we must have $a = 23$ and $b = 5$.

91. If $a + 3i = 5 + 3bi + 2a$, then $a + 3i = (5 + 2a) + 3bi$, and this implies that $a = 5 + 2a$, while $3 = 3b$. Thus, $-a = 5$, or $a = -5$ and $b = 1$.

93. If $i(2b + 6) - 3 = 4(bi + a)$, then $-3 + (2b + 6)i = 4a + 4bi$. Equating the real parts and imaginary parts gives $-3 = 4a$, or $a = \frac{-3}{4}$, and $2b + 6 = 4b$, or $2b = 6$, $b = 3$.

95. If we let $z = 6 - 5i$, then
$$4i - 3z = 4i - 3(6 - 5i)$$
$$= 4i - 18 + 15i = -18 + 19i.$$

97. Let $z = a + bi$, so that $\bar{z} = a - bi$.
Then $\bar{\bar{z}} = (\bar{\bar{z}}) = (\overline{a - bi}) = a + bi$, which is z. Hence, $\bar{\bar{z}} = z$.

98. Let $z = a + bi$, so that $\bar{z} = a - bi$. Thus, if $\bar{z} = z$, then $a + bi = a - bi$, which is possible if and only if the real parts are identical (i.e. $a = a$) and the imaginary parts are equal. Hence, we must have $b = -b$, or $2b = 0$, so that $b = 0$.

99. Let $z = a + bi$, so that $-z = -a - bi$, and $(\overline{-z}) = -a + bi$. Also, $\bar{z} = a - bi$ and $-(\bar{z}) = -a + bi$. Hence $(\overline{-z}) = -(\bar{z})$.

100. Let $z = a + bi$, so that $\bar{z} = b - bi$.
Then $z\,\bar{z} = (a + bi)(a - bi) =$
$a^2 - b^2i^2 = a^2 - b^2(-1) = a^2 + b^2$
a real number.

101. If $z_1 = a + bi$ and $z_2 = c + di$,
then $z_1 + z_2 = z_2 + z_1$.
Proof: $z_1 + z_2 = (a + bi) + (c + di)$
$$= (a + c) + (b + d)i$$
$$= (c + a) + (d + b)i$$
$$= (c + di) + (a + bi)$$
$$= z_2 + z_1$$

102. Prove $z_1 z_2 = z_2 z_1$
Proof: $z_1 z_2 = (a + bi)(c + di)$
$$= (ac - bd) + (ad + bc)i$$
$z_2 z_1 = (c + di)(a + bi)$
$$= (ca - db) + (cb + da)i$$
$$= (ac - bd) + (ad + bc)i$$
$$= z_1 z_2$$

103. Prove $(z_1 + z_2) + z_3 = z_1 + (z_2 + z_3)$.
Proof: Let $z_1 = a_1 + ib_1$, $z_2 = a_2 + ib_2$, and $z_3 = a_3 + ib_3$.
Then $(z_1 + z_2) = (a_1 + a_2) + (b_1 + b_2)i$,
so that $(z_1 + z_2) + z_3 = [(a_1 + a_2) + (b_1 + b_2)i] + (a_3 + ib_3)$
$$= [(a_1 + a_2) + a_3] + [(b_1 + b_2) + b_3]i$$
$$= [a_1 + (a_2 + a_3)] + [b_1 + (b_2 + b_3)]i,$$
since the associative property for addition holds for real numbers $a_1, a_2, a_3, b_1, b_2, b_3$,
$$= (a_1 + b_1 i) + [(a_2 + a_3) + (b_2 + b_3)i]$$
$$= z_1 + (z_2 + z_3)$$

105. Prove that $z_1(z_2 + z_3) = z_1 z_2 + z_1 z_3$
Proof: Let $z_1 = a_1 + b_1 i$, $z_2 = a_2 + b_2 i$
$z_3 = a_3 + b_3 i$. Then $z_2 + z_3 = (a_2 + a_3) +$

$(b_2 + b_3)i$, so that $z_1(z_2 + z_3) =$

$(a_1 + b_1 i)[(a_2 + a_3) + (b_2 + b_3)i]$

$= a_1(a_2 + a_3) + a_1(b_2 + b_3)i +$

   $b_1 i(a_2 + a_3) + b_1 i(b_2 + b_3)i$

$= a_1 a_2 + a_1 a_3 +$

   $(a_1 b_2 + a_1 b_3 + a_2 b_1 + a_3 b_1)i -$

   $b_1(b_2 + b_3)$

$= [a_1 a_2 - b_1 b_2) + (a_1 b_2 + a_2 b_1)i] +$

   $[(a_1 a_3 - b_1 b_3) + (a_1 b_3 + a_3 b_1)]$

$= (a_1 + b_1 i)(a_2 + b_2 i) + (a_1 + b_1 i) \cdot$

   $(a_3 + b_3 i)$

$= z_1 z_2 + z_1 z_3$

107. Let $z_1 = a + bi$ and $z_2 = c + di$ be

   complex numbers. Then $z_1 z_2 =$

   $(a + bi)(c + di)$

   $= (ac - bd) + (ad + bc)i$,

   which is a complex number

109. If $z = 4 - 3i$, then $8z - z^2$

   $= 8(4 - 3i) - (4 - 3i)^2$

   $= 32 - 24i - (16 - 24i + 9i^2)$

   $= 32 - 24i - 16 + 24i + 9$,

   $[i^2 = -1]$, $= 25$.

111. $(a + bi)^2 = a^2 - b^2 + 2abi$, and

   if $(a + bi)^2$ is real, then we must

   have $2ab = 0$. This implies that

   either $a = 0$ or $b = 0$. Hence, the

   solution is all real numbers or all

   imaginary numbers.

115. $\frac{\sqrt{2}}{2} + \frac{\sqrt{2}}{2}i$ is a square root of i

   because $(\frac{\sqrt{2}}{2} + \frac{\sqrt{2}}{2}i)^2 = \frac{2}{4} +$

      $2(\frac{\sqrt{2}}{2})(\frac{\sqrt{2}}{2}i) - \frac{2}{4} = i$.

Chapter 1 Review Exercises

Selected Solutions

1. commutative property of multipli-
    cation $6 \cdot 4 = 4 \cdot 6$

5. $4 \cdot 6 + 4 \cdot 12 = 4(6 + 12)$
    distributive property

9. $(4 + 2 \cdot 8) \div 3 = (4 + 16) \div 3$
    $\qquad\qquad = 20 \div 3 = \frac{20}{3}$

13. 6 is the only natural number in K

17. $-\sqrt{7}$, $\frac{\pi}{4}$, and $\sqrt{11}$ are the irrational
    numbers in K

21. $\sqrt{36} = 6$, so the answer is a, b, c,
    d, and f; natural, whole, integer,
    rational, and real.

25. e and f; irrational and real

29. $|6 - 4| = 2$, $-|-2| = -2$, $|8 + 1| = 9$,
    and $-|3 - (-2)| = -5$, so the proper
    numerical order is $-|3 - (-2)|$,
    $-|-2|$, $|6 - 4|$, and $|8 + 1|$ or -5,
    -2, 2, 9.

31. $|3 - \sqrt{7}|$
    Since $9 > 7$ it follows that
    $3 = \sqrt{9} > \sqrt{7}$.
    Thus $|3 - \sqrt{7}| = -\sqrt{7}$.

35. (a) A, -2 $d(A, B) = |-2 - (-1)|$
        B, -1 $= |-2 + 1|$
        C, 10 $= |-1| = 1$
    (b) $d(A, B) + d(B, C) = 1 + d(B, C)$
                      $= 1 + |-1 - 10|$
                      $= 1 + |-11|$
                      $= 1 + 11$
                      $= 12$

39. $|x + y| = -|x| - |y|$
$\quad\quad\quad = -(|x| + |y|)$

is true only if $x = y = 0$.

Since $-(|x| + |y|) \le 0$ and $|x + y| \ge 0$

$|x + y| = -(|x| + |y|)$ is true only if

$|x + y| = 0$ and $-(|x| + |y|) = 0$

so, $x = y = 0$ is the only choice.

43. We have

$(-6x^2 - 4x + 11) + (-2x^2 - 11x + 5)$

$= -6x^2 - 4x + 11 - 2x^2 - 11x + 5$

$= -8x^2 - 15x + 16$

47. $(x + 2y - z)^2$

$= (x + 2y - z)(x + 2y - z)$

$= x(x + 2y - z) + 2y(x + 2y - z) - z(x + 2y - z)$

$= x^2 + 2xy - xz + 2xy + 4y^2 - 2yz - xz - 2yz + z^2$

$= x^2 + 4xy + 4y^2 - 2xz - 4yz + z^2$

51. $7z^2 - 9z^3 + z = = z(9z^2 - 7z - 1)$

or $z(7z - 9z^2 + 1)$

55. $30m^5 - 35m^4n - 25m^3n^2$

$\quad = 5m^3(6m^2 - 7mn - 5n^2)$

$\quad = 5m^3(3m - 5n)(2m + n)$

59. $(x - 1)^2 - 4$

$= [(x - 1) - 2][(x - 1) + 2]$

$= (x - 3)(x + 1)$

63. $3(m - n) + 4k(m - n) = (m - n)(3 + 4k)$

67. $y^{2k} - 9 = (y^k - 3)(y^k + 3)$

71. $\dfrac{x^2 + x - 2}{x^2 + 5x + 6} \div \dfrac{x^2 + 3x - 4}{x^2 + 4x + 3}$

$= \dfrac{(x + 2)(x - 1)}{(x + 3)(x + 2)} \div \dfrac{(x + 4)(x - 1)}{(x + 3)(x + 1)}$

$= \dfrac{(x + 2)(x - 1)}{(x + 3)(x + 2)} \cdot \dfrac{(x + 3)(x + 1)}{(x + 4)(x - 1)}$

$= \dfrac{x + 1}{x + 4}$

75. $\dfrac{1}{4y} + \dfrac{8}{5y} = \dfrac{5}{20y} + \dfrac{32}{20y} = \dfrac{37}{20y}$

79. $\dfrac{\frac{1}{p} + \frac{1}{q}}{1 - \frac{1}{pq}} \cdot \dfrac{pq}{pq} = \dfrac{q + p}{pq - 1}$

83. $\dfrac{(p^4)(p^{-2})}{(p^{-6})} = \dfrac{p^2}{p^{-6}} = p^2 \cdot p^6 = p^8$

87. $\dfrac{(2x^{-3})^2(3x^2)^{-2}}{6(x^2y^3)} = \dfrac{4x^{-6} \cdot 3^{-2}x^{-4}}{6x^2y^3}$

$= \dfrac{4x^{-10}}{9 \cdot 6x^2y^3}$

$= \dfrac{2}{9 \cdot 3x^{12}y^3}$

$= \dfrac{2}{27x^{12}y^3}$

91. $\sqrt{\dfrac{7}{3r}} = \sqrt{\dfrac{7}{3r} \cdot \dfrac{3r}{3r}} = \dfrac{\sqrt{21r}}{\sqrt{9r^2}} = \dfrac{\sqrt{21r}}{3r}$

95. $(\sqrt[3]{2} + 4)(\sqrt[3]{2^2} - 4\sqrt[3]{2} + 16)$

$= \sqrt[3]{2}(\sqrt[3]{2^2} - 4\sqrt[3]{2} + 16) + 4(\sqrt[3]{2} - 4\sqrt[3]{2} + 16)$

$= \sqrt[3]{2^3} - 4\sqrt[3]{2^2} + 16\sqrt[3]{2} + 4\sqrt[3]{2} - 16\sqrt[3]{2} + 64$

$= 2 + 64 = 66$

99. $\dfrac{3}{\sqrt{5}} - \dfrac{2}{\sqrt{45}} + \dfrac{6}{\sqrt{80}}$

$= \dfrac{3}{\sqrt{5}} - \dfrac{2}{3\sqrt{5}} + \dfrac{6}{4\sqrt{5}}$

$= \dfrac{3}{\sqrt{5}} - \dfrac{2}{3\sqrt{5}} + \dfrac{3}{2\sqrt{5}}$

$= \dfrac{18}{6\sqrt{5}} - \dfrac{4}{6\sqrt{5}} + \dfrac{9}{6\sqrt{5}}$

$= \dfrac{23}{6\sqrt{5}} \left(\dfrac{\sqrt{5}}{\sqrt{5}}\right) = \dfrac{23\sqrt{5}}{30}$

103. $\dfrac{1}{\sqrt{5} + 2} = \dfrac{1}{\sqrt{5} + 2} \quad \dfrac{\sqrt{5} - 2}{\sqrt{5} - 2}$

$$= \dfrac{\sqrt{5} - 2}{5 - 4}$$

$$= \sqrt{5} - 2$$

107. $(8r^{\frac{3}{4}}s^{\frac{2}{3}})(2r^2s^{\frac{5}{3}}) = 16r^{(\frac{3}{4}+\frac{3}{2})}s^{(\frac{2}{3}+\frac{5}{3})}$

$$= 16r^{\frac{9}{4}}s^{\frac{7}{3}}$$

111. $\dfrac{m^{2+p}m^{-2}}{m^{3p}} = m^{(2+p)-2-3p}$

$$= m^{-2p}$$

$$= \dfrac{1}{m^{2p}}$$

115. $(p + p^{\frac{1}{2}})(3p - 5)$

$$= 3p^2 + 3p^{\frac{3}{2}} - 5p - 5p^{\frac{1}{2}}$$

119. $(6 - 5i) + (2 + 7i) - (3 - 2i)$

$$= (6 + 2 - 3) + i(-5 + 7 + 2)$$

$$= 5 + 4i$$

123. $(2 + 6i)^2 = 4 + 24i + 36i^2$

$$= 4 - 36 + 24i$$

$$= -32 + 24i$$

127. $i^{17} = i^{16} \cdot i = (1^4)^4 \cdot i$

$$= (1)^4 \cdot i = i, \text{ since } 1^4 = 1.$$

131. $\dfrac{2 + i}{1 - 5i} \cdot \dfrac{1 + i}{3 - i} = \dfrac{2 + 3i + i^2}{3 - 16i + 5i^2}$

$$= \dfrac{2 - 1 + 3i}{3 - 5 - 16i}$$

$$= \dfrac{1 + 3i}{-2 - 16i} \cdot \dfrac{-2 + 16i}{-2 + 16i}$$

$$= \dfrac{-2 + 10i + 48i^2}{4 - 256i^2}$$

$$= \dfrac{-2 - 48 + 10i}{4 + 256}$$

$$= \dfrac{-50 + 10i}{260}$$

$$= \dfrac{-5 + i}{26}$$

$$= -\dfrac{5}{26} + \dfrac{1}{26}i$$

135. $\sqrt{-12} = \sqrt{4(-3)} = 2\sqrt{-3} = 2\sqrt{3}i$ or $2i\sqrt{3}$

137. $(|a| + a)(|a| - a) = |a|^2 - a^2 = 0,$

$\quad$ since $|a|^2 = a^2.$

138. $\sqrt{[2a^4+(b^2-a^2)^2-(a^2-b^2)^2][a^6-(-a^2)^3]}$

$$= \sqrt{[2a^4 + 0][a^6 + a^6]}$$

$\quad$ since $(b^2 - a^2)^2 = (a^2 - b^2)^2$

$$= \sqrt{2a^4 \cdot 2a^6} = \sqrt{4a^{10}} = 2|a|^5$$

139. $b(a - c)^2 + a(b + c)^2 = c^2(ab + c^2)$

Proof: $b(a - c)^2 + a(b + c)^2$

$$= b(a^2 - 2ac + c^2) + a(b^2 + 2bc + c^2)$$

$$= a^2b - 2abc + bc^2 + ab^2 + 2abc + ac^2$$

$$= a^2b + bc^2 + ab^2 + ac^2$$

$$= a^2b + b(a + b) + ab^2 + a(a + b)$$

$$\text{since } a + b = c^2$$

$$= a^2b + ab + b^2 + ab^2 + a^2 + ab$$

$$= a^2b + 2ab + b^2 + ab^2 + a^2$$

$$= a^2 + 2ab + b^2 + a^2b + ab^2$$

$$= (a + b)^2 + ab(a + b)$$

$$= (a + b)[(a + b) + ab]$$

$$= c^2(c^2 + ab) \text{ since } a + b = c^2$$

141. $x + |x| = x - |x|$ $\qquad$ Find x.
Subtract x; giving $|x| = -|x|$.
$x = 0$ is the only solution.

142. If $(x + 1)^2 = (|x| + 1)^2$ then $x \geq 0$.
Proof: $(x + 1)^2 = x^2 + 2x - 1$ and
$(|x| + 1)^2 = |x|^2 + 2|x| + 1 = x^2 +$
$2|x| + 1$. Since $(x+1)^2 = (|x| + 1)^2$

then, $x^2 + 2x + 1 = x^2 + 2|x| + 1$.
Simplifying gives
$$x = |x|.$$
Therefore $x \geq 0$.

143. $0 < a < 1$ and $a + b = 1$, so that
$(a + b)^2 = 1$ or $a^2 + 2ab + b^2 = 1$,
which implies $a^2 + b^2 = 1 - 2ab <$
1, since $2ab > 0$.

145. Find the order relations among 1,
a, a^2, $\sqrt{a}$, $\frac{1}{a}$, b, b^2, $\sqrt{b}$, and $\frac{1}{b}$ if
$\sqrt{b} < a < b$. We can assume $a > 0$,
$b > 0$ since the numbers $\sqrt{a}$, $\frac{1}{a}$, $\sqrt{b}$,
$\frac{1}{b}$ exist. If $\underline{a < b}$, then $\underline{\sqrt{a} < \sqrt{b}}$
and $a^2 < b^2$. Also, if $\sqrt{a} < \sqrt{b}$,
then $\sqrt{a}\sqrt{a} < \sqrt{a}\sqrt{b}$, or $a < \sqrt{ab}$, and
$\sqrt{a}\sqrt{b} < \sqrt{b}\sqrt{b}$, or $\sqrt{ab} < b$. Thus,
$\underline{a < b}$. Using $0 < a < b$, we have
$\frac{1}{a} > \frac{1}{b}$, or $\frac{1}{b} < \frac{1}{a}$. Since $\sqrt{b} < a$,
then $(\sqrt{b})^2 < a^2$, or $\underline{b < a^2}$. We have
$\underline{\sqrt{a} < \sqrt{b} < a < b < a^2 < b^2}$ and
$\frac{1}{b} < \frac{1}{a}$. Since $\sqrt{a} < a = \sqrt{a}\sqrt{a}$, we
can multiply by $\frac{1}{\sqrt{a}}$ to arrive at
$1 < \sqrt{a}$, and since $\sqrt{a} < a$ we have
$1 < a$, so that $\frac{1}{a} < 1$. Thus, we
can conclude that $\frac{1}{b} < \frac{1}{a} < 1 < \sqrt{a} <$
$\sqrt{b} < a < b < a^2 < b^2$.

146. Find the order relations among
1, a, a^2, $\sqrt{a}$, $\frac{1}{a}$, b, b^2, b, $\frac{1}{b}$, if
$b < a < \sqrt{b}$.
Since $b < \sqrt{b}$, $\sqrt{b} \cdot \sqrt{b} < \sqrt{b}$ or $\sqrt{b} < 1$.
Thus, $b < a < \sqrt{b} < 1$.

Next, since $a < \sqrt{b}$, $a^2 < (\sqrt{b})^2 = b$,
so, $a^2 < b < a < \sqrt{b} < 1$.
Since $b < a$, $\sqrt{b} < \sqrt{a}$ and since $a < 1$,
$\sqrt{a} < 1$, so,
$a^2 < b < a < \sqrt{b} < \sqrt{a} < 1$.
Since $b < a < 1$, $1 < \frac{1}{a} < \frac{1}{b}$; so
$a^2 < b < a < \sqrt{b} < \sqrt{a} < 1 < \frac{1}{a} < \frac{1}{b}$.
Finally, since $b < a$, $b^2 < a^2$, so we
get the final set of relations:
$b^2 < a^2 < b < a < \sqrt{b} < \sqrt{a} < 1 < \frac{1}{a} < \frac{1}{b}$.

147. If $a > 0$, show that $a + \frac{1}{a} \geq 2$
Proof: Since $a > 0$, if we could
show that $a^2 + 1 \geq 2a$ then we would
be done. Since $a^2 + 1 \geq 2a$ is
equivalent to $a^2 - 2a + 1 \geq 0$, we
will show that $a^2 - 2a + 1 \geq 0$.
We know $a^2 - 2a + 1 = (a - 1)^2 \geq 0$.
so $a + \frac{1}{a} \geq 2$.

Chapter 1 Test

1. (a) Find $-|-6 + 3| - |3| + |-7|$.

    (b) If $A = -3$, $B = 2$, and $C = 5$, find $d(B, A) + d(C, A)$.

2. Perform the addition $(-3x^2 + 5x - 6) + (5x^2 - 4x - 2)$.

3. Evaluate $(3x + 2)(x^2 - 3x - 7)$.

4. Perform the multiplication $(2x - 3)(4x^2 + 6x + 9)$.

5. Simplify $\dfrac{(2a^2)^3 (5a^3)^2}{(2a^3)^3}$, assuming $a \neq 0$.

6. Factor (a) $2x^2 + 5x - 12$, and (b) $15x^2 + 17x - 42$.

7. Factor $81x^4 - 16$ as completely as possible.

8. Factor $27x^3 + 8y^3$ as completely possible.

9. Perform the indicated operation and simplify $\dfrac{x^2 + 2x - 3}{x^2 - 3x + 2} \div \dfrac{x^2 - 9}{x^2 - 4}$.

10. Simplify $\dfrac{2}{3a} - \dfrac{1}{5a}$.

11. Simplify the expression $\dfrac{\frac{a}{b} + \frac{b}{a}}{\frac{1}{ab}}$.

12. Simplify the expression $(\dfrac{x + h}{x + h + 2} - \dfrac{x}{x + 2}) \div h$, if $h \neq 0$.

13. Rewrite the expression $\dfrac{x^{-1} - y^{-1}}{x^{-1}y^{-1}}$ using only positive exponents and simplify.

14. Simplify the expression $\dfrac{(4a^{-3})^{-2}(2a^2)^3}{8(2a^{-2})^4}$, if $a \neq 0$.

15. Perform the multiplication $(\sqrt[3]{3} - 2)(\sqrt[3]{9} + 2\sqrt[3]{3} + 4)$.

16. Evaluate $(2x - y + 3a)^2$.

17. Simplify the expression $\dfrac{\sqrt[3]{8t^5r^3}\sqrt[3]{2t^3r^7}}{\sqrt[3]{81t^4r^2}}$.

18. Express $\dfrac{4}{\sqrt{3}} + \dfrac{3}{\sqrt{12}} - \dfrac{17}{\sqrt{48}}$ as a single fraction whose denominator is free of radicals.

19. Evaluate $(27a^9)^{-2/3}$.

20. Express $\dfrac{4}{2 + \sqrt{3}}$ as a fraction whose denominator is free of radicals.

21. Express $\dfrac{\sqrt{x + h} - \sqrt{x}}{h}$ as a fraction whose numerator is free of radicals, if $h \neq 0$.

22. Find the product $\dfrac{1}{2}(3x^{1/6})(-2x^{3/2})(-5x^{3/4})$.

23. Simplify the expression $2x[\dfrac{1}{2}(x + 2)^{-1/2}] + 2(x + 2)^{1/2}$ to arrive at a single fraction whose numerator is free of radicals.

24. Show that $\sqrt{1 + (\dfrac{1}{2}x^{1/2} - \dfrac{1}{2}x^{-1/2})^2}$ can be simplified to the fraction $\dfrac{x + 1}{2\sqrt{x}}$, if $x > 0$.

25. Find the product $(5 + 2i)(3 - 4i)$.

26. Perform the division $\dfrac{7 - 4i}{2 + i}$ and express the quotient in $a + bi$ form

27. Evaluate $(2 - 3i)^3$ and express the product in $a + bi$ form.

28. Evaluate $\dfrac{3 - i}{1 + i} + \dfrac{1 - i}{2i}$ and place the result in $a + bi$ form.

29. Show that $\sqrt{15 + 4\sqrt{14}} = 2\sqrt{2} + \sqrt{7}$.

30. Show that $2 + 3i$ is a square root of $-5 + 12i$. Also, show that $-2 - 3i$ is a square root of $-5 + 12i$.
    (Answers for this test are on page 359.)

CHAPTER 2   Equations and Inequalities

Section 2.1   Linear Equations

Additional Examples

Example 1   Solve the equation

$$5[x + 6(\frac{2x + 1}{3}) + 2] = 3x + 9.$$

Solution   Simplifying from inside out we have

$$5[x + 6(\frac{2x + 1}{3}) + 2] = 3x + 9$$

$$5[x + 2(2x + 1) + 2] = 3x + 9,$$

since $6/3 = 2$,

$$5[x + 4x + 2 + 2] = 3x + 9$$

$$5[5x + 4] = 3x + 9$$

$$25x + 20 = 3x + 9$$

$$25x - 3x = 9 - 20$$

$$22x = -11$$

$$x = -\frac{1}{2}.$$

$x = -\frac{1}{2}$ is a solution and the

solution set is $\{-\frac{1}{2}\}$.

Example 2   Solve the equation

$$\frac{2}{3} + \frac{1}{6}x = \frac{7}{2} - \frac{1}{5}x.$$

Solution   Arranging all terms involving x on one side of the equation, and all constant terms on the other side gives

$$\frac{2}{3} + \frac{1}{6}x = \frac{7}{2} - \frac{1}{5}x$$

$$\frac{1}{6}x + \frac{1}{5}x = \frac{7}{2} - \frac{2}{3}$$

$$(\frac{1}{6} + \frac{1}{5})x = \frac{7}{2} - \frac{2}{3}$$

$$(\frac{5 + 6}{30})x = \frac{21 - 4}{6}, \text{ using } \frac{a}{b} \pm \frac{c}{d} = \frac{ad \pm bc}{bd},$$

$$\frac{11}{30}x = \frac{17}{6}$$

$$x = \frac{17}{6} \div \frac{11}{30}$$

$$x = \frac{17}{6} \cdot \frac{30}{11}$$

$$x = \frac{(17)(5)}{(1)(11)}, \text{ cancelling 6,}$$

$$x = \frac{85}{11}.$$

The solution set is the set $S = \{\frac{85}{11}\}$.

Example 3   Find a value of k so that the equation

$$-3(x + 2k) - 3 = 4k + 3 \text{ has the}$$

solution set $S = \{5\}$.

Solution   Using the algebraic properties to simplify gives

$$-3(x + 2k) - 3 = 4k + 3$$

$$-3x - 6k - 3 = 4k + 3$$

$$-3x = 4k + 3 + 6k + 3,$$

adding 6k and 3 to both sides,

$$-3x = 10k + 6$$

$$x = \frac{10k + 6}{-3}.$$

Since $x = (10k + 6)/-3$ is a solution, this number must be 5 since the solution set is $\{5\}$. Hence,

$$\frac{10k + 6}{-3} = 5$$

$$10k + 6 = -15$$

$$10k = -21, \text{ so that } k = \frac{-21}{10}.$$

Example 4   Solve the equation

$$\frac{3}{3p + 2} - \frac{4}{2p - 1} = \frac{-5}{2p - 1}.$$

Solution   To solve this equation, we shall clear the fractions. A common denominator is $(3p + 2)(2p - 1)$. Multiplying both sides by $(3p + 2)(2p - 1)$ gives

$$(\frac{3}{3p+2})(3p+2)(2p-1) - (\frac{4}{2p-1})(3p+2)(2p-1)$$

$$= (\frac{-5}{2p - 1})(3p + 2)(2p - 1),$$

or $3(2p - 1) - 4(3p + 2) = -5(3p + 2)$,

provided $p \neq -\frac{2}{3}$ and $p \neq \frac{1}{2}$. Hence,

$$6p - 3 - 12p - 8 = -15p - 10$$

$$-6p - 11 = -15p - 10$$

$$-6p + 15p = -10 + 11$$

$$9p = 1$$

$$p = \frac{1}{9}.$$

The solution set is the set $S = \{1/9\}$.

Selected Solutions

1. $x^2 + 5x = x(x + 5)$ is an identity, since it is just a statement of the distributive property which is true for all values of x.

5. $\frac{m + 3}{m} = 1 + \frac{3}{m}$ is an identity:

$\frac{m + 3}{m} = \frac{m}{m} + \frac{3}{m} = 1 + \frac{3}{m}$

9. $3x - 5 = 7$

$-6x + 10 = 14$

Not equivalent; the solution to the first is 4, the solution to the second is -2/3.

13. $\frac{x}{x - 2} = \frac{2}{x - 2}$

$x = 2$

Not equivalent, since x = 2 is not in the domain of the first.

17. $4x - 1 = 15$

add 1: $4x = 16$

divide by 4: $x = 4$

The solution set is {4}.

21. $\frac{5}{6}k - 2k + \frac{1}{3} = \frac{2}{3}$

$5k - 12k + 2 = 4$ multiply by 6

$-7k + 2 = 4$ combine

$-7k = 2$ subtract 2

$k = -\frac{2}{7}$ divide by -7

The solution set is the set $\{\frac{-2}{7}\}$.

25. $2[m - (4 + 2m) + 3] = 2m + 2$

$2[m - 4 - 2m + 3] = 2m + 2$

$2[-m - 1] = 2m + 2$

$-2m - 2 = 2m + 2$

$-4 = 4m$, so that

$m = -1$

The solution set is {-1}.

27. $\frac{3x - 2}{7} = \frac{x + 2}{5}$

$5(3x - 2) = 7(x + 2)$ multiply by 35

$15x - 10 = 7x + 14$ combine

$15x = 7x + 24$ add 10

$8x = 24$ subtract 7x

$x = 3$ divide by 8

The solution set is {3}.

29. $\frac{3k - 1}{4} = \frac{5k + 2}{8}$

$2(3k - 1) = 5k + 2$ multiply both sides by 8

$6k - 2 = 5k + 2$

$6k = 5k + 4$ add 2 to both sides

$k = 4$ subtract 5x from both sides

The solution set is {4}.

33. $\frac{1}{4p} + \frac{2}{p} = 3$

$1 + 8 = 12p$ multiply by 4p

$9 = 12p$, so that $p = \frac{3}{4}$.

The solution set is $\{\frac{3}{4}\}$.

37. $\frac{2r}{r - 1} = 5 + \frac{2}{r - 1}$

$2r = 5(r - 1) + 2$ multiply by r - 1

$2r = 5r - 3$ combine

$2r + 3 = 5r$ add 3

$3 = 3r$ subtract 2r

$1 = r$ divide

The equation has no solution since r = 1 is not in the domain of the original equation. The solution set is ∅.

41. $\frac{4}{x - 3} - \frac{8}{2x + 5} + \frac{3}{x - 3} = 0$

multiply by $(x - 3)(2x + 5)$

$4(2x + 5 - 8(x - 3) + 3(2x + 5) = 0$

combine

$8x + 20 - 8x + 24 + 6x + 15 = 0$

$6x + 59 = 0$

$6x = -59$

$x = \frac{-59}{6}$

The solution set is $\{\frac{-59}{6}\}$.

45. $\dfrac{2p}{p - 2} = 3 + \dfrac{4}{p - 2}$

$2p = 3(p - 2) + 4$ multiply by $p - 2$

$2p = 3p - 6 + 4$

$2p = 3p - 2$ combine

$-p = -2$, so that $p = 2$. However, $p = 2$ does not check since we cannot divide by zero. The solution set is $S = \emptyset$.

49. $(3x - 4)^2 - 5 = 3(x + 5)(3x + 2)$

$9x^2 - 24x + 16 - 5 = 3(3x^2 + 17x + 10)$,

$9x^2 - 24x + 11 = 9x^2 + 51x + 30$,

$-75x = 19$, "combine like terms"

$x = \dfrac{-19}{75}$.

The solution set is $\{\dfrac{-19}{75}\}$.

53. $ax + b = 3(x - a)$

$ax + b = 3x - 3a$ multiply

$ax = 3x - b - 3a$ add $-b$

$ax - 3x = -b - 3a$ subtract $3x$

$x(a - 3) = -b - 3a$ factor

$x = \dfrac{-b - 3a}{a - 3}$ divide by $(a - 3)$

$x = \dfrac{3a + b}{3 - a}$ multiply by $\dfrac{-1}{-1}$

57. $a^2x + 3x = 2a^2$

$x(a^2 + 3) = 2a^2$ factor

$x = \dfrac{2a^2}{a^2 + 3}$ divide

61. Let $f = 800$, $q = 36$, and $n = 18$ to find

$u = f \cdot \dfrac{n(n + 1)}{q(q + 1)} = 800 \dfrac{18(19)}{36(37)}$

$= \dfrac{800(1)(19)}{2(37)} = \dfrac{400(19)}{37} \approx \$205.41.$

65. Given $x^2 + 2x - 15 = x^2 - 3x$, factoring both sides gives $(x + 5)(x - 3) = x(x - 3)$, but cancelling the term $(x - 3)$ is improper _if_ you are cancelling zero. Note that the correct method of solution would be

$x^2 + 2x - 15 = x^2 - 3x$,

$2x - 15 = -3x$,   subtracting x^2

$5x - 15 = 0$,   adding $3x$

$5x = 15$,   adding 15

$x = 3$.   dividing by 5.

The solution set is $\{3\}$, and hence, cancelling the term $x - 3$ is improper.

67. $-5x + 11x - 2 = k + 4$ is equivalent to $6x - 2 = k + 4$ or $6x - 6 = k$. Substituting $x = 2$ gives $6(2) - 6 = k$, or $k = 6$. Hence, $k = 6$ will make the original equation have the solution $x = 2$.

69. Letting $x = 2$ in the equation $\sqrt{x + k} = 0$ gives $\sqrt{2 + k} = 0$. If $k = -2$, then $\sqrt{2 + k} = \sqrt{2 - 2} = 0$. Hence, $k = -2$ will make the original equation have the solution $x = 2$.

71. $9.06x + 3.59(8x - 5)$

$= 12.07x + .5612$,

$9.06x + 28.72x - 17.95$

$= 12.07x + .5612$,

$37.78x - 12.07x$

$= .5612 + 17.95$,

or $25.71x = 18.5112$, so that

$x = \dfrac{18.5112}{25.71} = 0.72.$

The solution set is $\{0.72\}$.

75. $\dfrac{2.63r - 8.99}{1.25} - \dfrac{3.90r - 1.77}{2.45} = r,$

this gives,

$2.45(2.63r - 8.99) - 1.25(3.90r - 1.77)$
$= (1.25)(2.45)r,$

multiplying each term by
(1.25)(2.45),

$6.4435r - 22.0255 - 4.8750r + 2.2125$
$= 3.0625r,$

$1.5685r - 3.0625r$
$= 22.0255 - 2.2125$

$-1.4940r = 19.8130$

$r = -\dfrac{19.8130}{1.4940} = -13.261714$

or

$r = -13.26$, rounded to the
nearest hundreth.

Section 2.2 Formulas and Applications

Additional Examples

Example 1 Solve the equation

$$A = \frac{24f}{b(p + 1)}$$

for p.

Solution Assuming the denominator is
not zero, we have

$$A = \frac{24f}{b(p + 1)}$$

$$b(p + 1)A = 24f$$

$$p + 1 = \frac{24f}{bA}$$

$$p = \frac{24f}{bA} - 1.$$

Example 2 If John can paint the dining
room in his house in three hours,
while his wife Mary can paint the
same room in 4 hours working alone,
how long will it take for both of
them working together to paint the
room.

Solution If John can paint the room
in 3 hours, he completes 1/3 of the
job each hour. Similarly, Mary
paints 1/4 of the room each hour.
Let x be the number of hours it
takes for them to complete the
painting of the room working together,
then they complete 1/x of the painting job each hour. Consider the
table below.

	$\begin{pmatrix}\text{Amount of}\\\text{work}\\\text{per hour}\end{pmatrix}$ x	$\begin{pmatrix}\text{Number}\\\text{of}\\\text{hours}\end{pmatrix}$	= Work
John	$\frac{1}{3}$	1	$\frac{1}{3}$
Mary	$\frac{1}{4}$	1	$\frac{1}{4}$
Together	$\frac{1}{x}$	1	$\frac{1}{x}$

Then we have (work done by John) +
(work by Mary) = work together, or
$1/x = 1/3 + 1/4$. This gives

$$\frac{1}{x} = \frac{4 + 3}{12}, \ \frac{1}{x} = \frac{7}{12}, \text{ or } x = \frac{12}{7}.$$

Hence it will take them 12/7 of an
hour or approximately 1 hour, 43
minutes.

Example 3 A boat that can travel at a
rate of r miles per hour in still
water makes a 36 mile trip downstream
in 3 hours while it takes 4 hours to
make the return trip upstream in the
boat. Find the rate of the current
of the stream.

Solution We are given that the boat
travels at a rate of r miles per hour
in still water. Let x be the rate of
the current of the stream (in miles
per hour). Using the formula,
distance = (rate) x (time),
we have the following:

(a) Traveling downstream, the boat,
aided by the velocity of the water,
travels at a rate of r + x miles per

hour and completes the 36 mile trip in 3 hours. Hence,

$$36 = (r + x)(3),$$

or $3(r + x) = 36$.

(b) Traveling upstream, the boat, impeded by the velocity of the water, travels at a rate of $r - x$ miles per hour and completes the 36 mile trip in 4 hours. Hence,

$$36 = (r - x)(4),$$

or $4(r - x) = 36$.

We wish to solve for x. To do so, let us consider the results obtained in (a) and (b). In (a) we have

$$3(r + x) = 36$$
$$r + x = 12,$$

or $\quad\quad r = 12 - x,$

and in (b) we find that

$$4(r - x) = 36$$
$$r - x = 9,$$

or $\quad\quad r = 9 + x.$

Equating the two values for r gives

$$9 + x = 12 - x$$
$$x + x = 12 - 9$$
$$2x = 3,$$

or $\quad\quad x = \frac{3}{2}$ miles per hour

The current in the stream is 1.5 miles per hour.

Example 4   A bank lends a certain amount of money to Alex at 14% annual rate, lends Burt $1000 less than the amount Alex received at a 17% annual rate, and lends Carol $2000 more than Alex received at a 12% annual rate. If the combined interest over a one year period amounts to $1,252.50, how much money was lent to each person.

Solution   Let x be the amount of money the bank lent to Alex. Then Burt borrowed x - 1000 dollars, and Carol borrowed x + 2000 dollars. The amount of interest Alex owes for one year is .14x and similarly,

Burt owes .17(x - 1000), and Carol owes .12(x + 2000). Since the total interest for the year is $1252.50 we have

$$.14x + .17(x - 1000) + .12(x + 2000)$$
$$= 1252.50$$
$$.14x + 17x + .12x - 170 + 240$$
$$= 1252.50$$
$$.43x = 1252.50 - 70$$
$$.43x = 1182.50$$
$$x = \frac{1182.50}{.43}$$
$$x = \frac{118250}{43}$$
$$x = \$2750.$$

Hence, Alex borrowed $2750, Burt borrowed $1750, and Carol borrowed $4750.

Selected Solutions

1.   PV = k for V

divide by P: $V = \frac{k}{p}$

5.   Solve $V = V_0 + gt$ for g.

$V - V_0 = gt$, subtract V_0

$\frac{V - V_0}{t} = g$, divide by t.

9.   Solve $A = \frac{1}{2}(B + b)h$ for B.

$\quad\quad 2A = (B + b)h \quad\quad$ multiply by 2

$\quad\quad 2A = Bh + bh \quad\quad$ multiply

$\quad 2A - bh = Bh \quad\quad\quad\quad$ subtract bh

$\quad\quad\quad B = (2a - bh)/h \quad$ divide by h

or $\quad\quad B = \frac{2A}{h} - b$

13. $g = \frac{4\pi^2 \ell}{t^2}$ for ℓ

$gt^2 = 4\pi^2 \ell \quad\quad\quad\quad$ multiply by t^2,

$\frac{gt^2}{4\pi^2} = \ell \quad\quad\quad\quad\quad$ divide by $4\pi^2$

17. Solve $A = \dfrac{24f}{B(p+1)}$ for f.

$AB(p+1) = 24f$,   multiply by $B(p+1)$

$f = \dfrac{AB(p+1)}{24}$,   divide by 24

21. Draw a picture, label it.

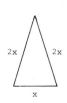

let x = length of the shortest side

2x = length of the other sides

perimeter = x + 3x + 2x

30 = 5x

x = 6

The short side is 6 cm long.

23. If the box contains 11 nickels, then there is 11(.05) = $.55 in the box. In order for the box to contain $2.30, we must add $2.30 - $.55 = $1.75 to the box. If x is the number of quarters to be added, then .25x = 1.75, or x = 7. Hence, 7 quarters must be added.

25. Make a chart:

% alcohol	amount of solution	amount of alcohol
10	7	(.10)7 = .7
100	x	1.00x = x
30	x + 7	.30(x + 7)

.7 + x = .30(x + 7)

.7 + x = .3x + 2.1

.7x = 1.4

x = 2

Add 2 liters.

$\dfrac{x}{50} + \dfrac{x}{55} = 32$

$\left(2d = (50 + 55)32 \right)$

$2d =$

27. Make a chart. Change all prices to price per kilogram:

Type of nut	Price per kg	Number of kg in mix	Total value
cashews	$16	10	160
hazelnuts	$12	8	96
peanuts	$4	x	4x
mixture	$10	18 + x	10(18+ x)

The total value of the three nuts should equal the value of the mix.

160 + 96 + 4x = 10(18 + x)

256 + 4x = 180 + 10x

76 = 6x

$x = \dfrac{38}{3}$ or $12\frac{2}{3}$kg

29. Make a table:

% Isooctane	liters
99	200
94	x
97	200 + x

we then have

.99(200) + .94x = .97(200 + x)

198 + .94x = 194 + .97x

4 = .03x

or $x = \dfrac{4}{.03} = \dfrac{400}{3}$

= 133.33...

Answer: add $133\frac{1}{3}$ liters of 94 octane gasoline.

31. Make a chart; use d = rt so t = d/r

	d	r	t
A to F	x	50	$\dfrac{x}{50}$
F to A	x	55	$\dfrac{x}{55}$

$\dfrac{x}{50} + \dfrac{x}{55} = 32$

11x + 10x = 17600   multiply by 5·10·11

21x ≈ 17600

x ≈ 838

The distance is about 840 miles

33. Make a chart:

	d	r	t
Janet	5x	5	x
Russ	7x	7	x

Find x when $7x - 5x = \frac{1}{2}$

$$2x = \frac{1}{2}$$

$$x = \frac{1}{4} \text{ hour or } 15$$
minutes.

35. Make a chart. Change the times to hours.

	d	r	t
upstream	$\frac{1}{3}(x-5)$	$x-5$	$\frac{1}{3}$
downstream	$\frac{1}{4}(x+5)$	$x+5$	$\frac{1}{4}$

$x =$ boat speed,

$5 =$ current speed

$\frac{1}{3}(x-5) = \frac{1}{4}(x+5)$ same distance traveled

$4(x - 5) = 3(x + 5)$

$4x - 20 = 3x + 15$

$x = 35$ kph

37. Let x = the time it takes them working together.

Mark can clean $\frac{1}{9}$ of the house in 1 hour, Wendy $\frac{1}{6}$ of the house in one hour, and together they can clean $\frac{1}{x}$ of the house in one hour. Thus,

$$\frac{1}{9} + \frac{1}{6} = \frac{1}{x}$$

$$\frac{2 + 3}{18} = \frac{1}{x}$$

$$\frac{5}{18} = \frac{1}{x}$$

$$\frac{18}{5} = x.$$

It takes them $\frac{18}{5}$ hours $= 3\frac{3}{5}$ hours $= 3$ hours 36 minutes.

39. Let x = the time it takes A to produce the maximum pollution.

2x = the time it takes B to produce the maximum pollution.

$$\frac{1}{x} + \frac{1}{2x} = \frac{1}{26}$$

multiply by 26x: $26 + 13 = x$

$$39 = x$$

B takes 78 hours and A takes 39 hours.

41. Let x = the time required to fill the pool with both pipes open.

$\frac{1}{5} - \frac{1}{8} = \frac{1}{x}$ (filled - emptied)

$$\frac{3}{40} = \frac{1}{x}$$

$$x = \frac{40}{3} = 13\frac{1}{3} \text{ hours,}$$

or x = 13 hours and 20 minutes.

43. Let x = the regular price. Then .85x = sale price.

$.85x = 49$

$x = \$57.65$

45. Let x = amount invested at 13%. Then 20,000 - x is invested at 16%. Then

$.13x + .16(20,000 - x) = 2840$

$.13x + 3200 - .16x = 2840$

$-.03x = -360$

$$x = \frac{-360}{-.03}$$

$$= \frac{36000}{3}$$

$$= 12,000$$

Thus, $12,000 was invested at 13% and $8,000 was invested at 16%.

49. Let x = price of land with 15% profit 120,000 - x = price of land with 10% loss.

Total profit $= .15x - .10(120000 - x)$
$$= 5500$$

$.15x - 12000 + .10x = 5500$

$.25x = 17,500$

$x = 70,000$

She paid $70,000 for the profitable land and $50,000 for the unprofitable land.

51. Let x = weekly pay before deductions
    then x - .26x = take home pay = 198
$$.74x = 198$$
$$x = \$267.57$$

53. Let x be the amount invested at 7%, so that 20,000 - x is the amount invested at 10%. Then if we attempt to solve the problem we arrive at
$$.07x + .10(20,000 - x) = 2500$$
$$.07x - .10x + 2000 = 2500$$
$$-.03x = 500$$
$$x = \frac{500}{-.03}$$
$$= \frac{-50000}{3}$$
$$= -16,666.67$$

which is an absurd solution. Note that if all $20,000 was invested at the larger rate of 10%, the annual interest would be .10(20,000) = $2,000. Thus, the problem as stated has no solution.

55. Let x = amount invested at 12%. Then 2x is the amount invested at 10%, and x + 2x = 60,000. Hence, 3x = 60,000, or x = 20,000: $20,000 invested at 12% and $40,000 invested at 10%.
    Note: .12(20,000) + .10(40,000) = 2400 + 4000 = $6400, the required amount of interest. However, we were given more information than was necessary to solve the problem.

57. Let x = number of $5 bills. Then n - x is the number of $10 bills and we have the equation
5x + 10(n - x) = v, or -5x + 10n = v.
Thus 5x = 10n - v, or $x = \frac{10n - v}{5}$

is the number of $5 bills. Also,
$$n - x = n - \frac{10n - v}{5} = \frac{v - 5n}{5} \text{ is}$$
the number of $10 bills.

58. Let 0 < a < b < c < 100. Let x = amount of a% solution. Make a chart.

%	amount of solution	amount of pure
c	m	.01cm
a	x	.01ax
b	m + x	.01b(m + x)

.01cm + .01ax = .01b(m + x)
Multiply by 100:
$$cm + ax = b(m + x)$$
$$cm + ax = bm + bx$$
$$ax - bx = bm - cm$$
$$(a - b)x = m(b - c)$$
$$x = \frac{m(b - c)}{a - b} \text{ liters}$$

59. Let x = number of individuals. We can estimate by assuming the ratio of $\frac{\text{individuals}}{\text{marked}}$ remains constant. Then
$$\frac{x}{100} = \frac{b}{c}, \text{ or } x = \frac{100b}{c}.$$

60. Let x = amount at m%
    then B - x = amount at n%
$$.01mx + .01n(B - x) = I$$
Multiply by 100:
$$mx + n(B - x) = 100I$$
$$mx + nB - nx = 100I$$
$$mx - nx = 100I - nB$$
$$(m - n)x = 100I - nB$$
$$x = \frac{100I - nB}{m - n} \quad \text{amount at m\%}$$
$$B - x = \frac{mB - 100I}{m - n} \quad \text{at n\%}$$

Section 2.3 Quadratic Equations

Additional Examples

Example 1   Solve the equation
$(2x - 1)(3x + 2) = -1$.

Solution No conclusion can be drawn from the product of two numbers equal to -1. Multiplying and rearranging terms gives

$$(2x - 1)(3x + 2) = -1$$
$$6x^2 + x - 2 = -1$$
$$6x^2 + x - 1 = 0.$$

This equation factors to give

$$(3x - 1)(2x + 1) = 0.$$

Hence,

$$3x - 1 = 0 \quad \text{or} \quad 2x + 1 = 0$$
$$3x = 1 \quad \text{or} \quad 2x = -1$$
$$x = \frac{1}{3} \quad \text{or} \quad x = -\frac{1}{2}.$$

The solution set is the set

$$S = \{-\frac{1}{2}, \frac{1}{3}\}.$$

Example 2   Solve the equation
$\frac{1}{x} + \frac{1}{x - 2} = 3$.

Solution We note that we cannot let x be the numbers 0 or 2 because we cannot divide by zero. A common denominator is $x(x - 2)$. Multiplying by $x(x - 2)$ and simplifying gives

$$\frac{1}{x} + \frac{1}{x - 2} = 3$$
$$(\frac{1}{x} + \frac{1}{x - 2})x(x - 2) = 3x(x - 2),$$

provided $x \neq 0, 2$,

$$\frac{1}{x} \cdot x(x - 2) + \frac{1}{x - 2} \cdot x(x - 2)$$
$$= 3x(x - 2)$$
$$(x - 2) + x = 3x(x - 2)$$
$$2x - 2 = 3x^2 - 6x$$
$$0 = 3x^2 - 6x - 2x + 2$$

or $3x^2 - 8x + 2 = 0.$

Using the quadratic formula with $a = 3$, $b = -8$, and $c = 2$, we have

$$x = \frac{-b \pm \sqrt{b^2 - 4ac}}{2a}$$
$$x = \frac{8 \pm \sqrt{64 - 4(3)(2)}}{2(3)}$$
$$x = \frac{8 \pm \sqrt{64 - 24}}{6}$$
$$x = \frac{8 \pm \sqrt{40}}{6}$$
$$x = \frac{8 \pm 2\sqrt{10}}{6}$$
$$x = \frac{4 \pm \sqrt{10}}{3}.$$

The solution set is the set

$$S = \{\frac{4 - \sqrt{10}}{3}, \frac{4 + \sqrt{10}}{3}\}.$$

Example 3 Use the quadratic formula to solve the quadratic equation

$$(3 + 2i)x^2 - 4x + (3 - 2i) = 0.$$

Solution Using $a = 3 + 2i$, $b = -4$, and $c = 3 - 2i$, we have

$$x = \frac{-b \pm \sqrt{b^2 - 4ac}}{2a}$$
$$x = \frac{4 \pm \sqrt{16 - 4(3 + 2i)(3 - 2i)}}{2(3 + 2i)}$$
$$x = \frac{4 \pm \sqrt{16 - 52}}{6 + 4i}$$
$$x = \frac{4 \pm \sqrt{-36}}{6 + 4i}$$
$$= \frac{4 \pm 6i}{6 + 4i}.$$

The numbers $\frac{4 + 6i}{6 + 4i}$ and $\frac{4 - 6i}{6 + 4i}$ are solutions. However,

$$\frac{4 - 6i}{6 + 4i} = \frac{4 - 6i}{6 + 4i} \cdot \frac{6 - 4i}{6 - 4i}$$
$$= \frac{24 - 24 - 52i}{36 + 16}$$
$$= \frac{-52i}{52}$$
$$= -i$$

and

$$\frac{4 + 6i}{6 + 4i} = \frac{4 + 6i}{6 + 4i} \cdot \frac{6 - 4i}{6 - 4i}$$
$$= \frac{24 + 24 + 20i}{36 + 16}$$
$$= \frac{48 + 20i}{52}$$

$$= \frac{12 + 5i}{13}$$

$$= \frac{12}{13} + \frac{5}{13}i.$$

The solution set is the set

$$S = \{-i, \frac{12}{13} + \frac{5}{13}i\}.$$

Example 4 The sum of a number and its reciprocal is 169/60. Find the number.

Solution Let x be the number. Then we have

$$x + \frac{1}{x} = \frac{169}{60}.$$

A common denominator is 60x. Multiplying by 60x gives the following:

$$60x(x + \frac{1}{x}) = 60x(\frac{169}{60})$$

$$60x^2 + 60 = 169x$$

$$60x^2 - 169x + 60 = 0.$$

By trial and error, the equation factors into

$$(12x - 5)(5x - 12) = 0,$$

so that

$$12x - 5 = 0 \quad \text{or} \quad 5x - 12 = 0$$

$$x = \frac{5}{12} \quad \text{or} \quad x = \frac{12}{5}.$$

These numbers are reciprocals and they add to give 169/60. Hence, the number is either 5/12 or 12/5.

Selected Solutions

3. $x^2 = 27$

$$x = \sqrt{27} \quad \text{or} \quad x = -\sqrt{27}$$

$$x = 3\sqrt{3} \quad \text{or} \quad x = -3\sqrt{3}$$

The solution set is $\{-3\sqrt{3}, 3\sqrt{3}\}$.

5. $(m - 3)^2 = 5$

$$m - 3 = \pm\sqrt{5}$$

$$m = 3 \pm \sqrt{5}$$

The solution set is $\{3 \pm \sqrt{5}\}$.

9. $p^2 - 5p + 6 = 0$

$$(p - 3)(p - 2) = 0 \quad \text{Factor}$$

$$p - 3 = 0 \quad \text{or} \quad p - 2 = 0$$

$$p = 3 \quad \text{or} \quad p = 2$$

The solution set is $\{2, 3\}$.

11. $6z^2 - 5z - 50 = 0$

$$6z^2 + 15z - 20z - 50 = 0 \quad \text{Factor}$$

$$3z(2z + 5) - 10(2z + 5) = 0$$

$$(2z + 5)(3z - 10) = 0$$

$$2z + 5 = 0, \quad \text{or} \quad 3z - 10 = 0$$

$$2z = -5 \quad \text{or} \quad 3z = 10$$

$$z = \frac{-5}{2} \quad \text{or} \quad z = \frac{10}{3}$$

The solution set is $\{\frac{-5}{2}, \frac{10}{3}\}$.

15. $p^2 - 8p + 15 = 0$

$$p^2 - 8p = -15$$

and $\frac{1}{2}(-8) = -4$, so we add $(-4)^2 = 16$ to both sides.

$$p^2 - 8p + 16 = 1$$

$$(p - 4)^2 = 1$$

$$p - 4 = \pm\sqrt{1} = \pm 1$$

so $p = 4 \pm 1$

Hence, $p = 5$ or $p = 3$.

The solution set is $\{3, 5\}$.

17. $x^2 - 2x - 4 = 0$

$$x^2 - 2x = 4.$$

Then $\frac{1}{2}(-2) = -1$, so add $(-1)^2 = 1$ to both sides.

$$x^2 - 2x + 1 = 4 + 1$$

$$(x - 1)^2 = 5,$$

so $x - 1 = \pm\sqrt{5}$ or $x = 1 \pm \sqrt{5}.$

The solution set is $\{1 \pm \sqrt{5}\}$.

21. $m^2 - m - 1 = 0$

Using the quadratic formula with $a = 1$, $b = -1$, $c = -1$ gives

$$m = \frac{-(-1) \pm \sqrt{(-1)^2 - 4(1)(-1)}}{2(1)}$$

$$= \frac{1 \pm \sqrt{5}}{2}$$

The solution set is $\{\frac{1 \pm \sqrt{5}}{2}\}$.

23. $2s^2 + 2s = 3$

$2s + 2s - 3 = 0$.

Use the quadratic formula with $a = 2$, $b = 2$, $c = -3$:

$$s = \frac{-2 \pm \sqrt{(2)^2 - 4(2)(-3)}}{2(2)}$$

$$s = \frac{-2 \pm \sqrt{28}}{4} = \frac{-2 \pm 2\sqrt{7}}{4}$$

$$s = \frac{2(-1 \pm \sqrt{7})}{4} = \frac{-1 \pm \sqrt{7}}{2}$$

The solution set is $\{\frac{-1 \pm \sqrt{7}}{2}\}$.

27. $n^2 + 4 = 3n$

Get equal to 0 as $n - 3n + 4 = 0$. Here $a = 1$, $b = -3$, $c = 4$. Use the quadratic formula.

$$n = \frac{-(-3) \pm \sqrt{(-3)^2 - 4(1)(4)}}{2(1)}$$

$$= \frac{3 \pm \sqrt{9 - 16}}{2}$$

$$= \frac{3 \pm \sqrt{-7}}{2}$$

$n = \frac{3 \pm i\sqrt{7}}{2}$.   The solution set is $\{\frac{3 \pm i\sqrt{7}}{2}\}$.

29. $2m^2 = m - 1$

Get equal to 0.

$2m^2 - m + 1 = 0$

$a = 2$, $b = -1$, $c = 1$.

$$m = \frac{-(-1) \pm \sqrt{(-1)^2 - 4(2)(1)}}{2(2)}$$

$$= \frac{1 \pm \sqrt{1 - 8}}{4} = \frac{1 \pm \sqrt{-7}}{4}$$

$$= \frac{1 \pm i\sqrt{7}}{4}.$$ the solution set is $\{\frac{1 \pm i\sqrt{7}}{4}\}$.

33. $4 - \frac{11}{x} - \frac{3}{x^2} = 0$

$x^2(4 - \frac{11}{x} - \frac{3}{x^2}) = 0 \cdot x^2$, if $x \neq 0$

$4x^2 - 11x - 3 = 0$

$(4x + 1)(x - 3) = 0$

$x = -\frac{1}{4}$, 3.

The solution set is $\{-\frac{1}{4}, 3\}$.

35. $2 - \frac{5}{r} + \frac{3}{r^2} = 0$

$r^2(2 - \frac{5}{r} + \frac{3}{r^2}) = r^2 \cdot 0$, if $r \neq 0$

$2r^2 - 5r + 3 = 0$

$(2r - 3)(r - 1) = 0$

$r = \frac{3}{2}$, 1.

The solution set is $\{1, \frac{3}{2}\}$.

39. $2m^2 = m + 2$ becomes $2m^2 - m - 2 = 0$, with $a = 2$, $b = -1$, $c = -2$.

$$m = \frac{-(-1) \pm \sqrt{(-1)^2 - 4(2)(-2)}}{2(2)}$$

$$= \frac{1 \pm \sqrt{1 + 16}}{4}$$

$$= \frac{1 \pm \sqrt{17}}{4}$$

Since $\sqrt{17} \approx 4.123$

$$m \approx \frac{1 \pm 4.123}{4}$$

or $m \approx \frac{1 + 4.123}{4} = \frac{5.123}{4} \approx 1.281$

or $m \approx \frac{1 - 4.123}{4} = \frac{-3.123}{4} \approx -.781$

Solution set is $\{1.281, -.781\}$.

41. $x^2 - 2 = 3x$

$x^2 - 3x - 2 = 0$. Use quadratic formula with $a = 1$, $b = -3$, $c = -2$.

$$x = \frac{-(-3) \pm \sqrt{(-3)^2 - 4(1)(-2)}}{2(1)}$$

$$x = \frac{3 \pm \sqrt{9 + 8}}{2}$$

$$x = \frac{3 \pm \sqrt{17}}{2} \approx 3.562, -.562$$

The solution set is $\{3.562, -.562\}$.

45. $\sqrt{2}p^2 - 3p + \sqrt{2} = 0$

$a = \sqrt{2}, \; b = -3, \; c = \sqrt{2}$

$p = \dfrac{-(-3) \pm \sqrt{(-3)^2 - 4(2)(2)}}{2\sqrt{2}}$

$p = \dfrac{3 \pm \sqrt{9 - 8}}{2\sqrt{2}} = \dfrac{3 \pm \sqrt{1}}{2\sqrt{2}}$

$p = \dfrac{3 \pm 1}{2\sqrt{2}} \cdot \dfrac{\sqrt{2}}{\sqrt{2}} = \dfrac{(3 \pm 1)\sqrt{2}}{4} = \sqrt{2}, \; \dfrac{\sqrt{2}}{2}$

The solution set is $\{\dfrac{\sqrt{2}}{2}, \; \sqrt{2}\}$.

47. $x^2 + ix + 1 = 0$

$a = 1, \; b = i, \; c = 1$

$x = \dfrac{-i \pm \sqrt{i^2 - 4(1)(1)}}{2(1)}$

$x = \dfrac{-i \pm \sqrt{-5}}{2}$

$x = \dfrac{-i \pm i\sqrt{5}}{2} = i(\dfrac{-1 \pm \sqrt{5}}{2})$

The solution set is $\{i(\dfrac{-1 \pm \sqrt{5}}{2})\}$.

51. $(1 + i)x^2 - x + (1 - i) = 0$

$a = 1 + i, \; b = -1, \; c = 1 - i$

$x = \dfrac{-(-1) \pm \sqrt{(-1)^2 - 4(1 + i)(1 - i)}}{2(1 + i)}$

$x = \dfrac{1 \pm \sqrt{1 - 4(2)}}{2(1 + i)}$

$x = \dfrac{1 \pm i\sqrt{7}}{2(1 + 1)} \cdot \dfrac{1 - i}{1 - i}$

$x = \dfrac{(1 \pm i\sqrt{7})(1 - i)}{4}$

$x = \dfrac{(1 - i) \pm (1 - i)i\sqrt{7}}{4}$

$x = \dfrac{(1 - i) \pm (i\sqrt{7} + \sqrt{7})}{4}$

$[-i \cdot i\sqrt{7} = -i^2\sqrt{7} = -(-1)\sqrt{7} = \sqrt{7}]$

55. By the sum of two cubes formula

$x^3 + 27 = 0$ becomes

$(x + 3)(x^2 - 3x + 9) = 0.$

Hence, $x + 3 = 0$ or $x^2 - 3x + 9 = 0.$

then $x = -3$ or

$x = \dfrac{3 \pm \sqrt{9 - 4(1)(9)}}{2}$

$x = \dfrac{3 \pm \sqrt{-27}}{2}$

$x = \dfrac{3 \pm 3\sqrt{3}i}{2}.$

The solution set is

$\{-3, \; \dfrac{3}{2} \pm \dfrac{3\sqrt{3}}{2}i\}.$

57. Factoring the difference of two cubes $x^3 - 64 = 0$ becomes

$(x - 4)(x^2 + 4x + 16) = 0$

$x = 4$ or $x = \dfrac{-4 \pm \sqrt{16 - 64}}{2}$

$x = \dfrac{-4 \pm \sqrt{-48}}{2}$

$x = \dfrac{-4 \pm 4\sqrt{3}i}{2}$

$x = -2 \pm 2\sqrt{3}i.$

The solution set is $\{4, \; -2 \pm 2\sqrt{3}i\}.$

61. $x^2 + 8x + 16 = 0$

$a = 1, \; b = 8, \; c = 16$

$b^2 - 4ac = 64 - 4(1)(16) = 64 - 64 = 0$

Therefore, there is one rational solution.

65. $4p^2 = 6p + 3$ becomes

$4p^2 - 6p - 3 = 0.$

$a = 4, \; b = -6, \; c = -3,$ so that

$b^2 - 4ac = 36 - 4(4)(-3)$

$= 36 + 48$

$= 84 > 0.$

There are two real solutions. They are irrational.

67. $9k^2 + 11k + 4 = 0$

We have $a = 9, \; b = 11$ and $c = 4.$ This gives

$b^2 - 4ac = (11)^2 - 4(9)(4)$

$= 121 - 144 = -23.$

Hence, there are no real solutions. The solutions are conjugate complex numbers.

69. $s = \frac{1}{2}gt^2$ becomes $2s = gt^2$.

Dividing by g gives $t^2 = \frac{2s}{g}$, and

hence $t = \pm\sqrt{\frac{2s}{g}}$. Rationalizing the

denominator we have

$t = \pm\sqrt{\frac{2s}{g}} \cdot \frac{\sqrt{g}}{\sqrt{g}} = \pm\frac{\sqrt{2sg}}{g}$.

71. $L = \frac{d^4k}{h^2}$ for h

$h^2 = \frac{d^4k}{L}$

$h = \frac{\pm d^2\sqrt{k}}{\sqrt{L}} \cdot \frac{\sqrt{L}}{\sqrt{L}} = \pm\frac{d^2\sqrt{kL}}{L}$

75. Solve $s = 2\pi rh + 2\pi r^2$ for r by

writing as $2\pi r^2 + 2\pi hr - s = 0$.

Let $a = 2\pi$, $b = 2\pi h$ and $c = -s$ and

use the quadratic formula to

arrive at

$r = \frac{-2\pi h \pm \sqrt{4\pi^2 h^2 - 4(2\pi)(-s)}}{4\pi}$

$r = \frac{-2\pi h \pm 2\sqrt{\pi^2 h^2 + 2\pi s}}{4\pi}$

$r = \frac{-\pi h \pm \sqrt{\pi^2 h^2 + 2\pi s}}{2\pi}$,

or we could write $r^2 + hr - \frac{s}{2\pi} = 0$

and get

$r = \frac{-h \pm \sqrt{h^2 + \frac{2s}{\pi}}}{2}$.

77. Let x = the first integer

x + 2 = the next consecutive even

integer

$x(x + 2) = 288$

$x^2 + 2x - 288 = 0$

$(x + 18)(x - 16) = 0$

$x = -18$ or $x = 16$,

either -18 and -16 or 16 and 18.

79. Let x = one integer

10 - x = the other

$x^2 + (10 - x)^2 = 148$

$x^2 + 100 - 20x + x^2 = 148$

$2x^2 - 20x - 48 = 0$

$x^2 - 10x - 24 = 0$

$(x - 12)(x + 2) = 0$

$x = 12, -2$

The integers are 12 and -2.

81. Let l = the length and w = the

width.

The perimeter is $300 = 2(l + w)$

area is $5000 = lw$

$300 = 2(l + w)$

gives $l = 150 - w$

$5000 = (150 - w)w$

$5000 = 150w - w^2$

$w^2 - 150w + 5000 = 0$

$(w - 100)(w - 50) = 0$

$w = 100$ or $w = 50$

w = 100 implies l = 50, and w = 50

implies l = 100, so either way the

rectangle has dimensions 50 meters

by 100 meters.

83. Make a sketch.

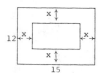

$(12 - 2x)(15 - 2x) = 108$

$180 - 54x + 4x^2 = 108$

$4x^2 - 54x + 72 = 0$

$2x^2 - 27x + 36 = 0$

$(2x - 3)(x - 12) = 0$

$2x - 3 = 0$ or $x - 12 = 0$

$x = \frac{3}{2}$ or $x = 12$

rejected (too wide)

The dimensions of the rug are

12 - 2x by 15 - 2x, so the rug

should be 9 ft. by 12 ft.

85. Make a chart. Use $t = \frac{d}{r}$.

Let x be the rate Steve travels.

	d	r	t
Steve	100	x	$\frac{100}{x}$
Dolores	100	x + 10	$\frac{100}{x + 10}$

$$\frac{100}{x} - \frac{1}{3} = \frac{100}{x + 10}$$

Thus, $\frac{300 - x}{3x} = \frac{100}{x + 10}$

$$300(x + 10) - x(x + 10) = 300x$$

$$300x + 3000 - x^2 - 10x = 300x$$

$$x^2 + 10x - 3000 = 0$$

Use the quadratic formula with a = 1, b = 10, c = -3000.

$$x = \frac{-10 \pm \sqrt{10^2 - 4(1)(-3000)}}{2}$$

$$x = \frac{-10 \pm \sqrt{100 + 12000}}{2}$$

$$x = \frac{-10 \pm \sqrt{12100}}{2}$$

$$x = \frac{-10 \pm 110}{2}$$

$$x = \frac{100}{2} = 50 \text{ or } \frac{-120}{2} = -60$$

Discard the negative solution. His speed is 50 mph.

87. Make a sketch. Let x denote the length of the shorter leg.

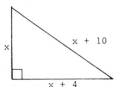

$$x^2 + (x + 4)^2 = (x + 10)^2$$

$$x^2 + x^2 + 8x + 16 = x^2 + 20x + 100$$

$$x^2 - 12x - 84 = 0$$

Use the quadratic formula:

$$x = \frac{12 \pm \sqrt{(-12)^2 - 4(1)(-84)}}{2}$$

$$x = \frac{12 \pm \sqrt{144 + 336}}{2}$$

$$x = \frac{12 \pm \sqrt{480}}{2}$$

$$x = \frac{12 \pm 4\sqrt{30}}{2}$$

$$x = 6 \pm 2\sqrt{30} \quad \text{discard the negative solution}$$

$$x = 6 + 2\sqrt{30} \approx 16.95$$

$$x + 4 = 10 + 2\sqrt{30} \approx 20.95$$

$$x + 10 = 16 + 2\sqrt{30} \approx 26.95$$

89. For a quadratic equation to have exactly one solution it is necessary that the discriminant $b^2 - 4ac = 0$.

$9x^2 + kx + 4 = 0$ implies a = 9, b = k, and c = 4.

$$o = b^2 - 4ac = k^2 - 4(9)(4)$$

$$0 = k^2 - 144$$

$$k = 12 \text{ or } k = -12$$

93. $kr^2 + (2k + 6)r + 16 = 0$

$$0 = b^2 - 4ac = (2k + 6)^2 - 4(k)(16)$$

$$0 = 4k^2 + 24k + 36 - 64k$$

$$0 = 4k^2 - 40k + 36$$

$$0 = k^2 - 10k + 9$$

$$0 = (k - 9)(k - 1)$$

$$k = 9, 1$$

95. Since r_1 and r_2 are solutions to the quadratic equation $ax^2 + bx + c = 0$, then r_1 and r_2 are solutions to $x^2 + \frac{b}{a}x + \frac{c}{a} = 0$, where $a \neq 0$.

Thus we must have the factoring $x^2 + \frac{b}{a}x + \frac{c}{a} = (x - r_1)(x - r_2)$.

Since $(x - r_1)(x - r_2)$

$$= x^2 - r_1x - r_2x + r_1r_2$$

$$= x^2 - (r_1 + r_2)x + r_1r_2,$$

we must have $-(r_1 + r_2) = \frac{b}{a}$, or

$$r_1 + r_2 = \frac{-b}{a}.$$

96. Following up from Exercise 95 we can also conclude that $r_1 r_2 = \frac{c}{a}$.

97. Consider $(x - m)(x - n) = k^2$, with m, n and k real. Then
$$x^2 - mx - nx + mn = k^2$$
$$x^2 - (m + n)x + (mn - k^2) = 0.$$
Using the quadratic formula with $a = 1$, $b = -(m + n)$, and $c = mn - k^2$ gives
$$x = \frac{(m + n) \pm \sqrt{(m + n)^2 - 4(mn - k^2)}}{2}$$
$$x = \frac{(m + n) \pm \sqrt{m^2 + 2mn + n^2 - 4mn + 4k^2}}{2}$$
$$x = \frac{(m + n) \pm \sqrt{m^2 - 2mn + n^2 + 4k^2}}{2}$$
$$x = \frac{(m + n) \pm \sqrt{(m - n)^2 + 4k^2}}{2}.$$
These solutions are real because for all m, n, k we have $(m - n)^2 \geq 0$, $4k^2 \geq 0$, and hence the discriminant $b^2 - 4ac = (m - n)^2 + 4k^2 \geq 0$.

98. If $m = -4$ is a solution to $km^2 + 10m - 8 = 0$, then $k(16) + 10(-4) - 8 = 0$, so that $16k - 48 = 0$ or $k = 3$. Hence, the equation is
$$3m^2 + 10m - 8 = 0$$
$$(m + 4)(3m - 2) = 0,$$
so the other solution is $m = \frac{2}{3}$.

99. (a) $4x^2 - 2xy + 3y^2 = 2$; solve for x by writing the equation as $4x^2 - 2yx + (3y^2 - 2) = 0$ and use the quadratic formula with $a = 4$, $b = -2y$, and $c = 3y^2 - 2$.
$$x = \frac{2y \pm \sqrt{4y^2 - 4(4)(3y^2 - 2)}}{8}$$
$$= \frac{2y \pm \sqrt{4y^2 - 48y^2 + 32}}{8}$$

$$= \frac{2y \pm \sqrt{32 - 44y^2}}{8}$$
$$= \frac{2y \pm 2\sqrt{8 - 11y^2}}{8}$$
$$= \frac{y \pm \sqrt{8 - 11y^2}}{4}$$

101. Starting with $ax^2 + bx + c = 0$, we multiply every term by 4a to get
$$4a^2x^2 + 4abx + 4ac = 0,$$
$$4a^2x^2 + 4abx = -4ac.$$
Then, if we add b^2 to both sides the left hand side becomes a perfect square,
$$4a^2x^2 + 4abx + b^2 = b^2 - 4ac$$
$$(2ax + b)^2 = b^2 - 4ac.$$
Then, taking the square root of both sides gives
$$\sqrt{(2ax + b)^2} = \sqrt{b^2 - 4ac},$$
$$|2ax + b| = \sqrt{b^2 - 4ac}, \text{ since}$$
$$\sqrt{n^2} = |n|, \text{ and hence,}$$
$$2ax + b = \pm\sqrt{b^2 - 4ac},$$
$$2ax = -b \pm \sqrt{b^2 - 4ac},$$
$$x = \frac{-b \pm \sqrt{b^2 - 4ac}}{2a}.$$

Section 2.4

Equations Reducible to Quadratics

Additional Examples

Example 1   Solve the equation
$$6(r - 2)^{2/5} - 7(r - 1)^{1/5} = 3$$
by using a suitable substitution.

Solution   If we let $u = (r - 2)^{1/5}$, then $u^2 = (r - 2)^{2/5}$, and substitution gives

$$6u^2 - 7u = 3$$
$$6u^2 - 7u - 3 = 0$$
$$(2u - 3)(3u + 1) = 0.$$

Hence,

$$2u - 3 = 0 \quad \text{or} \quad 3u + 1 = 0$$
$$u = \frac{3}{2} \quad \text{or} \quad u = -\frac{1}{3}.$$

Substituting $u = (r - 2)^{1/5}$ leads to

$$(r - 2)^{1/5} = \frac{3}{2} \text{ or } (r - 2)^{1/5} = -\frac{1}{3}.$$

Raising the terms to the fifth power gives the following:

$$(r - 2)^{1/5} = \frac{3}{2} \qquad (r - 2)^{1/5} = -\frac{1}{3}$$
$$r - 2 = \left(\frac{3}{2}\right)^5 \qquad r - 2 = \left(-\frac{1}{3}\right)^5$$
$$r - 2 = \frac{243}{32} \qquad r - 2 = \frac{-1}{243}$$
$$r = 2 + \frac{243}{32} \qquad r = 2 - \frac{1}{243}$$
$$r = \frac{64 + 243}{32} \qquad r = \frac{486 - 1}{243}$$
$$r = \frac{307}{32} \qquad r = \frac{485}{243}.$$

The solution set is the set

$$S = \left\{\frac{307}{32}, \frac{485}{243}\right\}.$$

Example 2 Solve the equation
$$x + 3\sqrt{x + 4} = 14.$$

Solution To solve this equation, we isolate the radical on one side, square both sides, and solve as follows:

$$x + 3\sqrt{x + 4} = 14$$
$$3\sqrt{x + 4} = 14 - x$$
$$(3\sqrt{x + 4})^2 = (14 - x)^2$$
$$9(x + 4) = 196 - 28x + x^2$$
$$9x + 36 = 196 - 28x + x^2$$
$$0 = -9x - 36 + 196 - 28x + x^2$$
$$x^2 - 37x + 160 = 0$$
$$(x - 5)(x - 32) = 0$$
$$x = 5 \quad \text{or} \quad x = 32.$$

Since extraneous solutions are sometimes introduced when both sides of an equation are squared,

we must check the two possible solutions. Substituting $x = 5$ in the equation $x + 3\sqrt{x + 4} = 14$ gives

$$5 + 3\sqrt{5 + 4} = 5 + 3\sqrt{9}$$
$$= 5 + 3 \cdot 3$$
$$= 5 + 9$$
$$= 14,$$

so that 5 checks as a solution. Substitution of $x = 32$ gives

$$5 + 3\sqrt{32 + 4} = 5 + 3\sqrt{36}$$
$$= 5 + 3 \cdot 6$$
$$= 5 + 18$$
$$= 23$$
$$\neq 14,$$

so that 32 is not a solution. The solution set is the set $S = \{5\}$.

Example 3 Solve the equation
$$\sqrt{2\sqrt{x} + 2} = 1 - \sqrt{x}.$$

Solution To solve this equation we must square both sides, combine terms and square again to eliminate all radicals. These steps give the following results:

$$\sqrt{2\sqrt{x} + 2} = 1 - \sqrt{x}$$
$$\left(\sqrt{2\sqrt{x} + 2}\right)^2 = (1 - \sqrt{x})^2 \quad \text{squaring both sides}$$
$$2\sqrt{x} + 2 = 1 - 2\sqrt{x} + x$$
$$2\sqrt{x} + 2\sqrt{x} = 1 - 2 + x$$
$$4\sqrt{x} = x - 1$$
$$(4\sqrt{x})^2 = (x - 1)^2$$
$$16x = x^2 - 2x + 1$$
$$0 = x^2 - 18x + 1 \quad \text{or}$$
$$x^2 - 18x + 1 = 0.$$

This equation will not factor, so we will use the quadratic formula to find solutions. Using $a = 1$, $b = -18$, and $c = 1$, we have

$$x = \frac{18 \pm \sqrt{324 - 4}}{2} = \frac{18 \pm \sqrt{320}}{2}$$
$$= \frac{18 \pm 8\sqrt{5}}{2} = 9 \pm 4\sqrt{5}.$$

We must test the possible solutions $9 - 4\sqrt{5}$ and $9 + 4\sqrt{5}$. Substitution into the equation $\sqrt{2\sqrt{x} + 2} = 1 - \sqrt{x}$ is no simple chore. We can use a calculator to show the following:

(a) For $x = 9 + 4\sqrt{5}$,

$$\sqrt{2\sqrt{x} + 2} = \sqrt{2(4.236) + 2}$$
$$= \sqrt{10.472} \approx 3.236,$$

and $1 - \sqrt{x} = -3.236$.

Thus, $9 + 4\sqrt{5}$ is not a solution.

(b) For $x = 9 - 4\sqrt{5}$,

$$\sqrt{2\sqrt{x} + 2} = \sqrt{2.4721} \approx 1.5723,$$

and $1 - \sqrt{x} = .7639$. Hence, there are no solutions and the solution set is $\emptyset$.

Selected Solutions

1. $m^4 + 2m^2 - 15 = 0$

If we let $u = m^2$, then we have the equation $u^2 + 2u - 15 = 0$, so that

$$(u + 5)(u - 3) = 0$$
$$u + 5 = 0 \text{ or } u - 3 = 0$$
$$u = -5 \quad \text{or} \quad u = 3.$$

However, this is

$$m^2 = -5 \text{ or } \quad m^2 = 3.$$

There are no real numbers m such that $m^2 = -5$ and the solutions to $m^2 = 3$ are $m = \pm\sqrt{3}$. The solution set is $\{\pm\sqrt{3}\}$.

Another way to arrive at a solution and not use a substitution is to merely factor. That is,

$$m^4 + 2m^2 - 15 = 0$$
$$(m^2 + 5)(m^2 - 3) = 0$$
$$m^2 = -5, \quad \text{or} \quad m^2 = 3$$

no solutions: or $m = \pm\sqrt{3}$
The solution set is $\{\pm\sqrt{3}\}$.

5. $(g - 2)^2 - 6(g - 2) + 8 = 0$

Let $x = g - 2$:

$$x^2 - 6x + 8 = 0$$
$$(x - 2)(x - 4) = 0$$
$$x = 2 \quad \text{or} \quad x = 4$$

Substitute back:

$$g - 2 = 2 \qquad g - 2 = 4$$
$$g = 4 \qquad\qquad g = 6.$$

The solution set is $\{4, 6\}$.

9. $6(k + 2)^4 - 11(k + 2)^2 + 4 = 0$

Letting $x = (k + 2)^2$ gives

$$6x^2 - 11x + 4 = 0$$
$$(3x - 4)(2x - 1) = 0$$
$$x = \frac{4}{3} \quad \text{or} \quad x = \frac{1}{2}.$$

Then we have either

$$(k + 2)^2 = \frac{4}{3} \quad \text{or} \quad (k + 2)^2 = \frac{1}{2}$$
$$(k + 2) = \pm\frac{2}{\sqrt{3}} \quad \text{or} \quad k + 2 = \pm\frac{1}{\sqrt{2}}$$
$$k + 2 = \frac{\pm 2\sqrt{3}}{3} \quad \text{or} \quad k + 2 = \frac{\pm\sqrt{2}}{2}$$
$$k = -2 \pm \frac{2\sqrt{3}}{3}$$
$$\text{or} \qquad k = -2 \pm \frac{\sqrt{2}}{2}.$$

The solution set is

$$\left\{-2 \pm \frac{2\sqrt{3}}{3}, \ -2 \pm \frac{\sqrt{2}}{2}\right\},$$
$$\text{or} \ \left\{\frac{-6 \pm 2\sqrt{3}}{3}, \ \frac{-4 \pm \sqrt{2}}{2}\right\}.$$

11. $7p^{-2} + 19p^{-1} = 6$

Let $x = p^{-1}$ and arrive at

$$7x^2 + 19x = 6$$
$$7x^2 + 19x - 6 = 0$$
$$(7x - 2)(x + 3) = 0$$
$$x = \frac{2}{7} \quad \text{or} \quad x = -3$$

Substitute back to arrive at

$$p^{-1} = \frac{2}{7} \text{ or } p^{-1} = -3$$
$$p = \frac{7}{2} \text{ or } \quad p = -\frac{1}{3}.$$

The solution set is $\left\{-\frac{1}{3}, \frac{7}{2}\right\}$.

13. $(r - 1)^{2/3} + (r - 1)^{1/3} = 12$

Letting $x = (r - 1)^{1/3}$ gives

$$x^2 + x - 12 = 0$$
$$(x + 4)(x - 3) = 0$$
$$x = -4 \quad \text{or} \quad x = 3.$$

Substitute back to arrive at

$$(r - 1)^{1/3} = -4 \quad \text{or} \quad (r - 1)^{1/3} = 3$$
$$r - 1 = -64 \text{ or} \qquad r - 1 = 27$$
$$r = -63 \text{ or} \qquad\quad r = 28.$$

The solution set is $\{-63, 28\}$.

17. $3 + \dfrac{5}{p^2 + 1} = \dfrac{2}{(p^2 + 1)^2}$

Letting $x = \dfrac{1}{p^2 + 1}$ gives

$$3 + 5x = 2x^2, \text{ or}$$

$$2x^2 - 5x - 3 = 0$$
$$(2x + 1)(x - 3) = 0; \quad x = -\frac{1}{2} \text{ or } x = 3.$$

Substitute back to arrive at

$$\frac{1}{p^2 + 1} = -\frac{1}{2} \quad \text{or} \quad \frac{1}{p^2 + 1} = 3$$

$$p^2 + 1 = -2 \quad \text{or} \quad p^2 + 1 = \frac{1}{3}$$

$$p^2 = -3 \quad \text{or} \quad p^2 = -\frac{2}{3}$$

no solution   ;   no solution.
The solution set is $\emptyset$.

21. $1 + 3(r^2 - 1)^{-1} = 28(r^2 - 1)^{-2}$

Letting $x = (r^2 - 1)^{-1}$ gives

$$1 + 3x = 28x^2, \text{ or } 28x^2 - 3x - 1 = 0,$$
$$(7x + 1)(4x - 1) = 0$$
$$x = -\frac{1}{7} \quad \text{or} \quad x = \frac{1}{4}.$$

Substitute back to arrive at

$$(r^2 - 1)^{-1} = -\frac{1}{7} \text{ or } (r^2 - 1)^{-1} = \frac{1}{4}$$

$$\frac{1}{r^2 - 1} = -\frac{1}{7} \text{ or } \qquad \frac{1}{r^2 - 1} = \frac{1}{4}$$

$$r^2 - 1 = -7 \text{ or} \qquad r^2 - 1 = 4$$

$$r^2 = -6 \text{ or} \qquad r^2 = 5$$

no solution   ; $r = \pm\sqrt{5}$.
The solution set is $\{\pm\sqrt{5}\}$.

25. $\left(\dfrac{k^2 + 3k}{4}\right)^2 - \dfrac{11}{6}\left(\dfrac{k^2 + 3k}{4}\right) + \dfrac{1}{2} = 0$

Letting $x = \left(\dfrac{k^2 + 3k}{4}\right)$ gives

$$6x^2 - 11x + 3 = 0$$

When we multiply by 6 to remove fractions,

$$6x^2 - 11x + 3 = 0$$
$$(2x - 3)(3x - 1) = 0$$
$$x = \frac{3}{2} \text{ or } x = \frac{1}{3}.$$

Substitute back to arrive at

$$\frac{k^2 + 3k}{4} = \frac{3}{2} \text{ or } \qquad \frac{k^2 + 3k}{4} = \frac{1}{3}$$

$$k^2 + 3k = 6 \text{ or } \quad 3(k^2 + 3k) = 4$$

$$k^2 + 3k - 6 = 0 \text{ or } 3k^2 + 9k - 4 = 0.$$

Neither of these factors so we use the quadratic formula on each, arriving at

$$k = \frac{-3 \pm \sqrt{9 + 24}}{2} \text{ or } k = \frac{-9 \pm \sqrt{81 + 48}}{6}$$

$$k = \frac{-3 \pm \sqrt{33}}{2} \quad \text{or} \quad k = \frac{-9 \pm \sqrt{129}}{6}$$

The solution set is

$$\left\{\frac{-3 \pm \sqrt{33}}{2}, \frac{-9 \pm \sqrt{129}}{6}\right\}.$$

29. $\qquad \sqrt{2m + 1} = 2\sqrt{m}$

$$(\sqrt{2m + 1})^2 = (2\sqrt{m})^2$$
$$2m + 1 = 4m$$
$$1 = 2m, \text{ or } m = \frac{1}{2}.$$

The solution set is $\{\frac{1}{2}\}$.

33. $\sqrt{4k + 5} - 2 = 2k - 7$

$$\sqrt{4k + 5} = 2k - 5$$
$$(\sqrt{4k + 5})^2 = (2k - 5)^2$$
$$4k + 5 = 4k^2 - 20k + 25$$
$$0 = 4k^2 - 24k + 20$$
$$0 = k^2 - 6k + 5$$
$$0 = (k - 1)(k - 5)$$
$$k = 1, 5$$

Test k = 1:

$\sqrt{4 \cdot 1 + 5} - 2 = \sqrt{9} - 2 = 3 - 2 = 1$

$\quad 2(1) - 7 = -5$; no

Test k = 5:

$\sqrt{4 \cdot 5 + 5} - 2 = \sqrt{25} - 2 = 5 - 2 = 3$

$\quad 2(5) - 7 = 10 - 7 = 3$; yes

The solution set is {5}.

37. $\quad \sqrt{y} = \sqrt{y - 5} + 1$

$\quad (\sqrt{y})^2 = (\sqrt{y - 5} + 1)^2$

$\quad y = (y - 5) + 2\sqrt{y - 5} + 1$

$\quad y = y - 4 + 2\sqrt{y - 5}$

$\quad 4 = 2\sqrt{y - 5}$

$\quad 2 = \sqrt{y - 5}$

$\quad 2^2 = (\sqrt{y - 5})^2$

$\quad 4 = y - 5$

$\quad y = 9$

Check the proposed answer, y = 9.

$\quad \sqrt{9} = 3$

$\sqrt{9 - 5} + 1 = 2 + 1$

$\quad\quad\quad = 3$

The answer checks. The solution set is {9}.

41. $\quad \sqrt{y + 2} = \sqrt{2y + 5} - 1$

$\quad (\sqrt{y + 2})^2 = (\sqrt{2y + 5} - 1)^2$

$\quad y + 2 = (2y + 5) - 2\sqrt{2y + 5} + 1$

$\quad y + 2 = 2y + 6 - 2\sqrt{2y + 5}$

$\quad 2\sqrt{2y + 5} = y + 4$

$\quad (2\sqrt{2y + 5})^2 = (y + 4)^2$

$\quad 4(2y + 5) = y^2 + 8y + 16$

$\quad 8y + 20 = y^2 + 8y + 16$

$\quad 0 = y^2 - 4$

$\quad y^2 = 4$

$\quad y = \pm 2$

Check each answer:

y = 2:

$\quad \sqrt{2 + 2} = 2$

$\sqrt{4 + 5} - 1 = 3 - 1 = 2$

$\quad\quad y = 2$ checks

y = -2:

$\quad \sqrt{0} = 0$

$\sqrt{1} - 1 = 0$

$\quad y = -2$ checks

The solution set is {-2, 2}.

43. $\sqrt{2\sqrt{7x + 2}} = \sqrt{3x + 2}$

Squaring both sides gives

$\quad 2\sqrt{7x + 2} = 3x + 2$. Hence,

$\quad (2\sqrt{7x + 2})^2 = (3x + 2)^2$

$\quad 4(7x + 2) = 9x^2 + 12x + 4$

$\quad 0 = 9x^2 - 16x - 4$

$\quad 0 = (9x + 2)(x - 2)$

$\quad x = -\frac{2}{9}$ or x = 2.

Text x = 2:

$\sqrt{2\sqrt{7x + 2}} = \sqrt{2\sqrt{7(2) + 2}}$

$\quad\quad = \sqrt{2\sqrt{16}} = \sqrt{2 \cdot 4} = \sqrt{8}$

$\sqrt{3x + 2} = \sqrt{3(2) + 2} = \sqrt{8}$

Test x = $-\frac{2}{9}$:

$\sqrt{2\sqrt{7(-\frac{2}{9}) + 2}} = \sqrt{2\sqrt{\frac{-14}{9} + \frac{18}{9}}}$

$\quad\quad = \sqrt{2\sqrt{\frac{4}{9}}} = \sqrt{2 \cdot \frac{2}{3}}$

$\quad\quad = \sqrt{\frac{4}{3} \cdot \frac{\sqrt{3}}{\sqrt{3}}} = \frac{\sqrt{12}}{3}$

$\sqrt{3(-\frac{2}{9}) + 2} = \sqrt{\frac{-6}{9} + \frac{18}{9}} = \sqrt{\frac{12}{9}}$

$\quad\quad = \frac{\sqrt{12}}{3}$

Both check.

The solution set is $\{-\frac{2}{9},\ 2\}$.

45. $\sqrt{x} + 2 = \sqrt{4 + 7\sqrt{x}}$

Squaring both sides gives,

$\quad (\sqrt{x} + 2)^2 = 4 + 7\sqrt{x}$ or

$\quad x + 4\sqrt{x} + 4 = 4 + 7\sqrt{x}$. Thus

$\quad x - 3\sqrt{x} = 0$

$\quad x = 3\sqrt{x}$

$\quad x^2 = 9x$

$\quad x^2 - 9x = 0$

$\quad x(x - 9) = 0$

$\quad x = 0$ or x = 9

Check x = 0: | Check x = 9:

$\sqrt{x} + 2 = \sqrt{0} + 2$ | $\sqrt{x} + 2 = \sqrt{9} + 2$

$= 2$ | $= 3 + 2 = 5$

$\sqrt{4 + 7\sqrt{x}} = \sqrt{4 + 7\cdot 0}$ | $\sqrt{4 + 7\sqrt{x}} = \sqrt{4 + 7\sqrt{9}}$

$= \sqrt{4} = 2$ | $= \sqrt{4 + 7(3)}$

                     | $= \sqrt{25} = 5$

Solution set is $\{0, 9\}$.

49. $\sqrt[3]{t^2 + 2t - 1} = \sqrt[3]{t^2 + 3}$.

Cubing both sides gives

$t^2 + 2t - 1 = t^2 + 3$

$\qquad 2t = 4$, so that $t = 2$.

test $t = 2$:

$\sqrt[3]{2^2 + 2(2) - 1} = \sqrt[3]{7}$ and

$\sqrt[3]{2^2 + 3} = \sqrt[3]{7}$.

Hence, the solution set is $\{2\}$.

53. $\sqrt[4]{q - 15} = 2$

$(\sqrt[4]{q - 15})^4 = 2^4$

$q - 15 = 16$

$q = 31$

obviously $q = 31$ checks, so the solution set is $\{31\}$.

57. $(z^2 + 24z)^{1/4} - 3 = 0$

$(z^2 + 24z)^{1/4} = 3$

$z^2 + 24z = 3^4$

$z^2 + 24z - 81 = 0$

$(z + 27)(z - 3) = 0$

$z = -27, \quad z = 3$.

Test $z = -27$:

$[(-27)^2 + 24(-27)]^{1/4} - 3 = ?$

$[729 - 648]^{1/4} - 3 =$

$(81)^{1/4} - 3 =$

$3 - 3 = 0$

Test $z = 3$

$(3^2 + 72)^{1/4} - 3 = ?$

$(9 + 72)^{1/4} - 3 =$

$(81)^{1/4} - 3 =$

$3 - 3 = 0$

The solution set is $\{-27, 3\}$.

59. $\qquad (2r - 1)^{2/3} = r^{1/3}$

Cubing both sides gives

$[(2r - 1)^{2/3}]^3 = [r^{1/3}]^3$

$(2r - 1)^2 = r$

$4r^2 - 4r + 1 = r$

$4r^2 - 5r + 1 = 0$

$(4r - 1)(r - 1) = 0$

$r = 1, \frac{1}{4}$.

The solution set is $\{1, \frac{1}{4}\}$.

61. $\qquad k^{2/3} = 2k^{1/3}$

Cubing both sides gives $k^2 = 8k$.

$k^2 - 8k = 0$

$k(k - 8) = 0$

$k = 0, \quad k = 8$.

Both check, so the solution set is $\{0, 8\}$.

We could also solve this as follows:

$k^{2/3} = 2k^{1/3}$

$k^{2/3} - 2k^{1/3} = 0$

$k^{1/3}(k^{1/3} - 2) = 0$

$k^{1/3} = 0$ or $k^{1/3} = 2$

$k = 0$ or $\qquad k = 8$.

63. $p(2 + p)^{-1/2} + (2 + p)^{1/2} = 0$

To solve by factoring we factor out $(2 + p)^{-1/2}$ and arrive at

$(2 + p)^{-1/2}[p + (2 + p)] = 0$

$(2 + p)^{-1/2}(2p + 2) = 0,$

$(2 + p)^{-1/2} = 0$ or $2p + 2 = 0$

$\dfrac{1}{\sqrt{2 + p}} = 0$ or $\qquad 2p = -2$

No solution $\qquad\qquad p = -1$

The solution set is $\{-1\}$ since $p = -1$ checks in the original equation.

Another way to solve is as follows:

$p(2 + p)^{-1/2} = -(2 + p)^{1/2}$

$p^2(2 + p)^{-1} = (2 + p) \qquad$ Squaring

$$p^2 = (2 + p)^2 \quad \text{Multiply by } (2 + p)$$

$$p^2 = 4 + 4p + p^2$$

$$-4p = 4 \quad \text{or} \quad p = -1.$$

The solution set is $\{-1\}$.

65. $(1 + 5r)^{1/3} - 2(1 + 5r)^{-2/3} = 0$

By factoring,

$$(1 + 5r)^{-2/3}[(1 + 5r) - 2] = 0$$

$$\frac{5r - 1}{(1 + 5r)^{2/3}} = 0,$$

and a fraction can be zero only when the numerator is zero, in this case when $r = \frac{1}{5}$.

Checking $r = \frac{1}{5}$ gives

$$(1 + 1)^{1/3} - 2(1 + 1)^{-2/3} = \,?$$

$$2^{1/3} - 2(2)^{-2/3} =$$

$$2^{1/3} - 2^{1-2/3} =$$

$$2^{1/3} - 2^{1/3} = 0.$$

The solution set is $\{\frac{1}{5}\}$.

We could also solve as follows.

$$(1 + 5r)^{1/3} = 2(1 + 5r)^{-2/3}$$

$$1 + 5r = 8(1 + 5r)^{-2} \quad \text{by cubing}$$

$$(1 + 5r)^3 = 8 \quad \text{multiplying by } (1 + 5r)^2$$

$$1 + 5r = 2 \quad \text{taking the cube root.}$$

so that $5r = 1$ or $r = \frac{1}{5}$.

67. $6p^4 - 41p^2 + 63 = 0$

let $x = p^2$:

$$6x^2 - 41x + 63 = 0$$

Use the quadratic formula.

$$x = \frac{41 \pm \sqrt{1681 - 1512}}{12}$$

$$x = \frac{41 \pm \sqrt{169}}{12}$$

$$x = \frac{41 \pm 13}{12}$$

$$x = \frac{9}{2}, \frac{7}{3}$$

Hence,

$$p^2 = \frac{9}{2} \qquad \text{or} \quad p^2 = \frac{7}{3}$$

$$p = \pm \frac{3}{\sqrt{2}} = \pm \frac{3\sqrt{2}}{2} \quad \text{or} \quad p = \pm\frac{\sqrt{21}}{3}.$$

Rounded to the nearest thousandth we have

$$p = \pm 2.121 \quad \text{or} \quad p = \pm 1.528.$$

71. $d = k\sqrt{h}$ for h

$$\frac{d}{k} = \sqrt{h}$$

$$\left(\frac{d}{k}\right)^2 = (\sqrt{h})^2$$

$$\frac{d^2}{k^2} = h$$

$$h = \left(\frac{d}{k}\right)^2$$

75. $x^{2/3} + y^{2/3} = a^{2/3}$ for y

$$y^{2/3} = a^{2/3} - x^{2/3}$$

$$y^2 = (a^{2/3} - x^{2/3})^3$$

$$y = \pm(a^{2/3} - x^{2/3})^{3/2}$$

Section 2.5 Inequalities

Additional Examples

Example 1 Solve the inequality

$$\frac{x^2 - 1}{x^2 - 9} \geq 0.$$

Solution Factoring the expression leads to

$$\frac{(x - 1)(x + 1)}{(x - 3)(x + 3)} \geq 0.$$

```
x - 1   ----|  ---- |---- |++++ |++++
x + 1   ----|  ---- |++++ |++++ |++++
x - 3   ----|  ---- |---- |---- |++++
x + 3   ---- ++++ ++++ ++++ |++++
        ┼────┼────┼──┼──┼──┼──┼──┼──
       -4 -3 -2  -1 0 1  2  3  4
            -3     -1   1    3
```

We make a sign graph by marking off each number that makes the numerator or denominator zero. We note that

the expression is positive in each
of the intervals $(-\infty, -3)$, $(-1, 1)$,
and $(3, \pm\infty)$. Testing each end point,
we cannot use $x = \pm 3$ because they
make the denominator 0. The
numbers ± 1 are solutions since they
make the expression zero. The
solution set is $S = (-\infty, -3) \cup$
$[-1, 1] \cup (3, \pm\infty)$.

Example 2 Solve the inequality

$$\frac{6x^2 + 5x - 6}{(x - 4)^3} < 0.$$

Solution Factoring the numerator gives

$$\frac{(2x + 3)(3x - 2)}{(x - 4)^3} < 0.$$

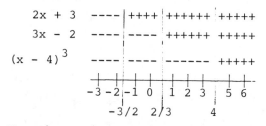

We make a sign graph, marking off
the numbers $-3/2$ and $2/3$, that make
the numerator zero, and 4, which
makes the denominator zero. Also,
it should be noted that the cube
of a number has the same sign as
the number itself. That is,

$(x - 4)^3$ is positive when $(x - 4)$
is positive, and negative when
$(x - 4)$ is negative. The solution
set is the set $S = (-\infty, -3/2) \cup$
$(2/3, 4)$ since we want the given
expression to be negative.

Example 3 Verify that if $a > 0$ and

$b > 0$ and if $a^2 > b^2$, then $a > b$.
Solution We are given that a and b
are positive real numbers and that
$a^2 > b^2$. Hence, we have

$$a^2 > b^2$$

$$a^2 - b^2 > 0$$

$$(a - b)(a + b) > 0.$$

Since $a > 0$ and $b > 0$, then
obviously $a + b > 0$. If $(a + b)$ is
a positive number and the product
of $(a - b)$ and $(a + b)$ is positive,
then $(a - b)$ must be positive since
$(+)(+) = +$. The term $a - b$ cannot
be negative since this would give
$(-)(+) = +$, which is false. Thus,
we must have

$$a - b > 0,$$

or $a > b,$

which verifies the desired conclusion.
We should note that the general

statement $a^2 > b^2$ does not imply the
inequality $a > b$. For example,

$(-5)^2 = 25 > (3)^2 = 9,$

but -5 is _not_ > 3.

Selected Solutions

1. $-1 < x < 4$ in interval notation
implies that x is in the interval
$(-1, 4)$

5. $2 > x \geq 1$ implies that $1 \leq x < 2$,
so that in interval notation, x is
in the interval $[1, 2)$.

9. $(-4, 3)$ is the interval consisting
of all real numbers x such that
$-4 < x < 3$.

13. The interval $[-2, 6)$
is the set of all real numbers x
such that $-2 \leq x < 6$.

17. $2x + 1 \leq 9$
      $2x \leq 8$
      $x \leq 4$
    Solution: $(-\infty, 4]$

21. $2(m + 5) - 3m + 1 \geq 5$

$\quad\quad 2m + 10 - 3m + 1 \geq 5$

$\quad\quad\quad\quad\quad -m + 11 \geq 5$

$\quad\quad\quad\quad\quad\quad\quad -m \geq -6$

$\quad\quad\quad\quad\quad\quad\quad\quad m \leq 6$

Solution: $(-\infty, 6]$

25. $\dfrac{4x + 7}{-3} \leq 2x + 5$.   Multiplying by -3

gives

$4x + 7 \geq -3(2x + 5)$, [Note $\leq$ changes
$\quad\quad\quad\quad\quad\quad\quad\quad\quad\quad$ to $\geq$],

$4x + 7 \geq -6x - 15$

$\quad 10x \geq -22$

$\quad\quad x \geq \dfrac{-22}{10}$

$\quad\quad x \geq -\dfrac{11}{5}$

The solution set is $[-\dfrac{11}{5}, +\infty)$.

29. $-10 > 3r + 2 > -16$

$\quad -12 > 3r > -18,$ subtract -2

$\quad\; -4 > r > -6$ multiply by $1/3$ and

$\quad\; -6 < r < -4$ change order

The solution set is $(-6, -4)$

33. $-4 < 1 - 3x < 2$.

We wish to isolate the x term. To do so, first add -1 throughout

$-5 < -3x < 1$.

Then multiply each term by -3, making sure to change the direction of each inequality. We have

$\dfrac{-5}{-3} > x > \dfrac{1}{-3}$, or

$-\dfrac{1}{3} < x < \dfrac{5}{3}$.

The solution is the interval $(-\dfrac{1}{3}, \dfrac{5}{3})$.

37. $y^2 - 10y + 25 < 25$

$\quad\quad y^2 - 10y < 0$

$\quad\quad\; y(y - 10) < 0$

$y(y - 10)$ is negative when the factors have opposite signs. As shown in the sign graph below, this occurs when $0 < y < 10$.

```
y       - - - | + + + | + + +
y - 10  - - - | - - - | + + +
       _____|_____|_____
              0      10
```

Solution: $(0, 10)$

41. $\quad\quad 2k^2 - 9k > -4$

$2k^2 - 9k + 4 > 0$

$(2k - 1)(k - 4) > 0$

This product will be positive when both factors have the same sign. As shown in the sign graph below, this occurs when $k < \dfrac{1}{2}$ or $k > 4$.

```
2k - 1  - - - | + + + | + + +
k - 4   - - - | - - - | + + +
       _____|_____|_____
              1/2     4
```

Solution: $(-\infty, \dfrac{1}{2}) \cup (4, +\infty)$.

45. $\quad\quad\quad x^3 - 4x \leq 0$

$x(x - 2)(x + 2) \leq 0$

This product will be negative when all three factors are negative or when just one factor is negative. As shown in the sign graph below, this occurs when $x < -2$ or $0 < x < 2$. The endpoints are

```
x      - - - | - - - | + + + | + + +
x - 2  - - - | - - - | - - - | + + +
x + 2  - - - | + + + | + + + | + + +
      _____|_____|_____|_____
            -2      0       2
```

also part of the final solution: $(-\infty, -2] \cup [0, 2]$

49. $\dfrac{m - 3}{m + 5} \leq 0$.

The quotient will be negative for the cases $\dfrac{+}{-}$ and $\dfrac{-}{+}$. The quotient will equal zero when the numerator $m - 3$ is zero. $m = -5$ is not acceptable. Consider the sign graph below.

```
m - 3   ----|-----|+++++
m + 5   ----|+++++|+++++
       ─────┼─────┼──────
          -5     3
```

The solution set is $(-5, 3]$.

53.
$$\frac{3}{x - 6} \leq 2$$

$$\frac{3}{x - 6} - 2 \leq 0$$

$$\frac{3 - 2(x - 6)}{x - 6} \leq 0 \qquad \text{Note: Do \underline{not}}$$

$$\frac{15 - 2x}{x - 6} \leq 0 \qquad \begin{array}{l}\text{multiply by} \\ (x - 6)! \text{ Why?}\end{array}$$

Form the sign graph.

```
+++|+++|---    15 - 2x    15 - 2x = 0
---|+++|+++    x - 6      x = 15/2
───┼───┼────
   6  15/2
```

The solution set is
$(-\infty, -6) \cup [\frac{15}{2}, +\infty)$.

57.
$$\frac{10}{3 + 2x} \leq 5.$$

To solve, subtract 5 from both sides to make the right hand side zero.

$$\frac{10}{3 + 2x} - 5 \leq 0$$

$$\frac{10 - 5(3 + 2x)}{3 + 2x} \leq 0 \quad \text{using } \frac{a}{b} - \frac{5}{1} = \frac{a - 5b}{b}$$

$$\frac{-5 - 10x}{3 + 2x} \leq 0$$

$x = -\frac{3}{2}$ makes the denominator zero
and
$x = -\frac{1}{2}$ makes the numerator zero.
The sign graph is below.

```
-5 - 10x  +++|+++|-----
3 + 2x    ---|+++|++++
          ───┼───┼────
            -3/2 -1/2
```

We are solving for ≤ 0, so the solution set is

$(-\infty, -\frac{3}{2}) \cup [-\frac{1}{2}, \infty)$. Note that $-\frac{1}{2}$

is a solution but $-\frac{3}{2}$ is not.

61.
$$\frac{3}{2r - 1} > \frac{-4}{r}$$

$$\frac{3}{2r - 1} + \frac{4}{r} > 0 \qquad \text{adding } \frac{4}{r}$$

$$\frac{3r + 4(2r - 1)}{r(2r - 1)} > 0 \quad \text{using } \frac{a}{b} + \frac{c}{d} = \frac{ad + bc}{bd}$$

$$\frac{11r - 4}{r(2r - 1)} > 0$$

We mark off $r = \frac{4}{11}$, $r = 0$, and

$r = \frac{1}{2}$ on the sign graph.

```
11r - 4   ----|---|++|++++
    r     ----|+++|++|++++
2r - 1    --- |---|--|++++
          ────┼───┼──┼────
             0  4/11 1/2
```

We are solving for >0, so the solution set is $(0, \frac{4}{11}) \cup (\frac{1}{2}, \infty)$.

65.
$$\frac{y + 3}{y - 5} \leq 1$$

$$\frac{y + 3}{y - 5} - 1 \leq 0$$

$$\frac{y + 3 - (y - 5)}{y - 5} \leq 0$$

$$\frac{8}{y - 5} \leq 0$$

The only number to mark off is $y = 5$. The numerator 8 is always positive.

```
8       ++++|+++++
y - 5   ----|+++++
        ────┼──────
            5
```

Since we are solving for ≤ 0, the solution set is $(-\infty, 5)$. Note that we cannot let $y = 5$.

66.
$$\frac{a + 2}{3 + 2a} \leq 5$$

$$\frac{a + 2}{3 + 2a} - 5 \leq 0$$

$$\frac{a + 2 - 5(3 + 2a)}{3 + 2a} \leq 0$$

$$\frac{-9a - 13}{3 + 2a} \leq 0$$

or
$$\frac{9a + 13}{3 + 2a} \geq 0 \qquad \begin{array}{l}\text{Multiplying} \\ \text{by } -1\end{array}$$

Form the sign graph using the end points,

$$9a + 13 = 0 \qquad 3 + 2a = 0$$
$$a = -\frac{13}{9} \qquad a = -\frac{3}{2}.$$

```
- - - - | - - | + + + +    9a + 13
- - - - | + + | + + + +    3 + 2a
_____|____|_____
       -3    -13
       ──    ───
        2     9
```

Note: $-\frac{13}{9} = \frac{-26}{18}$ and $-\frac{3}{2} = \frac{-27}{18}$.

The solution set is

$(-\infty, -\frac{3}{2}) \cup [-\frac{13}{9}, +\infty)$.   The endpoint $a = -3/2$ cannot be included because it causes a division by zero.

67. $\dfrac{2x - 3}{x^2 + 1} \geq 0$

In forming the sign graph, note that $x^2 + 1$ is always positive. Hence the only subdivision occurs at $x = 3/2$.

```
- - - - - | + + + +    2x - 3
+ + + + + | + + + +    x² + 1
_____|_____
          3
          ─
          2
```

The solution set is $[\frac{3}{2}, +\infty)$.

69. $\dfrac{(3x - 5)^2}{(2x - 5)^3} > 0$

The subdivisions occur at $x = 5/3$ and $x - 5/2$. Note that $(3x - 5)^2$ can never be negative, and $(2x - 5)^3$ is negative when $2x - 5$ is negative.

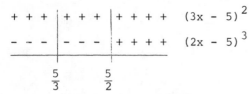

```
+ + + | + + + | + + + +    (3x - 5)²
- - - | - - - | + + + +    (2x - 5)³
_____|_____|_____
      5       5
      ─       ─
      3       2
```

The solution set is $(\frac{5}{2}, +\infty)$.

Note that $x = 5/2$ does not make the quotient > 0.

71. $\dfrac{(2x - 3)(3x - 8)}{(x - 6)^3} \geq 0$

Use a sign graph to decide what intervals satisfy the inequality.

Note that $(x - 6)^3$ is negative when $x - 6$ is negative.

```
2x - 3   - - - | - - - | + + + | + + +
3x + 8   - - - | + + + | + + + | + + +
x - 6    - - - | - - - | - - - | + + +
        _____|_____|_____|_____
           -8/3     3/2       6
```

The inequality is satisfied when $-\frac{8}{3} \leq x \leq \frac{3}{2}$ or $x > 6$.

Solution: $[-\frac{8}{3}, \frac{3}{2}] \cup (6, +\infty)$.

73. $x^2 - kx + 8 = 0$

There are real solutions if the discriminant $b^2 - 4ac$ is greater than or equal to zero. Here we use $a = 1$, $b = -k$, and $c = 8$.

Then, $b^2 - 4ac = k^2 - 4(1)(8)$
$= k^2 - 32$, and hence there are real solutions when

$$k^2 - 32 \geq 0$$
$$k^2 \geq 32$$
$$|k| \geq \sqrt{32} = 4\sqrt{2}.$$

Thus, there are real solutions if k is in $(-\infty, -4\sqrt{2}] \cup [4\sqrt{2}, +\infty)$.

77. Use revenue $\geq$ cost.

$$60x \geq 50x + 5000$$
$$10x \geq 5000$$
$$x \geq 500$$
$[500, +\infty)$

This implies that the company will at least break even by producing 500 units.

79. $60x \geq 70x + 500$

   $-10x \geq 500$

   $x \leq -50$

Since x must be positive, this product will never break even.

81. Find t when P > 0:

   $P = 4t^2 - 29t + 30 > 0$

   $(4t - 5)(t - 6) > 0.$

```
4t - 5   - - - | + + + | + + +
t - 6    - - - | - - - | + + +
         ──────┴───────┴──────
              5/4      6
```

Since we must have t > 0, she has been ahead when $0 < t < 5/4$ or when t > 6. The solution is $(0, \frac{5}{4}) \cup (6, +\infty).$

83. What values of x give $P = 3x^2 - 35x + 50 > 0$?

   $(3x - 5)(x - 10) > 0$

```
3x - 5   - - - | + + + | + + +
x - 10   - - - | - - - | + + +
         ──────┴───────┴──────
              5/3      10
```

P is positive when $0 \leq x < \frac{5}{3}$ or when x > 10. The solution set is $[0, \frac{5}{3}) \cup (10, +\infty).$

85. Let C denote a temperature in Celsius measure. Then if $0 \leq C \leq 30$, we have

   $0 \leq 9C \leq 270$

   $0 \leq \frac{9C}{5} \leq \frac{270}{5}$

   $0 \leq \frac{9C}{5} \leq 54$, so that

   $32 \leq \frac{9C}{5} + 32 \leq 54 + 32$, or

   $32 \leq \frac{9C}{5} + 32 \leq 86$, or $32 \leq F \leq 86$.

Hence, the temperature range in °F is from 32° F to 86° F.

87. If $\frac{1}{2} < \frac{3}{q} < \frac{2}{3}$, then we have

   $\frac{1}{2} < \frac{3}{q}$ and $\frac{3}{q} < \frac{2}{3}$

   $0 < \frac{3}{q} - \frac{1}{2}$ and $\frac{3}{q} - \frac{2}{3} < 0$

   $0 < \frac{6 - q}{2q}$ and $\frac{9 - 2q}{3q} < 0.$

```
6 - q  +++ | +++ | ---        9 - 2q  ++ | +++ | ---
2q     --- | +++ | +++  and   3q      -- | ++  | +++
       ────┴─────┴────        ───────────┴─────┴────
        0     6                       0    9/2
```

Solution A = (0, 6).   Solution B $= (-\infty, 0) \cup (\frac{9}{2}, \infty).$

For q to be a solution to the original inequality, q must satisfy both inequalities. This means that q must be an element of A and of B. That is $x \in A \cap B$. The numbers q that satisfy this are all numbers in $S = (\frac{9}{2}, 6).$

The solution set is $(\frac{9}{2}, 6).$

89. If b > 0 and $3b < \frac{1}{5bx} < \frac{2}{b}$, then

   $3b < \frac{1}{5bx}$ and $\frac{1}{5bx} < \frac{2}{b}$

   $0 < \frac{1}{5bx} - 3b$ and $\frac{1}{5bx} - \frac{2}{b} < 0$

   $0 < \frac{1 - 15b^2x}{5bx}$ and $\frac{(1 - 10x)}{5bx} < 0.$

```
1 - 15b²x   ++++ | +++ | ----
5bx         ---- | +++ | ++++
            ─────┴─────┴─────── , and
             0    1/15b²
```

```
1 - 10x   +++ | ++ | ----
5bx       --- | ++ | +++
          ────┴────┴──────
           0   1/10
```

$A = (0, \frac{1}{15b^2})$, and

$B = (-\infty, 0) \cup (\frac{1}{10}, \infty).$

A number x will be a solution to the original inequality only if x is in $S = A \cap B$. There are two cases depending on b.

(i) If $\dfrac{1}{15b^2} < \dfrac{1}{10}$, then $S = A \cap B = \Phi$.

Hence, if $15b^2 > 10$, so that $b^2 > \dfrac{2}{3}$, or $b > \dfrac{\sqrt{6}}{3}$, then the solution set is Φ.

(ii) If $o < b < \dfrac{\sqrt{6}}{3}$ [so that $\dfrac{1}{10} < \dfrac{1}{15b^2}$], then the solution set is $(\dfrac{1}{10}, \dfrac{1}{15b^2})$.

91. If $a > b > 0$, show that $\dfrac{1}{a} < \dfrac{1}{b}$.

Proof: $b < a$

divide by b: $1 < \dfrac{a}{b}$

The inequality does not reverse since $b > 0$. Similarly, $a > 0$, so divide by a: $\dfrac{1}{a} < \dfrac{1}{b}$.

92. Let $a = 2$, $b = -2$. Then $a > b$ but $\dfrac{1}{a} = \dfrac{1}{2} > 0$ and $\dfrac{1}{b} = -\dfrac{1}{2} < 0$ so $\dfrac{1}{a} > \dfrac{1}{b}$ in this case!

93. If $a > b > 0$, then $a^2 > b^2$

Proof: $b < a$ is given so multiply by b: $b^2 < ab$.

The inequality does not reverse since $b > 0$.

Since $b < a$, $ab < a^2$.

Thus $b^2 < ab < a^2$,

or $b^2 < a^2$, which is $a^2 > b^2$.

94. Let a and b be real numbers with $a > b > 0$. Then $\sqrt{a}$ and $\sqrt{b}$ exist.

We must have $n^2 \geq 0$ for any real number n, so that $(\sqrt{b} - \sqrt{a})^2 \geq 0$ even though $a > b$. Since $a \neq 0$ we must have $\sqrt{a} \neq \sqrt{b}$, and hence $(\sqrt{b} - \sqrt{a})^2 > 0$.

To verify the second part we can expand the last inequality to get

$$(\sqrt{b} - \sqrt{a})^2 > 0$$
$$b - 2\sqrt{a}\sqrt{b} + a > 0$$
$$a + b > 2\sqrt{ab}, \text{ or}$$
$$\dfrac{a + b}{2} > \sqrt{ab}$$

Now, since $a > b$ we have $\sqrt{a} > \sqrt{b}$. Then $\sqrt{a}\sqrt{b} > \sqrt{b}\sqrt{b}$,

$$\sqrt{ab} > \sqrt{b^2} = b, \text{ since } b > 0.$$

Hence, we have $b < \sqrt{ab} < \dfrac{a + b}{2}$.

95. $b > 0$. When is $b^2 > b$?

Let $0 < b < 1$. Multiply by b:

then $0 < b^2 < b$.

Let $b > 1$. Multiply by b:

then $b^2 > b$.

So $b^2 > b$ whenever $b > 1$.

97. Let a, b, c, d be positive and $ad < bc$.

then

$$ab + ad < ab + bc$$
$$a(b + d) < b(a + c)$$
$$\dfrac{1}{b} \cdot a(b + d) < \dfrac{1}{b} \cdot b(a + c)$$
$$\dfrac{a}{b}(b + d) < (a + c)$$
$$\dfrac{a}{b}(b + d)\dfrac{1}{(b + d)} < \dfrac{a + c}{b + d} \quad \text{since } b + d > 0$$
$$\dfrac{a}{b} < \dfrac{a + c}{b + d}.$$

99. Let n be a positive integer and solve

$$\dfrac{n - 1}{x} \leq \dfrac{n}{x + 1}.$$

we have

$$\dfrac{n - 1}{x} - \dfrac{n}{x + 1} \leq 0$$
$$\dfrac{(n - 1)(x + 1) - nx}{x(x + 1)} \leq 0 \quad \text{since } \dfrac{a}{b} - \dfrac{c}{d}$$
$$= \dfrac{ad - bc}{bd}$$
$$\dfrac{nx - x + n - 1 - nx}{x(x + 1)} \leq 0$$

$$\frac{(n-1)-x}{x(x+1)} \le 0.$$

Consider the sign graph with the number 0, -1, and n-1 marked off.

```
(n - 1) - x   +++ | ++ | ++++ | ----
        x     --- | -- | ++++ | ++++
      x + 1   ---- | ++ |+++++ |+++++
             ──────┼────┼──────┼─────
                  -1    0    (n - 1)
```

We have two cases; n = 1 and n > 1. The sign graph shown is for the case n > 1. Hence, if n > 1, the solution set is S = (-1, 0) ∪ [n - 1, ∞). Note that x = n - 1 makes the numerator zero and is a solution.

If n = 1, then the inequality reduces to $\dfrac{-x}{x(x+1)} \le 0$, or $\dfrac{-1}{x+1} \le 0$, with x ≠ 0. Here the sign graph is as shown below and the solution set is (-1, 0) ∪ (0, ∞).

```
    -1    ---- |-----
  x + 1   ---- |++++++
         ──────┼──────
            -1   0
```

Note that we must exclude x = 0.

Section 2.6   Absolute Value Equations
              and Inequalities

Additional Examples

Example 1 Solve the inequality
$$\left|\frac{2x + 3}{x - 1}\right| \le 3.$$

Solution This inequality is true if and only if
$$-3 \le \frac{2x + 3}{x - 1} \le 3.$$

We must solve each inequality separately, and for a number x to be a solution it must satisfy both inequalities simultaneously.

We have the following steps.

If $\dfrac{2x + 3}{x - 1} \ge -3$, then
$$\frac{2x + 3}{x - 1} + 3 \ge 0,$$
$$\frac{2x + 3 + 3(x - 1)}{x - 1} \ge 0,$$
so that $\dfrac{5x}{x - 1} \ge 0.$

Consider the sign graph below.

```
 5x    ----- | +++ | +++++
x - 1  ----- | --- | +++++
      ───┼─┼──────┼─┼─┼──
       -2 -1      2 3
          0   1
```

The solution set to this part is A = (-∞, 0] ∪ (1, +∞).

If $\dfrac{2x + 3}{x - 1} \le 3$, then
$$\frac{2x + 3}{x - 1} - 3 \le 0,$$
$$\frac{2x + 3 - 3(x - 1)}{x - 1} \le 0,$$
so that $\dfrac{6 - x}{x - 1} \le 0,$

Consider the sign graph below.

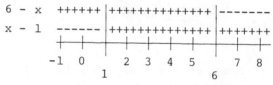

```
6 - x   ++++++ |+++++++++++++ |-------
x - 1   ------ |+++++++++++++ |+++++++
       ───┼─┼───┼─┼─┼─┼───┼─┼──
        -1  0    2  3  4  5    7  8
            1              6
```

The solution set for this inequality is the set B = (-∞, 1) ∪ [6, +∞). For x to be a solution to the given inequality, x must be in both A and B, or A ∩ B. The number x is in both A and B if x is in (-∞, 0] or [6, +∞). The solution set to the given inequality is the set S = (-∞, 0] ∪ [6, +∞).

Example 2 Solve the inequality
$$\left|\frac{x + 3}{x - 2}\right| > 4.$$

Solution This inequality will be true if either
$$\frac{x + 3}{x - 2} > 4 \quad \text{or} \quad -\left(\frac{x + 3}{x - 2}\right) > 4.$$

Solving each inequality separately
gives the following results.

If $\dfrac{x + 3}{x + 2} > 4$,

$$\frac{x + 3}{x - 2} - 4 > 0$$

$$\frac{(x + 3) - 4(x - 2)}{x - 2} > 0$$

$$\frac{11 - 3x}{x - 2} > 0$$

Consider the sign graph below.

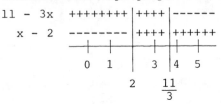

The solution set for this part is
the set A = (2, 11/3).

If $-\left(\dfrac{x + 3}{x - 2}\right) > 4$,

$$\frac{x + 3}{x - 2} < -4$$

multiply by (-1)

$$\frac{x + 3}{x - 2} + 4 < 0$$

$$\frac{x + 3 + 4(x - 2)}{(x - 2)} < 0$$

$$\frac{5x - 5}{(x - 2)} < 0$$

Consider the sign graph below.

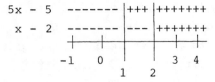

The solution set here is B = (1, 2).
We have that x is a solution if
either x is in A, or x is in B.
Hence, the solution set is
A ∪ B = (1, 2) ∪ (2, 11/3).

Example 3   Solve the inequality
$3x^2 - 8x + 1 > 0$.

Solution   The expression does not
    factor with integer coefficients.
    If we use the quadratic formula to
    determine the numbers x which makes
    $3x^2 - 8x + 1 = 0$, we have

$$x = \frac{8 \pm \sqrt{8^2 - 4(3)(1)}}{6}$$

$$= \frac{8 \pm \sqrt{64 - 12}}{6}$$

$$= \frac{8 \pm \sqrt{52}}{6}$$

$$= \frac{8 \pm 2\sqrt{13}}{6},$$

or

$$x = \frac{4 \pm \sqrt{13}}{3}.$$

Thus, $(4 - \sqrt{13})/3$, and $(4 + \sqrt{13})/3$
are numbers that make the expression
equal to zero. Let $f(x) = 3x^2 - 8x + 1$

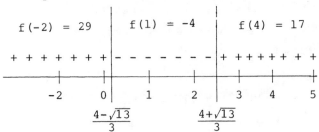

Making a sign graph, noting that
$4 - \sqrt{13} = .4$ and $4 + \sqrt{13} = 7.6$ for
reference, and testing reference
points to determine +, -, we have
the solution set

$$S = (-\infty, \frac{4 - \sqrt{13}}{3}) \cup (\frac{4 + \sqrt{13}}{3}, +\infty).$$

Selected Solutions

1. $|a - 2| = 1$
    Then we have either
    a - 2 = -1   or   a - 2 = 1
        a = 1   or   a = 3.
    The solution set is {1, 3}.

5. $|5 - 3x| = 3$
    We have either
    5 - 3x = -3   or   5 - 3x = 3
        -3x = -8   or   -3x = -2
        $x = \dfrac{8}{3}$ or $x = \dfrac{2}{3}$.

    The solution set is $\{\dfrac{2}{3}, \dfrac{8}{3}\}$.

7. $\left|\dfrac{z-4}{2}\right| = 5$

We have either

$\dfrac{z-4}{2} = -5$ or $\dfrac{z-4}{2} = 5$

$z - 4 = -10$ or $z - 4 = 10$

$z = -6$ or $z = 14.$

The solution set is $\{-6, 14\}$.

9. $\left|\dfrac{5}{r-3}\right| = 10$

We have either

$\dfrac{5}{r-3} = -10$ or $\dfrac{5}{r-3} = 10$

$5 = -10(r-3)$ or $5 = 10(r-3)$

$5 = -10r + 30$ or $5 = 10r - 30$

$10r = 25$ or $35 = 10r$

$r = \dfrac{5}{2}$ or $r = \dfrac{7}{2}.$

The solution set is $\{\dfrac{5}{2}, \dfrac{7}{2}\}$.

13. $|2k - 3| = |5k + 4|$

$2k - 3 = 5k + 4$ or $2k - 3 = -(5k + 4)$

$-7 = 3k$ or $7k = -1$

$-\dfrac{7}{3} = k$ or $k = -\dfrac{1}{7}$

The solution set is $\{-\dfrac{7}{3}, -\dfrac{1}{7}\}$.

17. $|x + 2| = |x - 1|$

$x + 2 = x - 1$ or $x + 2 = -(x - 1)$

$2 = -1$ or $x + 2 = -x + 1$

not possible or $2x = -1$

$x = -\dfrac{1}{2}$

The solution set is $\{-\dfrac{1}{2}\}$.

21. $|m| > 1$ means that

$m > 1$ or $m < -1$. The solution set is $(-\infty, -1) \cup (1, +\infty)$.

25. $|x| - 3 \le 7$

$|x| \le 10$

$-10 \le x \le 10$

The solution set is $[-10, 10]$.

29. $|3m - 2| > 4$ means that

$3m - 2 > 4$ or $3m - 2 < -4$

$3m > 6$ or $3m < -2$

$m > 2$ or $m < -\dfrac{2}{3}$

$m > 2$ or $m < -\dfrac{2}{3}.$

The solution set is

$(-\infty, -\dfrac{2}{3}) \cup (2, +\infty)$.

33. $\left|5x + \dfrac{1}{2}\right| - 2 < 5$

$\left|5x + \dfrac{1}{2}\right| < 7$

$-7 < 5x + \dfrac{1}{2} < 7$

$-7 - \dfrac{1}{2} < 5x < 7 - \dfrac{1}{2}$ subtract $\dfrac{1}{2}$

$-\dfrac{15}{2} < 5x < \dfrac{13}{2}$

$-\dfrac{3}{2} < x < \dfrac{13}{10}$ divide by 5

The solution set is $(-\dfrac{3}{2}, \dfrac{13}{10})$.

35. $\left|\dfrac{2x+3}{x}\right| < 1$

$-1 < \dfrac{2x+3}{x}$ and $\dfrac{2x+3}{x} < 1$

$\dfrac{2x+3}{x} > -1$ and $\dfrac{2x+3}{x} < 1$

$\dfrac{2x+3}{x} + 1 > 0$ and $\dfrac{2x+3}{x} - 1 < 0$

$\dfrac{2x+3+x}{x} > 0$ and $\dfrac{2x+3-x}{x} < 0$

$\dfrac{3x+3}{x} > 0$ and $\dfrac{x+3}{x} < 0$

$3x+3$ ---|+++|+++ $x+3$ ---|+++|+++

$\quad x$ ---|---|+++ $\quad x$ ---|---|+++

$\qquad\quad -1\quad 0$, $\qquad\quad -3\quad 0$

The quotient is   The fraction is
positive if   negative if
$x < -1$ or $x > 0$. $-3 < x < 0.$

Thus, $\left|\dfrac{2x+3}{x}\right| < 1$ if x satisfies

both inequalities. Hence, the
solution set is $(-3, -1)$.

37. $\left|\dfrac{6 + 2y}{y - 5}\right| > 2$

y is a solution if <u>either</u>

$\dfrac{6 + 2y}{y - 5} > 2$ <u>or</u> $\dfrac{6 + 2y}{y - 5} < -2$.

Then if $\dfrac{6 + 2y}{y - 5} > 2$,

$$\dfrac{6 + 2y}{y - 5} - 2 > 0$$

$$\dfrac{6 + 2y - 2(y - 5)}{y - 5} > 0$$

$$\dfrac{16}{y - 5} > 0.$$

This is true if $y > 5$ because then the quotient is positive. The solution set here is $S_1 = (5, +\infty)$.

Also, if $\dfrac{6 + 2y}{y - 5} < -2$,

$$\dfrac{6 + 2y}{y - 5} + 2 < 0$$

$$\dfrac{6 + 2y + 2y(y - 5)}{y - 5} < 0$$

$$\dfrac{4y - 4}{y - 5} < 0$$

```
- - - | + + + + | + + +    4y - 4
- - - | - - - - | - - -    y - 5
_____|_____|_____
       1         5
```

The solution set here is $s_2 = (1, 5)$.

To satisfy the original inequality x can be in either S_1 or S_2. Thus, the solution set to this exercise is $S_1 \cup S_2 = (1, 5) \cup (5, +\infty)$.

39. $\left|\dfrac{2}{q - 2}\right| \le 4$

$-4 \le \dfrac{2}{q - 2} \le 4$

$-4 \le \dfrac{2}{q - 2}$ and $\dfrac{2}{q - 2} \le 4$

$\dfrac{2}{q - 2} \ge -4$ $\qquad$ $\dfrac{2}{q - 2} \le 4$

$\dfrac{2}{q - 2} + 4 \ge 0$ $\qquad$ $\dfrac{2}{q - 2} - 4 \le 0$

$\dfrac{2 + 4q - 8}{q - 2} \ge 0$ $\qquad$ $\dfrac{2 - 4q + 8}{q - 2} \le 0$

$\dfrac{4q - 6}{q - 2} \ge 0$ and $\dfrac{10 - 4q}{q - 2} \le 0$

```
4q-6   - - - | + + + | + + +      10-4q   + + + | + + + | - - -
q-2    - - - | - - - | + + +      q-2     - - - | + + + | + + +
_____|_____|_____      _____|_____|_____
            3/2      2                          2      5/2
```

$(q \le \dfrac{3}{2}$ or $q > 2)$ and $(q < 2$ or $q \ge \dfrac{5}{2})$

Note: $q \ne 2$ because of a zero denominator. Simplified, this is the intersection of the two solution sets, or

$q \le \dfrac{3}{2}$ or $q \ge \dfrac{5}{2}$.

Solution: $(-\infty, \dfrac{3}{2}] \cup [\dfrac{5}{2}, +\infty)$

43. $\left|\dfrac{3z - 5}{2z}\right| > 4$

z is a solution if either $\dfrac{3z - 5}{2z} > 4$

or $\dfrac{3z - 5}{2z} < -4$.

Solve each part separetely. We have

$$\dfrac{3z - 5}{2z} > 4$$

$$\dfrac{3z - 5}{2z} - 4 > 0$$

$$\dfrac{3z - 5 - 4(2z)}{2z} > 0$$

$$\dfrac{-5z - 5}{2z} > 0$$

$$\dfrac{5z + 5}{2z} < 0.$$

```
- - - | + + | + + + +    5z + 5
- - - | - - | + + + +    2z
_____|_____|_____
     -1     0
```

The solution here is $S_1 = (-1, 0)$.

Also, $\dfrac{3z - 5}{2z} < -4$

$$\dfrac{3z - 5}{2z} + 4 < 0$$

$$\dfrac{3z - 5 + 4(2z)}{2z} < 0$$

$$\dfrac{11z - 5}{2z} < 0.$$

```
- - - | - - | + + +    11z - 5
- - - | + + | + + +    2z
_____|_____|_____
      0    5/11
```

The solution here is $S_2 = (0, \dfrac{5}{11})$.

z is a solution to the original inequality if z is in either S_1 or S_2. Thus, the solution set is $S_1 \cup S_2 = (-1, 0) \cup (0, \frac{5}{11})$.

47. If $|x + 1| = 2x$, then either

$$x + 1 = -2x \text{ or } x + 1 = 2x$$
$$3x = -1 \text{ or } \quad 1 = x.$$

Since $x = -\frac{1}{3}$ does not check, the solution set is $\{1\}$.

51.   If $|P| = |P|^2$, then solve by

$$|P|^2 - |P| = 0$$
$$|P|(|P| - 1) = 0$$
$$|P| = 0 \text{ or } |P| = 1$$
$$p = 0 \text{ or } \quad p = \pm 1.$$

The solution set is $\{0, \pm 1\}$.

55. $6|3r + 4|^2 + |3r + 4| = 2$

Let $x = |3r + 4|$ and write

$$6x^2 + x = 2$$
$$6x^2 + x - 2 = 0$$
$$(3x + 2)(2x - 1) = 0,$$

so that either

$$x = -\frac{2}{3} \quad \text{or} \quad x = \frac{1}{2}.$$

Hence,

$|3r + 4| = \frac{-2}{3}$ or $|3r + 4| = \frac{1}{2}$

no solution; or $3r + 4 = -\frac{1}{2}$ or $3r + 4 = \frac{1}{2}$

or $3r = -\frac{9}{2}$ or $3r = \frac{-7}{2}$

$r = \frac{-3}{2}$ or $r = \frac{-7}{6}$

The solution set is $\{\frac{-3}{2}, \frac{-7}{6}\}$.

57. $|r^2 - 3| < 1$ becomes

$$-1 < r^2 - 3 < 1$$
$$3 - 1 < r^2 < 3 + 1 \text{ or}$$
$$2 < r^2 < 4.$$

Consider each inequality separately. We must have

$$2 < r^2 \quad \text{and} \quad r^2 < 4$$
$$r^2 - 2 > 0 \quad \text{and} \quad r^2 - 4 < 0$$
$$(r - \sqrt{2})(r + \sqrt{2}) > 0 \quad \text{and} \quad (r - 2)(r + 2) < 0.$$

The solution set is   The solution set is
$A = (-\infty, -\sqrt{2}) \cup$ $B = (-2, 2)$
$(\sqrt{2}, \infty)$,

We see that r must be in A and B to be a solution to the original inequality. Hence, the solution set is

$S = A \cap B = (-2, -\sqrt{2}) \cup (\sqrt{2}, 2)$.

59. $|z^2 - 8| \geq 7$ means that either

$$z^2 - 8 \leq -7 \quad \text{or} \quad z^2 - 8 \geq 7$$
$$z^2 \leq 1 \quad \text{or} \quad z^2 \geq 15$$
$$\sqrt{z^2} \leq 1 \quad \text{or} \quad \sqrt{z^2} \geq \sqrt{15}$$
$$|z| \leq 1 \quad \text{or} \quad |z| \geq \sqrt{15},$$

Since $\sqrt{n^2} = |n|$,

$$-1 \leq z \leq 1 \quad \text{or} \quad z \geq \sqrt{15}$$
$$\text{or } z \leq -\sqrt{15}.$$

The solution set is   The solution set is
$A = [-1, 1]$. $B = (-\infty, -\sqrt{15}] \cup [\sqrt{15}, \infty)$.

Hence, z is a solution if z is in either A or B. The solution set is

$S = A \cup B = (-\infty, -\sqrt{15}] \cup [-1, 1] \cup [\sqrt{15}, \infty)$.

61. $|m + 2| \leq |4m - 1|$

$\frac{|m + 2|}{|4m - 1|} \leq 1$ so that $\left|\frac{m + 2}{4m - 1}\right| \leq 1$,

Thus, $-1 \leq \frac{m + 2}{4m - 1} \leq 1$.

$\frac{m + 2}{4m - 1} \geq -1$ and $\frac{m + 2}{4m - 1} < 1$

$\frac{m + 2}{4m - 1} + 1 \geq 0$ $\bigg|$ $\frac{m + 2}{4m - 1} - 1 < 0$

$$\frac{m + 2 + (4m - 1)}{4m - 1} \geq 0 \text{ and } \frac{m + 2 - (4m - 1)}{4m - 1} < 0$$

$$\frac{5m + 1}{4m - 1} \geq 0 \qquad\qquad \frac{3 - 3m}{4m - 1} < 0$$

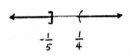

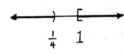

The solution here is

$$S_1 = (-\infty, -\tfrac{1}{5}] \cup (\tfrac{1}{4}, +\infty).$$

The solution here is

$$S_2 = (-\infty, \tfrac{1}{4}) \cup [1, +\infty).$$

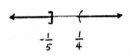 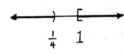

The solution set to the original inequality is the intersection of S_1 and S_2, which is

$$(-\infty, -\tfrac{1}{5}] \cup [1, \infty)$$

65. z is no less than 2 units from 12

$$|z - 12| \qquad \geq \qquad 2$$

means the distance from z to 12 is greater than or equal to 2. Thus, $|z - 12| \geq 2$.

69. If $|x - 2| < .0004$ then $|y - 7| < .00001$

71. If $|x - 2| < 3$, then
$-3 < x - 2 < 3,$
$-1 < x < 5$, by adding 2.
then
$-3 < 3x < 15$, and
$-3 + 5 < 3x + 5 < 20$, or
$2 < 3x + 5 < 20.$
Hence, m = 2 and n = 20.

73. If $|x - 1| < 10^{-6}$, then
$-10^{-6} < x - 1 < 10^{-6}$, and
multiplying by 7 gives
$-(7)(10^{-6}) < 7x - 7 < (7)10^{-6}.$
Since $7 < 10$, then $7 \cdot 10^{-6} < 10 \cdot 10^{-6}$
$= 10^{-5}$, and $-10 < -7$, so that
$(-10)(10^{-6}) < (-7)(10^{-6}).$
Hence,
$-10^{-5} = (-10)(10^{-6}) < (-7)(10^{-6})$
$< 7x - 7 < 7 \cdot 10^{-6} < 10^{-5}.$
This shows that
$-10^{-5} < 7x - 7 < 10^{-5}$, or
$$|7x - 7| < 10^{-5}.$$

75. $|4 + p| + |4 - p| \leq 8.$
Since $|a - b|$ means the distance between a and b, we have
$|4 + p| = |p + 4| = d(P, -4) = d_1$
and $|4 - p| = d(p, 4) = d_2.$ We
must have $d_1 + d_2 \leq 8.$ We see that
if $P < -4$, then d_2 alone is > 8.
Also, if $P > 4$, then $d_1 > 8$. Hence,
the solution set is $[-4, 4]$.

Note that $p = -4$ and $P = 4$ are both solutions.

Chapter 2 Review Exercises

Selected Solutions

3. $5y - 2(y + 4) = 3(2y + 1)$
$5y - 2y - 8 = 6y + 3$ Remove parentheses
$3y - 8 = 6y + 3$ Combine like terms
$3y - 8 - 3y = 6y + 3 - 3y$
$-8 = 3y + 3$

$$-11 = 3y$$

$$\frac{1}{3}(-11) = \frac{1}{3} \cdot 3y$$

$$\frac{-11}{3} = y$$

The solution set is $\{\frac{-11}{3}\}$.

5. $\frac{p}{2} - \frac{3p}{4} = 8 + \frac{p}{3}$

$12(\frac{p}{2} - \frac{3p}{4}) = 12(8 + \frac{p}{3})$ Multiply by common denominator = 12.

$6p - 9p = 96 + 4p$ Remove parenthesis

$-3p = 96 + 4p$ Combine like terms

$-7p = 96$

$p = \frac{-96}{7}$

The solution set is $\{\frac{-96}{7}\}$.

9. $(x - 3)(2x + 1) = 2(x + 2)(x - 4)$

$2x^2 - 5x - 3 = 2x^2 - 4x - 16$

Remove parentheses

$-5x - 3 = -4x - 16$

Add $-2x^2$ on both sides

$-3 = x - 16$

Add 5x on both sides

$13 = x$, add 16.

The solution set is $\{13\}$.

11. $3(x + 2b) + a = 2x - 6$

$3x + 6b + a = 2x - 6$ Remove parentheses

$x + 6b + a = -6$

$x = -6b - a - 6$

15. $2a + ay = 4y - 4a$ for y.

$ay - 4y = -4a - 2a$

$y(a - 4) = -6a$

$y = \frac{-6a}{a - 4}$ or $\frac{6a}{4 - a}$

17. $F = \frac{9}{5}C + 32$ for C.

$\frac{9}{5}C + 32 = F$

$\frac{9}{5}C = F - 32$

$C = \frac{5}{9}(F - 32)$

21. $\frac{1}{k} = \frac{1}{r_1} + \frac{1}{r_2}$ for r_1.

$\frac{1}{r_1} = \frac{1}{k} - \frac{1}{r_2}$

$\frac{1}{r_1} = \frac{r_2 - k}{kr_2}$

$r_1 = kr_2/(r_2 - k)$

23. $V = \pi r^2 L$ for L.

$L = V/(\pi r^2)$

27.   Let x = original price. Then .15x = discount and we have x - .15x = sale price.

Thus, .85x = 425, or x = \$500.

29. Let t = number of hours it takes second person to do the job alone. Then

Amount first person can do in 1 hour	Amount second person can do	Amount together
$\frac{1}{6}$ +	$\frac{1}{t}$ =	$\frac{1}{4}$

$\frac{1}{t} = \frac{1}{4} - \frac{1}{6}$

$\frac{1}{t} = \frac{1}{12}$, or t = 12.

The first person would need 12 hours.

33. $2a^2 + a - 15 = 0$

$(2a - 5)(a + 3) = 0,$

$a = \frac{5}{2}, -3.$

The solution set is $\{-3, \frac{5}{2}\}$.

35.
$$2q^2 - 11q = 21$$
$$2q^2 - 11q - 21 = 0$$
$$(2q + 3)(q - 7) = 0$$
$$q = -\frac{3}{2}, \ 7.$$

The solution set is $\{-\frac{3}{2}, \ 7\}$.

39. $a = i, \ b = -4, \ c = i$
$$x = \frac{4 \pm \sqrt{16 - 4(i)(i)}}{2i}$$
$$= \frac{4 \pm \sqrt{20}}{2i}$$
$$x = \frac{4 \pm 2\sqrt{5}}{2i} = \frac{2 \pm \sqrt{5}}{i} \cdot \frac{i}{i}$$
$$x = \frac{(2 \pm \sqrt{5})i}{-1} = (-2 \pm \sqrt{5})i$$
$$x = -2i \pm \sqrt{5}i$$

The solution set is $\{-2i \pm \sqrt{5}i\}$.

41.
$$8y^2 = 2y - 6$$
$$8y^2 - 2y + 6 = 0$$
Here $a = 8$, $b = -2$ and $c = 6$, so that $b^2 - 4ac = 4 - 4(8)(6)$
$= 4 - 192 = -188$. Thus, the equation has complex roots.

45. $25z^2 - 110z + 121 = 0$
Letting $a = 25$, $b = -110$, and $c = 121$, we have
$$b^2 - 4ac = (-110)^2 - 4(25)(121)$$
$$= 12,100 - 12,100 = 0.$$
Hence, the equation has one real solution.

47. Sketch.

wall

Know that
$\ell + 2w = 325$
and must have
$\ell w = 11,250$

Solve $\ell + 2w = 325$ for ℓ:
$$\ell = 325 - 2w$$

Substitute ℓ into $\ell w = 11,250$:
$$(325 - 2w)w = 11,250$$
$$325w - 2w^2 = 11,250$$
$$2w^2 - 325w + 11,250 = 0$$
$$(2w - 225)(w - 50) = 0$$
$$w = 50$$
$$\text{or} \quad w = \frac{225}{2}$$
If $w = 50$, then $\ell = 225$.
If $w = \frac{225}{2}$ then $\ell = 100$.

51.
$$(r + 1)^2 - 3(r + 1) = 4$$
$$(r + 1)^2 - 3(r + 1) - 4 = 0$$
Let $x = r + 1$, then solve:
$$x^2 - 3x - 4 = 0$$
$$(x - 4)(x + 1) = 0$$
$$x = 4, \ -1.$$
If $x = 4$, then $\quad r + 1 = 4$
$$r = 3.$$
If $x = -1$, then $\quad r + 1 = -1$, or
$$r = -2$$
The solution set is $S = \{-2, \ 3\}$.

53.
$$(2z + 3)^{2/3} + (2z + 3)^{1/3} = 6$$
$$(2z + 3)^{2/3} + (2z + 3)^{1/3} - 6 = 0$$
Let $x = (2z + 3)^{1/3}$, then solve:
$$x^2 + x - 6 = 0$$
$$(x + 3)(x - 3) = 0$$
$$x = -3, \ 2.$$
If $x = -3$ then $\quad (2z + 3)^{1/3} = -3,$
$$\text{cube:} \quad 2z + 3 = -27$$
$$2z = -30$$
$$z = -15.$$
If $x = 2$, then $\quad (2z + 3)^{1/3} = 2$
$$2z + 3 = 8$$
$$2z = 5$$
so that $\qquad\qquad z = \frac{5}{2}.$

The solution set is
$$S = \{-15, \ \frac{5}{2}\}.$$

57.　　　$\sqrt{4y - 2} = \sqrt{3y + 1}$

　　　$(\sqrt{4y - 2})^2 = (\sqrt{3y + 1})^2$　since

　　　　　　　　　　$(\sqrt{x})^2 = x$

　　　　　$4y - 2 = 3y + 1$

　　　　　　　　$y = 3$

　　Check this proposed solution:

　　　　　　　$y = 3:$

　　$\sqrt{(4 \cdot 3) - 2} = \sqrt{10}$

　　$\sqrt{(3 \cdot 3) + 1} = \sqrt{10}.$

　　$y = 3$ checks.　The solution set
　　is S = {3}.

59.　　　$\sqrt{p + 2} = 2 + p$

　　　$(\sqrt{p + 2})^2 = (2 + p)^2$

　　　　$p + 2 = p^2 + 4p + 4$

　　　　　　$0 = p^2 + 3p + 2$

　　　　　　$0 = (p + 2)(p + 1)$

　　　　　$p = -2$ or $p = -1$

　　Try -2: $\sqrt{-2 + 2} = 0$, $2 + (-2) = 0.$
　　Try -1: $\sqrt{-1 + 2} = \sqrt{1} = 1$, $2 + (-1)$
　　　　　　　　　　　　　　$= 1.$

　　They both work.　The solution set
　　is S = {-2, -1}.

63.　　　$\sqrt[3]{6y + 2} = \sqrt[3]{4y}$

　　　$(\sqrt[3]{6y + 2})^3 = (\sqrt[3]{4y})^3$

　　　　　$6y + 2 = 4y$

　　　　　　　$2y = -2$

　　　　　　　　$y = -1$

　　The solution set is S = {-1}.

65.　　　$\sqrt{3 + x} = \sqrt{3x + 7} - 2$

　　　$(\sqrt{3 + x})^2 = (\sqrt{3x + 7} - 2)^2$

　　　　　$3 + x = (3x + 7) - 4\sqrt{3x + 7} + 4$

　　　$4\sqrt{3x + 7} = 3x + 11 - (3 + x)$

　　　$4\sqrt{3x + 7} = 2x + 8$

　　　$2\sqrt{3x + 7} = x + 4$

　　　$(2\sqrt{3x + 7})^2 = (x + 4)^2$

　　　$4(3x + 7) = x^2 + 8x + 16$

　　　$12x + 28 = x^2 + 8x + 10$

　$x^2 - 4x - 12 = 0$

$(x - 6)(x + 2) = 0$

　　　　　$x = -2, \ x = 6$

　　Check $x = -2$:

　　　$\sqrt{3 + x} = \sqrt{3 - 2} = \sqrt{1} = 1$

　$\sqrt{3x + 7} - 2 = \sqrt{-6 + 7} - 2 = \sqrt{1} - 2$

　　　　　　　　　　　　　$= 1 - 2$

　　　　　　　　　　　　　$= -1$

　　$x = -2$ does not check.

　　Check $x = 6$:

　　　　$\sqrt{3 + x} = \sqrt{9} = 3$

　$\sqrt{3x + 7} - 2 = \sqrt{25} - 2 = 5 - 2 = 3$

　　$x = 6$ is the only solution.　The
　　solution set is S = {6}.

69.　$-9x < 4x + 7$

　　　$0 < 13x + 7$

　　$-7 < 13x$

　　$\dfrac{-7}{13} < x$

　　The solution set is S = $(\dfrac{-7}{13}, \ \infty).$

73.　$3r - 4 + r > 2(r - 1)$

　　　$4r - 4 > 2r - 2$

　　　$2r - 4 > -2$

　　　　　$2r > 2$

　　　　　$r > 1$

　　The solution set is S = $(1, \ \infty).$

75.　$5 \le 2x - 3 \le 7$

　　$8 \le 2x \le 10$

　　$4 \le x \le 5$

　　The solution set is S = [4, 5].

77.　$-5 < \dfrac{2p - 1}{-3} \le 2$

　　$15 > 2p - 1 \ge -6$　multiply by -3
　　　　　　　　　　　　and change dir-
　　　　　　　　　　　　ection of in-
　　　　　　　　　　　　equalities

　　$16 > 2p \ge -5$　　add 1

　　$8 > p \ge -\dfrac{5}{2}$　　multiply by 1/2

　$-\dfrac{5}{2} \le p > 8$　　rewrite

　　The solution set is S = [-5/2, 8).

81. $6m^2 - 11m - 10 < 0$

Factor as $(3m + 2)(2m - 5) < 0$.

Make a sign graph.

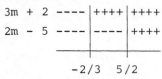

$3m + 2$ ---- $|$++++$|$++++

$2m - 5$ ---- $|$----$|$++++

$$-2/3 \quad 5/2$$

The product is negative when the two factors have opposite signs, giving the solution

$S = (-2/3, 5/2)$.

83. $z^3 - 16z \leq 0$

Factor as $z(z + 4)(z - 4) \leq 0$.

Make a sign graph showing the factors z, $z + 4$, $z - 4$.

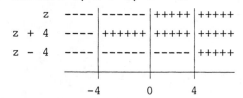

z ---- $|$------$|$+++++$|$+++++

$z + 4$ ---- $|$++++++$|$+++++$|$+++++

$z - 4$ ---- $|$------$|$-----$|$+++++

$$-4 \quad\quad 0 \quad\quad 4$$

The product is negative when $z < -4$ or when $0 < z < 4$.

Check the endpoints (because of $\leq$) to get the solution

$(-\infty, -4] \cup [0, 4]$.

87. To solve $\dfrac{3}{r - 1} \leq \dfrac{5}{r + 3}$

add $-\dfrac{5}{r + 3}$ on both sides.

$$\frac{3}{r - 1} - \frac{5}{r + 3} \leq 0$$

$$\frac{3(r + 3) - 5(r - 1)}{(r - 1)(r + 3)} \leq 0$$

$$\frac{3r + 9 - 5r + 5}{(r - 1)(r + 3)} \leq 0$$

$$\frac{-2r + 14}{(r - 1)(r + 3)} \leq 0$$

Make a sign graph showing $-2r + 14$, $r - 1$, and $r + 3$.

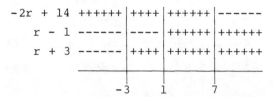

$-2r + 14$ ++++++$|$++++$|$++++++$|$------

$r - 1$ ------$|$----$|$++++++$|$++++++

$r + 3$ ------$|$++++$|$++++++$|$++++++

$$-3 \quad\quad 1 \quad\quad 7$$

The quotient is negative when $-3 < r < 1$ or $r > 7$.

Check the endpoints in the original inequality to get the solution, $(-3, 1) \cup [7, +\infty)$.

89. Find x where $-x^2 + 28x + 60 \geq 0$

$$x^2 - 28x - 60 \leq 0$$

$$(x + 2)(x - 30) \leq 0.$$

Make a sign graph for $x + 2$ and $x - 30$.

$x + 2$ ---- $|$+++++$|$++++++

$x - 30$ ---- $|$-----$|$++++++

$$-2 \quad\quad 30$$

The product is negative (so that profit is positive), when $-2 < x < 30$. However, we can't sell a negative number of pieces, so the solution is $[0, 30)$.

93. $|2 - y| = 3$

$2 - y = 3$ or $2 - y = -3$

$\quad -y = 1$ or $\quad\quad -y = -5$

$\quad\quad y = -1$ or $y = 5$

The solution set is $\{-1, 5\}$.

95. $\left|\dfrac{7}{2 - 3a}\right| = 9$

$\dfrac{7}{2 - 3a} = 9$ or $\dfrac{7}{2 - 3a} = -9$

$7 = 9(2 - 3a)$ or $7 = -9(2 - 3a)$

$7 = 18 - 27a$ or $7 = -18 + 27a$

$27a = 11$ or $25 = 27a$

$a = \dfrac{11}{27}$ or $a = \dfrac{25}{27}$

The solution set is $\{\dfrac{11}{27}, \dfrac{25}{27}\}$.

97. $|5r - 1| = |2r + 3|$

$5r - 1 = 2r + 3$ or $5r - 1 = -2(r + 3)$

$3r = 4$ or $5r - 1 = -2r - 3$

$r = \dfrac{4}{3}$ or $7r = -2$

$r = \dfrac{-2}{7}$

The solution set is $\{-\dfrac{2}{7}, \dfrac{4}{3}\}$.

99. $|M| \leq 7$

$-7 \leq M \leq 7$

The solution set is $[-7, 7]$.

101. $|b| \leq -1$ has no solution because $|b| \geq 0$ for any choice of b, so cannot be less than -1. The solution set is $\emptyset$.

105. $|3r + 7| > 5$

$3r + 7 > 5$ or $3r + 7 < -5$

$3r > -2$ or $3r < -12$

$r > \frac{-2}{3}$ or $r < -4$

The solution set is

$(-\infty, -4) \cup (-\frac{2}{3}, +\infty)$.

107. $\left|\frac{3r}{r-1}\right| \geq 3$

Start with

$\frac{3r}{r-1} \leq -3$ or $\frac{3r}{r-1} \geq 3$.

Solve each inequality separately.

$\frac{3r}{r-1} + 3 \leq 0$ or $\frac{3r}{r-1} - 3 \geq 0$

$\frac{3r + 3(r-1)}{r-1} \leq 0$ or $\frac{3r - 3(r-1)}{r-1} \geq 0$

$\frac{6r-3}{r-1} \leq 0$ or $\frac{3}{r-1} \geq 0$

Sign graphs give

$(\frac{1}{2}, 1)$ or $(1, +\infty)$.

The solution set is $[\frac{1}{2}, 1) \cup (1, \infty)$ since $r = \frac{1}{2}$ checks but $r = 1$ does not.

109. $f(x) = 2x[\frac{1}{2}(x^2 + 1)^{-1/2}(2x)]$

$+ 2(x^2 + 1)^{1/2}$

$= \frac{2x}{1} \cdot \frac{1}{2} \cdot \frac{1}{(x^2 + 1)^{1/2}} \cdot \frac{2x}{1}$

$+ 2(x^2 + 1)^{1/2}$

$= \frac{2x^2}{(x^2 + 1)^{1/2}} + \frac{2(x^2 + 1)^{1/2}}{1}$

$= \frac{2x^2 + 2(x^2 + 1)^{1/2}(x^2 + 1)^{1/2}}{(x^2 + 1)^{1/2}},$

using $\frac{a}{b} + \frac{c}{d} = \frac{ad + bc}{bd}$

$= \frac{2x^2 + 2(x^2 + 1)}{(x^2 + 1)^{1/2}}$

$f(x) = \frac{4x^2 + 2}{(x^2 + 1)^{1/2}},$ in simplified form

Note that $4x^2 + 2$ and $x^2 + 1$ are always positive, f(x) is always positive.

Thus,

(a) $f(x) > 0$ if x is in the interval $(-\infty, +\infty)$.

(b) $f(x) < 0$ is never true; that is, x is in $\emptyset$.

111. Draw the figure.

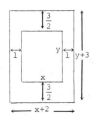

Let x denote the width of the printed area. Since the printed area is 36, then $x \cdot$ (height) = 36. Thus, in the figure, the height y is 36/x. The total area is then $A = (x + 2)(36/x + 3)$ or

$A = 36 + \frac{72}{x} + 3x + 6$

$A = 3x + \frac{72}{x} + 42$.

112.

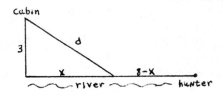

The distance d is the hypotenuse of the right triangle, so that

$d = \sqrt{x^2 + 9}$. Using distance = (rate) x (time), we have that if t, is the amount of time the hunter walks the (8 - x) miles alongside the river, then

$$t_1 = \frac{distance}{rate} = \frac{8 - x}{5} = \frac{8}{5} - \frac{1}{5}x$$

hours, and if t_2 is the amount of time the hunter walks from the river to the cabin, then

$$t_2 = \frac{\sqrt{x^2 + 9}}{2} = \frac{1}{2}\sqrt{x^2 + 9} \text{ hours.}$$

Hence, the total time is

$$t = t_1 + t_2 = \frac{8}{5} - \frac{1}{5}x + \frac{1}{2}\sqrt{x^2 + 9}.$$

113. Let $y = 2x + |2 - x|$.

   Case 1 If $x \leq 2$, then
   $|2 - x| = 2 - x$ and
   we have $y = 2x + 2 - x$
   $$y = x + 2$$
   or $x = y - 2$,

   Case 2 If $x > 2$, then
   $|2 - x| = x - 2$ and
   we have $y = 2x + x - 2$
   $$y = 3x - 2$$
   $$3x = y + 2$$
   or $x = \frac{y + 2}{3}.$

115. If $s < t$, then $|s - t| = t - s$ and we have

$$\frac{s + t - |s + t|}{2} = \frac{s + t - (t - s)}{2}$$

$$= \frac{2s}{2} = s,$$

the smaller of s and t.

119. If x is in the interval [2, 7],

   then $2 \leq x \leq 7$ and hence,

   $\frac{1}{7} \leq \frac{1}{x} \leq \frac{1}{2}$. This implies that

   $-\frac{1}{2} \leq \frac{1}{x} \leq \frac{1}{2}$ and $\left|\frac{1}{x}\right| \leq \frac{1}{2}$.

   Thus, $M = \frac{1}{2}$.

121. Using $|a + b| \leq |a| + |b|$ with
   $a = x^2$ and $b = -2x + 1$ gives

   $$|x^3 - 2x + 1| \leq |x^3| + |-2x + 1|$$

   $$= |x^3| + |2x - 1|, \text{ since}$$

   $|c| = |-c|$. Then using $x \in (-2, 3)$,
   we have $-2 < x < 3$, so that
   $-4 < 2x < 6$, and $-5 < 2x - 1 < 5$.
   Thus, $|2x - 1| < 5$. Also, if
   $-2 < x < 3$, then $(-2)^3 < x^3 < 3^3$,
   or $-8 < x^3 < 27$. Then,
   $-27 < x^3 < 27$, so that $|x^3| < 27$.
   Hence, $|x^3 - 2x + 1| \leq |x^3| + |2x - 1| < 5 + 27 = 32 = M$.

Chapter 2 Test

1. Solve the equation $\frac{1}{4} + \frac{4}{x} = \frac{1}{5} + \frac{5}{x}$.

2. Solve the equation $\frac{x + 3}{x - 1} = \frac{3}{5} - \frac{2x}{x - 1}$.

3. Solve the equation $(x + 5)(x - 6) = (x - 3)(x - 4)$.

4. Solve $4xy + 3 = 7y + 9$ for y.

5. Solve $\frac{1}{x} + \frac{1}{r} = \frac{1}{t}$ for r.

6. A movie theater charges adults $4 and children $2.50. If 500 tickets are sold and the total proceeds are $1,805.00, how many tickets of each kind were sold?

7. A mixture contains 24 liters of neutral solution and 8 liters of acid. How many liters of acid should be added to the present mixture to have a 40% acid mixture?

8. Solve the equations   (a) $(2x + 3)^2 = 24$ and (b) $(x + 2)^2 = \sqrt{2}$.

9. Solve the equation $6x^2 - 13x = -6$.

10. Solve the equation $4x^2 + 3x - 5 = 0$.

11. Solve the equation $2x^2 - 4x + 9 = 0$.

12. Solve the equation $2(\frac{1}{x} + 2)^2 + 3(\frac{1}{x} + 2) - 2 = 0$.

13. Solve the equation $7 - \sqrt{x + 5} = x$.

14. Solve the equation $\sqrt{2x + 1} - \sqrt{x - 3} = 2$.

15. Solve the equation $\sqrt{x + 3} + \sqrt{2x - 3} = 6$.

16. Solve the equation $(t - 1)^{2/3} - (t - 1)^{1/3} = 2$.

17. Find all values of k such that $4x^2 + kx + 1 = 0$ has equal roots.

18. The height of a window in a church is three times its width and the area of the window is 363 square feet. Find the dimensions of the window.

19. Find the solution set of the inequality $3t - 2(t + 4) \leq 6(1 - t)$.

20. Solve the inequality $x^2 - x - 6 \geq 0$.

21. Find the solution set of the inequality $-3 \leq \dfrac{4p + 3}{-3} < 5$.

22. Solve the inequality $\dfrac{x^2 - 4}{2x + 1} \leq 0$.

23. Solve the inequality $\dfrac{3t + 2}{2t - 1} \geq 1$.

24. Solve the inequality $\dfrac{3}{r + 2} \geq \dfrac{2}{r - 1}$.

25. Solve the equation $|4 - 3m| = 5$.

26. Solve the equation $\left|\dfrac{2 - 3a}{4a + 1}\right| = 2$.

27. Solve the inequality $|2x - 3| > 7$.

28. Solve the inequality $\left|\dfrac{3x - 2}{x + 1}\right| < 3$.

29. Find all values of k such that $x^2 - kx + 1 = 0$ has real solutions.

30. Find all numbers x such that $|x + 4| > 2|x - 3|$.

    (Answers for this test are on page 359.)

Cumulative Review Exercises,

Chapters 1 and 2

Selected Solutions

1. $-\frac{11}{3}$ is a rational number (c) and a real number (e).

5. The integers are closed with respect to subtraction since the difference of two integers is another integer.

9. $-|-7|$, $|-3|$, and $-|2|$
    $-|-7| = -7$, $|-3| = 3$ and $-|2| = -2$, so the proper numerical order is $-|-7|$, $-|2|$, $|-3|$.

13. $-|0| = -0 = 0$.

17. If $\frac{m}{3} > y$, then $m > 3y$, so that $m - 3y > 0$. Hence $|m - 3y| = m - 3y$.

21. $(r^{-3})(r^{-2})(r^5) = r^{-3-2+5} = r^0$
    $= 1$

25. $\dfrac{(5p^2q)^{-1}(5p^3q^{-2})^2}{5(pq)^{-3}(p^4q^{-2})^{-1}}$

    $= \dfrac{5^{-1}p^{-2}q^{-1}5^2p^6q^{-4}}{5p^{-3}q^{-3}p^{-4}q^2}$

    $= \dfrac{5^{-1+2}p^{-2+6}q^{-1-4}}{5p^{-3-4}q^{-3+2}}$

    $= \dfrac{5p^4q^{-5}}{5p^{-7}q^{-1}} = \dfrac{p^{4+7}}{q^{-1+5}} = \dfrac{p^{11}}{q^4}$

29. $(k - 7)(3k - 8)$
    $= k(3k - 8) - 7(3k - 8)$
    $= 3k^2 - 8k - 21k + 56$
    $= 3k^2 - 29k + 56$

33. $(y + z + 2)(3y - 2z + 5)$
    $= y(3y - 2z + 5) + z(3y - 2z + 5) + 2(3y - 2z + 5)$
    $= 3y^2 - 2yz + 5y + 3yz - 2z^2 + 5z + 6y - 4z + 10$
    $= 3y^2 + yz + 11y - 2z^2 + z + 10$

37. $3m^3 + 9m + 15m^5 = 3m(m^2 + 3 + 5m^4)$
    $= 3m(5m^4 + m^2 + 3)$

41. $8a^3 + 125 = (2a)^3 + (5)^3$
    $= (2a + 5)[(2a)^2 - (2a)(5) + (5)^2]$
    $= (2a + 5)(4a^2 - 10a + 25)$

45. $(z - 4)^2 - (z + 4)^2$
    $= [(z - 4) + (z + 4)][(z - 4) - (z + 4)]$
    $= [2z][-8] = 16z$

49. $\dfrac{3z^2 + z - 2}{4z^2 - z - 5} \div \dfrac{3z^2 + 11z + 6}{4z^2 + 7z - 15}$

    $= \dfrac{3z^2 + z - 2}{4z^2 - z - 5} \cdot \dfrac{4z^2 + 7z - 15}{3z^2 + 11z + 6}$

    $= \dfrac{(3z - 2)(z + 1)}{(4z - 5)(z + 1)} \cdot \dfrac{(4z - 5)(z + 3)}{(3z + 2)(z + 3)}$

    $= \dfrac{3z - 2}{3z + 2}$

53. $\dfrac{m^{-1} - n^{-1}}{(mn)^{-1}} = \dfrac{\frac{1}{m} - \frac{1}{n}}{\frac{1}{mn}}$

    $= \dfrac{\frac{n - m}{mn}}{\frac{1}{mn}}$

    $= \dfrac{n - m}{mn} \cdot \dfrac{mn}{1} = n - m$

57. $-\sqrt[4]{32} = -\sqrt[4]{16 \cdot 2}$
    $= -2\sqrt[4]{2}$

59. $\sqrt[3]{25} \cdot 3^4 \cdot 5^3 = \sqrt[3]{5^2 \cdot 3^4 \cdot 5^3}$

$= \sqrt[3]{3^4 \cdot 5^5}$

$= \sqrt[3]{3^3 \cdot 5^3 (75)}$

$= 3 \cdot 5 \sqrt[3]{75}$

$= 15 \sqrt[3]{75}$

63. $\sqrt{8} + 5\sqrt{32} - 7\sqrt{128}$

$= \sqrt{(4)(2)} + 5\sqrt{(16)(2)} - 7\sqrt{(64)(2)}$

$= 2\sqrt{2} + 20\sqrt{2} - 56\sqrt{2} = -34\sqrt{2}$

65. $\dfrac{1}{2 - \sqrt{7}} = \dfrac{1}{2 - \sqrt{7}} \cdot \dfrac{2 + \sqrt{7}}{2 + \sqrt{7}}$

$= \dfrac{2 + \sqrt{7}}{4 - 7}$

$= \dfrac{2 + \sqrt{7}}{-3} = -\left(\dfrac{2 + \sqrt{7}}{3}\right)$

67. $32^{-6/5} = \dfrac{1}{32^{6/5}} = \dfrac{1}{2^6} = \dfrac{1}{64}$

69. $(a - b)^{2/3} \cdot (a - b)^{-5/3}$

$= (a - b)^{2/3 - 5/3}$

$= (a - b)^{-3/3}$

$= (a - b)^{-1}$

$= \dfrac{1}{a - b}$

73. $\dfrac{r^{1/3} s^{5/3} t^{1/2}}{r^{-2/3} s^2 t^{-3/2}}$

$= r^{1/3 + 2/3} s^{5/3 - 2} t^{1/2 + 3/2}$

$= r^1 s^{-1/3} t^2 = \dfrac{r t^2}{s^{1/3}}$

77. $(1 + 3i)(2 - 5i)$

$= 1(2 - 5i) + 3i(2 - 5i)$

$= 2 - 5i + 6i - 15i^2$

$= 2 + i + 15$, since $i^2 = -1$

$= 17 + i$

81. $\dfrac{4 + 3i}{1 + 1} = \dfrac{4 + 3i}{1 + i} \cdot \dfrac{1 - i}{1 - i}$

$= \dfrac{(4 + 3i)(1 - i)}{1 + 1}$

$= \dfrac{4 + 3i - 4i - 3i^2}{2}$

$= \dfrac{7 - i}{2}$ since $i^2 = -1$

$= \dfrac{7}{2} - \dfrac{1}{2}i$

85. $\sqrt{-400} = \sqrt{400}\sqrt{-1} = 20i$

89. $i^{15} = i^{12} \cdot i^3$

$= (i^4)^3 \cdot i^3$

$= 1 \cdot i^3$ using $i^4 = 1$

$= i^3$

$= i^2 \cdot i = -i$

93. $\dfrac{-7r}{2} + \dfrac{3r - 5}{4} = \dfrac{2r + 5}{4}$

$-14r + 3r - 5 = 2r + 5$ multiply by 4

$-11r - 5 = 2r + 5$

$-13r = 10$

$r = -\dfrac{10}{13}$

The solution set is $\left\{\dfrac{-10}{13}\right\}$.

97. $V = V_0 + gt$. Solve for t.

$V - V_0 = gt$

$\dfrac{V - V_0}{g} = t$

101. Let x = length of shorter side. Then $x + 6$ is the length of each of the other two sides. Since the perimeter is 54 cm, we have

$x + (x + 6) + (x + 6) = 54$

$3x + 12 = 54$

$3x = 42$

$x = 14.$

The sides have lengths 14, 20, and 20.

105. Let x = number of pounds of $6 per pound coffee. Consider the table

pounds	price per pound	amount
20	4.50	4.50(20)
x	6.00	6.00(x)
20 + x	5.00	5.00(20 + x)

Then,

$$4.50(20) + 6.00(x) = 5.00(20 + x)$$
$$90 + 6x = 100 + 5x$$
$$x = 10 \text{ pounds}$$

107. Let x = speed of the boat in still water.

	speed of boat	time	distance
upstream	x − 2	t	15
downstream	x + 2	t	27

distance = (rate) x (time)

(a) $15 = (x - 2)t$ implies

$$t = \frac{15}{x - 2}, \text{ and}$$

(b) $27 = (x + 2)t$ implies

$$t = \frac{27}{x + 2}$$

Hence,

$$\frac{15}{x - 2} = \frac{27}{x + 2}.$$
$$15(x + 2) = 27(x - 2)$$
$$15x + 30 = 27x - 54$$
$$84 = 12x$$
$$x = 7$$

Speed is 7 km per hour.

109. $(5r - 3)^2 = 7$
$$5r - 3 = \pm\sqrt{7}$$
$$5r = 3 \pm \sqrt{7}$$
$$r = \frac{3 \pm \sqrt{7}}{5}$$

The solution set is the set $\{\frac{3 \pm \sqrt{7}}{5}\}$.

113. $4z^2 - 4z - 5 = 0$

Use the quadratic formula with a = 4, b = −4, c = −5.

$$z = \frac{-b \pm \sqrt{b^2 - 4ac}}{2a}$$
$$= \frac{4 \pm \sqrt{16 - 4(4)(-5)}}{8}$$
$$= \frac{4 \pm \sqrt{96}}{8} = \frac{4 \pm 4\sqrt{6}}{8} = \frac{1 \pm \sqrt{6}}{2}$$

The solution set is $\{\frac{1 \pm \sqrt{6}}{2}\}$.

117. $12y^2 - 4y + 3 = 0$

Using the quadratic formula with a = 12, b = −4, and c = 3 gives

$$y = \frac{4 \pm \sqrt{16 - 4(12)(3)}}{24}$$
$$= \frac{4 \pm \sqrt{16 - 144}}{24}$$
$$= \frac{4 \pm \sqrt{-128}}{24} \qquad 128 = 64 \cdot 2$$
$$= \frac{4 \pm 8\sqrt{2}\ i}{24}$$
$$= \frac{1 \pm 2\sqrt{2}i}{6}$$

The solution set is $\{\frac{1 \pm 2\sqrt{2}i}{6}\}$.

121. $z = 10a^2yb$. Solve for a.

$$\frac{z}{10yb} = a^2, \text{ so that}$$

$$a = \pm\sqrt{\frac{z}{10yb}} \cdot \frac{\sqrt{10yb}}{\sqrt{10yb}}$$

$$a = \pm\frac{\sqrt{10ybz}}{10yb}$$

125. Let x = the number of hours for B to complete the job. Person A does 1/5 of the job each hour. Person B does 1/x of the job each hour. Working together, A and B do 1/3 of the job each hour. Hence,

$$\frac{1}{x} + \frac{1}{5} = \frac{1}{3}.$$

Multiply by 15x to arrive at

$$15 + 3x = 5x$$
$$15 = 2x$$
$$x = \frac{15}{2}, \text{ or } 7\frac{1}{2} \text{ hours.}$$

129. $(m - 1)^{2/3} + 3(m - 1)^{1/3} = 10$

Let $u = (m - 1)^{1/3}$. Then

$u^2 + 3u - 10 = 0$

$(u - 2)(u + 5) = 0$

$\quad u - 2 = 0 \quad$ or $\quad u + 5 = 0$

$\quad\quad u = 2 \quad$ or $\quad\quad u = -5$

$\quad (m - 1)^{1/3} = 2 \quad$ or $\quad (m - 1)^{1/3} = -5$

$\quad\quad m - 1 = 8 \quad$ or $\quad\quad m - 1 = -125$

$\quad\quad\quad m = 9 \quad$ or $\quad\quad\quad m = -124$

The solution set is $\{-124, 9\}$.

133. $(z^2 - 18z)^{1/4} = 0$

Raise both sides to the fourth power.

$z^2 - 18z = 0$

$z(z - 18) = 0$

$\quad z = 0$ or $z = 18$

The solution set is $S = \{0, 18\}$.

137. $12m - 17 \geq 8m + 7$

$12m - 8m \geq 17 + 7$

$\quad 4m \geq 24$

$\quad m \geq 6$

The solution set is $[6, +\infty)$.

141. $y^2 + 6y \geq 0$

$y(y + 6) \geq 0$

Make a sign graph

```
    y   - - - | - - - - | + + + +
  y + 6 - - - | + + + + | + + + +
        _____|_____|_____
            -6         0
```

$y(y + 6) \geq 0$ if y is in the solution set $(-\infty, -6] \cup (0, +\infty)$.

145. $\dfrac{3}{y + 6} \geq \dfrac{1}{y - 2}$

$\dfrac{3}{y + 6} - \dfrac{1}{y - 2} \geq 0$

$\dfrac{3(y - 2) - (y + 6)}{(y + 6)(y - 2)} \geq 0$

$\dfrac{2y - 12}{(y + 6)(y - 2)} \geq 0$

Make a sign graph.

```
 2y - 12 - - - | - - - - | - - | + + +
  y + 6  - - - | + + + + | + + | + + +
  y - 2  - - - | - - - - | + + | + + +
         _____|_____|_____|_____
             -6         2     6
```

The solution set is $(-6, 2) \cup [6, +\infty)$.

149. $|2x + 5| > 3$

$2x + 5 > 3 \quad$ or $\quad -(2x + 5) > 3$

$\quad 2x > -2 \quad$ or $\quad -2x - 5 > 3$

$\quad x > -1 \quad$ or $\quad\quad -2x > 8$

$\quad x > -1 \quad$ or $\quad\quad x < -4$

The solution set is
$(-\infty, -4) \cup (-1, +\infty)$.

153. $|a - 2| = 1$

$a - 2 = 1$ or $a - 2 = -1$

$\quad a = 3$ or $\quad a = 1$

The solution set is $S = \{1, 3\}$.

155. $|3z - 1| = |2z + 5|$

$3z - 1 = 2z + 5 \quad$ or $\quad 3z - 1 = -(2z + 5)$

$3z - 2z = 5 + 1 \quad$ or $\quad 3z + 2z = -5 + 1$

$\quad\quad z = 6 \quad\quad$ or $\quad\quad 5z = -4$

$\quad\quad z = 6 \quad\quad$ or $\quad\quad z = -\dfrac{4}{5}$

The solution set is $S = \{-\dfrac{4}{5}, 6\}$.

CHAPTER 3 Functions and Graphs

Section 3.1 A Two-Dimensional Coordinate System

Additional Examples

Example 1 Verify whether or not the points $(6, -2)$, $(-2, 10)$, $(3, -4)$ are the vertices of a right triangle.

Solution Label the points $A(6, -2)$, $B(-2, 10)$, and $C(3, -4)$. Then we have

$$d(A,B) = \sqrt{(6 - (-2))^2 + (-2 - 10)^2}$$
$$= \sqrt{8^2 + (-12)^2}$$
$$= \sqrt{64 + 144}$$
$$= \sqrt{208},$$

$$d(A,C) = \sqrt{(6 - 3)^2 + (-2 - (-4))^2}$$
$$= \sqrt{3^2 + 2^2}$$
$$= \sqrt{9 + 4}$$
$$= \sqrt{13},$$

and

$$d(B,C) = \sqrt{(-2 - 3)^2 + (10 - (-4))^2}$$
$$= \sqrt{(-5)^2 + 14^2}$$
$$= \sqrt{25 + 196}$$
$$= \sqrt{221}.$$

Since $d^2(A, B) + d^2(A, C) = 208 + 13 = 221 = d^2(B, C)$, the points A, B, and C are the vertices of a right triangle. We can note that the side BC is the hypotenuse.

Example 2 Determine all values of c such that the distance between the points $(c, 9)$ and $(11, 2)$ is $\sqrt{130}$.

Solution The distance between the points $(c, 9)$ and $11, 2)$ is

$$\sqrt{(c - 11)^2 + (9 - 2)^2} = \sqrt{(c - 11)^2 + 7^2}$$
$$= \sqrt{(c - 11)^2 + 49}.$$

If the distance is $\sqrt{130}$, we solve for c as follows:

$$\sqrt{(c - 11)^2 + 49} = \sqrt{130}$$
$$(c - 11)^2 + 49 = 130, \text{ which implies}$$
$$(c - 11)^2 = 81.$$

Thus, $c - 11 = \pm 9$, so that

$$c = 2 \text{ or } 20.$$

Example 3 Find an equation of the set of all points (x, Y) that are 6 units from the point $(-3, 4)$.

Solution Using the notation for the points that $P(x, y)$ and $A(-3, 4)$ we have that $d(P, A) = 6$. Using the distance formula, we have

$$d(P,A) = \sqrt{(x - (-3))^2 + (y - 4)^2}$$
$$= \sqrt{(x + 3)^2 + (y - 4)^2}.$$

The equation is then

$$\sqrt{(x + 3)^2 + (y - 4)^2} = 6$$
$$\text{or} \quad (x + 3)^2 + (y - 4)^2 = 36.$$

This set of points is a circle with center at $(-3, 4)$ and radius 6.

Example 4 Given the points $A(0, -4)$ and $B(0, 4)$, find an equation of the set of all points $P(x, y)$ such that $d(A, P) + d(B, P) = 10$.

Solution Using the given points A and B we have

$$d(A,P) = \sqrt{(x - 0)^2 + (y + 4)^2}$$
$$= \sqrt{x^2 + (y + 4)^2},$$

and

$$d(B,P) = \sqrt{(x - 0)^2 + (y - 4)^2}$$
$$= \sqrt{x^2 + (y - 4)^2}.$$

Hence, an equation is

$$\sqrt{x^2 + (y + 4)^2} + \sqrt{x^2 + (y - 4)^2} = 10.$$

However, this can be greatly simplified as follows:

$$\sqrt{x^2 + (y + 4)^2} = 10 - \sqrt{x^2 + (y - 4)^2}$$
$$x^2 + (y + 4)^2 = \left(10 - \sqrt{x^2 + (y - 4)^2}\right)^2$$
$$x^2 + y^2 + 8y + 16 = 100 - 20\sqrt{x^2 + (y - 4)^2} + x^2 + (y - 4)^2$$
$$y^2 + 8y + 16 - 100 - (y^2 - 8y + 16) = -20\sqrt{x^2 + (y - 4)^2}$$
$$16y - 100 = -20\sqrt{x^2 + (y - 4)^2}$$
$$4y - 25 = -5\sqrt{x^2 + (y - 4)^2}$$
$$(4y - 25)^2 = 25[x^2 + (y - 4)^2]$$
$$16y^2 - 200y + 625 = 25x^2 + 25(y - 4)^2$$

$16y^2 - 200y + 625 = 25x^2 + 25(y^2 - 8y + 16)$

$16y2 - 200y + 625 = 25x^2 + 25y^2 - 200y + 400$

$225 = 25x^2 + 9y^2.$

If we divide by 225 we arrive at

$$\frac{x^2}{9} + \frac{y^2}{25} = 1,$$

which is the desired equation. (We will find later that the graph of this equation is an ellipse.)

Selected Solutions

For Exercises 1-17, see the graphs in the answer section of your text.

9. $y \leq 0$ means y is either negative or 0. Shade everything below the x-axis.

13. $|x| = 4$, $y \geq 2$.
    $|x| = 4$ means $x = 4$ or $x = -4$
    The graph includes all points with $x = 4$ or -4 and $y \geq 2$.

17. $2 \leq |x| \leq 3$, $y \geq 2$
    $2 \leq |x| \leq 3$ means either $2 \leq x \leq 3$
or $-3 \leq x \leq -2$.
    To graph $-3 \leq x \leq -2$ and $y \geq 2$, shade the region between the graphs of $x = -3$ and $x = -2$ and above and on the line $y = 2$.
    Graph $2 \leq x \leq 3$ and $y \geq 2$ similarly.

21. distance $= \sqrt{(x_1 - x_2)^2 + (y_1 - y_2)^2}$

The midpoint is $(\frac{x_1 + x_2}{2}, \frac{y_1 + y_2}{2})$.
    $P(-8, -2)$, $Q(-3, -5)$
    $d(P, Q) = \sqrt{(-8 - (-3))^2 + (-2 - (-5))^2}$
    $= \sqrt{(-5)^2 + 3^2}$
    $= \sqrt{25 + 9}$
    $= \sqrt{34}.$

Midpoint: $(\frac{-8 + (-3)}{2}, \frac{-2 + (-5)}{2})$
    $= (\frac{-11}{2}, \frac{-7}{2})$

25. $(5, 7)$, $(2, 14)$
    $d = \sqrt{(5 - 2)^2 + (14 - 7)^2}$
    $= \sqrt{3^2 + 7^2}$
    $= \sqrt{9 + 49}$
    $= \sqrt{58}$
    ≈ 7.616

29. endpoint $(-3, 6)$
    midpoint $(5, 8)$
    $\frac{-3 + x}{2} = 5$ $\frac{6 + y}{2} = 8$
    $-3 + x = 10$ $6 + y = 16$
    $x = 13$ $y = 10$
    Other endpoint: $(13, 10)$.

33. $A(-2, 5), B(1, 5), C(1, 9)$
    $d(A, B) = \sqrt{(1 + 2)^2 + (5 - 5)^2} = 3$
    $d(A, C) = \sqrt{(1 + 2)^2 + (9 - 5)^2}$
    $= \sqrt{9 + 16} = \sqrt{25} = 5$
    $d(B, C) = \sqrt{0^2 + 4^2} = 4$
    $d(A, B)^2 + d(B, C)^2 = 3^2 + 4^2 = 9 + 16$
    $= 25 = d(A, C)^2$
    The points form a right triangle.

37. $A(\sqrt{3}, 2\sqrt{3} + 3)$, $B(\sqrt{3} + 4, -\sqrt{3} + 3)$,
    $C(2\sqrt{3}, 2\sqrt{3} + 4)$
    $d(A, B)^2 = (\sqrt{3} + 4 - \sqrt{3})^2 +$
    $(2\sqrt{3} + 3 + \sqrt{3} - 3)^2$
    $= 4^2 + (3\sqrt{3})^2$
    $= 16 + 27$
    $= 43$
    $d(A, C)^2 = (2\sqrt{3} - \sqrt{3})^2 +$
    $(2\sqrt{3} + 4 - 2\sqrt{3} - 3)^2$
    $= (\sqrt{3})^2 + (1)^2$
    $= 3 + 1$
    $= 4$

$$d(B, C)^2 = (\sqrt{3} + 4 - 2\sqrt{3})^2 +$$
$$(-\sqrt{3} + 3 - 2\sqrt{3} - 4)^2$$
$$= (4 - \sqrt{3})^2 + (-1 - 3\sqrt{3})^2$$
$$= 16 - 8\sqrt{3} + 3 + 1 + 6\sqrt{3} + 27$$
$$= 47 - 2\sqrt{3}$$

This is not a right triangle since the Pythagorean theorem is not satisfied.

41. Let $A(0, -9)$, $B(3, 7)$, $C(-2, -19)$. Then, let $d_1 = d(A, B)$

$$= \sqrt{(3 - 0)^2 + (7 + 9)^2}$$
$$= \sqrt{9 + 256}$$
$$= \sqrt{265}$$
$$\approx 16.2788206$$

$$d_2 = d(B, C)$$
$$= \sqrt{(3 + 2)^2 + (7 + 19)^2}$$
$$= \sqrt{25 + 676}$$
$$= \sqrt{701}$$
$$\approx 26.4764046$$

$$d_3 = d(A, C)$$
$$= \sqrt{(0 + 2)^2 + (-9 + 19)^2}$$
$$= \sqrt{4 + 100}$$
$$= \sqrt{104}$$
$$\approx 10.198039$$

If the points lie on a straight line, then
$$d_3 + d_1 = d_2,$$
or $d(C, A) + d(A, B) = d(B, C)$. It can be shown that $(d_3 + d_1)^2 \neq d_2{}^2$ so that
$$d_3 + d_1 \neq d_2,$$
so that A, B, and C do not lie on a straight line.

45. Find y so that the distance between $(3, y)$ and $(-2, 9)$ is 12. Thus,

$$12 = \sqrt{(3 + 2)^2 + (y - 9)^2}$$
$$144 = 5^2 + y^2 - 18y + 81$$
$$0 = y^2 - 18y - 38$$

$$y = \frac{18 \pm \sqrt{18^2 - 4(1)(-38)}}{2}$$
$$y = \frac{18 \pm \sqrt{476}}{2}$$
$$y = 9 \pm \sqrt{119}.$$

49. $A(-2, 2)$, $B(13, 10)$, $C(21, -5)$, $D(6, -13)$

We need to show that the sides are the same length and that there is at least one right angle. We have

$$d(A, B) = \sqrt{15^2 + 8^2} = \sqrt{275 + 64}$$
$$= \sqrt{289} = 17,$$

$$d(B, C) = \sqrt{8^2 + 15^2} = \sqrt{289} = 17,$$

$$d(C, D) = \sqrt{15^2 + 8^2} = \sqrt{289} = 17,$$

$$d(D, A) = \sqrt{8^2 + 15^2} = \sqrt{289} = 17.$$

Show the angle at A is a right triangle.

$$d(B, D)^2 = 7^2 + 23^2 = 49 + 529 = 578$$
and $578 = d(A, B)^2 + d(A, D)^2$

53. Find all points (x, y) with $x = y$ such that the distance from $(1, 3)$ is equal to 4. We have

$$4 = \sqrt{(x - 1)^2 + (y - 3)^2}.$$

Since $x = y$:

$$4 = \sqrt{(x - 1)^2 + (x - 3)^2}$$
$$16 = x^2 - 2x + 1 + x^2 - 6x + 9$$
$$0 = 2x^2 - 8x - 6$$
$$0 = x^2 - 4x - 3$$
$$x = \frac{4 \pm \sqrt{4^2 - 4(1)(-3)}}{2}$$
$$x = \frac{4 \pm \sqrt{16 + 12}}{2}$$
$$x = \frac{4 \pm \sqrt{28}}{2}$$
$$x = 2 \pm \sqrt{7}$$

The points are $(2 + \sqrt{7}, 2 + \sqrt{7})$ and $(2 - \sqrt{7}, 2 - \sqrt{7})$.

57.   The distance between (ax_1, ay_1) and (ax_2, ay_2) is

$$d = \sqrt{(ax_2 - ax_1)^2 + (ay_2 - ay_1)^2}$$
$$= \sqrt{a^2(x_2 - x_1)^2 + a^2(y_2 - y_1)^2}$$
$$= \sqrt{a^2[(x_2 - x_1)^2 + (y_2 - y_1)^2]}$$
$$= |a|\sqrt{(x_2 - x_1)^2 + (y_2 - y_1)^2}$$
$$= a\sqrt{(x_2 - x_1)^2 + (y_2 - y_1)^2},$$

since $|a| = a$. This is $\underline{a}$ times the distance between (x_1, y_1) and (x_2, y_2).

59.   The diagonals of a rectangle are equal in length.
Proof: Draw a figure and label as shown.

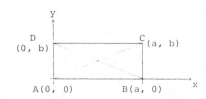

Diagonals are AC and BD, and

$$d(A, C) = \sqrt{(a - 0)^2 + (b - 0)^2}$$
$$= \sqrt{a^2 + b^2},$$
$$d(B, D) = \sqrt{(a - 0)^2 + (0 - b)^2}$$
$$= \sqrt{a^2 + b^2}.$$

61.   The diagonals of an isosceles trapezoid are equal.
Proof: See figure for notation.

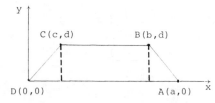

Since this is an isosceles trapezoid,

$$d(A, B) = d(C, D)$$
or $$\sqrt{(a - b)^2 + d^2} = \sqrt{c^2 + d^2}.$$
Squaring gives $(a - b)^2 = c^2$.
Thus, either $a - b = c$ or $a - b = -c$.

But $a - b$ cannot equal $-c$ since $a > b$.
Thus $a - b = c$ or, $a = b + c$.

$$d(A, C) = \sqrt{(c - a)^2 + d^2} \quad \text{substitute}$$
$$= \sqrt{(c - (b + c))^2 + d^2} \quad \begin{array}{l} b + c \\ \text{for } a \end{array}$$
$$= \sqrt{(c - b - c)^2 + d^2}$$
$$= \sqrt{b^2 + d^2}$$

$$d(B, D) = \sqrt{b^2 + d^2}$$

65.   Using the Pythagorean theorem with the hypotenuse having length $2x + 1$, we have

$$(2x + 1)^2 = x^2 + (2x - 1)^2$$
$$4x^2 + 4x + 1 = x^2 + 4x^2 - 4x + 1$$
$$0 = x^2 - 8x$$
$$x(x - 8) = 0$$
$$x = 0 \quad \text{or } x = 8.$$

The solution $x = 0$ is ridiculous, so the only solution for x is $x = 8$.

Section 3.2   Graphs

Additional Examples
Example 1   Sketch the graph of
$$6x^2 + 3y = 24.$$
Solution   If we solve the given equation for y, we have
$$3y = -6x^2 + 24$$
$$y = -2x^2 + 8.$$
Since the equation has no divisions or square roots, the set of numbers we can substitute for x is the set of all real numbers. Since x^2 is always nonnegative, $-2x^2 + 8$ is never larger than 8, and the value $y = 8$ occurs when $x = 0$. Also, substituting $x = +a$ or $x = -a$ gives the same value to y. We can plot some points as given in the table below.

x	0	±1	±2	±3	±4
y	8	6	0	-10	-24

The graph continues indefinitely in the manner shown.

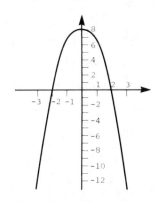

Example 2   Sketch the graph of
$$x^2 + y^2 + 4x - 6y = 12.$$
Solution   Rearranging terms and completing the square gives
$$x^2 + y^2 + 4y - 6y = 12$$
$$x^2 + 4x + y^2 - 6y = 12$$
$$x^2 + 4x + \underline{4} + y^2 - 6y + \underline{9} = 12 + 4 + 9$$
$$(x + 2)^2 + (y - 3)^2 = 25.$$
This is the equation of a circle with center at the point (-2, 3) and having radius 5. The graph can be sketched by marking off points 5 units vertically and horizontally from (-2, 3) and sketching the rough shape of a circle. More points could be located using a calculator if desired, but this isn't normally necessary.

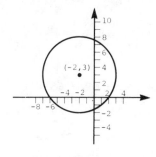

Example 3   Find the equation of the circle having points (-4, 5) and (7, 14) as end points of a diameter.

Solution   If the points (-4, 5) and (7, 14) are end points of a diameter, then the center of the circle is located at the midpoint of the segment joining the two points. Using the midpoint formula, the midpoint M has components
$$M\left(\frac{-4 + 7}{2}, \frac{5 + 14}{2}\right) = M\left(\frac{3}{2}, \frac{19}{2}\right).$$
The radius of the circle is the distance from M to either endpoint. Using the end point E(-4, 5), we have that
$$r = d(E, M) = \sqrt{\left(-4 - \frac{3}{2}\right)^2 + \left(5 - \frac{19}{2}\right)^2}$$
or
$$r = \sqrt{\left(\frac{-11}{2}\right)^2 + \left(-\frac{9}{2}\right)^2}$$
$$r = \sqrt{\frac{121}{4} + \frac{81}{4}}$$
$$r = \sqrt{\frac{202}{4}}$$
$$r = \frac{\sqrt{202}}{2}.$$
Hence, the equation of the circle is
$$\left(x - \frac{3}{2}\right)^2 + \left(y - \frac{19}{2}\right)^2 = \left(\frac{\sqrt{202}}{2}\right)^2$$
or
$$\left(x - \frac{3}{2}\right)^2 + \left(y - \frac{19}{2}\right)^2 = \frac{101}{2}.$$

Selected Solutions

See the answer section of your <u>text</u> for the graphs in Exercises 1-43.

1. y = 8x - 3
    Plot the intercepts:

x	y
0	-3
$\frac{3}{8}$	0

See graph in text.

5. $3y + 4x = 12$
    Plot the intercepts:

x	y
0	4
3	0

    See graph in text.

9. $y = -x^2$
    The graph looks like $y = x^2$ but
    opens down. See graph in text.

13. $y = 4 - x^2$
    The graph looks like $y = -x^2$ but
    is shifted up 4 units.

17. $4x = y^2$
    The graph opens to the right, and
    looks like $y = x^2$.

21. $y^2 = x + 2$
    The graph opens to the right, looks
    like $x = y^2$, but is shifted 2 units
    to the left.

25. $y = 1 - x^3$
    The graph looks like $y = -x^3$ but is
    shifted up one unit.

29. $y = |x| + 4$
    The graph is the same as the graph
    of $y = |x|$ shifted up 4 units.

33. $y = 3 - |x|$
    This graph is the graph of $y = -|x|$
    shifted three units upward. The
    graph of $y = -|x|$ is mirror image
    of $y = |x|$ about the x axis.

37. $x^2 + y^2 = 36$
    A circle, center at (0, 0), radius
    6.

41. $(x - 4)^2 + (y + 3)^2 = 4$
    This is a circle with center at
    (4, -3) and radius 2. See the graph
    in the text.

45. If the circle has center at (h, k)
    and has radius r, then the equation
    is $(x - h)^2 + (y - k)^2 = r^2$. Given
    a center at (1, 4) and radius $r = 3$,
    the equation is $(x - 1)^2 + (y - 4)^2$
    $= 9$.

49. If the center is at $C(-1, 2)$ and
    the circle passes through point
    $P(2, 6)$, then the radius is
    $r = d(C,P) = \sqrt{(2 + 1)^2 + (6 - 2)^2}$,
    $r = \sqrt{9 + 16} = \sqrt{25} = 5$.
    Hence, the equation is
    $(x + 1)^2 + (y - 2)^2 = 25$.

51. If the center is $C(-3, -2)$ and the
    circle is tangent to the x-axis,
    then the radius is the distance
    from C to the x-axis, or $r = 2$.
    Hence, the equation is
    $(x + 3)^2 + (y + 2)^2 = 4$.

53. $x^2 + 6x + y^2 + 8y = -9$
    $x^2 + 6x + \quad + y^2 + 8y + \quad = -9$
    $x^2 + 6x + \underline{9} + y^2 + 8y + \underline{16} = -9 + \underline{9} + \underline{16}$
    By completing the squares on x and y,
    $(x + 3)^2 + (y + 4)^2 = 4^2$.
    The center is $P(-3, -4)$, and $r = 4$.

57. $x^2 + 8x + y^2 - 14y + 65 = 0$
    $x^2 + 8x + \underline{16} + y^2 - 14y + \underline{49} = -65 + \underline{16} + \underline{49}$
    $(x + 4)^2 + (y - 7)^2 = 0$
    Center (-4, 7) and radius 0. This
    graph is the single point (-4, 7).

61. $x^2 - 2.84x + y^2 + 1.4y + 1.8664 = 0$

$x^2 - 2.84x + \underline{\quad} + y^2 + 1.4y + \underline{\quad}$

$\qquad = -1.8664 + \underline{\quad} + \underline{\quad}$

Since $\frac{1}{2}(-2.84) = -1.42$,

$\qquad (-1.42)^2 = 2.0164$,

$\qquad \frac{1}{2}(1.4) = .7$,

and $\qquad (.7)^2 = .49$,

we have

$(x^2 - 2.84x + 2.0164) +$

$(y^2 + 1.4y + .49)$

$= -1.8664 + 2.0164 + .49$

$(x - 1.42)^2 + (y + .7)^2 = .64$

$(x - 1.42)^2 + (y + .7)^2 = (.8)^2$

The center is $C(1.42, -.7)$ and the radius is $r = .8$.

65. Circle C_1 has center $(3, 4)$ and radius 5, and circle C_2 has center $(-1, -3)$ and radius 4. The circles would not intersect if the distance between their centers was more than the sum of the two radiuses, which is $5 + 4 = 9$. However,

$d[(3,4), (-1, -3)]$

$= \sqrt{(3 + 1)^2 + (4 + 3)^2}$

$= \sqrt{16 + 49}$

$= \sqrt{65}$

≈ 8.06225,

which is less than 9. Therefore, the circles intersect.

69. Given $x^2 + 2x + y^2 - 4y + 1 = 0$, we must find r and then the circumference is found by $C = 2\pi r$. Here we have

$x^2 + 2x + \underline{1} + y^2 - 4y + \underline{4} = -1 + \underline{1} + 4$,

or $(x + 1)^2 + (y - 2)^2 = 4$,

so that $r = 2$.

Hence, $\qquad C = 2\pi(2) = 4\pi$.

Also, $\qquad A = \pi r^2 = 4\pi$.

73. The point $P(\frac{-\sqrt{39}}{8}, \frac{5}{8})$ is on the unit circle $x^2 + y^2 = 1$, since

$(\frac{-\sqrt{39}}{8})^2 + (\frac{5}{8})^2 = \frac{39}{64} + \frac{25}{64} = \frac{64}{64} = 1$.

77. The circle with center at $(1, -4)$ having radius 6 has the equation $(x - 1)^2 + (y + 4)^2 = 36$.

(a) Testing $P(3, -2)$ we have

$(3 - 1)^2 + (-2 + 4)^2 = 2^2 + 2^2$

$\qquad = 4 + 4 = 8$.

P is not on the circle. P is inside the circle since $8 < 36$.

(b) Testing $Q(9, 1)$ we have

$(9 - 1)^2 + (1 + 4)^2 = 8^2 + 5^2$

$\qquad = 64 + 25 = 89$.

Q is not on the circle. Q is outside since $89 > 36$.

(c) Testing $R(7, -4)$ we have

$(7 - 1)^2 + (-4 + 4)^2 = 6^2 + 0^2$

$\qquad = 36$.

Hence, R is on the circle.

(d) Testing the point $S(0, 9)$ we have

$(0 - 1)^2 + (9 + 4)^2 = 1^2 + 13^2$

$\qquad = 1 + 169 = 170$.

Hence, S is not on the circle. S is outside.

Section 3.3   Symmetry and Translations

Additional Examples

Example 1   Use symmetry and point plotting to sketch the graph of

$4x^2 + 9y^2 = 36$.

Solution   In discussing the symmetry
of the graph we observe that:

(a) Replacing x by -x gives

$$4(-x)^2 + 9y^2 = 36 \quad \text{or}$$

$$4x^2 + 9y^2 = 36,$$

which is the same equation. Thus,
the graph is symmetric with respect
to the y-axis.

(b) Replacing y by -y gives the
same equation, so we have symmetry
to the x-axis.

(c) Replacing x by -x and y by -y
also gives the same equation. This
implies symmetry about the origin.

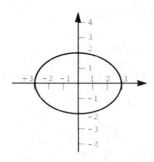

Plotting a few points will give a
fairly accurate graph. The intercepts are located in the table
below.

x	0	±3	±2
y	±2	0	±1.49

If $x = \pm 2$, then $y^2 = \dfrac{36 - 16}{9} = \dfrac{20}{9}$,
so that $y \approx \pm 1.49$.

Example 2   Using the graph of $y = x^2$
as a reference, explain how the
graph of $y = (x + 3)^2 + 5$ can be
obtained in comparison to $y = x^2$.
Sketch the graph of $y = (x + 3)^2 + 5$.

Solution   The graph of $y = x^2$ is a
parabola opening upward with the
low point at the origin. Even
though the graph of $y = x^2$ should
be a familiar graph, it is shown

below. To consider the graph of
$y = (x + 3)^2 + 5$, we note that this
can be written as $y - 5 = (x + 3)^2$.
Hence, in comparison to $y = x^2$, x
has been replaced by x + 3 and y has
be replaced by y - 5. This "shifts"
the graph of $y = x^2$ three units to
the left and 5 units upward. Note;
x = -3 gives y = 5.

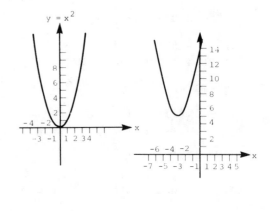

Selected Solutions
    For Exercises 1-31, see the answer
    section of your text.

1. Given P(5, -3), then (a) Q(5, 3) is
    symmetric to P with respect to the
    x-axis, (b) R(-5, -3) is symmetric
    to P with respect to the y-axis, and
    (c) S(-5, 3) is symmetric to P with
    respect to the origin.

5. Given P(-8, 0), the answers to (a),
    (b), (c) are (a) Q(-8, 0),
    (b) R(8, 0), and (c) S(8, 0).

9. $y = 4 - x^2$.
    Let $y = f(x) = 4 - x^2$. Since $f(-x)$
    $= f(x)$, we have symmetry with respect
    to the y axis. Also, the graph is
    a translation of $y = -x^2$, shifted

4 units upward. Some important
points are

x	±2	0
y	0	4

.

The graph is as shown.

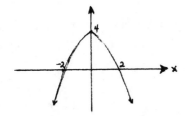

13. $x^2 + 2y^2 = 10$

Replacing x by -x gives the same
equation, so there is symmetry with
respect to the y-axis. Replacing
y by -y gives the same equation, so
there is symmetry with respect to
the x-axis. Also, we have symmetry
with respect to the origin.

Letting x = 0 gives $2y^2 = 10$, $y^2 = 5$,
or $y = \pm\sqrt{5}$. If y = 0, we have
$x^2 = 10$, or $x = \pm\sqrt{10}$. These are the
x and y intercepts. The graph is
the ellipse shown below.

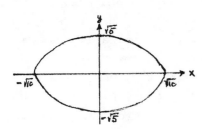

17. $y = 3|x|$

Replacing x by -x gives the same
equation since $|-x| = |x|$. Hence,
there is symmetry with respect to
the y-axis. Note the following
table

x	0	±1	±3
y_1	0	3	9

.

See the answer section of your text
for the graph.

21. $|y| = |x + 2|$

The graph consists of placing both
$y = |x + 2|$ and $y = -|x + 2|$ on
the same graph. $y = |x + 2|$ is a
"V" shaped graph with the V upward
and the vertex when x = -2.
$y = -|x + 2|$ is similar with the
V downward [Λ].

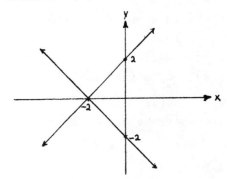

25. $\dfrac{x}{y} = -1$

We cannot have y = 0. However, if
$y \neq 0$ we have x = -y, or y = -x.
This is a line, but we must delete
the point (0, 0) from the line. See
the answer section in the text for
the graph.

29. $y = \dfrac{1}{1 + x^2}$

Replacing x by -x gives the same
equation, so the graph has symmetry
to the y-axis. The denominator
$1 + x^2$ can never be zero, so the
graph exists for every number x.
The numerator is never zero so that
y can never be 0. The graph never
crosses the x-axis and since $1 + x^2$
is always > 0, the graph lies <u>above</u>
the x-axis. Consider the table.

x	0	±1	±2	±5	±10	±100
y	1	$\frac{1}{2}$	$\frac{1}{5}$	$\frac{1}{26}$	$\frac{1}{101}$	$\frac{1}{10,001}$

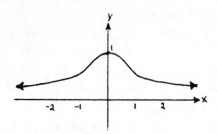

33. $y = x^2 + 2$

There is symmetry to the y-axis since replacing x by -x gives the same equation. The graph is the result of moving the graph of $y = x^2$ upward two units. See the graph in the answer section.

37. $y = -(x - 4)^2$

If we first "flip" $y = x^2$ downward we have the graph of $y = -x^2$

Note the "vertex" at (0, 0). Then we shift this graph (translate) so the vertex is at (4, 0). This is the graph of $y = -(x - 4)^2$.

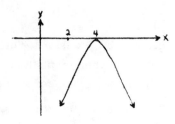

41. $y = -(x + 4)^2 + 2$

This can be written as

$y - 2 = -(x + 4)^2$.

First flip $y = x^2$ upside down and then shift the graph so the vertex is translated to the point (-4, 2). See the graph in the text.

43. The graph is reflected about the x-axis. For example: consider $y = x + 2$ and $y = -(x + 2) = -x - 2$.

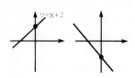

45. A graph symmetric to the x-axis but not the y-axis is the graph of $y^2 = x$.

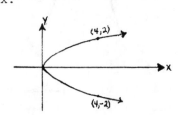

47. Prove a graph with symmetry to both the x-axis and the y-axis is also symmetric with respect to the origin. Proof: For convenience let us consider the equation of such a graph as $F(x, y) = 0$. As an example, rather than having the equation $x^2 - 3y^2 = 6x^4 - 7$, we write $x^2 - 3y^2 - 6x^4 + 7 = 0$. Since our graph has symmetry to the x-axis, $F(x, -y) = 0$ and $F(x, y) = 0$ are equivalent. That is $F(x, -y) = F(x, y)$. Similarly, symmetry to the y-axis implies $F(-x, y) = F(x, y)$. Consequently, replacing x by -x <u>and</u> y by -y gives $F(-x, -y)$. However, we can see from the above statements that

$F(-x, -y) = F(-x \ y)$ and

$F(-x, y) = F(x, y)$, so that

$F(-x, -y) = F(x, y)$. Thus, symmetry with respect to the origin.

Section 3.4   Functions

Additional Examples

Example 1   Determine the domain of

$$f(x) = \sqrt{\frac{x + 1}{x^2 - 9}} \, .$$

Solution   The domain of f consists of the set of all x such that

$$\frac{x + 1}{x^2 - 9} \geq 0.$$

Using a sign graph to determine the solution, we have

$$\frac{x + 1}{(x + 3)(x - 3)} \geq 0$$

The expression will be ≥ 0 in the set

$$S = (-3, -1] \cup (3, +\infty).$$

Hence, the domain of the function f is the set

$$(-3, -1] \cup (3, +\infty).$$

Example 2   Let $f(x) = 3x^2 - 6x + 2$ and determine

(a) $f(x + h)$, and

(b) $\dfrac{f(x + h) - f(x)}{h}$, if $h \neq 0$

Solution   (a) For the given function f we have

$$f(x + h) = 3(x + h)^2 - 6(x + h) + 2$$

$$f(x + h) = 3(x^2 + 2xh + h^2) - 6x - 6h + 2$$

or $f(x + h) = 3x^2 + 6xh + 3h^2 - 6x - 6h + 2$.
All like terms have been combined, so this is the desired result.

(b) We have already calculated $f(x + h)$, so that

$$\frac{f(x + h) - f(x)}{h}$$

$$= \frac{(3x^2 + 6xh + 3h^2 - 6x - 6h + 2) - (3x^2 - 6x + 2)}{h}$$

$$= \frac{6xh + 3h^2 - 6h}{h}$$

$$= \frac{h(6x - 6 + 3h)}{h}$$

$$= 6x - 6 + 3h, \text{ provided } h \neq 0.$$

Example 3   Find the intervals where the function $f(x) = 2x^2 - 8$ is increasing and decreasing.

Solution   The graph of $f(x) = 2x^2 - 8$ is the parabola

$$y = 2x^2 - 8.$$

This graph is similar to the parabola $y = 2x^2$, which opens upward and has the origin as its lowest point, or its vertex. The graph $y = 2x^2 - 8$ has an identical shape as the graph $y = 2x^2$, just shifted 8 units downward. Since $y = 2x^2$ is decreasing on the left of the y-axis, and increasing on the right of the y-axis, the graph $y = 2x^2 - 8$ is also decreasing and increasing over the same intervals. The conclusion is that

(a) $f(x) = 2x^2 - 8$ is decreasing over the interval $(-\infty, 0]$,

(b) $f(x) = 2x^2 - 8$ is increasing over the interval $[0, +\infty)$.

Selected Solutions

1. From the graph,

    (a) $f(-2) = 0$ (b) $f(0) = 4$

    (c) $f(1) = 2$ (d) $f(4) = 4.$

5. $f(x) = 3x - 1$ so that

$$f(0) = 3(0) - 1 = 0 - 1 = -1.$$

9. If $g(x) = |x^2 - 8|$, then $g(2)$

$$= |4 - 8| = |-4| = 4.$$

13. $f(1) = 3(1) - 1 = 3 - 1 = 2$ and
$g(1) = |1 - 8| = |-7| = 7.$
Hence, $f(1) + g(1) = 2 + 7 = 9.$

17.   If $f(x) = 3x - 1$, then
$f(-2m) = 3(-2m) - 1 = -6m - 1.$

21.   If $g(x) = |x^2 - 8|$, then
$$g(5p - 2) = |(5p - 2)^2 - 8|$$
$$= |25p^2 - 20p + 4 - 8|$$
$$= |25p^2 - 20p - 4|.$$

25.   Since $g(m) = |m^2 - 8|$ and
$f(m) = 3m - 1$, we have
$g(m) \cdot f(m) = (3m - 1)\,|m^2 - 8|.$

29. $f(x) = -4.6x^2 - 8.9x + 1.3$
$$f(3) = -4.6(3)^2 - 8.9(3) + 1.3$$
$$= -4.6(9) - 26.7 + 1.3$$
$$= -41.4 - 25.4$$
$$= -66.8$$

33.   For $f(x) = 2x - 1$, the domain of
f is $(-\infty, \infty)$ and hence, Range $f =$
$(-\infty, \infty)$. The range can be seen by
the fact that $y = 2x - 1$ is a line
with slope 2.

37. $f(x) = \sqrt{8 + x}$
We can use only numbers x such that
$8 + x \geq 0$. Thus, we must have
$x \geq -8$. The domain $f = [-8, \infty)$.
Noting that $f(-8) = \sqrt{0} = 0$, that
$\sqrt{n}$ is never negative and that is x
gets "very large" [say $x = 10^{25}$,
$x = 10^{100}$, etc.] then $f(x)$ is very
large, we have Range $f = [0, \infty)$.

41. $R(x) = (x - 4)^{1/2} = \sqrt{x - 4}$
We must have $x - 4 \geq 0$, or $x \geq 4$.
This gives domain $R = [4, \infty)$ and by
the same reasoning used in 37,
Range $f = [0, \infty)$.

45. $g(x) = \dfrac{2}{x^2 - 3x + 2} = \dfrac{2}{(x - 1)(x - 2)}$
Since we cannot divide by zero,
domain $g = \{x : x \neq 1, x \neq 2\}$. In
intervals;
domain $g = (-\infty, 1) \cup (1, 2) \cup (2, \infty).$

49. $f(x) = |x - 4|$
Any number x can be used and $|x - 4|$
exist. Hence, domain $f = (-\infty, \infty)$.
Since for all n, $|n| \geq 0$, and since
$f(4) = 0$, we see that Range $f =$
$[0, \infty).$

53. $f(x) = \sqrt{36 - x^2}$
Only numbers x such that $36 - x^2 \geq 0$
can be used since we cannot take
the square root of a negative
number. We have $\qquad 36 - x^2 \geq 0$
$\qquad\qquad\qquad (6 - x)(6 + x) \geq 0$

$6 + x \quad ---\,|\,+++\,|\,+++++$
$6 - x \quad +++\,|\,+++\,|\,-----$
$\qquad\qquad\overline{\qquad\qquad\qquad}$
$\qquad\qquad -6 \quad\ 6$

The solution set is the domain f.
Thus, Domain $f = [-6, 6]$, noting
that -6 and 6 are acceptable. Note
that $f(0) = \sqrt{36} = 6$ and $f(\pm 6) = 0$.
Then for all $x \in [-6, 6]$ we have
$0 \leq f(x) \leq 6$. That is Range $f =$
$[0, 6].$

57.   From the graph we have Domain $f =$
$[-5, 4]$ and we see that for all
$x \in [-5, 4]$ that $-2 \leq f(x) \leq 6$.
Thus, Range $f = [-2, 6].$

61.   From the graph f is defined for
$-3 \leq x \leq 4$ and that $f(x)$ ranges between $-6 \leq f(x) \leq 8$. Hence, Domain
$f = [-3, 4]$, and Range $f = [-6, 8].$

63. $\qquad\qquad f(x) = x^2 - 4$
(a) $f(x + h) = (x + h)^2 - 4$
$\qquad\qquad\quad = x^2 + 2xh + h^2 - 4$

(b) $f(x + h) - f(x)$

$= (x^2 + 2xh + h^2 - 4) - (x^2 - 4)$

$= x^2 + 2xh + h^2 - 4 - x^2 + 4$

$= 2xh + h^2$

(c) $\dfrac{f(x + h) - f(x)}{h} = \dfrac{2xh + h^2}{h}$

$= \dfrac{h(2x + h)}{h}$

$= 2x + h,$

if $h \neq 0$.

65. $f(x) = 6x + 2$

(a) $f(x + h) = 6(x + h) + 2$

$= 6x + 6h + 2$

(b) $f(x + h) - f(x)$

$= (6x + 6h + 2) -$

$(6x + 2) = 6h$

(c) $\dfrac{f(x + h) - f(x)}{h} = \dfrac{6h}{h} = 6,$

if $h \neq 0$.

69. (a) f is increasing over the set
$A = (-\infty, -3] \cup [3, +\infty)$.
(b) f is decreasing over the set
$B = [-3, 3]$.

73. (a) f is increasing over the entire set of real numbers.
(b) f is never decreasing.

77. $y = x^2 + 4$ is the graph $y = x^2$
shifted upward four units. Thus,
y is decreasing over the set A =
$(-\infty, 0]$ and y is increasing over
the set $B = [0, +\infty)$.

81. $y = x + |x|$ If $x \geq 0$, then
$|x| = x$, and if $x < 0$, then $|x| =$
$-x$. Hence, if $x \geq 0$, $y = 2x$, and
if $x < 0$, $y = 0$. That is, y is
constant over $(-\infty, 0]$ and y is increasing over the set $[0, +\infty)$.

85. $f(x) = x^4 + x^2 + 5$

$f(-x) = (-x)^4 + (-x)^2 + 5$

$= x^4 + x^2 + 5 = f(x)$

Therefore, f is an even function.

89. $f(x) = \dfrac{2}{x - 6}$

$f(-x) = \dfrac{2}{(-x) - 6} = \dfrac{2}{-x - 6},$

so that f is neither even nor odd.

93. $f(x) = |x - c|$ for (a) c = -2
and (b) c = 1.
(a) $f(x) = |x + 2|$ is the graph
$y = |x|$ shifted 2 units to the left.
(b) $f(x) = |x - 1|$ is the graph
$y = |x|$ shifted 1 unit to the right.
See the final graphs in textbook.

97. Graph $y = f(x - 1)$ using the given
graph. The graph of $f(x - 1)$ is
the given graph, shifted one unit
to the right. See final graph in
textbook.

101. Volume = length x width x height.
In the figure $h = x$, $\ell = 16 - 2x$,
and $w = 12 - 2x$. Hence,

$V = (16 - 2x)(12 - 2x)x = 4x^3 - 56x^2 + 192x.$

105. $f(x) = x^2 - 3x$
We have

$f(\tfrac{1}{x}) = (\tfrac{1}{x})^2 - 3(\tfrac{1}{x}) = \dfrac{1}{x^2} - \dfrac{3}{x},$

$f(\tfrac{1}{x}) = \dfrac{1 - 3x}{x^2},$ while

$\dfrac{1}{f(x)} = \dfrac{1}{x^2 - 3x}.$

Hence, $f(\tfrac{1}{x})$ does not equal $\dfrac{1}{f(x)}$ for

all x. Note that letting $x = 1$ gives

$f(\tfrac{1}{1}) = \dfrac{1 - 3}{1} = -2$, while $\dfrac{1}{f(1)} =$

$\dfrac{1}{1 - 3} = -\dfrac{1}{2}.$

109. Let $f(x)$ be an even function. Then, by definition $f(-x) \equiv f(x)$. Hence, the equation $y = f(x)$ remains unchanged when we replace x by $-x$. This shows the graph is symmetric with respect to the y-axis.

111. The graph could not be symmetric with the y-axis because if $(-1, y)$ were a point on the graph then $(1, y)$ would have to be, too. But $-1 < 1$ and, in order to be increasing, we would need $y < y$, an impossibility.

113. The area A of a circle is given by $A = \pi r^2$. We can write $A(r) = \pi r^2$. Also, the circumference C is given by $C = 2\pi r$, or $C(r) = 2\pi r$.

Section 3.5   Algebra of Functions

Additional Examples

Example 1   Let $f(x) = 2/(x + 1)$ and $g(x) = \sqrt{3 - x}$. Find $f \circ g$, $g \circ f$, and the domain of each.

Solution   The domain of f is $(-\infty, -1) \cup (-1, +\infty)$ and the domain of g is $(-\infty, 3]$. We have

(a) $(f \circ g)(x) = f[g(x)]$

$$= \frac{2}{g(x) + 1}$$

$$= \frac{2}{\sqrt{3 - x} + 1}$$

Every number in the domain of $f \circ g$ must be in the domain of g. We could write

$$\frac{2}{\sqrt{3 - x} + 1} = \frac{2}{\sqrt{3 - x} + 1} \cdot \frac{\sqrt{3 - x} - 1}{\sqrt{3 - x} - 1}$$

$$= \frac{2\sqrt{3 - x} - 2}{(3 - x) - 1}$$

$$= \frac{2\sqrt{3 - x} - 2}{2 - x}.$$

It appears we cannot let $x = 2$. We have

$$(f \circ g)(x) = \frac{2\sqrt{3 - x} - 2}{2 - x},$$

and domain of $f \circ g = (-\infty, 2) \cup (2, 3]$.

(b) $(g \circ f)(x) = g[f(x)]$

$$= \sqrt{3 - f(x)}$$

$$= \sqrt{3 - \frac{2}{x + 1}}$$

$$= \sqrt{\frac{3(x + 1) - 2}{x + 1}}$$

$$= \sqrt{\frac{3x + 1}{x + 1}}$$

The domain of $g \circ f$ is the set of all x such that

$$\frac{3x + 1}{x + 1} \geq 0.$$

Note that $x = -1$ is excluded here. From the sign graph we conclude that

$$\text{dom } g \circ f = (-\infty, -1) \cup [-\tfrac{1}{3}, +\infty).$$

$$3x + 1 \quad \text{----} \mid \text{--} \mid \text{+++++}$$
$$x + 1 \quad \text{----} \mid \text{++} \mid \text{+++++}$$

Example 2   For

$$f(x) = 2x^3 + 5 \text{ and } g(x) = \sqrt[3]{\frac{x - 5}{2}},$$

show that $(f \circ g)(x) = x$ and $(g \circ f)(x) = x$.

Solution   We have

(a) $(f \circ g)(x) = f[g(x)]$

$$= 2[g(x)]^3 + 5$$

$$= 2\left[\sqrt[3]{\frac{x - 5}{2}}\right]^3 + 5$$

$$= 2\left(\frac{x - 5}{2}\right) + 5$$

$$= x - 5 + 5$$

$$= x, \text{ and}$$

(b) $(g \circ f)(x) = g[f(x)]$

$$= \sqrt[3]{\frac{f(x) - 5}{2}}$$

$$= \sqrt[3]{\frac{(2x^3 + 5) - 5}{2}}$$

$$= \sqrt[3]{\frac{2x^3}{2}}$$

$$= \sqrt[3]{x^3}$$

$$= x.$$

Selected Solutions

1. $f(x) = 4x - 1$, $g(x) = 6x + 3$

$(f + g)(x) = (4x - 1) + (6x + 3)$

$= 10x + 2$, domain: $(-\infty, \infty)$

$(f - g)(x) = (4x - 1) - (6x + 3)$

$= -2x - 4$, domain: $(-\infty, \infty)$

$(f \cdot g)(x) = (4x - 1)(6x + 3)$

$= 24x^2 + 6x - 3$,

domain: $(-\infty, \infty)$

$(\frac{f}{g})(x) = \frac{4x - 1}{6x + 3}$ domain: all real numbers except $x = -\frac{1}{2}$

5. $f(x) = \sqrt{2x + 5}$, $g(x) = \sqrt{4x - 9}$

Function	Domain
$(f+g)(x) = \sqrt{2x+5} + \sqrt{4x-9}$	$[\frac{9}{4}, +\infty)$
$(f-g)(x) = \sqrt{2x+5} - \sqrt{4x-9}$	$[\frac{9}{4}, +\infty)$
$(f \cdot g)(x) = \sqrt{(2x+5)(4x-9)}$	$[\frac{9}{4}, +\infty)$
$(\frac{f}{g})(x) = \frac{\sqrt{2x + 5}}{\sqrt{4x - 9}}$	$(\frac{9}{4}, +\infty)$

9. If $f(x) = 4x^2 - 2x$,

then $f(3) = 4(9) - 6 = 30$,

and if $g(x) = 8x + 1$,

then $g(3) = 24 + 1 = 25$.

Hence,

$(f + g)(3) = f(3) + g(3) = 30 + 25 = 55$.

13. $(\frac{f}{g})(-1) = \frac{4(-1)^2 - 2(-1)}{8(-1) + 1}$

$= \frac{4 + 2}{-8 + 1}$

$= \frac{6}{-7}$

$= \frac{-6}{7}$

17. $(f \circ g)(2) = f(g(2))$

$= f(8(2) + 1)$

$= f(16 + 1)$

$= f(17)$

$= 4(17)^2 - 2(17)$

$= 1122$

21. $(f \circ g)(k) = f(g(k))$

$= f(8k + 1)$

$= 4(8k + 1)^2 - 2(8k + 1)$

$= 4(64k^2 + 16k + 1) - 16K - 2$

$= 256k^2 + 48k + 2$

25. $f(x) = 5x + 3$, $g(x) = -x^2 + 4x + 3$

$(f \circ g)(x) = 5(-x^2 + 4x + 3) + 3$

$= -5x^2 + 20x + 18$

$(g \circ f)(x) = -(5x + 3)^2 + 4(5x + 3) + 3$

$= -25x^2 - 30x - 9 + 20x + 12 + 3$

$= -25x^2 - 10x + 6$

29. $f(x) = \frac{1}{x}$, $g(x) = x^2$

$(f \circ g)(x) = \frac{1}{x^2}$

$(g \circ f)(x) = (\frac{1}{x})^2 = \frac{1}{x^2}$

33. $f(x) = \frac{1}{x - 5}$, $g(x) = \frac{2}{x}$

$(f \circ g)(x) = f(g(x))$ $(g \circ f)(x) = g(f(x))$

$= f(\frac{2}{x})$ $= \frac{2}{f(x)}$

$= \frac{1}{\frac{2}{x} - 5}$ $= 2(x - 5)$

$= \frac{x}{2 - 5x}$

37. From the graphs, $f(1) = 1$ and $g(1) = 3$.

Hence, $f(1) + g(1) = 1 + 3 = 4$.

41. By definition, $(f \circ g)(x) = f[g(x)]$.

From the graph $g(2) = 2$ and $f(2) = 1$. Thus,

$(f \circ g)(2) = f[g(2)] = f(2) = 1$.

43. From the graphs we see that $f(-4) = -2$, and that $g(-2) = 2$. Thus,

$(g \circ f)(-4) = g[f(-4)] = g(-2) = 2$.

45. $f(x) = 3x$, $g(x) = \frac{1}{3}x$

$(f \circ g)(x) = f(g(x))$ $(g \circ f)(x) = \frac{1}{3}(f(x))$

$\qquad\qquad\qquad = 3g(x)$ $\qquad\qquad\qquad\qquad = \frac{1}{3}3x$

$\qquad\qquad\qquad = 3 \cdot \frac{1}{3}x$ $\qquad\qquad\qquad\qquad = x$

$\qquad\qquad\qquad = x$

49. $f(x) = x^3 + 6$, $g(x) = \sqrt[3]{x - 6}$

$\quad (f \circ g)(x)$ $\qquad\qquad (g \circ f)(x)$

$= f(g(x))$ $\qquad\qquad = g((f(x))$

$= (g(x))^3 + 6$ $\qquad = g(x^3 + 6)$

$= (\sqrt[3]{x - 6})^3 + 6$ $\quad = \sqrt[3]{x^3 + 6 - 6}$

$= x - 6 + 6$ $\qquad\qquad = \sqrt[3]{x^3}$

$= x$ $\qquad\qquad\qquad = x$

53. $h(x) = \sqrt{x^2 - 1}$
Let $f(x) = \sqrt{x}$ and $g(x) = x^2 - 1$.
Then $(f \circ g)(x) = \sqrt{x^2 - 1}$.

57. $P(x) = 2x^2 + 1$, $f(a) = 3a + 2$

$(P \circ f)(a) = P(f(a))$

$\qquad\qquad = 2(f(a))^2 + 1$

$\qquad\qquad = 2(3a + 2)^2 + 1$

$\qquad\qquad = 2(9a^2 + 12a + 4) + 1$

$\qquad\qquad = 18a^2 + 24a + 9$

59. $r(t) = 4t$, $A(r) = \pi r^2$

$(A \circ r)(t) = A(r(t))$

$\qquad\qquad = \pi (4t)^2$

$\qquad\qquad = 16t^2\pi$

At time t, $(A \circ r)(t)$ gives the area
the oil slick covers.

61.   Let f and g be increasing on the
same interval I. Then for all x_1
and x_2 in I with $x_1 < x_2$, we have
$f(x_1) < f(x_2)$, and $g(x_1) < g(x_2)$.
Thus, $(f + g)(x_1) = f(x_1) +$
$g(x_1) < f(x_2) + g(x_2)$
$= (f + g)(x_2)$. This implies f + g
is increasing on I.

63.   If f and g are increasing on the
interval I, no conclusion can be
made regarding the function f - g.
To illustrate this consider the
case where $f(x) = x$ and $g(x) = 2x$.
f and g are increasing on I = [0, 10]
but $(f - g)(x) = f(x) - g(x) = -x$,
which is decreasing on I. However,
letting $f(x) = 2x^2$ and $g(x) = x^2$,
f and g are increasing on I =
[0, 10], and $(f - g)(x) = f(x) -$
$g(x) = x^2$ is also increasing on I.

65.   If $f(x) = ax + b$ and $g(x) = cx + d$,
then
$(f \circ g)(x) = f[g(x)] = a(cx + d) + b$
$\qquad\qquad\qquad = acx + (ad + b)$,
and
$(g \circ f)(x) = g[f(x)] = c(ax + b) + d$
$\qquad\qquad\qquad = acx + (bc + d)$.
We see that f ∘ g and g ∘ f are
identical when $ad + b = bc + d$.
If a and b are given, then we see
that c and d must satisfy bc +
$(1 - a)d = b$. For example, if
$f(x) = 3x + 6$, $g(x) = cx + d$,   then
$(f \circ g)(x) = 3cx + (3d + 6)$,   and
$(g \circ f)(x) = 3cx + 6c + d)$.   Hence,
$\quad 6c - 2d = 6$.
One solution is $g(x) = 2x + 3$.

67.   Let $h(x) = \frac{1}{2}[f(x) - f(-x)]$. Then,

$\qquad h(-x) = \frac{1}{2}[f(-x) - f(x)]$

$\qquad\qquad = -\frac{1}{2}[f(x) - f(-x)] = -h(x)$.

This implies h is odd.

68.   Let $f(x)$ be any function.

Then $f(x) = \frac{1}{2}(f(x) + f(-x)) +$

$\qquad\qquad \frac{1}{2}(f(x) - f(-x))$,

and $\frac{1}{2}(f(x) + f(-x))$ is an even

function while $\frac{1}{2}(f(x) - f(-x))$ is an

odd function.

69. The sum of two even functions is even.

Proof: Let $f(x)$ and $g(x)$ be even functions; so that

$$f(x) = f(-x) \text{ and } g(x) = g(-x).$$

Let $h(x) = f(x) + g(x)$.

Then $h(-x) = f(-x) + g(-x)$

$$= f(x) + g(x)$$

$$= h(x).$$

So $h(x)$ is an even function.

71. The sum of two odd functions is odd.

Proof: Let $f(-x) = -f(x)$ and $g(-x) = -g(x)$.

Define $h(x) = f(x) + g(x)$.

Then $h(-x) = f(-x) + g(-x)$

$$= -f(x) + (-g(x))$$

$$= -(f(x) + g(x))$$

$$= -h(x).$$

73. The product of an odd function and an even function is odd.

Proof: Let $f(-x) = f(x)$ (even) and $g(-x) = -g(x)$ (odd).

Define $h(x) = f(x)g(x)$. Then

$$h(-x) = f(-x)g(-x)$$

$$= f(x)(-g(x))$$

$$= -f(x)g(x)$$

$$= -h(x).$$

Section 3.6   Inverse Functions

Additional Examples

Example 1   Let $f(x) = (2\sqrt{x} + 3)^2$ and determine the domain and range of f. Verify whether or not f is one to one. If f is one to one, find f^{-1} and find the domain of f^{-1}.

Solution   In considering the domain of f, the term $\sqrt{x}$ implies that we can consider only values of x such that $x \geq 0$. Adding 3 and squaring gives no restrictions, so the domain of f is the set $S = \{x: x \geq 0\} = [0, +\infty)$.

The range of f can be determined by noting that $\sqrt{x}$ is always nonnegative and its smallest value occurs at $x = 0$. Thus, $(2\sqrt{x} + 3)^2$ has its smallest value when $x = 0$, and this value if $(2\sqrt{0} + 3)^2 = 9$. For larger x, $(2\sqrt{x} + 3)^2$ is larger and as $x \rightarrow \infty$ we have $(2\sqrt{x} + 3)^2 \rightarrow +\infty$. We conclude that the range of f is $[9, +\infty)$.

For convenience we use the notation dom $f = [0, +\infty)$ and ran $f = [9, +\infty)$.

To consider whether or not f is one to one, let $x_1 \neq x_2$, where x_1 and x_2 are both in dom f. We can easily conclude that $\sqrt{x_1} \neq \sqrt{x_2}$ and hence, $2\sqrt{x_1} + 3 \neq 2\sqrt{x_2} + 3$. Since both $2\sqrt{x_1} + 3$ and $2\sqrt{x_2} + 3$ are positive, we have

$$(2\sqrt{x_1} + 3)^2 \neq (2\sqrt{x_2} + 3)^2.$$

Hence, $f(x_1) \neq f(x_2)$, so that f is one to one on $[0, +\infty)$.

If f is one to one on its domain, then f^{-1} exists. To determine f^{-1} we consider the relationship

$$y = (2\sqrt{x} + 3)^2$$

and solve for x.

$$y = (2\sqrt{x} + 3)^2$$

$$\sqrt{y} = 2\sqrt{x} + 3$$

$$\sqrt{y} - 3 = 2\sqrt{x}$$

$$\sqrt{x} = \frac{\sqrt{y} - 3}{2}$$

$$x = \left(\frac{\sqrt{y} - 3}{2}\right)^2$$

$$x = \frac{1}{4}(\sqrt{y} - 3)^2$$

Interchanging x and y gives

$$y = \frac{1}{4}(\sqrt{x} - 3)^2,$$

so that

$$f^{-1}(x) = \frac{1}{4}(\sqrt{x} - 3)^2.$$

Since it is always true that dom f^{-1} = ran f, we have

dom f^{-1} = [9, +∞).

Example 2   Show that the functions

$f(x) = 2x^3 - 1$ and $g(x) = \sqrt[3]{\dfrac{x + 1}{2}}$

are inverse functions.

Solution   We must show that

$(f \circ g)(x) = x$ and $(g \circ f)(x) = x$.

We have $(f \circ g)(x) = f[g(x)]$

$$= 2(g(x))^3 - 1$$

$$= 2(\sqrt[3]{\frac{x + 1}{2}})^3 - 1$$

$$= 2(\frac{x + 1}{2}) - 1$$

$$= (x + 1) - 1$$

$$= x,$$

and $(g \circ f)(x) = g[f(x)]$

$$= \sqrt[3]{\frac{f(x) + 1}{2}}$$

$$= \sqrt[3]{\frac{(2x^3 - 1) + 1}{2}}$$

$$= \sqrt[3]{\frac{2x^3}{2}}$$

$$= \sqrt[3]{x^3}$$

$$= x.$$

Hence, f an g are inverse functions.

Example 3   If the function $f(x) = \sqrt{2x - 1}$ is one to one, find an equation for the inverse function f^{-1} and then graph f and f^{-1} on the same graph. Also, find the domain of f and f^{-1}.

Solution   The domain of f is the set of all x such that $2x - 1 \geq 0$, or $x \geq 1/2$. That is, dom f = [1/2, +∞). To show f is one to one, let x_1 and x_2 be in the domain of f with $x_1 \neq x_2$. If $x_1 \neq x_2$, then $2x_1 - 1 \neq 2x_2 - 1$, and hence, $\sqrt{2x_1 - 1} \neq \sqrt{2x_2 - 1}$. Thus, $x_1 \neq x_2$ implies $f(x_1) \neq f(x_2)$. We conclude that f is one to one.

To find f^{-1} we solve $y = \sqrt{2x - 1}$, x is in [1/2, +∞), for x. This gives

$$y^2 = 2x - 1$$

$$x = \frac{y^2 + 1}{2}.$$

Interchanging x and y gives

$$y = \frac{x^2 + 1}{2},$$

so that

$$f^{-1}(x) = \frac{x^2 + 1}{2}.$$

The domain of f^{-1} is the range of f, and considering $f(x) = \sqrt{2x - 1}$ for x is in [1/2, +∞), we see that f(1/2) = 0, and as x → +∞, f(x) → +∞. Thus, the range of f is the set [0, +∞). Hence, dom f^{-1} = [0, +∞). Consider the table below for points on each graph.

x	f(x)
1/2	0
1	1
2	$\sqrt{3}$
5/2	2
5	3
13	5

x	$f^{-1}(x)$
0	1/2
1	1
2	5/2
3	5
5	13
$\sqrt{3}$	2

Note the interchange of points in the tables.

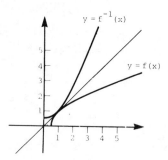

Selected Solutions

1.   The graph represents a function since every vertical line drawn would intersect the graph <u>at most once</u>. The graph represents a one-to-one function since <u>every horizontal line</u> drawn would intersect the graph <u>at most once</u>.

5. The vertical line test shows the graph is a function. However, the graph is not the graph of a one-to-one function because there is one horizontal line that would intersect the graph in more than one point. The particular horizontal line is the one that coincides with the graph when $x \geq 0$.

7. $y = 4x - 5$ Here, the function is $f(x) = 4x - 5$. Suppose $a \neq b$, then $4a \neq 4b$ and, so $f(a) = 4a - 5 \neq 4b - 5 = f(b)$. Thus $a \neq b$ implies that $f(a) \neq f(b)$. For this reason, the function is one-to-one.

9. $y = 6 - x$ Let $f(x) = 6 - x$ and suppose $a \neq b$. Then $-a \neq -b$ and hence $6 - a \neq 6 - b$. Thus, $f(a) \neq f(b)$. This shows that "if $a \neq b$, then $f(a) \neq f(b)$." For this reason the function is one-to-one.

11. $y = (x - 2)^2$ The function here is $f(x) = (x - 2)^2$. Let $a = 1$ and $b = 3$, then $a \neq b$, $f(1) = (1 - 2)^2 = (-1)^2 = 1$ and $f(b) = f(3) = (3 - 2)^2 = 1^2 = 1$. So $f(a) = f(b)$. f is not one-to-one because we have found two numbers a and b with $a \neq b$ but $f(a) = f(b)$. The function is not one-to-one.

13. $y = \sqrt{36 - x^2}$ This is not one-to-one. Let $a = 1$ and $b = -1$. Then $f(1) = \sqrt{36 - 1^2} = \sqrt{36 - 1} = \sqrt{35}$ and $f(-1) = \sqrt{36 - (-1)^2} = \sqrt{36 - 1} = \sqrt{35}$. Again, $a \neq b$ but $f(a) = f(b)$ so that the function is not one-to-one.

17. $y = x^3 - 1$ If $a \neq b$ then $a^3 \neq b^3$ and so, $f(a) = a^3 - 1 \neq b^3 - 1 = f(b)$. This is one-to-one.

21. $y = \dfrac{1}{x + 2}$ The function is $f(x) = \dfrac{1}{x + 2}$. Let $a \neq b$. Then $a + 2 \neq b + 2$, and hence $\dfrac{1}{a + 2} \neq \dfrac{1}{b + 2}$, or $f(a) \neq f(b)$. We have shown that if $a \neq b$, then $f(a) \neq f(b)$. Hence, f is one-to-one.

25. The pair of functions in the graph are inverses since their graphs are mirror images with respect to the line $y = x$.

29. The pair of functions on the graph are not inverses because they are not mirror images with respect to the line $y = x$.

33. Let $f(x) = 5x - 5$ and $g(x) = \frac{1}{5}x + 1$. Then $(f \circ g)(x) = f(\frac{1}{5}x + 1)$ $= 5(\frac{1}{5}x + 1) - 5 = x + 5 - 5 = x$, and $(g \circ f)(x) = g(5x - 5) = \frac{1}{5}(5x - 5) + 1 = x - 1 + 1 = x$. Hence, f an g are inverse to each other, that is, $f^{-1} = g$ and $g^{-1} = f$.

37. Let $f(x) = \dfrac{2}{x + 6}$ and $g(x) = \dfrac{6x + 2}{x}$. Then $(f \circ g)(x) = f(\dfrac{6x + 2}{x})$

$= \dfrac{2}{(\frac{6x + 2}{x}) + 6} = \dfrac{2}{\frac{6x + 2 + 6x}{x}}$

$= \dfrac{2x}{12x + 2}$.

Since $(f \circ g)(x) \neq x$ we cannot have $f^{-1} = g$, or $g^{-1} = f$.

39. Let $f(x) = x^2 + 3$ on domain $[0, \infty)$ and let $g(x) = \sqrt{x - 3}$ on domain $[3, \infty)$. We have $(f \circ g)(x) = f[g(x)] = f(\sqrt{x - 3})$

$= (\sqrt{x - 3})^2 + 3$

$= (x - 3) + 3 = x$, and

$(g \circ f)(x) = g[f(x)] = g(x^2 + 3)$

$$= \sqrt{(x^2 + 3) - 3} = \sqrt{x^2}$$

$$= |x| = x, \text{ since } x > 0.$$

Also, note that the range of f is [3, ∞) since f(0) = 3 and if x > 0, then f(x) > 3. Thus, domain g = range f. In addition, note that the range of g is [0, ∞) since g(3) = 0, and if x > 3, then g(x) > 0. Thus, domain f = range g.

We conclude that f^{-1} = g and g^{-1} = f.

41. Let f(x) = -|x + 5| on domain [-5, ∞) and let g(x) = |x - 5| on domain [5, ∞).

Consider x = -4 in the domain of f. We have f(-4) = -|-4 + 5| = -|1| = -1. However, -1 is not in the domain of g. That is, range f ≠ domain g. We can <u>not</u> have f and g being a pair of inverses.

45. The graph of an inverse is the mirror image with respect to the line y = x of the graph of the function.

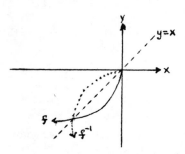

49. Let y = 4x - 5. Then f(x) = 4x - 5. To find the inverse we first inter-change x and y, then solve for y.
1. Start with y = 4x - 5.
2. Write x = 4y - 5, interchanging x, y.

3. 4y = x + 5

$$y = \frac{x + 5}{4}, \text{ solving for y}$$

4. Then $f^{-1}(x) = \frac{x + 5}{4}$, <u>or</u>

$$y = \frac{x + 5}{4}$$

is the inverse function.
Note the tables below.

x	y = 4x - 5	x	y = $\frac{x + 5}{4}$
1	-1	-1	1
2	3	3	2

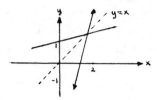

53. $y = -x^3 - 2$ is one-to-one
Interchange x and y and get
$x = -y^3 - 2$,
$y^3 = -x - 2 = -(x + 2)$,
$y = -\sqrt[3]{x + 2}$.
Hence, for $f(x) = -x^3 - 2$ we have
$y = f^{-1}(x) = -\sqrt[3]{x + 2}$.
For the graphs note the tables.

x	y = $-x^3 - 2$	x	y = $-\sqrt[3]{x + 2}$
0	-2	6	$-\sqrt[3]{8}$ = -2
-1	-1	-1	$-\sqrt[3]{1}$ = -1
-2	6	-2	0
1	-3	-3	1

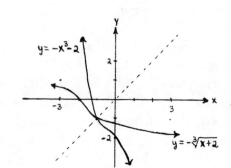

57. $y = -x^2 + 2$ is not one-to-one, as seen in the graph. There are horizontal lines ($y = 0$, for example) that intersect the graph more than once. This function has no inverse.

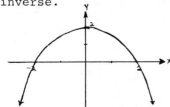

61. $y = \dfrac{-6x + 5}{3x - 1}$, domain $= (-\infty, \frac{1}{3}) \cup (\frac{1}{3}, \infty)$.

Interchange x and y, then solve for y:

$$x = \frac{-6y + 5}{3y - 1}$$

$$x(3y - 1) = -6y + 5$$

$$3xy - x = -6y + 5$$

$$3xy + 6y = x + 5$$

$$y(3x + 6) = x + 5$$

$$y = \frac{x + 5}{3x + 6}.$$

Hence, $f^{-1}(x) = \dfrac{x + 5}{3x + 6}$,

domain $(-\infty, -2) \cup (-2, \infty)$.

The graph of $y = f(x) = \dfrac{-6x + 5}{3x - 1}$

is below.

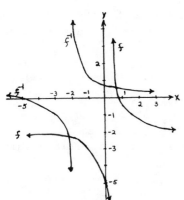

x	f(x)
-2	-17/7
-1	-11/4
0	-5
1	-1/2
2	-7/5
3	-13/8

x	$f^{-1}(x)$
-3	-2/3
-4	-1/6
-1	4/3
0	5/6
2	7/12

65. From the graph we see that $f(4) = 4$, so that $f^{-1}(4) = 4$.

67. From the graph we see that $f(2) = 0$, so that $f^{-1}(0) = 2$.

69. From the graph we see that $f(-2) = -3$, so that $f^{-1}(-3) = -2$.

73. $f(x) = -4x + 3$ and $g(x) = 2x^3 - 4$, so that

$$(f \circ g)(x) = f(g(x)) = -4(g(x)) + 3$$
$$= -4(2x^3 - 4) + 3$$
$$= -8x^3 + 19.$$

Letting $y = (f \circ g)(x) = -8x^3 + 19$, then to find $(f \circ g)^{-1}$, interchange x and y, which gives

$$x = -8y^3 + 19.$$

Solving for y,

$$8y^3 = -x + 19$$

$$y^3 = \frac{19 - x}{8}$$

$$y = \frac{\sqrt[3]{19 - x}}{2} = \frac{1}{2}\sqrt[3]{19 - x}.$$

Thus, $(f \circ g)^{-1}(x) = \frac{1}{2}\sqrt[3]{19 - x}$.

75. $f(x) = -4x + 3$ and $g(x) = 2x^3 - 4$. To find f^{-1} and g^{-1} consider the following steps:

$$f(x) = -4x + 3 \qquad g(x) = 2x^3 - 4$$
$$y = -4x + 3 \qquad y = 2x^3 - 4$$

Interchange x and y, then solve for y.

$$x = -4y + 3 \qquad x = 2y^3 - 4$$
$$4y = 3 - x \qquad 2y^3 = x + 4$$
$$y = \frac{1}{4}(3 - x) \qquad y = \sqrt[3]{\frac{x + 4}{2}}$$
$$= f^{-1}(x) \qquad\qquad = g^{-1}(x)$$

Then,

$$(g^{-1} \circ f^{-1})(x) = g^{-1}[f^{-1}(x)] = g^{-1}[\frac{3 - x}{4}]$$

$$= \sqrt[3]{\frac{(\frac{3-x}{4}) + 4}{2}}$$

$$= \sqrt[3]{\frac{3 - x + 16}{8}}$$

$$= \sqrt[3]{\frac{19 - x}{8}},$$

or $(g^{-1} \circ f^{-1})(x) = \frac{1}{2}\sqrt[3]{19 - x}$.

77. We wish to show that if f is a $1 - 1$ function then f^{-1} is unique.

Proof:

Suppose that there are two inverse functions to f, say f_1^{-1} and f_2^{-1}.

Then for each acceptable x, we have $f[f_1^{-1}(x)] = x$ and $f[f_2^{-1}(x)] = x$.

If f_1^{-1} and f_2^{-1} were different inverse functions, then this would imply that for some x_0, $f_1^{-1}(x_0) \neq f_2^{-1}(x_0)$. Since f is one-one, then we must have

$$f[f_1^{-1}(x_0)] \neq f[f_2^{-1}(x_0)].$$

However,

$$f[f_1^{-1}(x_0)] = x_0 \text{ and } f[f_2^{-1}(x_0)] = x_0.$$

Hence, for <u>all</u> x we <u>must</u> have $f_1^{-1}(x) = f_2^{-1}(x)$ which implies $f_1^{-1} = f_2^{-1}$. Thus, the inverse is unique.

Section 3.7   Variation

Additional Examples

Example 1   Write an equation for each of the following:

(a) z varies directly as x^2 and y, and inversely as 2s and t^3.

(b) u is proportional to 3b and c^2, and inversely proportional to 4d.

Solution   (a) This can be written as the equation

$$z = k \cdot \frac{x^2 y}{(2s)t^3}$$

or $z = \frac{kx^2 y}{2st^3}$, where k is a constant.

(b) The equation is

$$u = k \cdot \frac{(3b)c^2}{4d},$$

or $u = \frac{3kbc^2}{4d}$, where k is a constant.

Example 2   If r varies directly as x^2, and inversely as y and w^2, and if r = 72/81 when x = 2, y = 1/2 and w = 3, find r if x = 3, y = 2, and w = 1.

Solution   The equation for r is

$$r = \frac{kx^2}{yw^2}, \text{ k a constant.}$$

Letting r = 72/81, x = 2, y = 1/2, and w = 3, gives

$$\frac{72}{81} = \frac{k(4)}{(1/2)(9)} \text{ or } \frac{8k}{9} = \frac{72}{81}.$$

Thus, $k = \frac{72}{81} \cdot \frac{9}{8} = 1$, so that $r = \frac{x^2}{yw^2}$. Then, if x = 3, y = 2 and w = 1, we have

$$r = \frac{(3)^2}{2(1)^2} = \frac{9}{2}.$$

Example 3   Suppose an object is dropped from the top of the World Trade Center in New York City. The distance d, measured in feet, the object has fallen t seconds after it has been dropped is directly proportional to the square of the time t. If the object falls 4 feet in 1/2 a second, what is the distance the object will fall in 4 seconds.

Solution   Since the distance d is directly proportional to the square of the time t, we have

$$d = kt^2,$$

where t is measured in seconds and d in feet. We are given that d = 4 when t = 1/2. Substitution gives

$$4 = k\left(\frac{1}{2}\right)^2$$

$$4 = k\left(\frac{1}{4}\right)$$

$$16 = k.$$

We conclude that the relationship between d and t is

$$d = 16t^2.$$

Hence, when t = 4 seconds, we have d = 16(16) = 256 feet. That is, the object falls 256 feet in 4 seconds.

Selected Solutions

1. "a varies directly as b" can be written as a = kb, where k is a constant.

5. "r varies jointly as s and t" can be written as r = kst, where k is a constant.

9. m = kxy

    10 = k(4)(7),

    $k = \frac{5}{14}$, so that $m = \frac{5}{14}xy$. Then,

    $m = \frac{5}{14}(11)(8) = \frac{220}{7}$.

13. $a = \frac{kmn^2}{y^3}$

    $9 = k(4)(9)^2/3^3$

    $9 = 12k$

    $\frac{3}{4} = k$,

    so,

    $a = 3mn^2/(4y^3)$. Then

    $a = 3(6)(2)^2/(4 \cdot 5^3)$

    $a = \frac{18}{125}$.

17. We have $m = kp^2r^4$. If p doubles we replace p by 2p. If r triples we replace r with 3r. Then we have

    $k(2p)^2(3r)^4 = k(4p^2)(81r^4)$

    $= 324kp^2r^4$.

    We see that m is multiplied by 324 if p doubles and r triples.

21. R = resistance, d = diameter

    $R = \frac{k}{d^2}$

    $.4 = k/(.01)^2$

    $k = .00004$

    $R = .00004/(.03)^2$

    R = .044 ohms

25. Let I = interest, P = principle, and t = time. This gives the formula I = kPt, k a constant.

We are given that when P = 1000 and t = 2, then I = 110. This gives

    110 = k(1000)(2)

    $k = \frac{110}{2000} = .055$.

Hence, I = (.055)Pt. Then if P = 5000 and t = 5, the interest earned is

    I = (.055)(5000)(5) = $1,375.

29. Let w = weight, v = speed, and r = radius. Then we have

    $F = \frac{kwv^2}{r}$ and hence

    $3000 = \frac{k(2000)(30)^2}{500}$,

    $k = \frac{5}{6}$, so that

    $F = (5/6)(wv^2)/r$. Thus the

force needed for a curve r = 800 at 60 mph is

    $F = \frac{5(2000)(60)^2}{6(800)}$, or

    F = 7500 pounds.

33. P = population, r = rank

    $P = \frac{k}{r}$

    $1000000 = \frac{k}{8}$

    k = 8000000

    P = 8000000/2 = 4,000,000

35. Let N = number of long distance calls, P_1, P_2 are populations and d = distance. Then we have

    $N = \frac{kp_1p_2}{d}$

    $10000 = \frac{k(50,000)(125,000)}{500}$

    k = .0008

    $N = \frac{.0008(20,000)(80,000)}{800}$

    N = 1600 calls.

37. $R = \frac{k\ell}{r^4}$

    $25 = \frac{k(12)}{(.2)^4}$ implies

$$k = \frac{25(.2)^4}{12} = \frac{1}{300} \text{ so}$$

$$R = \frac{\ell}{300r^4}.$$

If $r = .3$, $\ell = 12$, then

$$R = \frac{12}{300(.3)^4}$$

$$\approx 4.938$$

39.   Let d = distance and y = yield.

$$d = k\sqrt[3]{y}$$

$$3 = k\sqrt[3]{100} \text{ implies}$$

$$k = \frac{3}{\sqrt[3]{100}} . \text{ Hence,}$$

$$d = \frac{3}{\sqrt[3]{100}}\sqrt[3]{y} = 3\sqrt[3]{\frac{y}{100}}$$

If $y = 1500$, then $d = 3\sqrt[3]{\frac{1500}{100}}$

$= 3\sqrt[3]{15} \approx 7.4$ km.

41. w = weight, h = height

$$w = kh^3$$

when $h = 20$, $w = 7$, gives

$7 = k(20)^3$. Hence, $k = \frac{7}{8000}$, so

$$w = \frac{7h^3}{8000}.$$

If $h = 67$, then $w = \frac{7(67)^3}{8000}$

$$\approx 263.17 \text{ pounds}$$

or approximately 263 pounds.

Chapter 3 Review Exercises

Selected Solutions

All graphs can be found in the answer section of your textbook.

1. $x < 0$

The set of all points to the left of the y-axis.

5. $P(3, -1), Q(-4, 5)$

$$d(P, Q) = \sqrt{(3 - (-4)^2 + (-1 - 5)^2}$$

$$= \sqrt{7^2 + (-6)^2}$$

$$= \sqrt{49 + 36}$$

$$= \sqrt{85}$$

midpoint $(\frac{3 + (-4)}{2}, \frac{-1 + 5}{2}) = (\frac{-1}{2}, 2)$

9. $P(-1, 2)$, $Q(-10, 5)$, $R(-4, k)$

There are four possible values of k that give a right triangle. One value when $(-1, 2)$ has the right angle, one value when $(-10, 5)$ has the right angle, and two values when $(-4, k)$ has the right angle. We are going to find these values by using the Pythagorean theorem and assuming the right angle is at the various vertices.

Find the distances (squared):

We have

$$d(P,Q)^2 = (-10 + 1)^2 + (5 - 2)^2$$

$$= 81 + 9 = 90 = d_1^2,$$

$$d(P,R)^2 = (-4 + 1)^2 + (k - 2)^2$$

$$= 9 + (k - 2)^2 = d_2^2, \text{ and}$$

$$d(Q,R) = (-4 + 10)^2 + (k - 5)^2$$

$$= 36 + (k - 5)^2 = d_3^2.$$

Assume the right angle is at $(-1, 2)$.

Then $d_3^2 = d_1^2 + d_2^2$, or

$$36 + (k - 5)^2 = 90 + 9 + (k - 2)^2$$

$$(k - 5)^2 = 63 + (k - 2)^2$$

$$k^2 - 10k + 25 = 63 + k^2 - 4k + 4$$

$$-6k = 42$$

$$k = -7.$$

Assume the right angle is at $(-10, 5)$. Then $d_2^2 = d_1^2 + d_3^3$, or

$$9 + (k - 2)^2 = 90 + 36 + (k - 5)^2$$

$$9 + k^2 - 4k + 4 = 126 + k^2 - 10k + 25$$

$$6k = 138$$

$$k = 23.$$

Finally, assume the right angle is

$(-4, k)$, then $d_1^2 = d_2^2 + d_3^2$, or

$90 = 9 + (k - 2)^2 + 36 + (k - 5)^2$

$45 = k^2 - 4k + 4 + k^2 - 10k + 25$

$0 = 2k^2 - 14k - 16$

$0 = k^2 - 7k - 8$

$0 = (k - 8)(k + 1)$

$k = 8, -1$.

The possible values of k are
$-7, 23, 8, -1$.

13. The medians to the two equal sides
of an isosceles triangle are equal
in length.

Proof: For notation see the figure.

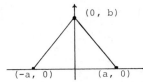

(0, b)

(-a, 0)   (a, 0)

We need to show that the distance
between $(-a, 0)$ and the midpoint of
(0   (0, b), $(a, 0)$ is equal to the distance between $(a, 0)$ and the midpoint of $(0, b)$, $(-a, 0)$.

The midpoint of $(a, 0)$, $(0, b)$ is

$(\frac{a}{2}, \frac{b}{2})$.

The distance between $(\frac{a}{2}, \frac{b}{2})$ and

$(-a, 0)$ is

$$\sqrt{(\frac{a}{2} - (-a))^2 + (\frac{b}{2} - 0)^2} = \sqrt{(\frac{3a}{2})^2 + (\frac{b}{2})^2}$$
$$= \sqrt{\frac{9a^2 + b^2}{4}}$$

The midpoint of $(-a, 0)$, $(0, b)$ is

$(-\frac{a}{2}, \frac{b}{2})$.

The distance between $(-\frac{a}{2}, \frac{b}{2})$ and

$(a, 0)$ is

$$\sqrt{(a - (-\frac{a}{2}))^2 + (0 - \frac{b}{2})^2} = \sqrt{(\frac{3a}{2})^2 + (\frac{b}{2})^2}$$
$$= \sqrt{\frac{9a^2 + b^2}{4}}$$

The distances are the same.

17. $y = \frac{1}{2}x^2$ is a function and the
function $y = f(x) = \frac{1}{2}x^2$ has domain
$f = (-\infty, \infty)$. See the graph in the
text.

21. $y = \sqrt{x - 7}$ is a function.
Domain: all $x \geq 7$, or $[7, +\infty)$.
See the graph in the text.

25. The general equation of a circle is
$(x - h)^2 + (y - k)^2 = r^2$, which gives
$(x + 8)^2 + (y - 1)^2 = r^2$.
Since it passes through $(0, 16)$,
r = distance between $(0, 16)$ and
$(-8, 1)$ and we have

$8^2 + (15)^2 = r^2$

$64 + 225 = r^2$

$r^2 = 289$.

So, the equation is

$(x + 8)^2 + (y - 1)^2 = 289$.

29. $x^2 + 7x + y^2 + 3y + 1 = 0$

$x^2 + 7x + y^2 + 3y = -1$

Complete the square on x and y,
which gives

$x^2 + 7x + (\frac{7}{2})^2 + y^2 + 3y + (\frac{3}{2})^2$

$= -1 + (\frac{7}{2})^2 + (\frac{3}{2})^2$

$(x + \frac{7}{2})^2 + (y + \frac{3}{2})^2 = -1 + \frac{49}{4} + \frac{9}{4}$

$(x + \frac{7}{2})^2 + (y + \frac{3}{2})^2 = \frac{54}{4}$.

Center $(-\frac{7}{2}, -\frac{3}{2})$ and radius $r = \frac{\sqrt{54}}{2}$

$= \frac{3\sqrt{6}}{2}$.

33. $y^3 = x + 1$
Replacing y by $-y$ gives

$(-y)^3 = x + 1$

$-y^3 = x + 1$.

This is not the same equation so the graph is <u>not</u> symmetric to the x-axis. Replacing x by -x gives

$y^3 = -x + 1$.

This is not the same equation so the graph is <u>not</u> symmetric to the y-axis. Replacing x by -x <u>and</u> y by -y gives $(-y)^3 = (-x) + 1$, or

$-y^3 = -x + 1$

$y^3 = x - 1$.

This is not the same equation so the graph is <u>not</u> symmetric to the origin. The graph is <u>not</u> symmetric to the line y = x since the point (0, 1) lies on the graph but (1, 0) does not.

37. $|x| = |y|$

The graph would consist of y = |x| and y = -|x| plotted on the same graph.

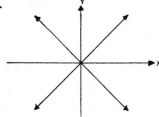

This <u>is</u> symmetric to the x-axis, the y-axis, the origin, and the line y = x.

41. $|y| = -x$

Reflect the graph of Exercise 35 about the x-axis.

45. $y = -4 + |x|$

Any value can replace x. The domain is all real numbers, or $(-\infty, \infty)$.

49. $y = \dfrac{8 + x}{8 - x}$

The domain includes all real numbers except 8, or $(-\infty, 8) \cup (8, \infty)$.

53. $y = f(x) + 3$

The graph is shifted upward 3 units. See final graph in the textbook.

57. $y = f(x + 3) - 2$

The graph is shifted to the left 3 units <u>and</u> downward two units. See final graph in the textbook.

61.

$f(x) = -x^3 + 2x^2$

$f(x + h) = -(x + h)^3 + 2(x + h)^2$

$\qquad = -(x^3 + 3x^2h + 3xh^2 + h^3) +$

$\qquad\quad 2(x^2 + 2xh + h^2)$

$\qquad = -x^3 - 3x^2h - 3xh^2 - h^3 +$

$\qquad\quad 2x^2 + 4xh + 2h^2$

$f(x + h) - f(x)$

$= -3x^2h - 3xh^2 - h^3 + 4xh + 2h^2$,

subtracting $-x^3 + 2x^2$.

$\dfrac{f(x + h) - f(x)}{h}$

$= \dfrac{h(-3x^2 - 3xh - h^2 + 4x + 2h)}{h}$

$= -3x^2 = 3xh - h^2 + 4x + 2h$, if $h \neq 0$.

65. $g(x) = \dfrac{x}{|x|}$, $x \neq 0$

$g(-x) = \dfrac{-x}{|-x|} = -\dfrac{x}{|x|} = -g(x)$

Thus, g is an odd function.

69.

$f(x) = 3x^2 - 4$, $g(x) = x^2 - 3x - 4$

$(f + g)(x) = f(x) + g(x)$

$\qquad = (3x^2 - 4) + (x^2 - 3x - 4)$

$\qquad = 4x^2 - 3x - 8$.

73. $(f + g)(2k) = f(2k) + g(2k)$, and

$\qquad f(2k) = 3(2k)^2 - 4 = 12k^2 - 4$,

and $g(2k) = (2k)^2 - 3(2k) - 4$

$\qquad\qquad = 4k^2 - 6k - 4$.

Thus $(f + g)(2k) = 16k^2 - 6k - 8$.

77. The domain of f · g is the set of all real numbers, $(-\infty, +\infty)$.

81. $f(x) = \sqrt{x - 2}$ and $g(x) = x^2$

$(f \circ g)(-6) = f[g(-6)] = f[(-6)^2]$
$= f(36) = \sqrt{36 - 2} = \sqrt{34}$.

85. $y = -(x + 1)^2$
The graph of $y = x^2$, shifted one unit to the left and inverted, gives the graph of $y = -(x + 1)^2$. Hence the function is increasing on $(-\infty, -1]$ and decreasing on $[-1, +\infty)$.

89. Not one-to-one. The horizontal line $y = -1$ intersects the graph in two points.

93. $y = -x^2 + 11$
$x_1 = -1$ and $x_2 = +1$ give the same value to y, namely, $y = 10$. The function is not one-to-one.

97. $f(x) = 12x + 3$
To find the inverse function, write $y = 12x + 3$ and interchange x and y to get
$x = 12y + 3$
$12y = x - 3$
$y = \dfrac{x - 3}{12}$.

Therefore, $f^{-1}(x) = \dfrac{1}{12}(x - 3)$.

101. $f(x) = \sqrt{25 - x^2}$ with domain f = [0, 5] implies the range of f is [0, 5]. Write $y = \sqrt{25 - x^2}$ and interchange x and y to get

$x = \sqrt{25 - y^2}$
$x^2 = 25 - y^2$
$y^2 = 25 - x^2$
$y = \sqrt{25 - x^2}$

So $f^{-1}(x) = \sqrt{25 - x^2}$ with domain f^{-1} = range f = [0, 5]. The graph of both f and f^{-1} is the portion of the circle $x^2 + y^2 = 25$ that lies in quadrant I.

105. We have $Y = \dfrac{kMN^2}{W^3}$.

109. $Z = \dfrac{kJ^2M^3}{W^4}$

If $125 = \dfrac{k(3)^2(5)^3}{(1)^4}$,

then $k = \dfrac{125}{(9)(125)} = \dfrac{1}{9}$ and hence,

$Z = \dfrac{J^2M^3}{9W^4}$.

When J = 2, M = 7, and W = 3, we have

$Z = \dfrac{(2)^2(7)^3}{9(3)^4} = \dfrac{(4)(343)}{9(81)} = \dfrac{1372}{729}$.

113. Suppose Alec converted 1000 U.S. dollars to Canadian money at a 12% premium. Then Alec had 1000 + .12 (1000) = 1.12(1000) = 1120 Canadian dollars. If he immediately converts back to U.S. dollars he receives $1120 - .12(1120) = (1 - .12)(1120) = .88(1120) = $985.60.

The conversion function changing U.S. dollars to Canadian dollars is as follows.

Let x be the amount of U.S. currency, then the amount of Canadian exchange is $y = x + .12x = 1.12x$. The conversion function is $f(x) = 1.12x$.

Similarly, the conversion function to change x Canadian dollars into U.S. dollars is $g(x) = x - .12x = .88x$.

The inverse function of f is found by considering $y = 1.12x$ and interchanging x and y to get

$$x = 1.12y$$

$$y = \frac{1}{1.12}x$$

or $y \approx (.8928571429)x$

That is, $f^{-1}(x) = \frac{1}{1.12}x$, and this is not $g(x)$.

117. $f(x) = \begin{cases} 0 & \text{if } x < 0 \\ 2x & \text{if } 0 \le x \le 1 \\ 0 & \text{if } x > 1 \end{cases}$

$g(x) = \begin{cases} 1 & \text{if } x < 0 \\ x/2 & \text{if } 0 \le x \le 1 \\ 1 & \text{if } x > 1 \end{cases}$

$(f \circ g)(x) = f[g(x)] = \begin{cases} f(1) & \text{if } x < 0 \\ f(\frac{x}{2}) & \text{if } 0 \le x \le 1 \\ f(1) & \text{if } x > 1 \end{cases}$

$\qquad = \begin{cases} 2 & \text{if } x < 0 \\ x & \text{if } 0 \le x \le 1 \\ 2 & \text{if } x > 1 \end{cases}$

That is,

$(f \circ g)(x) = \begin{cases} 2 & \text{if } x < 0 \\ x & \text{if } 0 \le x \le 1 \\ 2 & \text{if } x > 1 \end{cases}$

121. $f(x) = \begin{cases} x & \text{if } x < 1 \\ x^2 & \text{if } 1 \le x \le 9 \\ 27\sqrt{x} & \text{if } x > 9 \end{cases}$

Thus, write

$y = \begin{cases} x & \text{if } x < 1 \\ x^2 & \text{if } 1 \le x \le 9 \\ 27\sqrt{x} & \text{if } x > 9 \end{cases}$

Interchange x and y to get

$x = \begin{cases} y & \text{if } y < 1 \\ y^2 & \text{if } 1 \le y \le 9 \\ 27\sqrt{y} & \text{if } y > 9 \end{cases}$

which implies

$f^{-1}(x) = y = \begin{cases} x & \text{if } y < 1 \\ x & \text{if } 1 \le x \le 81 \\ (\frac{x}{27})^2 & \text{if } x > 81 \end{cases}$

123. Let $f(x) = x + 1$. Then we have

$f(x^2) = x^2 + 1$ and

$[f(x)]^2 = (x + 1)^2 = x^2 + 2x + 1$.

For this example we see that

$f(x^2) \neq [f(x)]^2$.

125. Let $f(x) = x + 1$. Then we have

$f(xy) = xy + 1$ and

$f(x) \cdot f(y) = (x + 1)(y + 1)$

$\qquad\qquad = xy + x + y + 1$.

For this example we have

$f(xy) \neq f(x)f(y)$.

Chapter 3 Test

1. Graph the set of points (x, y) such that $|x - 1| < 2$ and $|y| \geq 3$.

2. For P(-2, 3) and Q(4, -7), find d(P, Q) and the mid point of segment PQ.

3. Determine whether or not the points (2, -3), (-1, -1), and (3, 4) are the vertices of a right triangle.

4. Find all numbers x such that the point (x, 3) is five units from the point (2, 6).

5. Graph $(x + 2)^2 + (y - 1)^2 = 9$. Is this a function? Give reasons to support your answer.

6. Graph $y = \sqrt{x - 1}$. Is this a function? Give reasons to support your answer.

7. Find the equation of the circle of radius 4 having center at (-3, 4).

8. Find the center and radius of the circle $x^2 + y^2 + 4x - 8y + 11 = 0$ and sketch the graph of the circle.

9. Discuss the symmetry of the graph $y = 3x^2 + 5$ with respect to the x-axis, y-axis, origin, and the line y = x.

10. Graph $y = |x|$ and using this graph, obtain the graph of $y = |x - 1| + 2$.

11. Give the domain of the function $f(x) = \sqrt{2x - 1}$.

12. Give the domain of $f(x) = \sqrt{\dfrac{x - 2}{x + 3}}$.

13. Give the domain and range of $f(x) = 4 - x^2$.

14. Let $f(x) = \dfrac{2x + 1}{x - 2}$ and find $\dfrac{f(x) - f(4)}{x - 4}$ and simplify for $x \neq 2$, $x \neq 4$.

15. Let f have the graph as shown for $-2 \leq x \leq 2$.

     Sketch the graph of $y + 2 = f(x)$.

16. Decide whether the function $f(x) = 3x^3 - x$ is even, odd, or neither. What conclusion can be drawn regarding symmetry?

17. Let $f(x) = \sqrt{x + 2}$ and $g(x) = x^2 + 1$ and find   (a) $(f \cdot g)(2)$, and (b) $(g/f)(7)$.

18. If $f(x) = \sqrt{4 - x}$ and $g(x) = x^2 - 1$, find the domain of f/g.

19. Let $f(x) = \dfrac{x + 1}{x - 4}$ and $g(x) = \dfrac{1}{x - 1}$. Find $(f \circ g)(2)$ and $(g \circ f)(2)$.

20. Let $f(x) = x^2 + x + 1$ and $g(x) = 2x - 1$. Find $(g \circ f)(x)$.

21. For $f(x) = \dfrac{2x + 3}{x}$ and $g(x) = x^2 + 1$, find $(f \circ g)(x)$.

22. Find the intervals where $y = -x^2 + 2$ is increasing and decreasing.

23.   In figures A, B, and C, we have three graphs. Determine which of these represent the graph of a function. Give reasons for the conclusions.

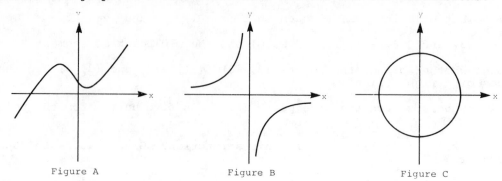

Figure A   Figure B   Figure C

24.   For the graphs in figures A, B, and C that are functions, which of these functions are also one to one function?   Give reasons for the conclusion.

25.   Justify the statement that $y = 2x^3 + 1$ is a one to one function.

26.   The function $f(x) = 3x - 6$ is a one to one function. Find an equation for the inverse function f^{-1}.

27.   The function $f(x) = \dfrac{3}{2x - 1}$, $x \neq \dfrac{1}{2}$, is a one to one function. Find an equation for $f^{-1}(x)$ and determine the domain of f^{-1}.

28.   Write an equation for the statement, "x varies jointly as a and the square of b, and inversely as the square root of c."

29.   If m varies directly as p, and inversely as the square of q, and if m = 2 when p = 3 and q = 2, find m when p = 2 and q = 5.

30.   Suppose the weight w of a body in space varies inversely as the square of its distance d from the center of the earth. Assuming the surface of the earth is 4000 miles from the center of the earth, find the weight of an object which weighs 200 pounds on the earth's surface and is in space 2000 miles from the surface of the earth.

    (Answers for this test are on page 360.)

CHAPTER 4   Polynomial and Rational
            Functions

Section 4.1   Linear Functions

Additional Examples

Example 1   The Fahrenheit temperature
    (F) is related to Celsius tempera-
    ture (C) by a linear equation.
    Water freezes at 32°F or 0°C, and
    boils at 212°F or 100°C.
    (a) Write a linear equation expres-
    sing C in terms of F.
    (b) What is the Celsius temperature
    when the Fahrenheit temperature is
    77°F.

Solution   We can think of this problem
    as finding the equation of the line
    passing through the points (32, 0)
    and (212, 100), where F is measured
    on the horizontal axis and C on the
    vertical axis.   The slope of the
    line is

$$m = \frac{100 - 0}{212 - 32} = \frac{100}{180} = \frac{5}{9}.$$

    Using the point (32, 0) in the
    point slope formula we have

$$C - 0 = \frac{5}{9}(F - 32).$$

    Hence, the solution in part (a)
    is C = 5/9(F - 32).
    In (b), let F = 77 to arrive at

$$C = \frac{5}{9}(77 - 32) = \frac{5}{9}(45) = 25°$$

Example 2   Graph the function

$$y = \begin{cases} 2x + 3 & \text{if } x < -3 \\ -x + 1 & \text{if } -3 \le x < 2 \\ 2x - 1 & \text{if } x \ge 2. \end{cases}$$

Solution   We note that
    (1) if x is in (−∞, −3) then
         y = 2x + 3;
    (2) if x is in [−3, 2), then
         y = −x + 1;
    (3) if x is in [2, +∞), then
         y = 2x − 1.

In each interval we have a linear
function. Hence the graph consists
of three parts; each part being a
portion of a line. Appropriately
choosing numbers x in the desired
intervals, we have the following
table.

y = 2x + 3

x	−6	−4	close to −3
y	−9	−5	close to −3

y = −x + 1

x	−3	1	close to 2
y	4	0	close to −1

y = 2x − 1

x	2	6
y	3	11

Plotting these points and noting
the restrictions on x gives the
following graph.

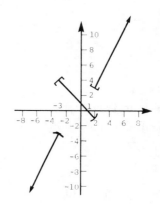

Selected Solutions
    1.   Graph x − y = 4.
         Note that if x = 0, then −y = 4, or
         y = −4. Hence, the y-axis intercept
         is −4. Another way of thought is
         that the point (0, −4) is on the
         line. Note that if y = 0, then
         x = 4. The point (4, 0) is on the
         line, or the x-axis intercept is 4.

Hence, the following graph.

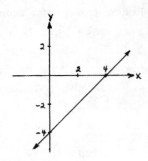

5.   Graph $3x - y = 6$.

Finding the x-axis and y-axis inter-cepts as in exercise 1, we have the following table.

x	0	2
y	-6	0

Hence the following graph.

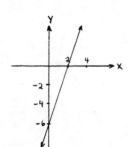

I. $x = 0$: $0 - y = 6$

$-y = 6$

$y = 6$

II. $y = 0$: $3x - 0 = 6$

$3x = 6$

$x = 2$

9.   Graph $4x - 3y = 9$.

Finding the intercepts gives the following table.

x	0	9/4
y	-3	0

I. $x = 0$: $0 - 3y = 9$ II. $y = 0$: $4x - 0 = 9$

$-3y = 9$ $4x = 9$

$y = -2$ $x = \frac{9}{4}$

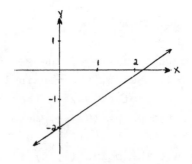

13.   Graph $y = -5$.

For every real number x we have $y = -5$. Hence, the graph is the horizontal line five units below the x-axis. See the answer section in the text for the graph.

17.   Graph $x = -5y$.

Two points on a line are all that is needed for the graph. Letting $x = 0$ gives $y = 0$ and when $x = 5$, $y = -1$. The graph follows:

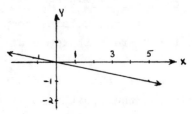

21.   Graph the line through $(3, -4)$ with slope $m = \frac{-1}{3}$.

If we find one additional point we have enough information to graph the line. The slope m measures the ratio of the change in y divided by the change in x. Since $m = \frac{-1}{3}$, if we add 3 to the x-value of $(3, -4)$ and -1 to its y-value, we arrive at another point on the line. Hence, $Q(3 + 3, -4 -1) = Q(6, - 5)$ is a point on the line. Hence, the following graph.

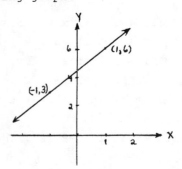

25.   Graph the line through $(3, \frac{2}{3})$ having an undefined slope is a vertical line

through $(3, \frac{2}{3})$. Note that every point (x, y) on the line has $x = 3$.

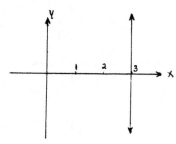

29. Given $P(8, 4)$ and $Q(-1, -3)$, we have

$$m = \frac{4 - (-3)}{8 - (-1)} = \frac{7}{9}.$$

33. Given $P(2, 3)$ and $Q(2, 7)$, we have

$m = \frac{3 - 7}{2 - 2} = \frac{-5}{0}$. Since we cannot divide by zero, the slope of the line is undefined. This is the case for a vertical line.

37. Given the line $y = 4x - 5$ we can find two points on the line by choosing numbers for x and finding y. We have the following table.

x	0	1
y	-5	-1

The slope is $m = \dfrac{y_2 - y_1}{x_2 - x_1} = \dfrac{-5 - (-1)}{0 - 1}$

$$= \frac{-5 + 1}{-1} = \frac{-4}{-1} = 4.$$

41. Given the line $y = 4$ we can find two points on the line by choosing numbers for x and finding y. Note that for <u>every</u> choice of x we have $y = 4$. Hence, two points are $P(1, 4)$ and $Q(2, 4)$. The slope is

$$m = \frac{4 - 4}{1 - 2} = \frac{0}{-1} = 0.$$

45. Given $P(-1.978, 4.806)$ and $Q(3.759, 8.125)$ we have

$$m = \frac{8.125 - 4.806}{3.759 - 1.978} = \frac{3.319}{1.781} = 1.8635598.$$

49. Given the points $X(1,3)$, $Y(-4, 73)$ and $Z(5, -50)$ we have

$$M_{xy} = \frac{73 - 3}{-4 - 1} = \frac{70}{-5} = -14, \text{ and}$$

$$M_{xz} = \frac{-50 - 3}{5 - 1} = \frac{-53}{4} = -13.25.$$

Since these slopes are not equal we can conclude that X, Y, and Z do <u>not</u> lie on a straight line. We do not need to calculate M_{yz}.

53. Graph $g(x) = \begin{cases} 4 - x & \text{if } x < 2 \\ 1 + 2x & \text{if } x \geq 2. \end{cases}$

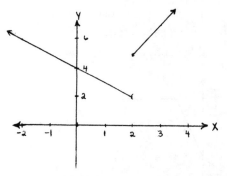

57. Graph $h(x) = \begin{cases} 2 + x & \text{if } x < -4 \\ -x & \text{if } -4 \leq x \leq 5 \\ 3x & \text{if } x > 5. \end{cases}$

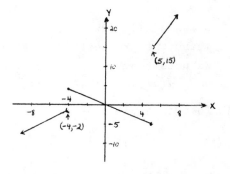

Note that <u>if $x < -4$</u> but "getting close" to -4, then $h(x)$ is "getting close" to $2 + (-4) = -2$. Also, if $x > 5$ but "getting close" to 5, then $h(x)$ is "getting close" to $3(5) = 15$.

61. If $i(t) = \begin{cases} 40t + 110 & \text{if } 0 \leq t \leq 3 \\ 220 & \text{if } 3 < t \leq 8 \\ -80t + 860 & \text{if } 8 < t \leq 10 \\ 60 & \text{if } 10 < t \leq 24, \end{cases}$

then

(a) 7 a.m. implies t = 1, and
     i(1) = 40(1) + 100 = 140;

(b) 9 a.m. implies t = 3, and
     i(3) = 40(3) + 100 = 220;

(c) 10 a.m. implies t = 4, and
     i(4) = 220;

(d) noon implies t = 6, and
     i(6) = 220;

(e) 2 p.m. implies t = 8, and
     i(8) = 220;

(f) 5 p.m. implies t = 11, and
     i(11) = 60;

(g) midnight implies t = 18, and
     i(18) = 60.

The graph of i follows.

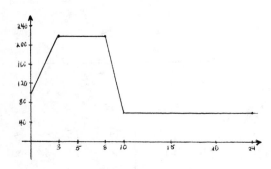

65.   Graph g(x) = [2x - 1], where [r]
      means the greatest integer in r.
      We note that 2x -1 is an integer
      when x = ..., -1 $-\frac{1}{2}$, 0, $\frac{1}{2}$, 1, ...

      That is g(-1) = [-3] = -3,

                $g(-\frac{1}{2})$ = [-2] = -2,

                g(0) = [-1] = -1,

                $g(\frac{1}{2})$ = [0] = 0,

                g(1) = [1] = 1.

      Also, note that if $0 < x < \frac{1}{2}$,

                  0 < 2x < 1,
                 -1 < 2x < 0,

      so that g(x) = [2x - 1] = -1.

Hence, the graph looks like steps.

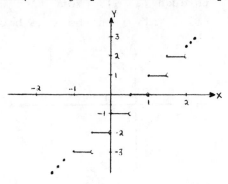

69.   Graph h(x) = [3x] - 1. The term
      [3x] changes every $\frac{1}{3}$ unit. That is,
      if $0 \leq x < \frac{1}{3}$, then $0 \leq 3x < 1$ and
      [3x] = 0; if $\frac{1}{3} \leq x < \frac{2}{3}$, then
      $1 \leq 3x < 2$ and [3x] = 1; if
      $\frac{2}{3} \leq x < 1$, then $2 \leq 3x < 3$ and
      [3x] = 2; and so on. This graph is
      a "step graph" with the width of
      each step being $\frac{1}{3}$ of a unit.

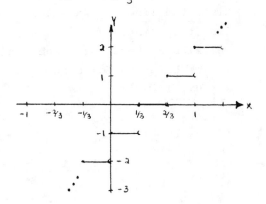

73.   If a letter weighs x ounces and it
      costs 30¢ if $0 < x \leq 1$, and 27¢ for
      each ounce or fraction of an ounce
      above 1 ounce, then the cost L of
      mailing a letter x ounces can be
      written as L(x) = 30 + 27[x - 1].

77.   If p = 16 - $\frac{5}{4}$x, then

   (a) when x = 0, p = 16 - $\frac{5}{4}$(0) = $16;

   (b) when x = 4, p = 16 - $\frac{5}{4}$(4) = 16 - 5 = $11;

   (c) when x = 8, p = 16 - $\frac{5}{4}$(8) = 16 - 10 = $6;

(d) If p = 6 and p = 16 - $\frac{5}{4}$x, then

$$6 = 16 - \frac{5}{4}x$$

$$-10 = \frac{5}{4}x$$

$$-40 = -5x$$

$$x = 8.$$

(e) If p = 11, then 11 = 16 - $\frac{5}{4}$x

$$-\frac{5}{4}x = -5,$$

$$x = \left(-\frac{4}{5}\right)(-5) = 4.$$

(f) If p = 16, then 16 = 16 - $\frac{5}{4}$x,
so that x = 0.

(g) The graph of p = 16 - $\frac{5}{4}$x is a
line with all of the points found
above on the line. The y-axis
intercept is (0, 16). See the
graph in the text.

(h) If p = $\frac{3}{4}$x and p = 0, then

$$0 = \frac{3}{4}x, \text{ or } x = 0.$$

(i) If p = 10, then 10 = $\frac{3}{4}$x,

$$3x = 40, \text{ or } x = \frac{40}{3}.$$

(j) If p = 20, then 20 = $\frac{3}{4}$x,

$$3x = 80, \text{ or } x = \frac{80}{3}.$$

(k) See the graph in the text.

(l) The equilibrium is the point of
intersection of the graph. If
p = $\frac{3}{4}$x and p = 16 - $\frac{5}{4}$x, then

$$\frac{3}{4}x = 16 - \frac{5}{4}x$$

$$\frac{8}{4}x = 16$$

$$x = 8.$$

Hence, x = 8 is the equilibrium
supply.

(m) The equilibrium price is

$$p = \frac{3}{4}(8) = \$6.$$

Section 4.2   Equations of a Line

Additional Examples

Example 1   Write the equation of the
line passing through the point
P(-2, 3) having slope m = -3 in
standard form Ax + By = C.

Solution   Using the point slope formula
we have   y - 3 = -3(x - (-2))

$$y - 3 = -3(x + 2)$$

$$y - 3 = -3x - 6$$

or   3x + y = -3.

Example 2   Write the equation in standard form for the line through (2, -1)
that is perpendicular to the line
2x - 5y = 6.

Solution   We need to solve the equation
2x - 5y = 6 for y. We have

$$-5y = -2x + 6 \text{ or }$$

$$y = \frac{2}{5}x - \frac{6}{5}.$$

The coefficient of x is the slope
of this line. We see that the slope
is $\frac{2}{5}$. The slope m of any line perpendicular to this line is the
negative reciprocal of $\frac{2}{5}$. That is,
m = $-\frac{5}{2}$. The desired equation is
then found as

$$y - (-1) = -\frac{5}{2}(x - 2)$$

$$y + 1 = -\frac{5}{2}(x - 2)$$

$$2(y + 1) = -5(x - 2)$$

$$2y + 2 = -5x + 10$$

$$5x + 2y = 8.$$

Selected Solutions

1. The equation of the line through
P(1, 3) having slope m = -2 is

$$y - 3 = -2(x - 1)$$

$$y - 3 = -2x + 2$$

$$2x + y = 5.$$

5. If $P(2, 0)$ and $m = -\frac{3}{4}$, the equation

is $y - 0 = -\frac{3}{4}(x - 2)$

$4y = -3(x - 2)$

$4y = -3x + 6$

$3x + 4y = 6.$

9. If the slope of a line is undefined, then the line is a vertical line and the equation of the line is x = constant. Since we are given the line passes through $P(-8, 1)$, the equation is $x = -8$.

13. The line through $P(-1, 3)$ and $Q(3, 4)$ has slope $m = \frac{4 - 3}{3 + 1} = \frac{1}{4}$. Hence, using either P or Q, we can find the equation of the line. Using Q we arrive at

$y - 4 = \frac{1}{4}(x - 3)$

$4y - 16 = x - 3$

or $x - 4y = -13.$

17. If the x-intercept is 3 and the y-intercept is -2, we have two points, $P(3, 0)$ and $Q(0, -2)$. The slope of the line is $m = \frac{0 - (-2)}{3 - 0} = \frac{2}{3}$. Using P the equation is

$y - 0 = \frac{2}{3}(x - 3)$

$3y = 2(x - 3)$

$3y = 2x - 6$

or $2x - 3y = 6$

21. The vertical line through $P(-6, 5)$ has the equation $x = -6.$

25. The line $x + 3y = 5$, when solved for y becomes $y = -\frac{1}{3}x + \frac{5}{3}$ and hence has slope $m = -\frac{1}{3}$. The slope of any line parallel to $x + 3y = 5$ has the same slope $m = -\frac{1}{3}$. If $P(-1, 4)$

lies on the line, the equation is

$y - 4 = -\frac{1}{3}(x + 1)$

$3(y - 4) = -(x + 1)$

$3y - 12 = -x - 1$

or $x + 3y = 11$

29. The line $x + y = 4$ can be written as $y = -x + 4$. The slope is $m_1 = -1$. The slope of a line perpendicular to this line has slope

$m_2 = \frac{-1}{m_1} = \frac{-1}{-1} = 1$

If $P(3, -4)$ is on the line, the equation of the desired line is

$y + 4 = 1(x - 3)$

$y + 4 = x - 3$

or $x - y = 7.$

33. The line $y = 2x$ has slope $m = 2$ as does every line parallel to $y = 2x$. If the x-intercept is -2, then $P(-2, 0)$ is on the line. The equation is

$y - 0 = 2(x + 2)$

$y = 2x + 4$

or $2x - y = -4.$

37. The slope of the line through $P(4, 3)$ and $Q(2, 0)$ is $m = \frac{3 - 0}{4 - 2} = \frac{3}{2}$ and the equation of the line is

$y - 0 = \frac{3}{2}(x - 2)$

$2y = 3(x - 2)$

or $3x - 2y = 6.$

We see that $R(-18, -12)$ is <u>not</u> on the line since

$3(-18) - 2(-12) = -54 + 24 = -30 \neq 6.$

41. If $A(1, 3)$, $B(-\frac{5}{2}, 2)$, $C(-\frac{7}{2}, 4)$, and $D(2, 1)$, then

$M_{AC} = \frac{4 - 3}{-\frac{7}{2} - 1} = \frac{1}{-\frac{9}{2}} = -\frac{2}{9},$

$M_{BD} = \frac{2 - 1}{-\frac{5}{2} - 2} = \frac{1}{-\frac{9}{2}} = -\frac{2}{9},$

$M_{AD} = \dfrac{3-1}{1-2} = \dfrac{2}{-1} = -2$, and

$M_{BC} = \dfrac{4-2}{\frac{-7}{2}+\frac{5}{2}} = \dfrac{2}{-1} = -2$.

Hence, the line segments $\overline{AC}$ and $\overline{BD}$ are parallel and the line segments $\overline{AD}$ and $\overline{BC}$ are parallel. This shows the quadrilateral is a parallelogram.

43. (a) Prove two nonvertical parallel lines have the same slope.

Proof: Let ℓ_1 and ℓ_2 be nonvertical parallel lines (see the figure). Choose point A on ℓ_1 and point B on ℓ_2. Horizontal lines are drawn from these points to the y-axis, intersecting at points C and D respectively. Let E and F denote the points where ℓ_1 and ℓ_2 intersect the y-axis. Then,

  (i) angle ACE = angle BDF

      Both are right angles

  (ii) angle AEC = angle BFD

      Corresponding angles cut by a transversal (the y-axis)

(iii) triangle ACE is similar to triangle BDF

      They have equal angles

  (iv) $\dfrac{CE}{CA} = \dfrac{DF}{DB}$

      The ratio of lengths of sides of similar triangles are equal

  (v) slope $\ell_1 = \dfrac{CE}{CA}$, slope $\ell_2 = \dfrac{DF}{DB}$

      Definition

Thus, parallel lines have the same slope.

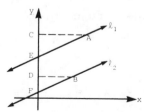

43. (b) Prove two lines with the same slope are parallel.

Proof: Let ℓ_1 and ℓ_2 be two distinct lines with the same slope m. Then ℓ_1 and ℓ_2 have equations $y = mx + b_1$ and $y = mx + b_2$, respectively. Suppose ℓ_1 and ℓ_2 are not parallel. Then they will intersect in some point, say (a, b). Thus, (a, b) satisfies each equation, which leads to

  $b = ma + b_1$ (ℓ_1)
  $b = ma + b_2$ (ℓ_2).

This implies $b_1 = b_2$, so that ℓ_1 and ℓ_2 have the same equation, and hence are the same line. Assuming ℓ_1 and ℓ_2 are not parallel leads to a contradiction with the given facts. Hence, ℓ_1 and ℓ_2 must be parallel.

45. The segment connecting P(a, b) and Q(b, a) has slope $m = \dfrac{b-a}{a-b} = -1$. The line $y = x$ has slope $m_2 = 1$ and hence is perpendicular to the line segment PQ. The mid-point of P and Q is the point R(c, d) where $c = \dfrac{a+b}{2}$, $d = \dfrac{b+a}{2}$. Thus, $c = d$, and the point R lies on the line $y = x$. This shows that $y = x$ is a perpendicular bisector of PQ.

47. Let P be the point (x_1, y_1) and M be (x_2, y_2). P and M both satisfy the equation for L. Since MQ measures the vertical change from P to M then the length of MQ is $y_2 - y_1$. Also, since $y_1 = m_1 x_1 + b$ and $y_2 = m_1 x_2 + b$,

$y_2 - y_1 = (m_1 x_2 + b) - (m_1 x_1 + b)$
$= m_1 (x_2 - x_1)$.

However, $x_2 - x_1$ is the length of PQ, which is 1. Thus MQ has length m_1.

49. Show triangles MPQ and PQN are similar. By definition, two triangles are similar if and only if corresponding angles are equal. Consider a line through M parallel to PQ. Then the angles labeled θ are equal. Angle PMQ and angle NPQ are equal since they are both supplementary to θ. Angle PQM = angle PQN since both are 90° angles. Then, we must have angle MPQ = angle PNQ because the angles in a triangle add to the same value, 180°. Hence, triangle MPQ is similar to triangle PQN. See the figure.

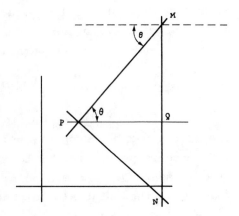

50. Show $\dfrac{m_1}{1} = \dfrac{1}{-m_2}$ and that $m_1 m_2 = -1$.

In exercise 49 we have shown triangles MPQ and PQN to be similar. This implies the quotients of the lengths of corresponding sides are equal. This gives

$$\frac{m_1}{1} = \frac{1}{-m_2}$$

Simplifying we have $m_1 m_2 = -1$.

53. If $f(x) = \dfrac{1}{x}$, then $f(x+h) = \dfrac{1}{x+h}$.

The slope of the line through $P(x, f(x))$ and $Q(x+h, f(x+h))$ is

$$m = \frac{f(x+h) - f(x)}{(x+h) - x} = \frac{\dfrac{1}{x+h} - \dfrac{1}{x}}{h},$$

$$m = \frac{\dfrac{x - (x+h)}{(x+h)(x)}}{h} = \frac{-h}{x(x+h)} \cdot \frac{1}{h}, \text{ or}$$

$$m = \frac{-1}{x(x+h)}, \text{ provided } h \neq 0.$$

57. The points on the line are $P(20, \$13,900)$ and $Q(10, \$7500)$. The slope is

$$m = \frac{13,900 - 7500}{20 - 10} = \frac{6400}{10} = 640.$$

The equation of the line is
$$y - 7500 = 640(x - 10)$$
or $\qquad y = 640x + 1100.$

61. The points on the line are $P(45, 42.5)$ and $Q(55, 67.5)$. The slope is

$$m = \frac{67.5 - 42.5}{55 - 45} = \frac{25}{10} = 2.5,$$

and the equation is
$$y - 42.5 = 2.5(x - 45)$$
or $\qquad y = 2.5x - 70.$

Section 4.3   Quadratic Functions

Additional Examples

Example 1   For the quadratic function
$$f(x) = -2x^2 = 3x + 2,$$
determine the intercepts of the graph, the vertex, and the axis. Graph the parabola described by the function.

Solution   Let $y = -2x^2 - 3x + 2$, move the constant term to the left hand side, factor out -2 from the right hand side, and complete the square on x. This gives the standard form,

$$y - 2 = -2(x^2 + \frac{3}{2}x)$$

$$y - 2 = -2[x^2 + \frac{3}{2}x + \frac{9}{16}] + 2(\frac{9}{16}),$$

since $\dfrac{3}{2} \times \dfrac{1}{2} = \dfrac{3}{4}$,

$$y - 2 - \dfrac{9}{8} = -2\left(x + \dfrac{3}{4}\right)^2$$

$$y - \dfrac{25}{8} = -2\left(x + \dfrac{3}{4}\right)^2.$$

The vertex is $\left(-\dfrac{3}{4}, \dfrac{25}{8}\right)$ and the axis is the line $x = -\dfrac{3}{4}$. To find the intercepts, $f(0) = 2$, and when $y = 0$ we have,

$$-2x^2 - 3x + 2 = 0$$
$$-(2x - 1)(x + 2) = 0$$
$$x = \dfrac{1}{2} \text{ or } x = -2.$$

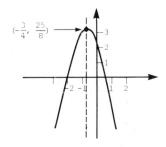

Example 2   A rectangular piece of ground along a stone wall is to be enclosed with 600 meters of fencing on three sides while the stone wall forms the remaining side. Determine the dimensions of the rectangle so the fenced area will be a maximum. What is the maximum area enclosed?

Solution

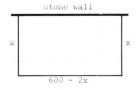

Using the dimensions in the figure, we have the area enclosed is

$$A = x(600 - 2x)$$
$$A = -2x^2 + 600x$$
$$A = -2(x^2 - 300x)$$
$$A = -2[x^2 - 300x + (150)^2 - (150)^2],$$

since 1/2 of coefficient of $x = 150$,

$$A = -2(x^2 - 300x + 22{,}500) + 45{,}000$$
$$A - 45{,}000 = -2(x - 150)^2.$$

Interpreting this result, we see that A is a quadratic function whose graph is a parabola with vertex at $x = 150$, $A = 45{,}000$. The parabola opens downward since the coefficient of $(x - 150)^2$ is negative. Thus, $A = 45{,}000$ is the largest value for A. This implies the maximum area is $A = 45{,}000$ square meters, which occurs when $x = 150$. The dimensions of the rectangle enclosing the maximum area are

$$x = 150 \text{ by } 600 - 2x = 600 - 300 = 300$$

that is,

150 m by 300 m.

Selected Solutions

1. Each graph has the form $y = ax^2$. It can be seen that the larger a is, the fatter the graph gets. See the graphs in the text.

5. If $y = (x - 2)^2$, the vertex is $(2, 0)$, the axis is the line $x = 2$, and it looks like $y = x^2$ shifted over two units to the right.

9. If $y = -2(x + 3)^2 + 2$, the vertex is $(-3, 2)$, it opens down, the axis is the line $x = -3$.

13. If $y = x^2 - 2x + 3$, complete the square to arrive at

$$y = (x^2 - 2x + 1) + 3 - 1$$
$$y = (x - 1)^2 + 2.$$

vertex $(1, 2)$, opens up, axis $x = 1$

17. $y = 2x^2 - 4x + 5$

$y = 2(x^2 - 2x + 1 - 1) + 5$

$y = 2(x^2 - 2x + 1) - 2 + 5$

$y = 2(x - 1)^2 + 3$

vertex (1, 3), axis x = 1, opens up.

21. The graph of $y = -0.9x^2 - 1.8x + .5$
is a parabola opening downward. If
x = 0, y = .5; is x = 1, y = -2.2;
if x = -1, y = 1.4; and if x = -2,
y = .5. See the graph in the text.

25. The parabola $y = -x^2 + 4$ opens
downward, and writing $y - 4 = -x^2$,
we see that the vertex is at the
point (0, 4). This is the highest
point on the graph, so the parabola
is increasing to the left of the
vertex. The interval I = (-∞, 0]
is the interval where the function
is increasing.

29. Solving $f(x) = x^2 + 8x + 13 = 0$.
We use the quadratic formula with
a = 1, b = 8, and c = 13. This gives

$x = \dfrac{-8 \pm \sqrt{8^2 - 4(1)(13)}}{2} = \dfrac{-8 \pm \sqrt{12}}{2}$

$x = \dfrac{-8 \pm 2\sqrt{3}}{2} = -4 \pm \sqrt{3}$.

The x-value of the vertex is half-
way between these numbers $-4 - \sqrt{3}$
and $-4 \pm \sqrt{3}$. The x-value of the
vertex is -4. The axis of the
parabola is the vertical line
x = -4.

33. In solving the inequality
$x^2 + 8x + 13 < 0$,
we note from exercise 29 that
$x^2 + 8x + 13 = 0$ at $r_1 = -4 - \sqrt{3}$
and $r_2 = -4 + \sqrt{3}$. Noting that
$\sqrt{3} \approx 1.73$, $r_1 \approx -5.73$, and $r_2 \approx$
2.27, make the following sign graph.

	r_1	r_2	
----	+++	+++	$x - r_1$
----	---	+++	$x - r_2$

we conclude that

$(x^2 + 8x + 13) = (x - r_1)(x - r_2) < 0$
on the interval
$S = (r_1, r_2) = (-4 - \sqrt{3}, -4 + \sqrt{3})$.

37. Write $f(x) = -(x - 1)^2 - 7$ as
$y + 7 = -(x - 1)^2$. The vertex is
the point V(1, -7). The distance
from V to the origin is

$d = \sqrt{1^2 + (-7)^2} = \sqrt{1 + 49} = \sqrt{50}$,

or $d = 5\sqrt{2}$ units.

41. Write $f(x) = x^2 - 5x + 4$ as
$y = x^2 - 5x + 4$ and complete the
square on x. We have $y - 4 = x^2 - 5x$,
and add $\dfrac{25}{4}$ to both sides to complete
the square. This gives

$y - 4 + \dfrac{25}{4} = x^2 - 5x + \dfrac{25}{4}$

$y + \dfrac{9}{4} = (x - \dfrac{5}{2})^2$.

The vertex is $V(\dfrac{5}{2}, \dfrac{9}{4})$ and the distance
from V to the origin is

$d = \sqrt{(\dfrac{5}{2})^2 + (\dfrac{9}{4})^2} = \sqrt{\dfrac{25}{4} + \dfrac{81}{16}} = \sqrt{\dfrac{181}{16}} = \dfrac{\sqrt{181}}{4}$.

45. We find the vertex of the parabola
$m = 10x - x^2$. The parabola opens
downward so the vertex gives the
largest value of M. We have

$M = -(x^2 - 10x)$

$M = -(x^2 - 10x + 25) + 25$

$M - 25 = -(x - 5)^2$.

The vertex is V(5, 25) and we can
conclude that 5 inches of rainfall
will produce 25 million mosquitoes.

49. If $p = 500 - x$, then

(a) the revenue function is given by $R(x) = px = 500x - x^2$.

(b) If we complete the square, we have

$$R = -(x^2 - 500x)$$

$$R - (250)^2 = -(x^2 - 500x + 250^2)$$

$$R - 62,500 = -(x - 250)^2.$$

The vertex is $V(250, 62,500)$, and from $R = 500x - x^2 = x(500 - x)$ we see that $R = 0$ when $x = 0$ <u>and</u> $x = 500$. See the graph in the text.

(c) From the vertex $V(250, 62,500)$ the price that gives a maximum revenue is $p = 500 - 250 = \$250$,

(d) The maximum revenue is $\$62,500$.

53. The graph of $y = x^2 - 10x + C$ will have exactly one x-intercept if the vertex lies on the x-axis. This will occur if $x^2 - 10x + C$ is a perfect square; that is if $C = 25$. Then

$$y = (x - 5)^2.$$

This is a parabola with vertex at $V(5, 0)$ opening upward.

57. Write $y = ax^2 + bx + C$

$$y - C = a(x^2 + \frac{b}{a}x)$$

$$y - C = a(x^2 + \frac{b}{a}x + \frac{b^2}{4a^2}) - \frac{b^2}{4a}$$

$$y - (\frac{-b^2}{4a} + C) = a(x + \frac{b}{2a})^2$$

$$y - (\frac{-b^2 + 4aC}{4a}) = a(x + \frac{b}{2a})^2.$$

The vertex is $V(-\frac{b}{2a}, \frac{-b^2 + 4ac}{4a})$.

61. (a) The distance from $P(x, y)$ to the line $y = -p$ is the distance from $P(x, y)$ to $Q(x, -p)$. This distance is

$$d_1 = \sqrt{(x - x)^2 + (y + p)^2}$$

$$= \sqrt{(y + p)^2} = |y + p| \text{ or } d_1 = y + p$$

since $y \geq 0$ and $p > 0$ in the given figure.

(b) It is reasonable, since when $x = 0$ the distance to the line is p units.

(c) The distance from $P(x, y)$ to the focus point $F(0, P)$ is

$$d_2 = \sqrt{(x - 0)^2 + (y - p)^2}$$

$$= \sqrt{x^2 + (y - p)^2}$$

If $P(x, y)$ is on the parabola, then $d_1 = d_2$ or

$$(y + p)^2 = x^2 + (y - p)^2$$

$$y^2 + 2py + p^2 = x^2 + y^2 - 2py + p^2$$

or $\qquad 4py = x^2$.

65. If the focus point is $F(8, 0)$ and the directrix is the line $x = -8$, then $d_1 = d_2$ in the figure, we have

$$d_1 = \sqrt{(x+8)^2 + (y-y)^2}$$

$$d_1 = \sqrt{(x + 8)^2}$$

and

$$d_2 = \sqrt{(x-8)^2 + (y-0)^2}$$

$$d_2 = \sqrt{(x - 8)^2 + y^2}.$$

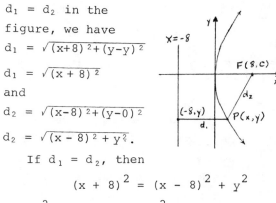

If $d_1 = d_2$, then

$$(x + 8)^2 = (x - 8)^2 + y^2$$

$$x^2 + 16x + 64 = x^2 - 16x + 64 + y^2$$

or $\qquad 32x = y^2$.

69. If $F(3, -4)$ is the focus and $x = 9$ is the directrix, then the distance from F to $P(x, y)$ is

$$d_2 = \sqrt{(x - 3)^2 + (y + 4)^2},$$

and the distance from $P(x, y)$ to the directrix $x = 9$ is

$$d_1 = \sqrt{(x - 9)^2 + (y - y)^2} = \sqrt{(x - 9)^2}.$$

If $d_1 = d_2$, then

$$(x - 3)^2 + (y + 4)^2 = (x - 9)^2$$

$$x^2 - 6x + 9 + (y + 4)^2 = x^2 - 18x + 81$$

$$(y + 4)^2 = -12x + 72$$

or $$(y + 4)^2 = -12(x - 6).$$

73. The parabola $y = -(x - 2)^2 + 9$ is a parabola opening downward. The largest value of y occurs at the vertex. If we write $y - 9 = -(x -)^2$, we see the vertex is (2, 9). Hence, y = 9 is the largest value of y.

(a) The largest possible value for $\sqrt{y}$ is $\sqrt{9} = 3$.

(b) The smallest value for $\frac{1}{y}$ is $\frac{1}{3}$.

Section 4.4   Ellipses and Hyperbolas

Additional Examples

Example 1   Sketch the graph of

$$\frac{(x - 2)^2}{4} - \frac{(y - 1)^2}{16} = 1.$$

Solution   The equation is in the standard form for a hyperbola. The center is the point (2, 1). Sketch horizontal and vertical dotted lines through the center. The asymptote lines are determined by finding the fundamental rectangle

$$\frac{(x - 2)^2}{4} - \frac{(y - 1)^2}{16} = 0$$

$$(x - 2)^2 = \frac{(y - 1)^2}{4}$$

$$(x - 2) = \pm\frac{(y - 1)}{2}.$$

So, if $y - 1 = \pm 2$ ($y = -1$ or 3), then $x - 2 = \pm 1$ ($x = 1$ or 3). The intercepts with the horizontal line $y = 1$ occur when

$$\frac{(x - 2)^2}{4} = 1$$

$$(x - 2)^2 = 4$$

$$x - 2 = \pm 2$$

$$x = 0 \quad \text{or} \quad x = 4.$$

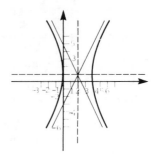

Example 2   Sketch the graph of

$$\frac{y}{5} = -\sqrt{1 + \frac{x^2}{4}}.$$

Solution   We note that $y < 0$ always because y is the negative of the square root of $1 + \frac{x^2}{4}$. Squaring both sides gives

$$\frac{y^2}{25} = 1 + \frac{x^2}{4}$$

$$\frac{y^2}{25} - \frac{x^2}{4} = 1,$$

a hyperbola with center at the origin, y-axis intercepts at $y = \pm 5$, foci on the x-axis, and asymptote lines

$$\frac{y^2}{25} - \frac{x^2}{4} = 0$$

$$y = \pm\frac{5}{2}x.$$

The points (2, 5), (2, -5), (-2, 5), and (-2, -5) are used to get the fundamental rectangle. Note that the graph consists of only the lower portion of the hyperbola. See the graph below.

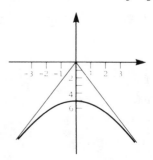

Selected Solutions

1. The equation $\frac{x^2}{9} + \frac{y^2}{4} = 1$ describes an ellipse with intercepts on the x-axis at ± 3 and on the y-axis at ± 2, with center at the origin. See the graph in the answer section of the text.

5. $x^2/6 + y^2/9 = 1$ is an ellipse with x-intercepts at $x = \pm\sqrt{6}$ and y-intercepts at $y = \pm\sqrt{9} = \pm 3$. See final graph in textbook.

9. $x^2 = 9 + y^2$

$x^2 - y^2 = 9$ is a hyperbola with x-axis intercepts at $x = \pm\sqrt{9} = \pm 3$. Note that the graph has no y-axis intercepts. The graph has asymptote lines of

$$x^2 - y^2 = 0$$
$$y^2 = x^2, \text{ or } y = \pm x.$$

See the graph in the textbook.

13. If $25x^2 - 4y^2 = -100$, then

$$\frac{y^2}{25} - \frac{x^2}{4} = 1.$$

This is a hyperbola with y-axis intercepts at ± 5 and having no x-axis intercepts. The asymptote lines are $\frac{y^2}{25} - \frac{x^2}{4} = 0$, or $y = \pm\frac{5}{2}x$.

See the graph in the text.

17. $\frac{64x^2}{9} + \frac{25y^2}{36} = 1$

$\frac{x^2}{(9/64)} + \frac{y^2}{(36/25)} = 1$ is an ellipse with x-intercepts at $x = \pm\sqrt{9/64} = \pm 3/8$ and y-intercepts at $y = \pm\sqrt{36/25} = \pm 6/5$. See final graph in textbook.

21. $\frac{(x - 3)^2}{16} - \frac{(y + 2)^2}{49} = 1$

This is a hyperbola, centered at $(3, -2)$. The asymptotes are

$$\frac{(x - 3)^2}{16} = \frac{(y + 2)^2}{49}$$

or $\quad (y + 2) = \pm\frac{7}{4}(x - 3)$.

That is, $\quad y = \frac{7}{4}x - \frac{29}{4}$

and $\quad y = -\frac{7}{4}x + \frac{13}{4}$.

Note: vertices of the hyperbola are at $(-1, -2)$ and $(7, -2)$. See final graph in textbook.

25. If $\frac{x}{4} = \sqrt{1 - \frac{y^2}{9}}$, then the graph is the right half of the ellipse

$$\frac{x^2}{16} + \frac{y^2}{9} = 1.$$

The graph has an x-axis intercept at $+4$ and y-axis intercepts at ± 3.

29. $x = -\sqrt{1 - \frac{y^2}{64}}$

This is the left half of the ellipse $x^2 = 1 - \frac{y^2}{64}$ or $\frac{x^2}{1} + \frac{y^2}{64} = 1$. x-intercept is $x = -1$, y-intercepts are $y = \pm\sqrt{64} = \pm 8$. See final graph in textbook.

31. Graph $y = -\sqrt{1 + \frac{x^2}{25}}$.

To recognize the graph, square and arrange terms to get

$$y^2 = 1 + \frac{x^2}{25}$$

$$\frac{y^2}{1} - \frac{x^2}{25} = 1,$$

which is a hyperbola centered at $(0, 0)$, having asymptotes $y = \pm\frac{1}{5}x$, and crossing the y-axis at ± 1.

Since $y = -\sqrt{1 + \frac{x^2}{25}}$, we want the lower half of the hyperbola. See final graph in textbook.

33. Given x-intercepts ±4, foci at (±2, 0). The center is the midpoint of the segment joining the foci so that C = (0, 0). The y-intercepts ±b satisfy the equation $b^2 + 2^2 = 4^2$ or $b^2 = 16 - 4 = 12$. The equation is

$$\frac{x^2}{4^2} + \frac{y^2}{b^2} = 1 \text{ or } \frac{x^2}{16} + \frac{y^2}{12} = 1.$$

37. The ellipse with center at (3, -2), a = 5, c = 3, and major axis vertical has the equation

$$\frac{(x - 3)^2}{a^2} + \frac{(y + 2)^2}{b^2} = 1,$$

where b^2 satisfies $a^2 - b^2 = c^2$. Hence, $b^2 = 25 - 9 = 16$, so the equation is

$$\frac{(x - 3)^2}{16} + \frac{(y + 2)^2}{25} = 1.$$

41. The hyperbola with asymptotes $y = \pm\frac{3}{5}x$, y-intercepts (0, 3) and (0, -3), has the equation

$$\frac{y^2}{b^2} - \frac{x^2}{a^2} = 1, \text{ where } b = 3 \text{ and } a = 5.$$

The equation is $\frac{y^2}{9} - \frac{x^2}{25} = 1.$

43. $\frac{x^2}{5013} + \frac{y^2}{4970} = 1$

The widest possible distance across this ellipse is the length of the major axis, or

$2a = 2\sqrt{5,013} \approx 2(70.802)$

≈ 141.6 million miles.

45. The method works because the string is fixed and the points where the string is fixed become the focus points of the ellipse. Every point touched by the pencil as it traces the curve satisfies the definition of an ellipse. The sum of the distances from the point to the two focus points is constant.

49. Consider an ellipse centered at the origin with major axis on the x-axis and focus points at $F_1(-c, 0)$ and $F_2(c, 0)$. If P(x, y) lies on the ellipse, then

$d(P, F_1) + d(P, F_2) = $ constant, say 2a. See the figure.

We have

$d(P, F_1) = \sqrt{(x + c)^2 + y^2}$

$d(P, F_2) = \sqrt{(x - c)^2 + y^2}.$

Then $d(P, F_1) + d(P, F_2) = 2a$

$(\sqrt{(x - c)^2 + y^2})^2 = (2a - \sqrt{(x+c)^2 + y^2})^2$

$x^2 - 2cx + c^2 + y^2 = 4a^2 - 4a\sqrt{(x+c)^2 + y^2} + x^2 + 2cx + c^2 + y^2$

$a\sqrt{(x + c)^2 + y^2} = a^2 + cx,$

$a^2(x^2 + 2cx + c^2 + y^2) = a^4 + 2a^2cx + c^2x^2,$

$x^2(a^2 - c^2) + a^2y^2 = a^2(a^2 - c^2),$

$$\frac{x^2}{a^2} + \frac{y^2}{a^2 - c^2} = 1.$$

We have a > c, so we let $a^2 - c^2 = b^2 > 0$ and write $\frac{x^2}{a^2} + \frac{y^2}{b^2} = 1.$

Section 4.5   Conic Sections

Additional Examples

Example 1   Sketch the graph of

$4y^2 + x - 8y = 3.$

Solution   We rewrite the equation as

$x - 3 = -4y^2 + 8y$

$x - 3 = -4(y^2 - 2y)$

$x - 3 - 4 = -4(y^2 - 2y + 1)$,

adding -4 to both sides,

$x - 7 = -4(y - 1)^2$.

The graph is a parabola with a horizontal axis, passing through the vertex located at the point (7, 1), and opening to the left. The horizontal axis is the line $y = 1$. Additional points to determine the shape are given below.

$x = -4y^2 + 8y + 3$

y	0	2
x	3	3

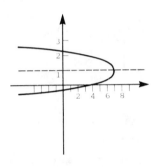

Example 2   Discuss and sketch the graph having the equation

$4x^2 - 16x - 25y^2 + 250y - 509 = 0$.

Solution   First place the equation in standard form by groups terms.

$4x^2 - 16x - 25y^2 + 250y = 509$

$4(x^2 - 4x + \underline{}) - 25(y^2 - 10y + \underline{}) = 509$

$4(x^2 - 4x + 4) - 25(y^2 - 10y + 25) = 509 + 16 - 625$

$4(x - 2)^2 - 25(y - 5)^2 = -100$

$\dfrac{(y - 5)^2}{4} - \dfrac{(x - 2)^2}{25} = 1$,

dividing by -100.

This is a hyperbola centered at (2, 5), opening upward and downward, symmetric with respect to the vertical line $x = 2$, and intercepting the line $x = 2$ when

$\dfrac{(y - 5)^2}{4} - 0 = 1$,

or $(y - 5)^2 = 4$

$y - 5 = \pm 2$

$y = 3 \text{ or } 7$.

The asymptote lines are

$\dfrac{(y - 5)^2}{4} - \dfrac{(x - 2)^2}{25} = 0$

or $y - 5 = \pm\dfrac{2}{5}(x - 2)$.

Letting $x = -3$ and 7, the fundamental rectangle has vertices (-3, 3), (-3, 7), (7, 3), (7, 7).

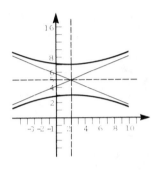

Selected Solutions

1. Write $x = y^2 + 2$ as $x - 2 = y^2$. This is the standard form for a parabola with vertex at V(2, 0), and the graph is the graph of $x = y^2$ shifted to the right two units.

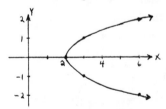

Note that when $x = 3$, $y^2 = 1$ or $y = \pm 1$.

5. Write $x = (y + 2)^2 - 1$ as $(x + 1) = (y + 2)^2$. This is a parabola opening to the right with vertex at V(-1, -2). The graph is the graph of $x = y^2$ shifted downward 2 units and to the left 1 unit. See the text for a graph.

9. Write $x = \frac{1}{2}(y + 1)^2 + 3$ as

   $(x - 3) = \frac{1}{2}(y + 1)^2$. This is a parabola opening to the right with vertex at V(3, -1). The graph is the graph of $x = \frac{1}{2}y^2$ shifted to the right 3 units and downward 1 unit. See the text for a graph.

13. Write $x = -2y^2 + 2y - 3$ as

   $x + 3 = -2(y^2 - y)$.

   We need $y^2 - y + (\frac{-1}{2})^2$ to complete the square, so we add $-2(\frac{-1}{2})^2 = -\frac{1}{2}$ to both sides, giving

   $x + 3 - \frac{1}{2} = -2(y^2 - y) - \frac{1}{2}$

   $x + \frac{5}{2} = -2(y^2 - y + \frac{1}{4})$

   $x + \frac{5}{2} = -2(y - \frac{1}{2})^2$.

   This is a parabola opening to the left with vertex at V($-\frac{5}{2}$, $\frac{1}{2}$).

   The graph is the graph of $x = -2y^2$ shifted to the left $\frac{5}{2}$ units and upward $\frac{1}{2}$ unit. See the text for a graph.

17. The graph of $\frac{x^2}{4} - \frac{y^2}{4} = 1$ is a hyperbola centered at the origin with x-axis intercepts at $x = \pm 4$ and no y-axis intercepts. The asymptote lines are when $\frac{x^2}{4} - \frac{y^2}{4} = 0$, or $y = \pm x$. See the final graph in the text.

21. Write $x^2 = 25 + y^2$ as

   $x^2 - y^2 = 25$

   $\frac{x^2}{25} - \frac{y^2}{25} = 1$.

   This is a hyperbola centered at (0, 0), with asymptote lines

$x^2/25 = y^2/25$, or $y = \pm x$. The x-intercepts are at $x = \pm 5$. See the final graph in textbook.

25. For $\frac{(x + 3)^2}{16} + \frac{(y - 2)^2}{16} = 1$,

   this is a circle of radius 4 and center at (-3, 2). See final graph in textbook.

29. If $(x + 7)^2 + (y - 5)^2 + 4 = 0$, then

   $(x + 7)^2 + (y - 5)^2 = -4$—the sum of two squares negative? This is an impossible equation; no graph.

33. If $x^2 - 6x + y = 0$ or $y = -x^2 + 6x$, then

   $y = -(x^2 - 6x + 9) + 9$ complete square on x

   or $y - 9 = -(x - 3)^2$.

   This is a parabola with vertex at the point (3, 9), and it opens downward. Note the intercepts at $x = 0$ and $x = 6$. See final graph in textbook.

37. If $4x^2 - 8x + 9y^2 + 54y = -84$, then

   $4(x^2 - 2x) + 9(y^2 + 6y) = -84$

   $4(x^2 - 2x + 1) + 9(y^2 + 6y + 9) = -84 + 4 + 81$

   $4(x - 1)^2 + 9(y + 3)^2 = 1$

   $\frac{(x - 1)^2}{1/4} + \frac{(y + 3)^2}{1/9} = 1$.

   This is an ellipse with center at (1, -3), a = 1/2, b = 1/3. See final graph in textbook.

Section 4.6   Graphs of Polynomial
                Functions

Additional Examples

Example 1   Sketch the graph of $y = x^3$,
    and make a rough sketch of the fol-
    lowing graphs by discussing the
    comparison to $y = x^3$.

        (i) $y = (x - 4)^3$

        (ii) $y = (x + 4)^3$

        (iii) $y = x^3 + 2$

        (iv) $y = 3x^3$

        (v) $y = -\frac{1}{5}x^3$

        (vi) $y = a(x + b)^3 + c$, a, b, c
                real numbers, $a \neq 0$.

Solution   The graph of $y = x^3$ is dis-
    cussed in the text, and a list of
    several points should be sufficient
    to sketch the graph.

x	-4	-2	-1	0	1	2	4
y	-64	-8	-1	0	1	8	64

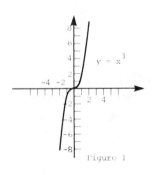

Figure 1

In discussing comparisons to the
other graphs the reader may wish to
plot several points in order to be
convinced regarding the conclusions.

    (i)   The graph of $y = (x - 4)^3$
is a graph having the identical
shape of $y = x^3$ but shifted horizontally +4 units. Note that letting x = 4 gives y = 0.

(See Figure 2)

    (ii) The graph of $y = (x + 4)^3$ is
identical to $y = x^3$ but shifted
horizontally -4 units (or 4 units
to the left). Note that x = -4
gives y = 0. (See Figure 2)

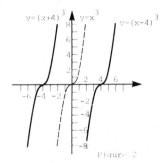

Figure 2

(iii) The graph of $y = x^3 + 3$ is
identical to the graph of $y = x^3$ but
shifted vertically +3 units (upward
3 units). Note that x = 0 gives
y = 3. Each point on $y = x^3$ is
elevated 3 units.   (See Figure 3)

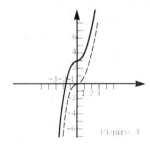

Figure 3

    (iv) The graph of $y = 3x^3$ rises
more rapidly than $y = x^3$. When
x = 2, $x^3 = 8$, but $3x^3 = 24$. The
graph appears narrow compared to
$y = x^3$. The coefficient 3 acts as
a "stretching" factor. (See Figure 4.)

    (v)   The graph of $y = -\frac{1}{5}x^3$ has a
stretching factor of -1/5. The negative sign inverts the graph and the
1/5 makes the graph rise less rapidly,
thereby giving the graph a fatter
appearance. (See Figure 4)

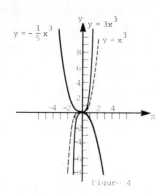

Figure 4

(vi)   Considering $y = a(x + b)^3 + c$, we conclude that if $a > 0$ the shape will be comparable to $y = x^3$, while $a < 0$ means the graph will be inverted. a will serve as a stretching factor, making the graph appear fatter if $|a| < 1$ and narrower if $|a| > 1$. The number b indicates a horizontal shift of $|b|$ units. If $b < 0$, the shift is $|b|$ units to the right, while $b > 0$ indicates a shift of b units to the left. The number c indicates a vertical shift of $|c|$ units, upward if $c > 0$ and downward if $c < 0$.

Example 2   Graph the polynomial function

$$f(x) = (x^2 - 1)(x^2 - 9).$$

Solution   We can factor f to arrive at $f(x) = (x + 1)(x - 1)(x + 3)(x - 3)$. Make a sign graph by marking the zeros -3, -1, 1, 3 of f and test numbers in each of the subdivisions $(-\infty, -3)$, $(-3, -1)$, $(-1, 1)$, $(1, 3)$, and $(3, +\infty)$ as to determine where f is positive and negative.

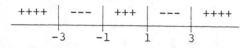

The table below gives the results.

x	-5	-2	0	2	4
y	384	-15	9	-15	105

For example, we calculate

$$f(-5) = (-5 + 1)(-5 - 1)(-5 + 3)(-5 - 3)$$
$$= (-4)(-6(-2)(-8)$$
$$= +384,$$
$$f(-2) = (-1)(-3)(1)(-5)$$
$$= -15, \text{ etc.}$$

The points in the table not only determine where f is positive and negative according to the sign graph, but they are points on the graph. Even though we will not plot the points $(-5, 384)$ and $(4, 105)$ because of their magnitude, these points will indicate how steeply the graph is changing. Also, note the zeros at -3, -1, 1, and 3.

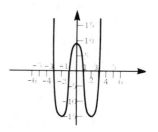

Selected Solutions

   The graphs are shown in your text for 1-27.

1. $f(x) = \frac{1}{4}x^6$

   Symmetric about y-axis since $f(-x) \equiv f(x)$.

5. $f(x) = \frac{1}{2}x^3 + 1$, or $(y - 1) = \frac{1}{2}x^3$, is symmetric about $(0, 1)$ since $y = x^3$ is symmetric about $(0, 0)$.

9. $f(x) = (x - 1)^4 + 2$, or $(y - 2) = (x - 1)^4$ is symmetric about the line $x = 1$ since $y = x^4$ is symmetric about the y-axis, or $x = 0$.

13. $f(x) = x^2(x - 2)(x + 3)^2$

The x-intercepts are 0, 2, -3.

  The intercepts divide the graph into four regions. Find the intervals where the function is positive (above the x-axis) or negative (below the x-axis) by substituting a point from each region into the equation.

region	sign of y-value	location of graph
$(-\infty, -3)$	–	below x-axis
$(-3, 0)$	–	below x-axis
$(0, 2)$	–	below x-axis
$(2, +\infty)$	+	above x-axis

17. If $f(x) = 3x^4 + 5x^3 - 2x^2$, we write

$f(x) = x^2(3x^2 + 5x - 2)$

$\qquad = x^2(3x - 1)(x + 2).$

The x-axis intercepts are

$\qquad x = 0, \frac{1}{3}, -2.$ We can make a

table as in #13 or an alternative (so you can make a choice of the method you wish to use) is to make a "sign graph" for f. This is accomplished by drawing a number line, marking the x-axis intercepts, then testing numbers in the open intervals by plugging into f.

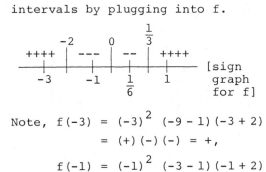

Note, $f(-3) = (-3)^2 (-9 - 1)(-3 + 2)$

$\qquad = (+)(-)(-) = +,$

$\quad f(-1) = (-1)^2 (-3 - 1)(-1 + 2)$

$\qquad = (+)(-)(+) = -,$

$\quad f(\frac{1}{6}) = (+)(-)(+) = -,$

$\quad f(1) = +$

See the graph in the text.

19. This is included to be compared to exercises 13 and 17. It is done both ways that were explained in 13 and 17.

If $f(x) = 2x^3(x^2 - 4)(x - 1)$, then

$\quad f(x) = 2x^3(x - 2)(x + 2)(x - 1).$

The x-intercepts are 0, 2, -2, 1. They divide the graph into 4 regions. Find the intervals where the function is positive (above the x-axis) or negative (below the x-axis) by substituting a point from each region into the equation.

region	sign of y-value	location of graph
$(-\infty, -2)$	+	above x-axis
$(-2, 0)$	–	below x-axis
$(0, 1)$	+	above x-axis
$(1, 2)$	–	below x-axis
$(2, +\infty)$	+	above x-axis

<u>alternatively</u>, draw a number line and "test" the intervals.

```
        -2    0     1     2
   ++++  |  --- |  ++ |  -- |  +++
  ───┼───────┼─────┼─────┼───── [sign
    -3     -1    1     3    3     graph
                 ─     ─           of f]
                 2     2
```

$f(-3) = (-)(-)(-)(-);$

$f(-1) = (-)(-)(+)(-) = -;$

$f(\frac{1}{2}) = (+)(-)(+)(-) = +$ etc.

See the graph in the text.

21. If $f(x) = x^4 - 4x^2$, then

$\quad f(x) = x^2(x + 2)(x - 2).$

the sign graph for f gives

```
        -2    0     2
   +++  |  --- |  --- |  +++
  ───┼───────┼─────┼───── [sign graph
    -3     -1    1     3    of f]
```

since $f(-3) = (+)(-)(-) = +;$

$\qquad f(-1) = (+)(+)(-) = -,$

$\qquad f(1) = (+)(+)(-) = -,$

and $\quad f(3) = (+)(+)(+) = +.$

See the graph in the text.

25. $A(x) = -.015x^3 + 1.058x$ for $0 \le x \le 8$

(a)

x	0	1	2	3	4
A(x)	0	1.043	1.996	2.769	3.272

x	5	6	7	8
A(x)	3.415	3.108	2.261	0.784

See final graph in textbook.

(b)   About 5 hours

(c)   Between about 1 and 7 hours

We want $A(x) > 1.5$ because A measures tenths of a percent.

29.   If $f(x) = 2x^3$, then

$$f(-x) = 2(-x)^3 = -2x^3 = -f(x).$$

Hence, f is an odd function. Note that x is raised to an odd power.

33.   If $f(x) = -x^5$, then $f(-x) = -(-x)^5$ $= -f(x)$. This implies that f is an odd function. Note that f has x raised only to odd powers.

37.   If $f(x) = x^4 + 3x^2 + 5$, then

$$f(-x) = (-x)^4 + 3(-x)^2 + 5$$

$$= x^4 + 3x^2 + 5 = f(x).$$

This implies that f is an even function. Note that f contains only even powers of x.

41.   For $y = x^3 + 4x^2 - 8x - 8$ we let $x = -3.8, -3.7, -3.6, -3.5, -3.4, -3.3, -3.2, -3.1,$ and -3, and find the y-value for each x. We do this in a table and round off the y-value to 3 decimals. Note that it may be simpler to calculate y as

$$y = (x^2 + 4x - 8)x - 8$$

$$= [(x + 4)x - 8]x - 8.$$

x	-3.8	-3.7	-3.6	-3.5
y	25.288	25.707	25.984	26.125

-3.4	-3.3	-3.2	-3.1	-3
26.136	26.023	25.792	25.449	25

Hence, an approximate maximum value is 26.136, which occurs when x = -3.4. an apparent minimum value is 25, which occurs at x = -3.

43.   This is included to give another example and to incorporate a system that can make the operations with a calculator more efficient

Consider $y = 2x^3 - 5x^2 - x + 1$, when x is in [-1, 0].

x	-1	-.9	-.8	-.7	-.5
y	-5	-3.608	-2.424	-1.436	0

x	-.4	-.3	-.2	-.1	0
y	0.472	0.796	0.984	1.048	1

Note: Using a calculator the following system may facilitate the computations:

$$2x^3 - 5x^2 - x + 1 = (2x^2 - 5x - 1)x + 1$$

$$= [(2x - 5)x - 1]x + 1.$$

Then for x = -.9, find $2(-.9) - 5$, multiply by (-.9), subtract 1, multiply by (-.9), then add 1 to get $f(-.9) = -3.608$.

The approximate minimum value is -5.
The approximate maximum value is 1.048.

45.   Using $y = x^4 - 7x^3 + 13x^2 + 6x - 28$, and for calculator purposes we write

$$y = (x^3 - 7x^2 + 13x + 6)x - 28$$

$$= [(x^2 - 7x + 13)x + 6]x - 28$$

$$y = ([x - 7)x + 13]x + 6)x - 28.$$

Then to calculate y at x = -1.9 on a calculator we input -1.9, subtract 7 [we now have x - 7], multiply by -1.9, add 13 [we now have $(x - 7) \cdot x + 13$], multiply by -1.9, add 6 [you can see what we have now], multiply by -1.9, and subtract 28. Using this technique we can fill out the following table.

x	-2.0	-1.9	-1.8	-1.7	-1.6
y	84	68.58	54.64	42.11	30.90

-1.5	-1.4	-1.3	-1.2	-1.1	-1
20.94	12.13	4.41	-2.31	-8.09	-13

The maximum value seems to be 84, and occurs at x = -2. The minimum value seems to be -13, and occurs at x = -1.

Section 4.7   Rational Functions

Additional Examples

Example 1   Graph
$$f(x) = \frac{3x - 1}{x^2 - 9}.$$

Solution   Factoring the denominator gives
$$f(x) = \frac{3x - 1}{(x - 3)(x + 3)}.$$

We can observe the following:

(i) Since the substitution of the numbers 3 and -3 for x cause a division by zero in f, the lines x = 3 and x = -3 are vertical asymptote lines.

(ii) $\frac{3x - 1}{x^2 - 9} \to 0$ as $|x| \to +\infty$, so y = 0 is a horizontal asymptote.

(iii) 3x - 1 = 0 when x = 1/3 so that f(1/3) = 0.

(iv) Some points on the graph are given below.

x	-6	-4	-2	0	2	4	6
y	-19/27	-13/7	7/5	1/9	-1	11/7	17/27

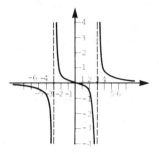

Example 2   Graph $f(x) = \dfrac{x^2 - 9}{x^2 - 1}$.

Solution   Factoring f gives
$$f(x) = \frac{(x + 3)(x - 3)}{(x + 1)(x - 1)}.$$

In this form we can observe that the graph of f will have vertical asymptote lines of x = -1 and x = 1. The graph will have x-axis intercepts at ±3 since f(-3) = 0 and f(3) = 0. The y-axis intercept is at 9 since f(0) = 9. The line y = 1 is a horizontal asymptote since
$$\frac{x^2 - 9}{x^2 - 1} \to 1 \text{ as } |x| \to +\infty.$$

Additional points are below.

x	±5	±2	±1/2
y	2/3	-5/3	35/3

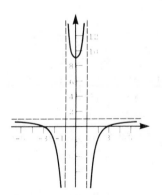

Selected Solutions

1. For the function $f(x) = \frac{2}{x - 5}$, we see that $x = 5$ is not in the domain since substitution of $x = 5$ makes the denominator zero. Hence, the graph has a <u>vertical asymptote line</u> of $x = 5$. We see that as $|x| \to \infty$, that is letting either $x \to -\infty$ or $x \to +\infty$, we have $\frac{2}{x - 5} \to 0$. Hence, the line $y = 0$ is a <u>horizontal asymptote line</u>.

5. We can write $f(x) = \frac{2 - x}{x + 2}$ as $f(x) = -1 + \frac{4}{x + 2}$, by ordinary long division. We see that the vertical line $x = -2$ is a <u>vertical asymptote line</u>, and since $\frac{4}{x + 2} \to 0$ as $|x| \to \infty$, we see that $y = -1$ is a <u>horizontal asymptote line</u>.

9. We write
$$f(x) = \frac{2}{x^2 - 4x - 3} = \frac{2}{(x - 1)(x - 3)}$$
and we see that the vertical lines $x = 1$ and $x = 3$ are <u>vertical asymptote lines</u>. Also, since $\frac{2}{(x - 1)(x - 3)} \to 0$ as $|x| \to \infty$, the horizontal line $y = 0$ is a <u>horizontal asymptote line</u>.

13. If $f(x) = \frac{(x - 3)(x + 1)}{(x + 2)(2x - 5)}$, then we see that the numbers making the denominator zero are -2 and $\frac{5}{2}$. Hence, the vertical lines $x = -2$ and $x = \frac{5}{2}$ are <u>vertical asymptote lines</u>. It can be realized that as $|x| \to \infty$, the terms in the numerator and denominator of f having the largest degree are the <u>only</u> terms that need to be considered.

These terms in $f(x) = \frac{(x - 3)(x + 1)}{(x + 2)(2x - 5)}$ are $\frac{x^2}{2x^2} = \frac{1}{2}$. That is, as $|x| \to \infty$, $f(x) \to \frac{1}{2}$. Hence, $y = \frac{1}{2}$ is a <u>horizontal asymptote line</u>.

17. See the graphs in the answer section of the text.

(a) The graph of $f(x) = \frac{1}{(x - 3)^2}$ has a vertical asymptote line $x = 3$. The graph is identical to $y = \frac{1}{x^2}$ shifted to the right 3 units.

(b) The graph of $f(x) = \frac{-2}{x^2}$ can be obtained by multiplying each y-value in the graph of $y = \frac{1}{x^2}$ by -2. The factor -2 inverts the graph and stretches the graph.

(c) Similarly, the graph of $f(x) = \frac{-2}{(x - 3)^2}$ is the graph of $y = \frac{-2}{x^2}$ shifted three units to the right.

21. The graph of $f(x) = \frac{3x}{(x + 1)(x - 2)}$ has vertical asymptote lines of $x = -1$ and $x = 2$. The degree of the denominator is one larger than the degree of the numerator so $f(x) \to 0$ as $|x| \to \infty$. Hence, $y = 0$ is a horizontal asymptote line. The final graph is in the text. Note that $f(0) = 0$.

25. The graph of $f(x) = \frac{3x}{x - 1}$ has a vertical asymptote of the vertical line $x = 1$ and a horizontal asymptote of the horizontal line $y = 3$. Note that $f(0) = 0$, so the graph intersects the x-axis at $x = 0$. See the final graph in the text.

25. The graph of $f(x) = \frac{x-5}{x+3}$ has the vertical asymptote line $x = -3$, the horizontal asymptote line $y = 1$ (since $\frac{x-5}{x+3} \to 1$ as $|x| \to \infty$), and intercepts the x-axis when $x = 5$ (since $f(5) = 0$). The final graph is in the text.

33. We can write $f(x) = \frac{x^2 - 3x + 2}{x - 3}$ in two different ways to gain valuable information. We can write

$$\frac{x^2 - 3x + 2}{x - 3} = \frac{(x-2)(x-1)}{x-3},$$

and by long division

$$\frac{x^2 - 3x + 2}{x - 3} = x + \frac{2}{x-3}.$$

We conclude that the vertical line $x = 3$ is a vertical asymptote line to the graph, the x-axis intercepts occur at $x = 1$ and $x = 2$, and since $\frac{3}{x-3} \to 0$ as $|x| \to \infty$, then for $|x|$ large the graph approaches the graph of $y = x$. The final graph is in the text.

37. We write $f(x) = \frac{x^2 + 2x}{2x - 1} = \frac{x(x+2)}{2x-1}$ or $\frac{x(x+2)}{2\left(x - \frac{1}{2}\right)}$. From this we can conclude that the graph has the vertical line $x = \frac{1}{2}$ as a vertical asymptote, the graph intersects the x-axis when $x = -2$ and $x = 0$. Also, when $|x|$ is large the graph approaches the graph $y = \frac{x}{2}$ since $\frac{x+2}{x - \frac{1}{2}} \to 1$ as $|x| \to \infty$. See the graph in the text.

41. The graph of $f(x) = \frac{(x-5)(x-2)}{x^2 + 9}$ has no vertical asymptotes since $x^2 + 9$ is never zero. The graph has x-axis intercepts at $x = 2$ and

$x = 5$. Also since

$$\frac{(x-5)(x-2)}{x^2 + 9} = \frac{x^2 - 7 + 10}{x^2 + 9}$$

acts like $\frac{x^2}{x^2} = 1$ as $|x| \to \infty$, the horizontal line $y = 1$ is a horizontal asymptote line for the graph, we can also note that since $x^2 + 9 > 0$ for all x, the sign graph for $(x-5)(x-2)$ is as shown below.

$$+++ \;|\; ---- \;|\; +++ \qquad (x-5)(x-2)$$

with marks at 2 and 5.

Thus, the graph lies above the x-axis for $x \in (-\infty, 2) \cup (5, \infty)$ and below for $x \in (2, 5)$. See the graph in the text.

45. The graph $f(x) = \frac{(2x-3)(x-4)}{x-4}$ is the same as the graph of $y = 2x - 3$ except when $x = 4$. f is not defined at $x = 4$. The graph is in the text.

49. (a) If $y = \frac{110,000}{x + 225}$, then we have the following table:

x	25	50	100	200	300	400
y	440	400	338.46	258.82	209.52	176

(b) The graph is in the text.

53. If $y(x) = \frac{80x - 8000}{x - 110} = \frac{80(x - 100)}{x - 110}$, then:

(a) $y(55) = \frac{80(-45)}{(-55)} = \frac{80(9)}{11} = \frac{720}{11}$

$= 65.4\overline{54}...$

Rounded off to the nearest 10 million, $y = \$655,000,000$.

(b) $y(60) = \frac{80(-40)}{-50} = \frac{80(4)}{5} = 64$, or $\$640$ million.

(c) $y(70) = \frac{80(-30)}{-40} = 60$, or $\$600$ million.

(d) $y(90) = \dfrac{80(-10)}{-20} = 40$, or

$400 million.

(e) $y(100) = \dfrac{80(0)}{-10} = 0$.

(f) See the graph in the text.

Chapter 4 Review Exercises

Selected Solutions

1. If $P(8, 7)$, $Q(\tfrac{1}{2}, -2)$, then

$m = \dfrac{7 - (-2)}{8 - \tfrac{1}{2}} = \dfrac{7 + 2}{\tfrac{16}{2} - \tfrac{1}{2}} = \dfrac{9}{\tfrac{15}{2}}$

$= 9 \cdot \dfrac{2}{15} = \dfrac{6}{5}$.

5. If $9x - 4y = 2$, then we solve for y and the coefficient of x is the slope $(y = mx + b)$. We have
$9x - 4y = 2$

$-4y = -9x + 2$

$y = \dfrac{9}{4}x - \dfrac{1}{2}$.

Thus, $m = \dfrac{9}{4}$.

9. If $y + 6 = 0$, then $y = -6$. The coefficient of x is 0. Hence, the slope is $m = 0$.

13. Writing $3y = x$ as $y = \tfrac{1}{3}x$ we can graph a line by plotting two points.

x	0	3
y	0	1

See the graph in the text.

17. If $P(-2, 4)$, $Q(1, 3)$, then

$m = \dfrac{4 - 3}{-2 - 1} = -\dfrac{1}{3}$, so the equation of the line is

$y - 3 = -\dfrac{1}{3}(x - 1)$

$3y - 9 = -x + 1$, or

$x + 3y = 10$.

21. Given $P(\tfrac{1}{5}, \tfrac{1}{3})$ and $m = -\tfrac{1}{2}$, the equation is

$y - \dfrac{1}{3} = -\dfrac{1}{2}(x - \dfrac{1}{5})$ and multiplication by 30 gives

$30y - 10 = -15(x - \dfrac{1}{5})$

$30y - 10 = -15x + 3$, or

$15x + 30y = 13$.

25. The line $8x + 5y = 3$ has slope $m = -\dfrac{8}{5}$, so the desired line has a slope of $m = \dfrac{5}{8}$. If the line passes through $(0, 5)$, then the equation is

$y - 5 = \dfrac{5}{8}(x - 0)$

$8y - 40 = 5x$, or

$5x - 8y = 40$.

29. We need only two points to graph a line. We are given $P(2, -4)$. Since the slope is $m = \dfrac{3}{4}$, then for every 3 units added to y, we add 4 to x. Hence, $Q(2 + 4, -4 + 3) = Q(6, -1)$ is a second point on the line. See the graph in the text.

33. $y = \begin{cases} 3x + 1 & \text{if } x < 2 \\ -x + 4 & \text{if } x \geq 2 \end{cases}$

If $x < 2$,   If $x \geq 2$,
$y = 3x + 1$. $y = -x + 4$.

x	y
0	1
1	4

x	y
2	2
4	0

as $x \to 2$ | $y \to 7$

See final graph in textbook.

37. Write $y = 3(x+1)^2 - 5$ as $y + 5 = 3(x+1)^2$. This is a parabola with vertex $(-1, -5)$ opening upward. The axis is the line $x = -1$. To find the x-intercepts let $y = 0$ and solve.

$$5 = 3(x+1)^2$$
$$(x+1) = \pm\sqrt{\frac{5}{3}}$$
$$x = -1 \pm \frac{\sqrt{15}}{3},$$

or $x \approx -2.29$ and $x \approx 0.29$.
See final graph in textbook.

41. Write $y = -(x+3)^2 - 9$ as $y + 9 = -(x+3)^2$. The vertex is $(-3, -9)$ and the axis is the line $x = -3$.

45. If $y = -3x^2 - 6x + 1$, then

$$y = -3(x^2 + 2x) + 1$$
$$y = -3(x^2 + 2x + 1) + 1 + 3$$
completing the square
$$y = -3(x+1)^2 + 4, \text{ or }$$
$$y - 4 = -3(x+1)^2.$$

The vertex is $(-1, 4)$ and the axis is the line $x = -1$.

47. Let x be one number. The second number is $11 - x$. We wish to maximize the product $y = x(11 - x)$.

$$y = -x^2 + 11x$$
$$y = -(x^2 - 11x + \frac{121}{4}) + \frac{121}{4}$$
complete the square
$$y - \frac{121}{4} = -(x - \frac{11}{2})^2$$

This is a parabola opening downward with vertex $(11/2, 121/4)$. The maximum value of the product y is $121/4$ and is found when $x = 11/2$. The two numbers are $11/2$ and $11 - 11/2 = 11/2$.

49. 180 meters of fence is given. See the figure.

The area is given by
$$A = x(\frac{180 - 2x}{2}) = x(90 - x)$$
$$= 90x - x^2$$
$$A = -(x^2 - 90x)$$
$$A = -(x^2 - 90x + 2025) + 2025,$$
since
$$(\frac{90}{2})^2 = 45^2 = 2025.$$
Hence
$A - 2025 = -(x - 45)^2$, a parabola opening downward, vertex $(45, 2025)$. The maximum area is $2025m^2$ and the dimensions of the rectangle are 45 x 45.

53. The graph of $\frac{x^2}{4} - \frac{y^2}{9} = 1$ is a hyperbola centered at $(0, 0)$ with x-intercepts at $x = \pm 2$, and asymptote lines
$$\frac{x^2}{4} = \frac{y^2}{9} \text{ or } y = \pm\frac{3}{2}x.$$
See final graph in textbook.

57. Write $\frac{25x^2}{9} + \frac{4y^2}{25} = 1$ as

$$\frac{x^2}{9/25} + \frac{y^2}{25/4} = 1.$$

This is an ellipse with center at $(0, 0)$ and intercepts $x = \pm 3/5$ and $y = \pm 5/2$. See final graph in textbook.

61. $$\frac{(y+2)^2}{4} - \frac{(x+3)^2}{9} = 1$$

This is a hyperbola centered at $(-3, -2)$ with asymptotes

$$\frac{(y + 2)^2}{4} = \frac{(x + 3)^2}{9} \text{ or}$$

$$y + 2 = \pm\frac{2}{3}(x + 3).$$

The vertices occur when $x = -3$ and

$$\frac{(y + 2)^2}{4} = 1$$

$$(y + 2)^2 = 4$$

$$y + 2 = \pm 2$$

$$y = 0, -4.$$

See final graph in textbook.

65. $y = -\sqrt{1 - \frac{x^2}{25}}$ is the <u>lower half</u> of

$y^2 = 1 - \frac{x^2}{25}$, or $\frac{x^2}{25} + \frac{y^2}{1} = 1$,

which is an ellipse with center at
(0, 0), and intercepts $x = \pm 5$ and
$y = \pm 1$. See final graph in textbook.

69.   If $f(x) = x^2(2x + 1)(x - 2)$, the
x-axis intercepts are at $x = 0$,
$x = -\frac{1}{2}$, and $x = 2$. Making a sign
graph for f gives the following.

A table gives some points on the
graph.

x	-2	-1	$-\frac{1}{4}$	1	3
y	80	3	$\frac{-7}{128}$	-3	63

See the graph in the text.

73.   The graph of $f(x) = \frac{8}{x}$ has a vertical
asymptote line $x = 0$, and since
$\frac{8}{x} \to 0$ as $|x| \to \infty$, the line $y = 0$
is a horizontal asymptote. A table
gives some points.

x	-16	-8	-1	1	8	16
y	$-\frac{1}{2}$	-1	-8	8	1	$\frac{1}{2}$

See the text for the graph.

77.   We write $f(x) = \frac{2x}{x^2 - 1} = \frac{2x}{(x + 1)(x - 1)}$.
The vertical lines $x = -1$ and $x = 1$
are vertical asymptotes. Since
$\frac{2x}{x^2 - 1} \to 0$ as $|x| \to \infty$, the line $y = 0$
is a horizontal asymptote line.
The x-axis intercept occurs at $x = 0$,
since $f(0) = 0$. Additional points
are given in the table

x	-3	-2	$-\frac{1}{2}$	$\frac{1}{2}$	2	3
y	$-\frac{3}{4}$	$-\frac{4}{3}$	$\frac{4}{3}$	$-\frac{4}{3}$	$\frac{4}{3}$	$\frac{3}{4}$

See the graph in the text.

81.   The center of the circle $(x - 4)^2 +$
$(y + 2)^2 = 9$ is $P(4, -2)$. If $m = \frac{2}{3}$,
the equation of the line

$$y + 2 = \frac{2}{3}(x - 4)$$

$$3y + 6 = 2x - 8, \text{ or}$$

$$2x - 3y = 14.$$

85.   Let $A(0, 7)$ and $B(12, 12)$ be vertices
of a square. If AB is a side, we
find that $M_{AB} = \frac{12 - 7}{12 - 0} = \frac{5}{12}$. Thus,
the adjacent sides have slope $\frac{-12}{5}$.
Let C be on the line perpendicular
to AB through A and $C = C(0 + 5, 7 - 12)$
$= C(5, -5)$. Find D from B in the
same fashion; $D(12 + 5, 12 - 12) =$
$D(17, 0)$. The vertices A, B, C, D
form a square. Also, finding E and
F above the line AB gives
$E(0 - 5, 7 + 12) = E(-5, 19)$ and
$F(12 - 5, 12 + 12) = F(7, 24)$. Then
A, B, E, F form a square.

Then, suppose AB is a diagonal.
There is one square having this
property.   The midpoint of AB is

$$M\left(\frac{0 + 12}{2},\ \frac{7 + 12}{2}\right) = M\left(6,\ \frac{19}{2}\right).$$

Since the medians of a square are
perpendicular bisectors, then the
other vertices are on the line perpendicular to AB passing through M
and 13 units apart.   These points

are $G\left(\frac{17}{2},\ \frac{7}{2}\right)$ and $H\left(\frac{7}{2},\ \frac{13}{2}\right).$

Chapter 4   Test

1. Determine the equation of the line passing through the points (6, -5) and (3, 2).

2. Determine the slope of the line   3. Graph the line 2x + 5y = 10.
   3x + 4y = 7.

4. Determine the equation of the line passing through (1, 2) and parallel to the line passing through the points (1, 5) and (5, 8).

5. Determine the equation of the line intersecting the x-axis at x = 4 and parallel to the line 2x + y = 6.

6. Determine the equation of the line through (1, 2) which is perpendicular to the line x - 3y = 7.

7. Graph $y = \begin{cases} 2x - 3 & \text{if } x \le 2 \\ -3x + 12 & \text{if } x > 2 \end{cases}$.

8. Graph the line passing through (-1, 3) and having slope $m = -\frac{2}{3}$.

9. Determine the vertex and axis of the quadratic function $y = (x - 5)^2 + 2$.

10. Determine the vertex and axis, and graph the parabola $y = -2x^2 + 4x + 3$.

11. Determine the intervals where the function $f(x) = 4x^2 - 4x - 5$ is increasing and decreasing.

12. Determine two real numbers whose sum is 26 and whose product is a maximum.

13. Determine two real numbers such that the sum of one of the numbers and twice the second number is 9/2 and whose product is a maximum.

In 14-18 identify each graph as an ellipse, parabola, or hyperbola. For a parabola determine the vertex, for an ellipse find the major and minor axis, and for a hyperbola find the asymptotes.

14. $25x^2 = 100 + 4y^2$ 15. $2x^2 - 4x = y - 4$

16. $9y^2 = -6x^2 + 54$ 17. $x^2 - 6x + 4y^2 + 40y + 45 = 0$

18. $x^2 + 72 = 9y^2 + 18y$ 19. $y + 4x^2 = 6$

20. Determine the asymptotes of the hyperbola $9x^2 - 16y^2 = 144$.

21. Graph $16x^2 + 4y^2 = 64$.   22. Graph $16x^2 - 4y^2 = 64$.

23. Find the equation of the line having slope m = -2, passing through the vertex of the parabola $y = 3x^2 + 12x = 7$.

24. Graph $\frac{y}{\sqrt{5}} = -\sqrt{1 - \frac{x^2}{9}}$.   25. Graph $y = \sqrt{x + 4}$.

26. Sketch the graph of $f(x) = x^3 - 4x$.

27. Sketch the graph of $f(x) = 2x(2 - x)(x + 3)$.

28. Determine the vertical and horizontal asymptotes for $f(x) = \frac{3x^2}{2x^2 - 8}$.

29. Determine the oblique asymptote of the graph of $f(x) = \frac{2x^2 - 1}{3x}$.

30. Sketch the graph of $f(x) = \frac{2x - 6}{x + 2}$.

(Answers for this test are on page 361.)

CHAPTER 5   Exponential and Logarithmic
            Functions

Section 5.1   Exponential Functions

Additional Examples

Example 1   Solve the following
    equations.

(a) $3^{1-2x} = 27$ (b) $2^{x^2} = 16$

(c) $(\frac{3}{2})^{x+1} = (\frac{81}{16})^2$

Solution   The key to the solution is
    to write $a^u = b$ in the form $a^u = a^v$
    and then solve $u = v$.

(a) Since $27 = 3^3$, we write

$3^{1-2x} = 3^3$, so that

$1 - 2x = 3$

$2x = -2$

$x = -1$

The solution set is $\{-1\}$.

(b) Since $16 = 2^4$, we have

$2^{x^2} = 2^4$

$x^2 = 4$

$x = \pm 2$.

The solution set is $\{-2, 2\}$.

(c) Since $\frac{81}{16} = (\frac{3}{2})^4$, we have

$(\frac{3}{2})^{x+1} = ((\frac{3}{2})^4)^2$

$(\frac{3}{2})^{x+1} = (\frac{3}{2})^8$

$x + 1 = 8$

$x = 7$.

The solution set is $\{7\}$.

Example 2   Solve the following
    equations.

(a) $(\frac{1}{3})^{2x+1} = 9^{2+x}$

(b) $5^{2-x} = \frac{1}{125}$

Solution   (a) Since $\frac{1}{3} = 3^{-1}$ and $9 = 3^2$

we can write

$(3^{-1})^{2x+1} = (3^2)^{2+x}$

$3^{-2x-1} = 3^{4+2x}$

$-2x - 1 = 4 + 2x$

$4x = -5$

$x = -\frac{5}{4}$

The solution set is $\{\frac{-5}{4}\}$.

(b) Since $125 = 5^3$, we have

$5^{2-x} = 5^{-3}$

$2 - x = -3$

$x = 5$.

The solution set is $\{5\}$.

Selected Solutions

1. $f(x) = 5^x - 1$ does not satisfy the
    definition of an exponential function
    in the text [that is, being of the
    form $f(x) = a^x$] but we note that the
    graph of f is the graph of $g(x) =$
    5^x (an exponential function) shifted
    1 unit downward.

5. If $f(x) = (\frac{2}{3})^x$, then $f(2) = (\frac{2}{3})^2 = \frac{4}{9}$.

9. The graph of $f(x) = 2^x$ is given be-
    low.

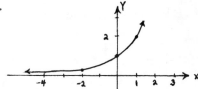

(a) The graph of $f(x) = 2^x + 1$ is
the graph of 2^x shifted upward 1
unit. See the graph in the answer
section of the text.

(b) The graph of $f(x) = 2^x - 4$ is
the graph of 2^x shifted downward 4
units. Note that at $x = 0$, $y = -3$.
See the graph in the text.

(c)   We have $f(x) = 2^{x+1} = 2 \cdot 2^x$. Hence, the graph of $f(x) = 2^{x+1}$ has the property that given any number x, the y number on $f(x) = 2^{x+1}$ is twice the y number on 2^x. Note the table:

x	-3	-2	-1	0	1	2
$y = 2^x$	$\frac{1}{8}$	$\frac{1}{4}$	$\frac{1}{2}$	1	2	4
$y = 2^{x+1}$	$\frac{1}{4}$	$\frac{1}{2}$	1	2	4	8

(d)   We have $f(x) = 2^{x-4} = 2^{-4} \cdot 2^x = (\frac{1}{16}) 2^x$

Note the table:

	-3	-2	-1	0	2	4	6
$y = 2^x$	$\frac{1}{8}$	$\frac{1}{4}$	$\frac{1}{2}$	1	4	16	64
$y = 2^{x-4}$	$\frac{1}{128}$	$\frac{1}{64}$	$\frac{1}{32}$	$\frac{1}{16}$	$\frac{1}{4}$	1	4

See the graph in the text.

13.   If $f(x) = (\frac{3}{2})^x$, we have the following table:

x	-2	-1	0	1	2
y	$\frac{4}{9}$	$\frac{2}{3}$	1	$\frac{3}{2}$	$\frac{9}{4}$

See the graph in the text.

17.   If $f(x) = 2^{x+1}$, we have the table:

x	-3	-2	-1	0	1	2	3
y	$\frac{1}{4}$	$\frac{1}{2}$	0	2	4	8	16

See the graph in the text.

21.   If $f(x) = 2^x + 2^{-x}$, we could graph $y = 2^x$ and $y = 2^{-x}$ on the same graph and add the ordinates. We could also plot the points in the following table and note that $f(-x) = 2^{-x} + 2^x = f(x)$.

x	-3	-2	-1	0
y	$\frac{1}{8} + 8 = \frac{65}{8}$	$\frac{1}{4} + 4 = \frac{17}{4}$	$\frac{1}{2} + 2 = \frac{5}{2}$	2

x	1	2	3
y	$2 + \frac{1}{2} = \frac{5}{2}$	$4 + \frac{1}{4} = \frac{17}{4}$	$8 + \frac{1}{8} = \frac{65}{8}$

See the graph in the text.

25.   The graph of $f(x) = \dfrac{e^x - e^{-x}}{2}$ can be seen in the text. Consider the table below: Note that $\dfrac{e^x - e^{-x}}{2} = \dfrac{e^{2x} - 1}{2e^x}$, or $\dfrac{1 - e^{-2x}}{2e^{-x}}$.

x	-2	-1	0	1	2
y	$\frac{1-e^4}{2e^2}$	$\frac{1-e^2}{2e}$	0	$\frac{e^2-1}{2e}$	$\frac{e^4-1}{2e^2}$

We see that $f(-x) = -f(x)$. The function is symmetric to the origin.

29.   Since $4 = 2^2$ we write

$$4^x = 2$$
$$(2^2)^x = 2$$
$$2^{2x} = 2$$
$$2x = 1$$

or $x = \frac{1}{2}$.

The solution set is $\{\frac{1}{2}\}$.
Note that by <u>inspection</u> we can see that $4^x = 2$ is true if $x = \frac{1}{2}$.

33.   Since $8 = 2^3$, we write

$$2^{3-y} = 8$$
$$2^{3-y} = 2^3$$
$$3 - y = 3$$
$$y = 0.$$

The solution set is $\{0\}$.

37. We have
$$4 = r^{\frac{2}{3}}$$
$$4^3 = (r^{\frac{2}{3}})^3$$
$$64 = r^2$$
$$r = \pm 8.$$
The solution set is $r = \{-8, 8\}$.

41. Since $5^2 = 25$ and $5^3 = 125$, we have
$$125^{-x} = 25^{3x}$$
$$(5^3)^{-x} = (5^2)^{3x}$$
$$5^{-3x} = 5^{6x} \quad \text{so that}$$
$$-3x = 6x$$
$$9x = 0$$
$$x = 0.$$
The solution set is $\{0\}$.

45. Since $\frac{1}{4} = (\frac{1}{2})^2$, we can write
$$(\tfrac{1}{2})^{-x} = (\tfrac{1}{4})^{x-1}$$
$$(\tfrac{1}{2})^{-x} = \left((\tfrac{1}{2})^2\right)^{x+1}$$
$$(\tfrac{1}{2})^{-x} = (\tfrac{1}{2})^{2x+2} \quad \text{so that}$$
$$-x = 2x + 2$$
$$-3x = 2$$
$$x = -\tfrac{2}{3}.$$
The solution set is $\{\frac{-2}{3}\}$.

49. Since $\frac{1}{125} = (\frac{1}{5})^3$, we have
$$(\tfrac{1}{5})^{|x-2|} = \tfrac{1}{125}$$
$$(\tfrac{1}{5})^{|x-2|} = (\tfrac{1}{5})^3 \quad \text{so that}$$
$$|x - 2| = 3.$$
This is true if $x - 2 = -3$ or if
$x - 2 = 3$. Thus, $x = -1$ or $x = 5$.
The solution set is $\{-1, 5\}$.

53. Let $a > 1$ and consider $y = a^x$. We
always have the table.

x	-2	-1	0	1	2
y	$\frac{1}{a^2}$	$\frac{1}{a}$	1	a	a^2

We can see that as a increases the
graph to the right of x = 0 increases
more rapidly and the graph to the
left of x = 0 tends to zero more
rapidly.

   Let $0 < a < 1$ and consider $y = a^x$.
From the same table we note that if
$0 < a < 1$ then the graph has the
following shape.
As a increases
(gets closer to 1),
the graph flattens out, getting
closer to the line $y = 1$.

57. We use P = 1593.24, i = .105 ($10\frac{1}{2}$%),
m = 4, and n = 14. The formula gives
$$A = 1593.24(1 + \tfrac{.105}{4})^{56}$$
$$= 1593.24(\tfrac{4.105}{4})^{56}$$
or A = \$6,799.21.

61. We use P = 5800, i = .13 (13%), and
n = 6 to find:

(a) $A = 5800(1 + \tfrac{.13}{1})^6$
$$= 5800(1.13)^6$$
$$= \$12,075.32;$$

(b) $A = 5800(1 + \tfrac{.13}{2})^{12}$
$$= 5800(1.065)^{12}$$
$$= \$12,348.76;$$

(c) $A = 5800(1 + \tfrac{.13}{365})^{2190}$
$$= \$12,650.77.$$

65. We have:

(a)
$$E(5) = (2,400,000)2^{\frac{1}{6}}$$
$$= 2,693,909 \quad \text{or}$$

approximating $E(50) \approx 2,690,000$;

(b)
$$E(10) = (2,400,000)2^{\frac{1}{3}}$$
$$= 3.023,811, \quad \text{or}$$

approximately $3,020,000$;

(c)
$$E(60) = (2,400,000)2^{2}$$
$$= 9,600,000;$$

(d)
$$E(120) = (2,400,000)2^{4}$$
$$= 38,400,000.$$

69. If we were to plot the points in the table, we would be tempted to join the points with a smooth graph giving no thought to intermediate points. Note, however, that if $x = \frac{1}{2}$, the number $y = (-2)^{\frac{1}{2}} = \sqrt{-2}$ does not exist. Similarly, $(-2)^{\frac{13}{2}}$, $(-2)^{\frac{15}{4}}$, $(-2)^{\frac{7}{8}}$, etc., do not exist. There are infinitely many numbers x for which $(-2)^{x}$ does not exist.

73. Consider the graphs of $f(x) = 3^{-x}$ and $g(x) = 1 - 2x$ plotted on the same graph.

x	f(x)	g(x)
-1	3	3
0	1	1
1	$\frac{1}{3}$	-1

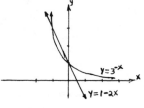

We can see that f and g are equal when $x = 0$ and $x = -1$. There are no additional points of intersection due to the nature of the graphs.

77. For any number $a > 0$ we have $(a^{x})^{2} = a^{2x}$. Hence, for every number $a > 0$ the function $f(x) = a^{x}$ has the property that $f(2x) = a^{2x} = (a^{x})^{2} = [f(x)]^{2}$.

81. Let $f(x) = e^{x}$. Then
$$f(x + h) = e^{x+h} = e^{x} \cdot e^{h}.$$
Hence we have that, provided $h \neq 0$,
$$\frac{f(x + h) - f(x)}{h} = \frac{e^{x+h} - e^{x}}{h}$$
$$= \frac{e^{x}e^{h} - e^{x}}{h}$$
$$= \frac{e^{x}(e^{h} - 1)}{h}.$$

Section 5.2   Logarithmic Functions

Additional Examples

Example 1   Evaluate

(a) $\log_8 \sqrt{\frac{1}{8}}$,

(b) $\log 100,000$, and

(c) $\log_{32} 2$.

Solution   In evaluations of this type we refer to the definition that $\log_a x = y$ if and only if $a^{y} = x$.

(a) If $n = \log_8 \sqrt{\frac{1}{8}}$, then $8^{n} = \sqrt{\frac{1}{8}}$. We have
$$8^{n} = \sqrt{\frac{1}{8}}$$
$$8^{n} = \left(\frac{1}{8}\right)^{1/2}$$
$$8^{n} = 8^{-1/2},$$
so that $n = -\frac{1}{2}$. Hence $\log_8 \sqrt{\frac{1}{8}} = -\frac{1}{2}$.

(b) If $n = \log 100,000$, or $n = \log_{10} 100,000$, then $10^{n} = 100,000$. Since $100,000 = 10^{6}$, we have $10^{n} = 10^{6}$, so that $n = 6$. Hence, $\log 100,000 = 6$.

(c) Let $n = \log_{32} 2$. Then $32^n = 2$, but since $32 = 2^5$, we have

$$32^n = 2$$
$$(2^5)^n = 2$$

or $2^{5n} = 2.$

This implies $5n = 1$, or $n = 1/5$.

Thus, $\log_{32} 2 = 1/5$.

Example 2   Graph $y = \log_{1/2} x$.

Solution   We note that in consideration of $\log_a x$ we have the domain $(0, +\infty)$. The graph $y = \log_{1/2} x$ can also be thought of as the graph of $(1/2)^y = x$. We can plot points without a calculator or a table if we substitute numbers for y and find corresponding x. Consider the table below.

x	$\frac{1}{16}$	$\frac{1}{8}$	$\frac{1}{4}$	$\frac{1}{2}$	1	2	4	8	16
y	4	3	2	1	0	-1	-2	-3	-4

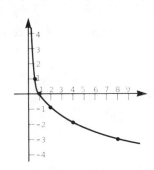

Example 3   Write

$$3 \log_a (x + 2) - 2 \log_a x + \frac{1}{2} \log_a \sqrt[3]{2x + 1}$$

as a single logarithm.

Solution   Using the properties of logarithms, we have

$$3 \log_a (x + 2) - 2 \log_a x + \frac{1}{2} \log_a \sqrt[3]{2x + 1}$$
$$= \log_a \frac{(x + 2)^3 (2x + 1)^{1/6}}{x^2}.$$

Selected Solutions

In most of the following exercises we will make use of the definition that

$\log_b a = n$ means that $b^n = a$.

1. Using the definition above we see that $3^4 = 81$ means the same as $\log_3 81 = 4$.

5. By definition, $(\frac{1}{2})^{-4} = 16$ means the same as $\log_{1/2} (16) = -4$.

9. By definition, $\log_6 36 = 2$ means the same as $6^2 = 36$.

13. By definition, $\log_{10} (.0001) = -4$ means the same as $10^{-4} = .0001$.

17. Let $n = \log_5 25$. Then $5^n = 25$, and since $5^2 = 25$ we have $n = 2$. Thus, $\log_5 25 = 2$.

21. Let $n = \log_{10} 0.001$. Using the definition we have

$$10^n = 0.001$$
$$10^n = 10^{-3}$$
$$n = -3.$$

Hence, $\log_{10} 0.001 = -3$.

25. Let $n = \log_4 \frac{\sqrt[3]{4}}{2}$. Using the definition we have $4^n = \frac{\sqrt[3]{4}}{2}$. Since $4 = 2^2$, we have $\sqrt[3]{4} = \sqrt[3]{2^2} = 2^{2/3}$, and hence $\frac{\sqrt[3]{4}}{2} = \frac{2^{2/3}}{2} = 2^{-1/3}$. Hence, we can now see that $4^n = \frac{\sqrt[3]{4}}{2}$ means $2^{2n} = 2^{-1/3}$, or $n = \frac{-1}{6}$.

Hence, $\log_4 \frac{\sqrt[3]{4}}{2} = -\frac{1}{6}$.

29. Let $n = \log_6 36^4$. Using the definition we have
$$6^n = 36^4$$
$$6^n = (6^2)^4$$
$$6^n = 6^8, \text{ so that}$$
$$n = 8.$$
Hence, $\log_6 36^4 = 8$.

33. Let $n = \log_e \sqrt{e}$. The definition gives
$$e^n = \sqrt{e}$$
$$e^n = e^{1/2} \quad \text{so that}$$
$$n = \frac{1}{2}.$$
Hence, $\log_e \sqrt{e} = \frac{1}{2}$.

37. Let $n = e^{\log_e x}$ taking $\log_e$ of both sides gives
$$\log_e n = \log_e e^{\log_e x}$$
or $\quad \log_e n = \log_e x$

Hence, $n = x$. We conclude that $e^{\log_e x} = x$. Note the comparison to the theorem in the text preceding Example 9 that states that
$$a^{\log_a x} = x.$$

41. To solve $\log_x 25 = -2$ we use the definition to rewrite this equation as
$$x^{-2} = 25$$
$$\frac{1}{x^2} = 25$$
$$x^2 = \frac{1}{25}$$
$$x = \pm\frac{1}{5}.$$

However, we must have the base b of a logarithm $\log_b$ as a positive number. That is, in considering $\log_b$ we must have $b > 0$. Hence, the only solution is $x = \frac{1}{5}$. The solution set is $\{\frac{1}{5}\}$.

45. Using the definition, we have
$$\log_y 8 = \frac{3}{4}$$
$$y^{\frac{3}{4}} = 8$$
$$y^{\frac{1}{4}} = 8^{\frac{1}{3}} = 2$$
$$y = 2^4 = 16.$$
The solution set is $\{16\}$.

49. Using the property that
$$\log_b \left(\frac{n}{d}\right) = \log_b n - \log_b d,$$
we have
$$\log_3 \left(\frac{2}{5}\right) = \log_3 2 - \log_3 5.$$

53. Using the logarithm properties, we have
$$\log_5 \frac{5\sqrt{7}}{3} = \log_5 5 + \log_5 \sqrt{7} - \log_5 3$$
$$= 1 + \frac{1}{2} \log_5 7 - \log_5 3.$$

57. We have
$$\log_k \frac{pq^2}{m} = \log_k P + \log_k q^2 - \log_k m$$
$$= \log_k P + 2 \log_k q - \log_k m.$$

61. Using the properties of logarithms we have
$$\log_a x + \log_a y - \log_a m = \log_a \frac{xy}{m}.$$

65. First of all, using the property that $\log_b n^k = k \log_b n$, we see that
$$-\frac{3}{4} \log_x a^6 b^8 = \log_x (a^6 b^8)^{-3/4}$$
$$= \log_x (a^{-9/2} b^{-6}),$$
and $\quad \frac{2}{3} \log_x a^9 b^3 = \log_x (a^9 b^3)^{2/3}$
$$= \log_x (a^6 b^2).$$
Hence,
$$-\frac{3}{4} \log_x a^6 b^8 + \frac{2}{3} \log_x a^9 b^3$$
$$= \log_x (a^{-9/2} b^{-6}) +$$
$$\log_x (a^6 b^2)$$

$$= \log_x (a^{-9/2+6}b^{-6+2})$$

$$= \log_x (a^{3/2}b^{-4}).$$

69. We have

$$2 \log_a (z+1) + \log_a (3z+2)$$

$$= \log_a (z+1)^2 + \log_a (3z+2)$$

$$= \log_a [(z+1)^2 (3z+2)]$$

73. The graphs of $y = \log_3 x$ and $y = 3^x$ will be symmetric with respect to the line $y = x$ since each function is the inverse of the other. This can be seen by the fact that

$y = \log_3 x$ means $3^y = x$.

See the desired graph in the answer section of the text, noting the tables:

x	$y = \log_3 x$
$\frac{1}{3}$	-1
1	0
3	1
9	2

x	$y = 3^x$
-1	$\frac{1}{3}$
0	1
1	3
2	9

77.. To graph $f(x) = \log_5 x$ consider the following table, noting that we evaluate $f(\frac{1}{5}) = \log_5 \frac{1}{5}$ by the definition. We see that $\log_5 \frac{1}{5} = -1$ since $5^{-1} = \frac{1}{5}$. We <u>choose</u> our x numbers so that y can be found without the use of a calculator. Note also that dom $f = (0, \infty)$.

x	$\frac{1}{25}$	$\frac{1}{5}$	1	5	25	125
y	-2	-1	0	1	2	3

These points illustrate the shape of the graph. See the graph in the answer section of the text.

81. In graphing $f(x) = \log_2 x^2$ we note that x cannot be zero but we can let x be negative since $x^2 > 0$. Hence, if we choose x so that x^2 is a power of 2, we have the following table:

x	$\pm\frac{1}{2}$	$\pm\frac{1}{\sqrt{2}}$	± 1
y	$\log_2 \frac{1}{4} = -2$	$\log_2 \frac{1}{2} = -1$	$\log_2 1 = 0$

x	$\pm\sqrt{2}$	± 2
y	$\log_2 2 = 1$	$\log_2 4 = 2$

See the graph in the answer section of the text.

85. We have

$$\log_{10} 6 = \log_{10} (2 \cdot 3) = \log_{10} 2 + \log_{10} 3$$

$$= 0.3010 + 0.4771 = 0.7781.$$

89. $\log_{10} 30 = \log_{10} (10 \cdot 3) = \log_{10} 10 + \log_{10} 3$

$$= 1 + 0.4771 = 1.4771.$$

93. (a) If the loudness of a whisper is $115 I_0$, then the decibel rating is

$$d = 10 \cdot \log_{10} \frac{I}{I_0} = 10 \cdot \log_{10} \frac{115 I_0}{I_0}$$

$$= 10 \cdot \log_{10} 115 \approx 10(2.0606978)$$

$$\approx 20.607, \text{ or } 21,$$

rounding off to the nearest decibel.

(b) If $I = 9,500,000 I_0$, then

$$d = 10 \cdot \log_{10} 9,500,000 \approx 69.777236,$$

or $d \approx 70$ decibels.

(c) If $I = 1,200,000,000 I_0$, then

$$d = 10 \cdot \log_{10} 1,200,000,000$$

$d = 10 \cdot \log_{10} \; (1.2 \times 10^9)$

$\quad = 10 [\log_{10} \; 10^9 + \log_{10} \; 1.2]$

$d = 10 [9 + \log_{10} \; 1.2]$

$\quad = 90 + 10 \; \log_{10} \; 1.2$

$d \approx 90 + 0.791812 + 90.791812,$

or $d \approx 91$ decibels.

(d)   If $I = 895,000,000,000 \; I_0$, then

$d = 10 \; \log_{10} \; (8.95 \times 10^{11})$

$\quad = 10 [\log_{10} \; 10^{11} + \log_{10} \; 8.95]$

$d = 10 [11 + \log_{10} \; 8.95]$

$\quad = 110 + 10 \; \log \; 8.95$

$d \approx 110 + 9.51823 = 119.51823,$

or $d = 120$ decibels.

(e)   If $I = 1.09 \times 10^{14} \; I_0$, then

$d = 10 \cdot \log_{10} \; (1.09 \times 10^{14})$

$\quad = 10 [14 + \log_{10} \; 1.09]$

$d = 140 + 10 \; \log_{10} \; 1.09$

$\quad \approx 140 + 0.374265,$

or $d = 140$ decibels.

97. Using a calculator and the y^x key, we have

$$3^{.003} \approx 1.0033013$$

and then

$(3^{.003})^{1001} \approx \underline{27.090113}.$

If we find

$3^{(.003 \times 1001)} = 3^{3.003}$

we find

$3^{(.003 \times 1001)} \approx \underline{27.089134}.$

The difference in answers is due to the round-off procedures built into the calculator.

99. If $f(x) = e^x$, then to find f^{-1} we (1) interchange x and y and (2) solve for y. That is, given $f(x) = e^x$ we write $y = e^x$. Interchang-

ing x and y gives $x = e^y$. Solving for y gives $\log_e x = y$, or $y = \ln x$. Hence, $f^{-1}(x) = \ln x$. See the graph in the text.

Section 5.3   Natural Logarithms

Additional Examples

Example 1   How long will it take an amount of money to triple if it is invested at a rate of 11% per year compounded quarterly?

Solution   Let P denote the amount of money initially invested, and A be the amount of money accumulated by this investment after t years. The formula for A as determined in the text is

$$A = P(1 + \frac{i}{m})^{mt},$$

where m is the number of times the interest is compounded in a year. In this example we have $m = 4$ and $i = 11\% = 0.11$. This gives

$$A = P(1 + \frac{0.11}{4})^{4t}$$

$$A = P(1.0275)^{4t}.$$

We need to determine the number t such that the initial investment has tripled, that is, such that $A = 3P$. Hence, we solve the equation

$$3P = P(1.0275)^{4t}$$

for t. Solving, we have

$$3 = (1.0275)^{4t}$$

$$\ln 3 = 4t \; \ln 1.0275$$

$$\frac{\ln 3}{4 \; \ln 1.0275} = t.$$

Using a calculator gives the values $\ln 3 = 1.09861$ and $\ln 1.0275 = .02713$, rounded to five decimals.

Hence,

$$t = \frac{1.09861}{4(.02713)} = \frac{1.09861}{0.10852} = 10.124.$$

We can conclude that the investment will definitely triple after 10.25 years, which is 10 years and one quarter.

Example 2   In an archaeological excavation an animal skull was found and it was determined that approximately 19.6% of the original amount of carbon-14 was still present. If the half-life of carbon-14 is 5600 years, find the age of the skull.

Solution   The formula for radioactive decay is

$$A = A_0 e^{-kt},$$

where A_0 is the original amount of the substance at time $t = 0$, t measured in years, k is the constant associated with the rate of decay (– because of decay), and A is the amount remaining after t years.

Our first step will be to determine the constant rate of decay k associated with carbon-14. We have been given the half life of carbon-14 is 5600 years. Hence, if A_0 is an initial amount of carbon-14, then after 5600 years the amount present is $\frac{1}{2}A_0$. This gives

$$\frac{1}{2}A_0 = A_0 e^{-k(5600)}$$

$$\frac{1}{2} = e^{-5600k}, \qquad \text{dividing by } A_0$$

$$\ln\frac{1}{2} = \ln e^{-5600k},$$

and since

$$\ln\frac{1}{2} = \ln 1 - \ln 2$$

$$= -\ln 2, \text{ and}$$

$$\ln e^{-5600k} = -5600k, \qquad \text{we have}$$

$$-\ln 2 = -5600k$$

or

$$k = \frac{\ln 2}{5600}.$$

Using a table for ln or a calculator, we have $\ln 2 = .69315$ rounded off to five decimals (here a calculator value is used). This implies that

$$k = \frac{.69315}{5600} = .0001238,$$

rounded to four significant digits.

We then conclude that for carbon-14 the radioactive decay formula

$$A = A_0 e^{-0.0001238t}$$

can be used to predict the amount of carbon-14 present after t years. We now turn to finding the number of years t for which only 19.6% of the original amount of carbon-14 remains. That is, if A_0 is the original amount, we want to find t so that $.196A_0$ remains. This gives

$$.196A_0 = A_0 e^{-0.0001238t}$$

$$.196 = e^{-0.0001238t}$$

$$\ln(.196) = \ln e^{-0.0001238t}$$

$$\ln(.196) = -0.0001238t$$

or

$$t = \frac{\ln(.196)}{0.0001238}.$$

We have $\ln(.196) = -1.62964$ (using a calculator and rounding to 5 decimal places), so that

$$t = \frac{1.62964}{0.0001238}$$

or

$$t = 13163.5.$$

We estimate that the animal skull is approximately 13,163 1/2 years old.

Selected Solutions

1. Using the fact that $\ln a = n$ means $\log_e a = n$, we see that $\underline{\ln e = 1}$, since $\log_e e = 1$.

5. We have $\ln e^{-3}$ because the definition of $\ln a = n$ means that $e^n = a$.

9. Using a calculator with an $\ln$ key we have $\ln 4 \approx 1.3862944$. Rounding this to four decimal places we write $\ln 4 = 1.3863$.

13. A calculator gives $\ln 350 \approx 5.8579332$, or $\ln 350 = 5.8579$, to four decimals.

17. Rounded to four decimals, we have $\ln 42 = 3.7377$.

21. Using the formula that
$$\log_b a = \frac{\ln a}{\ln b},$$
we have
$$\log_5 10 = \frac{\ln 10}{\ln 5} \approx \frac{2.3025851}{1.6094379},$$
or $\log_5 10 \approx 1.4306766$. Rounded to the nearest hundredth, $\log_5 10 = 1.43$.

25. We have
$$\log_{1/2} 3 = \frac{\ln 3}{\ln(1/2)} = \frac{\ln 3}{\ln(.5)}$$
$$\approx -1.5849625.$$
Note: We could have used
$$\ln\left(\tfrac{1}{2}\right) = \ln 1 - \ln 2 = -\ln 2.$$
Thus,
$$\log_{1/2} 3 = -\frac{\ln 3}{\ln 2} = \text{the same answer.}$$
Rounded to the nearest hundredth
$$\log_{1/2} 3 = -1.58.$$

29. We have
$$\log_{2.9} 7.5 = \frac{\ln 7.5}{\ln 2.9} \approx 1.8924417.$$
Rounded to the nearest hundredth we have $\log_{2.9} 7.5 = 1.89$.

33. In graphing $f(x) = \ln x$, we have dom $f = (0, \infty)$ and it is best to choose x numbers that are powers of e to sketch the graph. Consider the table:

x	$\dfrac{1}{e^3}$	$\dfrac{1}{e^2}$	$\dfrac{1}{e}$	1
$y = \ln x$	-3	-2	-1	0

x	e	e^2	e^3
$y = \ln x$	1	2	3

Note that $\dfrac{1}{e^3} = e^{-3} \approx 0.05$, $\dfrac{1}{e^2} = e^{-2}$ ≈ 0.135, $\dfrac{1}{e} \approx 0.37$, $e \approx 2.7818$, $e^2 \approx 7.39$, $e^3 \approx 20.09$. See the graph in the text.

35. Let $f(x) = x \ln x$ and using a calculator for two decimal approximations, consider the following table. Note: dom $f = (0, \infty)$.

x	$\dfrac{1}{e^2}$	$\dfrac{1}{e}$	1	e	e^2
y	$\dfrac{-2}{e^2} \approx -.27$	$\dfrac{-1}{e} \approx -.37$	0	$e \approx 2.7$	$2e^2 \approx 14.8$

Note: $\ln \dfrac{1}{e^2} = \ln e^{-2} = -2$, $\ln \dfrac{1}{e} = -1$, $\ln e = 1$.
See the graph in the book. Also, note that as x gets "closer and closer" to zero, the graph in the book seems to show that f gets close to zero. You can note that $x = \dfrac{1}{e^{200}}$ is very close to zero and $f(e^{-200}) = \dfrac{-200}{e^{200}}$, which is negative but very close to zero.

37. If the community has 2 species with 50 individuals each, then $P_1 = P_2$ $= \dfrac{50}{100} = \dfrac{1}{2}$ and hence,

$$H = -P_1 \log_2 P_1 - P_2 \log_2 P_2$$

$$H = -\frac{1}{2} \log_2 \left(\frac{1}{2}\right) - \frac{1}{2} \log_2 \left(\frac{1}{2}\right)$$

$$H = -\frac{1}{2}(-1) - \frac{1}{2}(-1),$$

using $\log_2 \left(\frac{1}{2}\right) = -1$,

$$H = \frac{1}{2} + \frac{1}{2}, \text{ or}$$

$$H = 1.$$

39.   If $S(n) = a \ln \left(1 + \frac{n}{a}\right)$ and

$$a = .36,$$

then $S(n) = .36 \ln \left(1 + \frac{n}{.36}\right).$

(a) $S(100) = .36 \ln \left(1 + \frac{100}{.36}\right)$

$$= .36 \ln (278.77\overline{7}...)$$

$$\approx 2.027$$

Hence $S(100) \approx 2.03.$

(b) $S(200) = .36 \ln \left(1 + \frac{200}{.36}\right)$

$$= .36 \ln (556.55\overline{5}...)$$

$$\approx 2.276$$

Hence $S(200) \approx 2.28.$

(c) $S(150) = .36 \ln \left(1 + \frac{150}{.36}\right)$

$$= .36 \ln (417.66\overline{6}...)$$

$$\approx 2.172$$

Hence $S(150) \approx 2.17.$

(d) $S(10) = .36 \ln \left(1 + \frac{10}{.36}\right)$

$$= .36 \ln (28.77\overline{7}...)$$

$$\approx 1.209$$

Hence $S(10) \approx 1.21.$

41.   If $y = y_0 e^{.4t}$, with time measured in years, and if $y_0 = 100$, then:

(a) $y(4) = 100e^{.4(4)} = 100 e^{1.6}$

$$y(4) \approx 100(4.9530324) = 495.3$$

Hence, there are 495 rabbits after 4 years.

(b)   If there are 30 rabbits after 3 months, then we have

$y\left(\frac{1}{4}\right) = 30.$ This gives

$$30 = y_0 e^{.4(1/4)}$$

$$30 = y_0 e^{.1}$$

$$y_0 = 30 e^{-.1} \approx 30(.9048374)$$

or $y_0 = 27.145.$

We conclude that $y_0 = 27.$

45.   (a)   The year 1810 corresponds to $t = -104$ and

$$N(-104) = \frac{197,273,000}{1 + e^{(.03134)(104)}}$$

$$\approx \frac{197,273,000}{27.032871}$$

$$\approx 7,297,523.1,$$

or   7,298,000 to the nearest thousand. The year 1900 corresponds to $t = -14$, and

$$N(-14) = \frac{197,273,000}{1 + e^{(.03134)(14)}}$$

$$\approx \frac{197,273,000}{2.5507831}$$

$$\approx 77,338,212$$

or   77,338,000, to the nearest thousand. The year 1970 corresponds to $t = +56.$ and

$$N(56) = \frac{197,273,000}{1 + e^{-(.03134)(56)}}$$

$$N(56) \approx \frac{197,273,000}{1.1729003}$$

$$\approx 168,192,470,$$

or   168,192,000, to the nearest thousand. The year 1980 corresponds to $t = 66$ and

$$N(66) = \frac{197,273,000}{1 + e^{-2.06844}}$$

$$\approx 175,138,510$$

or   175,139,000.

(b)   The population can never increase to 197,273,000 because the denominator $1 + e^{-.03134t}$ is greater than 1 for all t. Hence, N is less than 197,273,000 for all t.

49. Let $n = \dfrac{1}{\log_a b}$.   Then we have

$\log_a b = \dfrac{1}{n}$ and using the definition

of logarithms we have $a^{1/n} = b$.

Thus, $a = b^n$, and we can conclude

that $\log_b a = n$.   This shows that

$\dfrac{1}{\log_a b} = \log_b a$.

Section 5.4   Exponential and
              Logarithmic Equations

Additional Examples

Example 1   Solve the logarithmic
      equation $\log_3 x = 3 - \log_3 (x + 6)$.

Solution   Rearranging and using the
      properties of logarithms give the
      following:

$$\log_3 x = 3 - \log_3 (x + 6)$$
$$\log_3 x + \log_3 (x + 6) = 3$$
$$\log_3 x(x + 6) = 3$$

since $\log_a u + \log_a v = \log_a (uv)$

$$x(x + 6) = 3^3$$

since $\log_a u = v$ implies $u = a^v$

$$x(x + 6) = 27$$
$$x^2 + 6x - 27 = 0$$
$$(x + 9)(x - 3) = 0$$

so $x = -9$ or $x = 3$.

However, we note that $x = -9$ must
be discarded since $\log_3 x$ is not
defined for $x = -9$.   The solution
$x = 3$ does check since
$\log_3 3 = 1$ and $3 - \log_3 9 = 3 - 2 = 1$.
The solution set is $S = \{3\}$.

Example 2   If

$$y = \frac{e^x + e^{-x}}{e^x - e^{-x}}$$

solve for x in terms of y.

Solution   This function arises in
certain physical phenomenon and is
studied in calculus.   Using algebraic manipulations, we have

$$y = \frac{e^x + e^{-x}}{e^x - e^{-x}}$$

$$(e^x - e^{-x})y = e^x + e^{-x}$$

$$y \cdot e^x - y \cdot e^{-x} = e^x + e^{-x}$$

$$e^x(y - 1) = e^{-x}(y + 1) \quad \text{combining} \atop \text{terms}$$

$$e^x \cdot e^x(y - 1) = e^x e^{-x}(y+1) \quad \text{multiplying} \atop \text{by } e^x$$

$$e^{2x}(y - 1) = y + 1 \quad \text{since} \atop e^x \cdot e^{-x} = 1$$

$$e^{2x} = \frac{y + 1}{y - 1}$$

$$\ln(e^{2x}) = \ln\left(\frac{y + 1}{y - 1}\right) \quad \text{taking ln} \atop \text{of both} \atop \text{sides}$$

$$2x = \ln\frac{y + 1}{y - 1} \quad \text{since} \atop \ln e^u = u$$

$$x = \frac{1}{2} \ln\frac{y + 1}{y - 1}$$

The desired result.

Selected Solutions

1. If $3^x = 6$, then

$$\ln 3^x = \ln 6$$
$$x \ln 3 = \ln 6$$
$$x = \frac{\ln 6}{\ln 3} \approx 1.6309.$$

The desired solution set is
$\{1.631\}$.

5. If $3^{a + 2} = 5$, then
$$\ln 3^{a + 2} = \ln 5$$
$$(a + 2) \ln 3 = \ln 5$$
$$a + 2 = \frac{\ln 5}{\ln 3}$$
$$a = \frac{\ln 5}{\ln 3} - 2 \approx -0.5350265.$$

The solution set is $\{-0.535\}$.

9. If $4^{3m-1} = 12^{m+2}$, then

$$(3m - 1)\ln 4 = (m + 2)\ln 12$$
$$3m \ln 4 - \ln 4 = m \ln 12 + 2 \ln 12$$
$$m(3 \ln 4 - \ln 12) = \ln 4 + 2 \ln 12$$
$$m \ln\left(\frac{4^3}{12}\right) = \ln(4 \cdot 12^2)$$
$$m \ln\left(\frac{16}{3}\right) = \ln 576$$
$$m = \frac{\ln 576}{\ln(16/3)}$$
$$\approx 3.7970114.$$

The desired solution set is
{3.797}.

13. If $2e^{5a+2} = 8$, then

$$\ln(2e^{5a+2}) = \ln 8$$
$$\ln 2 + \ln e^{5a+2} = \ln 8$$
$$\ln 2 + (5a + 2) = \ln 8$$
$$5a + 2 = \ln 8 - \ln 2$$
$$5a = \ln\left(\frac{8}{2}\right) - 2$$
$$a = \frac{\ln 4 - 2}{5}$$

or $a \approx -0.1227411$.
The desired solution set is
{-0.123}.

17. If $\left(1 + \frac{r}{2}\right)^5 = 9$, we have

$$\left(1 + \frac{r}{2}\right) = \sqrt[5]{9}$$
$$\frac{r}{2} = \sqrt[5]{9} - 1$$

or $r = 2(\sqrt[5]{9} - 1)$.
Using the y^k key on the calculator
we have $\sqrt[5]{9} \approx 1.5518456$, so that
$r \approx 2(0.5518456) = 1.1036911$.
The desired solution set is
{1.104}.

21. $2^{x^2-1} = 12$, then

$$(x^2 - 1)\ln 2 = \ln 12$$
$$x^2 - 1 = \frac{\ln 12}{\ln 2}$$

$$x^2 = 1 + \frac{\ln 12}{\ln 2}$$
$$\approx 4.5849625$$

or $x = \pm 2.141526$.
The desired solution set is
{-2.141, 2.141}.

25. Using the definition that $\log_b a = n$
means $b^n = a$, we have that if

$$\log (t - 1) = 1,$$
then $t - 1 = 10^1 = 10$,
or $t = 11$.
The solution set is {11}.

29. If $\ln (y + 2) = \ln (y - 7) + \ln 4$,
then

$$\ln (y + 2) = \ln 4(y - 7)$$
$$y + 2 = 4(y - 7)$$

since $\ln x = \ln y$ is true if
and only if $x = y$

$$y + 2 = 4y - 28$$
$$3y = 30, \quad \text{so that } y = 10.$$

$y = 10$ checks since $\ln 12 =$
$\ln 3 + \ln 4$. The solution set is
{10}.

33. If $\ln (5 + 4y) - \ln (3 + y) = \ln 3$,
then

$$\ln \left(\frac{5 + 4y}{3 + y}\right) = \ln 3$$
$$\frac{5 + 4y}{3 + y} = 3$$
$$5 + 4y = 3(3 + y)$$
$$5 + 4y = 9 + 3y \quad \text{or} \quad y = 4.$$

$y = 4$ checks since $\ln 21 - \ln 7 =$
$\ln 3$. The solution set is {4}.

37. If $2 \ln (x - 3) = \ln (x + 5) + \ln 4$,
then

$$\ln (x - 3)^2 = \ln 4(x + 5)$$
$$(x - 3)^2 = 4x + 20$$
$$x^2 - 6x + 9 = 4x + 20$$
$$x^2 - 10x - 11 = 0$$
$$(x + 1)(x - 11) = 0$$
$$x = 1, 11.$$

Note that x = 1 does not check since ln (x - 3) is undefined at x = 1. That is, ln (-2) does not exist. The solution x = 11 checks since 2 ln 8 = ln 64, and ln 16 + ln 4 = ln 64. Hence, the solution set is {11}.

41. If $\log_3 (a - 3) = 1 + \log_3 (a + 1)$, then
$$\log_3 (a - 3) - \log_3 (a + 1) = 1$$
$$\log_3 \left(\frac{a - 3}{a + 1}\right) = 1$$
$$\left(\frac{a - 3}{a + 1}\right) = 3^1 = 3$$
$$a - 3 = 3(a + 1)$$
$$a - 3 = 3a + 3$$
$$2a = -6$$
or $a = -3$.

However, a = -3 does not check since $\log_3 (a - 3)$ would be $\log_3 (-6)$, and this does not exist. Hence, the solution set is S = ∅.

45. If $\log z = \sqrt{\log z}$, then squaring both sides gives $(\log z)^2 = \log z$, or
$$(\log z)^2 - \log z = 0$$
$$\log z [\log z - 1] = 0$$
$$\log z = 0 \quad \text{or} \quad \log z = 1$$
$$z = 1 \quad \text{or} \quad z = 10.$$
Both answers check since z = 1 gives $0 = \sqrt{0}$ and z = 10 give $1 = \sqrt{1}$. The solution set is {1, 10}.

49. If $(1.8)^{P + 4} = 9.31$, then
$$\ln (1.8)^{P + 4} = \ln 9.31$$
$$(P + 4) \ln (1.8) = \ln 9.31$$
$$P + 4 = \frac{\ln 9.31}{\ln 1.8}$$
$$\approx 3.7957464$$
or $P \approx -4 + 3.7957464$
$$= -0.2042536.$$
The desired solution set is {-0.204}.

53. If $P(t) = 100\, e^{-.1t}$ is the percent P of the initial amount after t days, and if P(t) = 1, we solve $1 = 100\, e^{-.1t}$ for t. This gives
$$\frac{1}{100} = e^{-.1t} \text{ and } e^{-a} = \frac{1}{e^a},$$
so $100 = e^{.1t}$
$$\ln 100 = \ln e^{.1t}$$
$$.1t = \ln 100$$
$$t = 10 \ln 100$$
or $t \approx 10(4.6051702)$
$$= 46.051702.$$
The answer is "approximately 46 days."

57. If $e^x - 6 + 5e^{-x} = 0$, then
$$e^x(e^x - 6 - 5e^{-x}) = e^x \cdot 0$$
$$e^{2x} - 6e^x - 5 = 0.$$
Let $u = e^x$. Then $u^2 = e^{2x}$, and we have the quadratic equation
$$u^2 - 6u - 5 = 0$$
$$(u - 1)(u - 5) = 0$$
so that $u = 1$ or $u = 5$.
Thus, $e^x = 1$ or $e^x = 5$,
$$x = \ln 1 = 0$$
or $x = \ln 5$.
The solution set is {0, ln 5}.

61. If $y = \dfrac{e^x - e^{-x}}{2}$, then
$$2y = e^x - e^{-x}$$
$$e^x - 2y - e^{-x} = 0$$
$$e^x(e^x - 2y - e^{-x}) = e^x \cdot 0$$
$$e^{2x} - 2y\, e^x - 1 = 0.$$
If we let $u = e^x$, we have the quadratic equation
$$u^2 - 2y\, u - 1 = 0.$$
Using the quadratic formula
$$u = \frac{-b \pm \sqrt{b^2 - 4ac}}{2a}$$

with $a = 1$, $b = -2y$, and $c = -1$ gives

$$u = \frac{2y \pm \sqrt{4y^2 + 4}}{2} = y \pm \sqrt{y^2 + 1}.$$

This is

$$e^x = y \pm \sqrt{y^2 + 1}.$$

We can note that $y - \sqrt{y^2 + 1}$ will always be a <u>negative</u> number for all y. Since e^x is never negative we must omit this. <u>Also</u>, since we will take the ln of both sides to solve for x, we cannot take the ln of a negative number. Hence,

$$e^x = y + \sqrt{y^2 + 1}, \text{ and}$$

$$x = \ln(y + \sqrt{y^2 + 1}).$$

65. If $A = \dfrac{Pi}{1 - (1 + i)^{-n}}$, then

$$A[1 - (1 + i)^{-n}] = Pi,$$

$$A - \frac{A}{(1 + i)^n} = Pi,$$

$$\frac{A}{(1 + i)^n} = A - Pi,$$

$$(1 + i)^n = \frac{A}{A - Pi},$$

$$n \ln(1 + i) = \ln\left(\frac{A}{A - Pi}\right),$$

or

$$n = \frac{\ln\left(\frac{A}{A - Pi}\right)}{\ln(1 + i)}.$$

69. If $\log_3 x = -1$, then $x = 3^{-1} = \frac{1}{3}$.
We know that the graph of $y = \log_b x$ is increasing, that is, if $x_1 > x_2$, then $\log_b x_1 > \log_b x_2$. Then, using this fact, we see that if $x > \frac{1}{3}$, then $\log_3 x > \log_3 \frac{1}{3} = -1$.
The solution set to $\log_3 x > 1$ is the interval $(\frac{1}{3}, \infty)$.

73. We can solve this inequality by changing both logarithms into ln x.
We have $\log_5 x = \dfrac{\ln x}{\ln 5}$ and $\log_{10} x = \dfrac{\ln x}{\ln 10}$. Noting that ln 5 and ln 10 are both positive and that ln 10 is larger than ln 5, we have the following:

$$\log_5 x < \log_{10} x,$$

$$\frac{\ln x}{\ln 5} < \frac{\ln x}{\ln 10},$$

$$\frac{\ln x}{\ln 5} - \frac{\ln x}{\ln 10} < 0,$$

$$\left(\frac{1}{\ln 5} - \frac{1}{\ln 10}\right) \ln x < 0,$$

$$\left(\frac{\ln 10 - \ln 5}{(\ln 5)(\ln 10)}\right) \ln x < 0.$$

Since the coefficient is positive, we have ln $x < 0$. This is true if $0 < x < 1$. Hence, the solution set is the interval $(0, 1)$.

77. Given the decibel formula
$d = 10 \log \dfrac{I}{I_0}$, we can solve for I and arrive at

$$\frac{d}{10} = \log \frac{I}{I_0},$$

$$\frac{I}{I_0} = 10^{d/10},$$

$$I = I_0 \, 10^{d/10}.$$

If $d = 86$, we have $I = I_0 \cdot 10^{8.6}$, or $I = 398{,}107{,}170 \, I_0$.
If $d = 89$, then $I = I_0 \cdot 10^{8.9}$, or $I = 794{,}328{,}230 \, I_0$.

The intensity level is almost twice as high. The calculated percent increase is

$$\frac{794{,}328{,}230 - 398{,}107{,}170}{398{,}107{,}170} \times 100$$

$$\approx 99.523\%,$$

that is, about a 100% increase.

81.   If $M = 434\ e^{-.08t}$, then

$$\frac{M}{434} = e^{-.08t} = \frac{1}{e^{.08t}},$$

$$e^{.08t} = \frac{434}{M},$$

$$\ln e^{.08t} = \ln\left(\frac{434}{M}\right),$$

$$.08t = \ln\left(\frac{434}{M}\right),$$

$$t = \frac{1}{.08}\ln\left(\frac{434}{M}\right).$$

We could also have

$$t = \frac{25}{2}\ln\left(\frac{434}{M}\right),$$

or $$t = -\frac{25}{2}\ln\left(\frac{M}{434}\right).$$

Section 5.5   Exponential Growth and
                       Decay

Additional Examples

Example 1   If 500 grams of a substance
     exist initially and 5 years later
     only 350 grams exist, determine the
     half-life of the substance, and
     determine how much of the substance
     will exist after 20 years.

Solution   We assume the substance is
     decaying continuously and the
     formula for such decay is
     $y(t) = y_0\ e^{kt}$. We have $y_0 = 500$
     grams and we are given that $y(5) =$
     350. This allows us to solve for
     the decay ratio k. We have

$$350 = 500\ e^{5k}$$

$$e^{5k} = \frac{350}{500} = \frac{7}{10}$$

$$5k = \ln\left(\frac{7}{10}\right), \text{ or } k = \frac{1}{5}\ln\left(\frac{7}{10}\right).$$

We have $k \approx -0.071335$. Note that
any results we obtain from this
point depend on the approximation
we use for k. This writer will use
the entire <u>six</u>-decimal approximation

above and use the formula

$$y = 500\ e^{kt},\ k = -0.071335.$$

(a)   To find the half-life we let
$y = \frac{500}{2} = 250$, and solve for t.
This gives

$$250 = 500\ e^{kt}$$

$$e^{kt} = \frac{1}{2}$$

$$kt = \ln\left(\frac{1}{2}\right) = -\ln 2$$

or $t = \frac{-\ln 2}{k} \approx \frac{-\ln 2}{-0.071335} \approx 9.71679.$
We conclude that the half-life of
the substance is approximately 9
years and 8.6 months.

(b)   We find that

$$y(20) = 500\ e^{20k}, \qquad k = -0.071335$$

$$y(20) = 500\ e^{-1.4267}$$

$$y(20) \approx 500(0.239884) = 119.94199.$$

Hence, there are approximately 120
grams of the substance remaining
after 20 years.

Example 2   Compare the result of in-
     vesting $5000 for a period of 5 years
     at a rate of 9% if the interest is
     compounded (a) quarterly, (b) daily,
     and (c) continuously.

Solution   For parts (a) and (b) we use
     the formula

$$A = A_0\left(1 + \frac{r}{n}\right)^{nt},$$

where A_0 is the initial investment,
r is the interest rate, n is the
number of times compounded per year,
and t is the number of years. We
have:

(a) $A = 5000\left(1 + \frac{.09}{4}\right)^{4(5)}$

$A = 5000(1 + .0225)^{20}$

$A \approx 5000(1.5605092)$, or

$A \approx \$7802.55.$

(b) $A = 5000\left(1 + \frac{.09}{365}\right)^{(365)(5)}$

$A = 5000(1 + .0002466)^{1825}$

$A \approx 5000(1.5682239)$, or

$A \approx \$7841.12$.

(c) In this part we use the formula

$$A = A_0 \ e^{rt} = 5000 \ e^{(.09)(5)}$$

$$A = 5000 \ e^{.45}$$

$A \approx 5000(1.5683122)$, or

$A \approx \$7841.56$.

Selected Solutions

1. Using the formula

$y = y_0 \ e^{kt}$, with $y_0 = 100$,

we know that when $t = 2$ months, or

$t = \frac{1}{6}$ year, that $y(\frac{1}{6}) = 125$, we

use this to find the rate k of

growth. This gives

$$125 = 100 \ e^{k(\frac{1}{6})}$$

$$e^{\frac{k}{6}} = \frac{125}{100} = \frac{5}{4}$$

$$\frac{k}{6} = \ln \frac{5}{4}$$

$$k = 6 \ \ln \left(\frac{5}{4}\right).$$

Rather that approximate k let us

use the formula with $k = 6 \ \ln \left(\frac{5}{4}\right)$.

We have

$$y = 100 \ e^{6t \ \ln \left(\frac{5}{4}\right)}, \ \underline{t \ in \ years}.$$

We wish to solve for t when $y = 500$.

This gives

$$500 = 100 \ e^{6t \ \ln \left(\frac{5}{4}\right)}$$

$$5 = e^{6t \ \ln \left(\frac{5}{4}\right)}$$

$$\ln 5 = 6t \ \ln \left(\frac{5}{4}\right)$$

$$t = \frac{\ln 5}{6 \ \ln \left(\frac{5}{4}\right)} = \frac{\ln 5}{6 \ \ln \ (1.25)},$$

or $t \approx 1.2020946$ years.

The answer is approximately 14.425

months. The text answer is "about

14 months."

5. Let A be the amount of chemical

that will dissolve in a solution at

temperature t. We use the formula

that $A(t)$ will be some constant C

times e^{kt}, i.e., $A(t) = C \ e^{kt}$.

Since $A(0) = 1$ we have $1 = C \ e^{\circ}$,

or $C = 1$. Thus, for all tempera-

tures t we have $A(t) = e^{kt}$.

Since $A(10) = 11$, we have

$$11 = e^{10k}$$

or $10k = \ln 11$

$$k = \frac{1}{10} \ \ln 11.$$

Hence, the formula is

$$A = e^{\frac{t}{10}(\ln 11)}.$$

Note: We could write

$$A = e^{\ln(11)^{\frac{t}{10}}} = (11)^{\frac{t}{10}}.$$

If $A = 15$, we solve for t to arrive

at

$$15 = e^{\frac{t}{10}(\ln 11)}$$

$$\ln 15 = \frac{t}{10}(\ln 11)$$

$$\frac{t}{10} = \frac{\ln 15}{\ln 11}$$

$$t = 10\left(\frac{\ln 15}{\ln 11}\right)$$

$$t \approx 10(1.1293447)$$

$$= 11.293447,$$

or about 11.3°.

9. The formula is $\frac{R}{r} = e^{\frac{t \ \ln 2}{5600}}$.

If $t = 11,200$, then we have

$$\frac{t \ \ln 2}{5600} = \frac{11,200 \ \ln 2}{5600} = 2 \ \ln 2 = \ln 4.$$

Thus, $\frac{R}{r} = e^{\ln 4} = 4$, or $r = \frac{1}{4}R$.

13. Using the formula

$$A(t) = A_0 e^{rt},$$

with $A_0 = \$2000$, $r = .08$, and $t = 1$,

gives

$$A = 2000\ e^{.08}$$
$$A = 2000(1.0832871)$$
$$A = \$2166.57.$$

17. We have

$$A = 5800\ e^{.13(6)} = 5800\ e^{.78}$$
$$A = 5800(2.1814723)$$

or $A = \$12,652.54.$

21. If $A = P\ e^{ni}$, then

$$\frac{A}{P} = e^{ni}$$

$$\ln\left(\frac{A}{P}\right) = ni$$

so that $i = \frac{1}{n}\ \ln\left(\frac{A}{P}\right).$

25. Using Newton's law of cooling we
have $f(t) = T_O + C\ e^{-kt}$. The
environment the lava is introduced
to is $T_O = 20°$. Also, we are given
that $f(0) = 800°$. This gives
$800 = 20 + C\ e^0$, or $C = 780$. Thus,
we have $f(t) = 20 + 780\ e^{-kt}$. To
solve for k we use the fact that
$f(5) = 410$. This gives

$$410 = 20 + 780\ e^{-k(5)}$$
$$390 = 780\ e^{-5k}$$
$$e^{5k} = \frac{780}{390} = 2$$
$$5k = \ln 2$$
$$k = \frac{1}{5}\ \ln 2.$$

Hence,
$$f(t) = 20 + 780\ e^{-\frac{1}{5}t\ \ln 2}.$$

Then,
$$f(15) = 20 + 780\ e^{\frac{-15}{5}\ \ln 2}$$
$$f(15) = 20 + 780\ e^{-3\ \ln 2}$$
$$f(15) = 20 + 780\ e^{\ln\left(\frac{1}{8}\right)}$$
$$f(15) = 20 + \frac{780}{8}$$
$$f(15) = 117.5°,$$

since $-3\ \ln 2 = \ln(2)^{-3} = \ln\left(\frac{1}{8}\right),$

and $e^{\ln\left(\frac{1}{8}\right)} = \frac{1}{8}.$

29. We wish to solve for t when
$G = 2G_0$. This gives

$$2G_0 = \frac{m \cdot G_0}{G_0 + (m-G_0)e^{-kmt}}$$

$$G_0 + (m - G_0)e^{-kmt} = \frac{m}{2}$$

$$(m - G_0)e^{-kmt} = \frac{m}{2} - G_0, \text{or } \frac{m-2G_0}{2}$$

$$e^{-kmt} = \frac{m - 2G_0}{2(m - G_0)}$$

$$e^{kmt} = \frac{2(m - G_0)}{m - 2G_0}.$$

We are given that $G_0 = 1000$,
$m = 2500$, $k = .0004$, and t is in
decades. Thus

$$kmt = \ln \frac{2(m - G_0)}{m - 2G_0}$$

$$(.0004)(2500)t = \ln \frac{2(1500)}{500}$$

$$t = \ln 6,$$

so that $t \approx 1.7917595,$
which means "about 1.8 years."

Section 5.6   Common Logarithms

Additional Examples

Example 1   Use logarithms to approximate

$$\frac{(3.11)^4}{6.7\sqrt{5.62}}.$$

Solution   Letting $N = \frac{(3.11)^4}{6.7\sqrt{5.62}}$ we have

$$\log N = 4\ \log(3.11) - \log 6.7$$

$$- \frac{1}{2}\ \log(5.62)$$

$$= 4(0.4928) - (0.8261)$$

$$- \frac{1}{2}(0.7497)$$

$$= 1.9712 - (0.8261) - (0.3749)$$

$$= 1.9712 - 1.2010$$

$$\log N = 0.7702.$$

Using the table we can see that
$N \approx 5.89$. That is

$$\frac{(3.11)^4}{6.7\sqrt{5.62}} \approx 5.89.$$

Example 2   Use logarithms to approximate

$$\sqrt[3]{242} + \sqrt[4]{176}.$$

Solution   This calculation must be treated with care because we should not try to use logarithms over a sum. That is, $\log(a + b)$ cannot be reduced. We must treat each term separately, calculating $\sqrt[3]{242}$, then $\sqrt[4]{176}$, and then adding the results. We have the following.

(a)   Let $N = \sqrt[3]{242}$. Then

$$N = (242)^{1/3}$$

$$\log N = \frac{1}{3} \log 242$$

$$= \frac{1}{3}(2.3838)$$

$$\log N = 0.7946.$$

Calculating the antilog gives

$$N \approx 6.232.$$

(b)   Let $M = \sqrt[4]{176}$. Then

$$M = (176)^{1/4}$$

$$\log M = \frac{1}{4} \log 176$$

$$= \frac{1}{4}(2.2455)$$

$$\log M = 0.5614.$$

Calculating the antilog gives

$$M \approx 3.643.$$

We conclude that $\sqrt[3]{242} + \sqrt[4]{176}$ ≈ 9.875. Using a calculator to calculate the result directly gives the result 9.8740003. Since both N and M were rounded upward in the third decimal place during the logarithmic solutions, we can see where the difference in the answers occurs. The logarithmic approximation again seems relatively accurate.

Selected Solutions

1.   The characteristic of 875 is 2 since $875 = 8.75 \times 10^2$.

5.   The characteristic of 0.00023 is -4 since $0.00023 = 2.3 \times 10^{-4}$.

9.   Since $0.000893 = 8.93 \times 10^{-4}$, and $\log 8.93 = 0.9509$, we have $\log 0.000893 = .9509 - 4$, or

$$\begin{array}{r} -4.0000 \\ 0.9509 \\ \hline -3.0491 \end{array}$$

$\log 0.000893 = -3.0491.$

13.   We have $\log 7.63 = 0.8825$.

17.   Since $0.008094 = 8.094 \times 10^{-3}$ and using a calculator gives $\log 8.094 = 0.9082$, we have $\log 0.008094$

$$= 0.9082 - 3, \text{ or } \begin{array}{r} -3.0000 \\ 0.9082 \\ \hline -2.0918 \end{array}$$

$\log 0.008094 = 2.0918.$

We note that on a calculator if we place in the number 0.008094, then push the log button we get -2.0918368.

21.   If N is a number such that $\log N = .8733 - 2$, we note in the table of common logarithms (Table 2 in the textbook) that the mantissa .8733 goes with the number 7.47. That is, $\log 7.47 = .8733$. Hence, $N = 0.0747$, moving the decimal two places to the left.

On a calculator we need the number $.8733 - 2.0000 = -1.1267$. Place -1.1267, push "inv" and "log". The result is $N = 0.0746965$.

25.   Using Table 2, the mantissa .8039 is not present. We see the following:

$$10 \left\{ \text{x} \left\{ \begin{array}{l} \log 6.360 = .8035 \\ \log n = .8039 \\ \log 6.370 = .8041 \end{array} \right\} 4 \right\} 6$$

Using the ratio $\frac{x}{10} = \frac{4}{6}$, we have

$6x = 40$, or $x = 6.666$. Rounding

off we use $x = 7$ and conclude that

$n = 6.367$. Hence, if N is a

number such that log N = .8039 −3,

we conclude that N = 0.006367, or

N = 0.00637.

Using a calculator, .8039 − 3.0000

is −2.1961 and "inv log" (−2.1961)

= .00636649. To three significant

digits, N = .00637.

29. Using the formula
$$\log_b x = \frac{\log x}{\log b},$$
we have, using e = 2.718281828,

$\ln .98 = \frac{\log .98}{\log e} = \frac{.9912 - 1}{.4343}$

$\quad = \frac{-0.0088}{0.4343} = -0.0202.$

We write, ln .98 = −0.02.

33. We have
$$\log_2 10 = \frac{\log 10}{\log 2} = \frac{1}{\log 2}$$

$\quad \approx \frac{1}{0.30103}$, or

$\log_2 10 = 3.32193$. We round

off to the nearest hundredth as

$\log_2 10 = 3.32.$

37. We have, using Table 2,
$$\log_4 12 = \frac{\log 12}{\log 4} = \frac{1.0792}{0.6021},$$ or

$\log_4 12 = 1.79239$. Rounded

to the nearest nundredth,

$\quad \log_4 12 = 1.79.$

41. If $100^{2x+1} = 17$, then

$(2x + 1) \log 100 = \log 17$, and

since log 100 = 2 and log 17

= 1.2304, we have

$2x + 1 = \frac{\log 17}{\log 100} = \frac{1.2304}{2} = .6152$

$\quad 2x = -1 + .6152 = -.3848$

$\quad\quad x = -.1924$, or $x \approx -.19.$

The solution set is $\{-.19\}$.

45. If $.01^{3x} = .005$, then

3x log (.01) = log (.005). We

have log (.01) = −2 and log (.005)

= .6990 − 3 = −2.3010. Hence,

$3x = \frac{\log (.005)}{\log (.01)} = \frac{-2.3010}{-2}$

$\quad 3x = 1.1505$

$\quad\quad x = 0.3835.$

Rounded to the nearest hundredth

we have x = 0.38. The solution set

is $\{.38\}$.

47. Let $n = (8.16)^{1/3}$.

Then log n = $\frac{1}{3}$ log 8.16

$\quad\quad \log n = \frac{1}{3}(.9117)$

$\quad\quad \log n = .3039$

so that n = 2.0132.

Rounded to three significant digits,

n = 2.01.

49. Let $N = \frac{(7.06)^3}{(31.7)(\sqrt{1.09}}$. Then we

have log N = 3 log 7.06 − log 31.7

$\quad\quad - \frac{1}{2} \log 1.09$

$\quad = 3(0.8488) - 1.5011$

$\quad\quad - \frac{1}{2}(0.0374)$

$\quad = 2.5464 - 1.5011 - 0.0187$

$\quad = 2.5464 - 1.5198$

$\quad \log N = 1.0266.$

The antilog of .0266 is 1.063.

Hence, $N \approx 10^{1.0266} \approx 10.63.$

Rounded to three significant digits,

N = 10.6.

51. Let $N = (115)^{1/2} + (35.2)^{2/3}$.

Calculate $a = (115)^{1/2}$ and

$b = (35.2)^{2/3}$ separately.

$a = (115)^{1/2}$ $b = (35.2)^{2/3}$

$\log a = \frac{1}{2} \log 115$ $\log b = \frac{2}{3} \log 35.2$

$= \frac{1}{2}(2.0607)$ $= \frac{2}{3}(1.5465)$

$\log a = 1.0303$ $\log b = 1.0310$

$a \approx 10.72$ $b \approx 10.74$

Hence $N \approx 21.46$ or 21.5 to three significant digits.

53. Using $n \approx -7600 \log r$, we have that:

(a) if $r \approx .9$, then

$n \approx -7600 \log (.9)$

$n \approx -7600 (-0.0458) = 348.$

We conclude that n is about 350 years.

(b) if $r = .3$, then

$n \approx -7600 \log (.3)$

$n \approx -7600 (-0.5229)$

$n \approx 3974.04.$

We conclude that n is about 4000 years.

(c) Using $r = \frac{1}{2} = .5$, we have

$n \approx -7600 \log (\frac{1}{2}) = 7600 \log 2$

$n \approx 7600(0.3010) \approx 2287.6.$

We conclude that n is about 2300 years.

57. The pH of a solution is given by $pH = -\log [H_3O^+]$, where $[H_3O^+]$ is the hydronium ion concentration.

In limes $[H_3O^+] = 1.6 \times 10^{-2}$, so the pH is

$pH = -\log (1.6 \times 10^{-2})$

$= -\log (1.6) - \log (10^{-2})$

$= -.2041 + 2 = 1.7959,$

or approximately 1.8.

61. Using the formula that $pH = -\log [H_3O^+]$, and given that the pH of beer is 4.8, we can solve for the $[H_3O^+]$ concentration as

$\log [H_3O^+] = -4.8$

$[H_3O^+] = 10^{-4.8} = 1.58 \times 10^{-5},$

or approximately 1.6×10^{-5}.

63. We use $A = \sqrt{s(s - a)(s - b)(s - c)}$, where $s = \frac{a + b + c}{2}$.

If $a = 114$, $b = 196$, and $c = 153$,

then $s = \frac{114 + 196 + 153}{2} = 231.5,$

and A

$= \sqrt{(231.5)(231.5-114)(231.5-196)(231.5-153)}$

$A = \sqrt{(231.5)(117.5)(35.5)(78.5)}.$

We have $\log A$

$= \frac{1}{2}[\log 231.5 + \log 117.5 + \log 35.5 + \log 78.5]$

$= \frac{1}{2}[2.3646 + 2.0700 + 1.5502 + 1.8949]$

$= \frac{1}{2}(7.8797),$ so that

$\log A = 3.9399.$

Taking the antilog, we have

$A \approx 8707.$

65. Using the formula $\log P = k \log a$ [Note: this is the same as $P = a^k$, but we use logarithms to find P assuming that $a^k = a^{.8}$ is to be found by using logarithms], with $k = .8$, we have the following:

(a) If $a = 230$, then

$\log P = .8 \log 230$

$\log P \approx .8(2.3617) \approx 1.8894.$

Then we find $P \approx 77.5$. We report a population of about 78.

(b) If $a = 95$, then

$\log P = .8 \log 95 \approx .8(1.9777)$

$\log P = 1.58216.$

This give $P \approx 38.2085$. We report a population of about 38.

(c) If $a = 20,000$, then

$\log P = .8 \log 20,000 \approx .8(4.3010)$

$\log P \approx 3.4408.$

This gives $P \approx 2759.3$. We report a population of about 2760, or, to the nearest hundred, about 2800.

Appendix: Interpolation

Selected Solutions

1. Using Table 2 on common logarithms we have the following.

$$10\left\{5\left\{\begin{array}{l} \log 2.340 = .3692 \\ \log 2.345 = n \\ \log 2.350 = .3711 \end{array}\right\} x\right\}19$$

Solving the proportion $\frac{5}{10} = \frac{x}{19}$,
we have $10x = 95$, or $x = 9.5$. We round this to $x = 9$ and conclude that $\log 2.345 \approx .3701$. Then we have $\log 2345 \approx 3.3701$.

5. From Table 2, we have the following.

$$10\left\{3\left\{\begin{array}{l} \log 6.270 = .7973 \\ \log 6.273 = n \\ \log 6.280 = .7980 \end{array}\right\} x\right\}7$$

Solving the proportion $\frac{3}{10} = \frac{x}{7}$, we have $10x = 21$, or $x = 2.1$. We then conclude that
$\log 6.237 \approx .7975$.
Then we have

$$\log .06273 = .7975-2, \text{ or}$$
$$\log .06273 = -1.2025, \text{ or}$$
$$\log .06273 = 8.7975-10.$$

Each of these answers is equivalent.

9. Let N be the number such that $\log N = 1.7942$. Using the mantissa .7942, we have the following.

$$10\left\{x\left\{\begin{array}{l} \log 6.220 = .7938 \\ \log n \quad = .7942 \\ \log 6.230 = .7945 \end{array}\right\}4\right\}7$$

Solving $\frac{x}{10} = \frac{4}{7}$, we have $7x = 40$,
or $x = 5.7$. We round to $x = 6$ and conclude that $\log 6.226 \approx .7942$.
Then we have that

$$\log 62.26 \approx 1.7942, \text{ or}$$
$$N \approx 62.26.$$

13. Let $\log N = 5.6930$. Using the mantissa .6930 in Table 2, we have the following.

$$10\left\{x\left\{\begin{array}{l} \log 4.930 = .6928 \\ \log n = .6930 \\ \log 4.940 = .6937 \end{array}\right\}2\right\}9$$

Solving $\frac{x}{10} = \frac{2}{9}$, we have $9x = 20$, or $x \approx 2$. We conclude that $\log 4.932 \approx .6930$.
Hence,

$$\log 493200 \approx 5.6930, \text{ or}$$
$$N \approx 493,200.$$

17. If we let $N = \frac{(26.13)(5.427)}{101.6}$, then we have
$\log N = \log(26.13) + \text{Log}(5.427) - \log(101.6)$.
Using Table 2 and interpolation we have:

$$10\left\{3\left\{\begin{array}{l} \log 2.610 = .4166 \\ \log 2.613 = n \\ \log 2.620 = .4183 \end{array}\right\} x\right\}17$$

$\frac{3}{10} = \frac{x}{17}$, $10x = 51$, $x = 5$,
hence, $\log 2.613 \approx .4171$.

$$10\left\{7\left\{\begin{array}{l} \log 5.420 = .7340 \\ \log 5.427 = m \\ \log 5.430 = .7348 \end{array}\right\} x\right\}8$$

$\frac{7}{10} = \frac{x}{8}$, $10x = 56$, $x \approx 6$,
$\log 5.427 \approx .7346$.

$$10\left\{6\left\{\begin{array}{l} \log 1.010 = .0043 \\ \log 1.016 = k \\ \log 1.020 = .0086 \end{array}\right\} x\right\}43$$

$\frac{6}{10} = \frac{x}{43}$, $10x = 258$, or $x \approx 26$.
We have $\log 1.016 = .0069$. Hence,
$\log N = \log 26.13 + \log 5.427 - \log(101.6)$
$\log N = 1.4171 + .7346 - 2.0069$
$\log N = 2.1517 - 2.0069 = 0.1448$.
Using Table 2 again we see that:

$$10\left\{x\left\{\begin{array}{l} \log 1.390 = .1430 \\ \log N = .1448 \\ \log 1.400 = .1461 \end{array}\right\}18\right\}31$$

and $\frac{x}{10} = \frac{18}{31}$ gives $31x = 180$, or $x \approx 6$.

Thus, log 1.396 $\approx$ .1448. We conclude that

$$\frac{(26.13)(5.427)}{101.6} \approx 1.396.$$

Using a calculator to check the accuracy we arrive at N = 1.3957432.

21. If we let N = $(.2374)^{.05}$, then log N = (.05) log (.2374). Using Table 2 we have:

$$10\left\{4\left\{\begin{array}{l}\log 2.370 = .3747 \\ \log 2.374 = n \\ \log 2.380 = .3766\end{array}\right\}x\right\}19$$

and $\frac{4}{10} = \frac{x}{19}$ gives 10x = 76, or

x $\approx$ 8. Thus, log 2.374 $\approx$ .3755 and log .2374 $\approx$ 0.3755-1 = -0.6245. Then we have

log N $\approx$ (.05)(-.6245) = -.03123, or

log N = .9688-1.

Using Table 2 again, we have:

$$10\left\{x\left\{\begin{array}{l}\log 9.300 = .9685 \\ \log n = .9688 \\ \log 9.310 = .9689\end{array}\right\}3\right\}4$$

and $\frac{x}{10} = \frac{3}{4}$ gives 4x = 30, or x $\approx$ 7.

We have log 9.307 $\approx$ .9688, and log .9307 $\approx$ .9688-1, so that N $\approx$ .9307.

25. Using L = $\frac{d^4}{h^2}$, with d = 2.143 and h = 12.25, gives

$$L = \frac{(2.143)^4}{(12.25)^2},$$

log L = 4 log (2.143)-2 log (12.25). Using Table 2, we have:

$$10\left\{3\left\{\begin{array}{l}\log 2.140 = .3304 \\ \log 2.143 = n \\ \log 2.150 = .3324\end{array}\right\}x\right\}20$$

$$\frac{3}{10} = \frac{x}{20}$$

$$x = 6.$$

Hence, log 2.143 $\approx$ .3310, and:

$$10\left\{5\left\{\begin{array}{l}\log 1.220 = .0864 \\ \log 1.225 = n \\ \log 1.230 = .0899\end{array}\right\}x\right\}35$$

$$\frac{5}{10} = \frac{x}{35}$$

$$x \approx 17.$$

Hence, log 1.225 = .0881 and log 12.25 = 1.0881. Now we have

log L = 4 log(2.143) - 2 log(12.25)

log L = 4(0.3310) - 2(1.0881)

log L = 1.3240 - 2.1762

log L = -0.8522 = 0.1478-1.

Using Table 2, we have:

$$10\left\{x\left\{\begin{array}{l}\log 1.400 = .1461 \\ \log n = .1478 \\ \log 1.410 = .1492\end{array}\right\}17\right\}31$$

and $\frac{x}{10} = \frac{17}{31}$ gives 31x = 170, or

x = 5.484. Using x $\approx$ 5 gives log 1.405 $\approx$ .1478. Hence, if log L = .1478-1, we conclude that L $\approx$ 0.1405.

Chapter 5 Review Exercises

Selected Solutions

1. If f(x) = 2^x, consider the table:

x	-3	-2	-1	0	1	2	3
y	1/8	1/4	1/2	1	2	4	8

See the graph in the answer section of the text.

3. If f(x) = $(\frac{1}{2})^{x+1}$, consider the following table:

x	-4	-3	-2	-1	0	1	2
y	8	4	2	1	1/2	1/4	1/8

See the graph in the text.

5. If f(x) = $(x-1) e^{-x} = \frac{x-1}{e^x}$, we have the following table (with each

calculation performed using a calculator and rounded to two decimals):

x	$f(x) = (x-1)\,e^{-x}$
-2	$-3\,e^2 \approx -22.17$
-1	$-2\,e \approx -5.44$
0	$-3 = -1$
1	0
2	$e^{-2} \approx 0.14$
3	$2\,e^{-3} \approx 0.1$

See the graph in the answer section of the text.

9. If $8^P = 32$, we use the fact that $2^3 = 8$ and $2^5 = 32$ to write
$$8^P = 32$$
$$(2^3)^P = 2^5$$
$$2^{3P} = 2^5, \quad \text{so that}$$
$$3p = 5, \quad \text{or } p = 5/3.$$
The solution set is $\{5/3\}$.

11. If $\dfrac{8}{27} = b^{-3}$, then
$$b^3 = \frac{27}{8}$$
$$b = \sqrt[3]{\frac{27}{8}} = \frac{3}{2}.$$
The solution set is $\{3/2\}$.

13. If $A(t) = 800\,e^{-.04t}$, then $A(0) = 800\,e^0 = 800$ grams.

15. Using the continually compounding interest formula $A = A_0\,e^{rt}$, with $A_0 = 1200$, $r = .10$, and $t = 4$, we have
$$A = 1200\,e^{(.10)4} = 1200\,e^{.4}$$
$$A \approx 1200(1.4918247) \approx \$1790.19.$$

17. The rate of increase is $r = .06$ per year. Using the formula $A = A_0 e^{rt}$ with $A = 2A_0$ (to consider twice the original amount A_0), we

solve for t. This gives
$$2A_0 = A_0\,e^{.06t}$$
$$2 = e^{.06t}$$
$$\ln 2 = .06t, \qquad \text{since } \ln e^n = n,$$
$$.06t = \ln 2$$
$$t = \frac{\ln 2}{.06} \approx 11.55245.$$
We conclude that the consumption will be doubled in about 12 years.

21. If $\left(\dfrac{1}{16}\right)^{1/4} = \dfrac{1}{2}$, the logarithmic form is $\log_{1/16}\left(\dfrac{1}{2}\right) = \dfrac{1}{4}$. This follows from the definition that $\log_b a = n$ if and only if $b^n = a$.

25. If $e^{.1} = 1.1052$, the logarithmic form is $\ln(1.1052) = .1$.

29. If $\log 3.45 = .537819$, the exponential form is $10^{.537819} = 3.45$.

33. Using the properties of exponents and the properties of logarithms, we can write
$$\log_5 x^2 y^4 \sqrt[5]{m^3 p}$$
$$= \log_5 x^2 y^4 m^{3/5} p^{1/5}$$
$$= \log_5 x^2 + \log_5 y^4 + \log_5 m^{3/5} + \log_5 p^{1/5}$$
$$= 2\log_5 x + 4\log_5 y + \frac{3}{5}\log_5 m + \frac{1}{5}\log_5 p.$$

37. Using Table 2, we have $\log 1.050 = 0.0212$, and hence, $\log 1050 = 3.0212$.

41. Using Table 2, we see that
$$\log 4.46 = .6493.$$
Hence, $\log 0.0446 = .6493-2$. Thus, the antilog of $.6493-2$ is $x = 0.0446$.

45. Let $N = \sqrt[5]{\dfrac{27.1}{4.33}}$. Using common

logarithms and Table 2, we have

$$\log N = \frac{1}{5} \log \frac{27.1}{4.33}$$

$$\log N = \frac{1}{5} \log 27.1 - \frac{1}{5} \log 4.33$$

$$\log N \approx \frac{1}{5}(1.4330) - \frac{1}{5}(0.6365)$$

or $\log N \approx .1593$.

From Table 2 we see that:

$$10 \left\{ x \left\{ \begin{array}{l} \log 1.440 = .1584 \\ \log N = .1593 \\ \log 1.450 = .1614 \end{array} \right\} 9 \right\} 30$$

and $\frac{x}{10} = \frac{9}{30}$ gives $x = 3$. Hence

$\log 1.443 \approx .1593$, and we conclude

that $\sqrt[5]{\frac{27.1}{4.33}} \approx 1.443$.

49. If $h(t) = .5 + \log t$, then
$h(10) = .5 + \log 10 = .5 + 1 = 1.5m$.

53. If $5^r = 11$, then

$$\ln 5^r = \ln 11$$

$$r \ln 5 = \ln 11$$

$$r = \frac{\ln 11}{\ln 5} \approx 1.4898961,$$

using a calculator. Rounded to
the nearest thousandth, the
solution set is $\{1.490\}$.

57. If $6^{2-m} = 2^{3m+1}$, then

$$\ln 6^{2-m} = \ln 2^{3m+1}$$

$$(2-m)\ln 6 = (3m + 1) \ln 2$$

$$2 \ln 6 - m \ln 6 = 3m \ln 2 + \ln 2$$

$$2 \ln 6 - \ln 2 = 3m \ln 2 + m\ln 6$$

$$m(3 \ln 2 + \ln 6) = 2 \ln 6 - \ln 2$$

$$m(\ln 8 + \ln 6) = \ln 36 - \ln 2$$

$$m(\ln 48) = \ln 18$$

$$m = \frac{\ln 18}{\ln 48} \approx 0.7466344.$$

Rounded to the nearest thousandth,
the solution set is $\{0.747\}$.

61. If $\ln 6x - \ln (x+1) = \ln 4$, then

$$\ln \frac{6x}{x+1} = \ln 4, \text{ and}$$

hence, $\qquad \frac{6x}{x+1} = 4$

$$6x = 4(x + 1)$$

$$6x = 4x + 4$$

$$2x = 4, \text{ or } x = 2.$$

The solution set is $\{2\}$.

65. If $y = \frac{5^x - 5^{-x}}{2}$, then

$$5^x - 5^{-x} = 2y$$

$$5^x - \frac{1}{5^x} = 2y$$

$$\frac{5^{2x} - 1}{5^x} = 2y$$

$$5^{2x} - 1 = 2y5^x$$

$$5^{2x} - 2y5^x - 1 = 0$$

Letting $u = 5^x$, we have

$u^2 - 2yu - 1 = 0$, which is a

quadratic equation in u. We can
use the quadratic formula with
$a = 1$, $b = -2y$, and $c = -1$. We
have

$$u = \frac{-b \pm \sqrt{b^2 - 4ac}}{2a} = \frac{2y \pm \sqrt{4y^2 + 4}}{2}$$

$$u = y \pm \sqrt{y^2 + 1}.$$

Since $u = 5^x$, we have

$$5^x = y \pm \sqrt{y^2 + 1}$$

$$\ln 5^x = \ln (y \pm \sqrt{y^2 + 1})$$

$$x \ln 5 = \ln (y \pm \sqrt{y^2 + 1})$$

$$x = \frac{\ln (y \pm \sqrt{y^2 + 1}}{\ln 5}.$$

However, we <u>must</u> note that
$y - \sqrt{y^2 + 1}$ is <u>negative</u> for all
real numbers y. Hence, the <u>only</u>
solution is

$$x = \frac{\ln (y + \sqrt{y^2 + 1})}{\ln 5}.$$

69. If $N = a + b \ln \frac{c}{d}$ and we wish to
solve for c, we write

$$N - a = b \ln \left(\frac{c}{d}\right)$$

$$\ln \left(\frac{c}{d}\right) = \frac{N - a}{b}$$

$$\frac{c}{d} = e^{\frac{N-a}{b}}$$

and $\qquad c = d\, e^{\frac{N-a}{b}}$.

71. Since $\ln e^A = A$, we see that
$\ln e^{-5.3} = -5.3$.

73. Using a calculator, we have
$$\ln 89 \approx 4.4886.$$
Note that in Table 1A we see that
$$e^{4.5} \approx 90.02,$$
which also states that
$$\ln 90.02 \approx 4.5.$$

77. Let $N = \log_{1/2}(9.45)$, so that
$$\left(\frac{1}{2}\right)^N = 9.45$$
$$N \ln \left(\frac{1}{2}\right) = \ln 9.45$$
or
$$N = \frac{\ln 9.45}{\ln(1/2)} = \frac{\ln 9.45}{-\ln 2}$$
$$\approx -3.2403.$$

81. Let $N = \log .009814$. We use Table 2 to evaluate $\log 9.814$. We have:
$$10\left\{ 4 \left\{ \begin{array}{l} \log 9.810 = .9917 \\ \log 9.814 = n \\ \log 9.820 = .9921 \end{array} \right\} x \right\} 4$$
and $\frac{4}{10} = \frac{x}{4}$ gives $10x = 16$, or $x \approx 2$. We have $\log 9.814 \approx .9919$. Hence,
$\log .009814 = .9919 - 3$ or
$\log .009814 = -2.0081.$

85. Using $A = P\left(1 + \frac{i}{m}\right)^{mn}$, with $A = 2000$, $i = .06$, $m = 4$, and $n = 8$, we have
$$2000 = P\left(1 + \frac{.06}{4}\right)^{(4)(8)}$$
$$2000 = P(1 + .015)^{32}$$
$$2000 = P(1.015)^{32}$$
$$P = \frac{2000}{(1.015)^{32}} \approx \frac{2000}{1.610\,3243}$$
or $P = \$1241.99.$

89. Use the formula $A = A_0 e^{rt}$ for continuously compounding, and let $A_0 = \$1$, $A = \$2$, and $r = .13$. Solving for t gives
$$2 = 1\,e^{.13t}$$
$$e^{.13t} = 2$$
$$.13t = \ln 2$$
$$t = \frac{\ln 2}{.13} \approx 5.3319.$$

We conclude that it would take approximately 5.33 years, or 5 years and 4 months.

91. If $R = \$1500$, $i = 14\% = .14$, and $n = 7$, then the amount is
$$A = R\left[\frac{(1 + i)^n - 1}{i}\right]$$
$$= 1500\left[\frac{(1 + .14)^7 - 1}{.14}\right]$$
$$= 1500\left[\frac{(1.14)^7 - 1}{.14}\right]$$
$$= 1500\left[\frac{2.50227 - 1}{.14}\right]$$
$$= 1500[10.73049]$$
$$A = \$16,095.74.$$

93. Using the formula
$$A_0 = R\left[\frac{(1 + i)^n - 1}{i}\right] \text{ for the}$$
amount accrued for the first 12 years with $R = 10,000$, $i = .12$, and $n = 12$, we have
$$A_0 = 10,000\left[\frac{(1.12)^{12} - 1}{.12}\right]$$
$$= 10,000\left[\frac{2.895976}{.12}\right]$$
$$A_0 \approx 10,000(24.133133) = \$241,331.33.$$
Manual then deposits this amount A for 9 years at 10% compounded semiannually. We then use the formula $A = A_0\left(1 + \frac{i}{m}\right)^{mt}$, where we use $A_0 = \$241,331.33$, $i = .10$, $m = 2$, and $t = 9$. This gives
$$A = A_0\left(1 + \frac{.10}{2}\right)^{18} = A_0(1.05)^{18}$$
$$A = 241,331.33(2.4066192)$$
or $A = \$580,792.62.$

97. We use the formula for $\ln x$,
$$\ln x \approx \left[\left(\frac{3A^2}{5} + 1\right)\frac{A^2}{3} + 1\right] 2A,$$
$$A = \frac{x - 1}{x + 1}, \text{ for } \frac{1}{2} \le x \le 3/2.$$

(a) If $x = .8$, then $A = \frac{.8 - 1}{.8 + 1} = -\frac{1}{9}$, and
$$\frac{3A^2}{5} = \frac{3}{(81)(5)} = \frac{1}{135}$$

$$\frac{3A^2}{5} + 1 = \frac{1}{135} + 1 = \frac{136}{135}$$

$$(\frac{3A^2}{5} + 1)\frac{A^2}{3} = (\frac{136}{135})(\frac{1}{3 \cdot 81})$$

$$= \frac{136}{(135)(243)}$$

$$\approx 0.0041457$$

$$(\frac{3A^2}{5} + 1)\frac{A^2}{3} + 1 = 1.0041457,$$

and finally,

$$\left[(\frac{3A^2}{5} + 1)\frac{A^2}{3} + 1\right]2A \approx [1.0041457](\frac{-2}{9}),$$

so that

$$\ln(0.8) \approx -0.2231435.$$

The accuracy of this result can be observed by a calculator check of $\ln(0.8) = -0.2231436$.

Similarly, if $x = 1.2$, then

$$A = \frac{1.2-1}{1.2+1} = \frac{.2}{2.2} = \frac{1}{11},$$

and

$$\frac{3A^2}{5} = \frac{3}{605},$$

$$\frac{3A^2}{5} + 1 = \frac{608}{605},$$

$$(\frac{3A^2}{5} + 1)\frac{A^2}{3} = (\frac{608}{605})(\frac{1}{363}),$$

$$(\frac{3A^2}{5} + 1)\frac{A^2}{3} + 1 \approx 1.0027685,$$

and

$$\left[(\frac{3A^2}{5} + 1)\frac{A^2}{3}+1\right]2A \approx (1.0027685)(\frac{2}{11}),$$

so that

$$\ln(1.2) \approx 0.1823215.$$

(b) We have that $\ln 2 = \ln(\frac{3}{2} \cdot \frac{4}{3})$,

or $\ln 2 = \ln\frac{3}{2} + \ln\frac{4}{3}$.

If $x = \frac{3}{2}$, $A = \frac{x-1}{x+1} = \frac{3/2 - 1}{3/2 + 1}$

$$= \frac{1/2}{5/2} = \frac{1}{5}, \quad \text{and}$$

$$\ln\frac{3}{2} \approx ((\frac{3A^2}{5} + 1)\frac{A^2}{3} + 1)2A$$

$$= \left[(\frac{3}{5^3} + 1)\frac{1}{3 \cdot 5^2} + 1\right]\frac{2}{5}$$

$$\approx [(1.024)\frac{1}{75} + 1]\frac{2}{5}$$

$$\approx (1.01365333...)\frac{2}{5}, \quad \text{so that}$$

$$\ln\frac{3}{2} \approx .40546.$$

If $x = \frac{4}{3}$, $A = \frac{x-1}{x+1} = \frac{1/3}{7/3} = \frac{1}{7}$, and

$$\ln\frac{4}{3} = \left[(\frac{3}{5 \cdot 7^2} + 1)\frac{1}{3 \cdot 7^2} + 1\right]\frac{2}{7}$$

$$\approx [(1.0606)\frac{1}{147} + 1]\frac{2}{7}$$

$$\approx (1.007215)\frac{2}{7}$$

$$\ln\frac{4}{3} \approx .28768.$$

Hence, $\ln 2 \approx .40545 + .28768$,
or $\ln 2 \approx .69314$.

(c) We have $\ln 3 = \ln(\frac{3}{2} \cdot 2) = \ln\frac{3}{2} +$

$\ln 2$ and from (b),

$$\ln 3 \approx .40545 + .69314$$

$$\ln 3 \approx 1.09860.$$

Also, $\ln 8 = \ln 2^3 = 3\ln 2$

$$\approx 3(.69314)$$

or $\ln 8 \approx 2.07942.$

99. Sterling's formula gives for "large" n,

$$n! \approx \sqrt{2\pi n}(\frac{n}{e})^n.$$

Hence,

$$100! \approx \sqrt{200\pi}(\frac{100}{e})^{100}.$$

If we use common logarithms to calculate the approximate on the right, we have

$$\log(100!) \approx \frac{1}{2}[\log 200 + \log \pi]$$

$$+ 100[\log 100 - \log e]$$

$$\log(100!) \approx \frac{1}{2}[2.3010 + .4971]$$

$$+ 100[2 - .4343]$$

$$\log(100!) = 1.3991 + 156.5700, \text{ or}$$

$$\log(100!) = 157.9691$$

Then, since $\log 9.313 \approx .9691$, we have that

$$100! \approx 9.313 \times 10^{157}.$$

Similarly, $200! \approx \sqrt{400\pi}(\frac{200}{e})^{200}$

$$\approx 7.88 \times 10^{374}.$$

Chapter 5 Test

1. Graph the exponential function $y = (\frac{1}{3})^{x-1}$.

2. Solve the exponential equation $16^{x+1} = 64$.

3. Solve the equation $(2a + 3)^x = (4a - 5)^x$ for a.

4. (a) Write $\log_5 (\frac{1}{125}) = -3$ in an exponential form.

    (b) Write $2^3 = 8$ in a logarithmic form.

5. Write $\log_4 x^3 y^2 \sqrt[5]{n^2 p^{-3}}$ as an appropriate sum, difference, and product of logarithms.

6. Solve the equation $\log_3 (x - 1) = -1$.

7. Solve the equation $\log_x (5x - 6) = 2$.

8. Evaluate $e^{-3 \ln 1/2}$.

9. Evaluate $\log_3 (\frac{\sqrt[4]{27}}{3})$.

10. Evaluate $\log_a (\frac{a^{-3} \sqrt[3]{a^4}}{a^{-5}})$.

11. Express $\frac{2}{3} \ln(2x + 1) - \frac{1}{3} \ln x + \frac{4}{3} \ln(2y)$ as a single logarithm.

12. If $\log 3 = 0.4771$ and $\log 2 = 0.3010$, find $\log 72$.

13. If $\ln 4 = 1.3862$ and $\ln 9 = 2.1972$, find $\ln 2/3$.

14. Solve the equation $\log_2 (x + 7) = 3 - \log_2 x$.

15. Solve the equation $\log_x (10x - 21) = 2$.

16. If $2000 is invested at an interest rate of 12% a year, compounded quarterly, what is the value of the investment after 18 months?

17. If $\log 3 = 0.4771$ and $\log 2 = 0.3010$, find $\log_3 32$.

18. If $\ln 2 = 0.6931$ and $\ln 5 = 1.6094$, find $\log_5 10$.

19. If $A = A_0 e^{-kt}$, solve for t.

20. Solve $12^{x-1} = 7$.

21. Solve $3^{x+4} = 5$.

22. Solve the equation $\ln(2x + 5) = \ln 6x - \ln(3x + 1)$.

23. Solve the equation $\log x^4 = (\log x)^3$.

24. Solve $y = \dfrac{e^x}{2(1 + e^x)}$ for x.

25. If a city having a population of 20,000 in 1986 is expected to increase in population at a rate of 7% a year, find the year in which the population has doubled.

26. If $y = e^{(t \ln 3)/7}$, is this equivalent to $y = (3)^{t/7}$? Justify your answer.

27. Use logarithms to approximate $(27.6)^{2.4}$.

28. Use logarithms to approximate $\sqrt{\dfrac{(6.2)^3}{(7.1)^2}}$.

(Answers for this test are on page 362.)

Chapter 6   Trigonometric Functions

Section 6.1   The Sine and Cosine Functions

Example 1   Find the coordinates of the point P on the unit circle which corresponds to s = π/3.

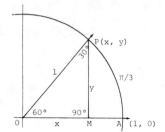

Solution   An arc of length π/3 is 2/3 as long as an arc of length π/2, so that point P is on a line making a 60° angle with the x-axis, as in the figure. Dropping a perpendicular from P produces a 30°-60° right triangle. The hypotenuse of this triangle has a length of 1 (we have a unit circle), with the short side of length 1/2 (our triangle is half of an equilateral triangle), and the medium side of length √3/2, since

$$(\tfrac{1}{2})^2 + (\tfrac{\sqrt{3}}{2})^2 = 1^2.$$

These results show that P has coordinates (1/2, √3/2).

Example 2   Find (a) sin π/3
(b) cos π/3   (c) sin π/6
(d) cos π/6.

Solution   A point with s = π/3 has coordinates (1/2, √3/2), as shown in Example 1. Thus, x = 1/2 and y = √3/2. By the definition of sine and cosine,

(a) $\sin \dfrac{\pi}{3} = y = \dfrac{\sqrt{3}}{2}$,

(b) $\cos \dfrac{\pi}{3} = x = \dfrac{1}{2}$.

By symmetry, π/6 leads to the point (√3/2, 1/2), with

(c) $\sin \dfrac{\pi}{6} = y = \dfrac{1}{2}$,

(d) $\cos \dfrac{\pi}{6} = x = \dfrac{\sqrt{3}}{2}$.

Selected Solutions

1. $\dfrac{5\pi}{4}$ corresponds to $P(-\dfrac{\sqrt{2}}{2},\ -\dfrac{\sqrt{2}}{2})$ on the unit circle.

5. 4π corresponds to $P(1, 0)$ on the unit circle.

9. $\dfrac{5\pi}{2}$ corresponds to $P(0, 1)$ on the unit circle.

13. 2.25π corresponds to $P(\dfrac{\sqrt{2}}{2},\ \dfrac{\sqrt{2}}{2})$ on the unit circle.

17.   If $P(\dfrac{2}{3}, \dfrac{\sqrt{5}}{3})$ corresponds to s, then the point corresponding to:

(a)   -s is $A(\dfrac{2}{3},\ \dfrac{-\sqrt{5}}{3})$,

(b)   s + 2π is $B(\dfrac{2}{3},\ \dfrac{\sqrt{5}}{3})$,

(c)   s + π is $C(-\dfrac{2}{3},\ \dfrac{-\sqrt{5}}{3})$,

(d)   π - s is $D(-\dfrac{2}{3},\ \dfrac{\sqrt{5}}{3})$.

21.   If $P(-\dfrac{1}{2}, \dfrac{\sqrt{3}}{2})$ corresponds to s, then the point corresponding to:

(a)   -s is $A(-\dfrac{1}{2},\ \dfrac{-\sqrt{3}}{2})$,

(b)   s + 2π is $B(-\dfrac{1}{2},\ \dfrac{\sqrt{3}}{2})$,

(c)   s + π is $C(\dfrac{1}{2},\ \dfrac{-\sqrt{3}}{2})$,

(d)   π - s is $D(\dfrac{1}{2},\ \dfrac{\sqrt{3}}{2})$.

25. If s is arc length on the unit circle, then s = 0 corresponds to P(1, 0). Hence, sin 0 = 0 and cos 0 = 1.

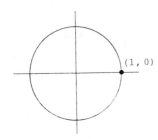

29. If s is arc length on the unit circle, then $s = \frac{3\pi}{2}$ corresponds to P(0, -1). Hence, $\sin \frac{3\pi}{2} = -1$, and $\cos \frac{3\pi}{2} = 0$.

33. If s is arc length on the unit circle, then $s = \frac{-\pi}{4}$ corresponds to $P(\frac{\sqrt{2}}{2}, \frac{-\sqrt{2}}{2})$. Hence, $\sin (-\frac{\pi}{4}) = \frac{-\sqrt{2}}{2}$, and $\cos (-\frac{\pi}{4}) = \frac{\sqrt{2}}{2}$.

37. s = 10 will terminate in quadrant III since $3\pi < 10 < \frac{7}{2}\pi$.

41. $\frac{-896.1}{-\pi} \approx 285.24$

Since -285π corresponds to π, $-896.1 \approx -285.24\pi = -285\pi - .24\pi$, which corresponds to $\pi - .24\pi$ $= .76\pi$, which terminates in the second quadrant.

45.

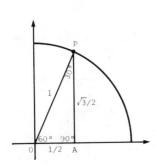

(a) Show that P is on the line $y = \sqrt{3}x$. Since $\pi/3$ corresponds to 60°, angle AOP = 60°. Then, since PAO = 90°, angle OPA = 30°. Thus, $x = \frac{1}{2}$ and $y = \frac{1}{2}\sqrt{3}$.

The slope of OP is $\frac{\Delta y}{\Delta x} = \frac{\frac{\sqrt{3}}{2}}{\frac{1}{2}} = \sqrt{3}$.

The equation of line OP is
$$y - 0 = \sqrt{3}(x - 0) \text{ or } y = \sqrt{3}x.$$

(b) The coordinates of P are $(\frac{1}{2}, \frac{\sqrt{3}}{2})$.

(c)

Arc	Coordinates
$\frac{-\pi}{3}$	$(\frac{1}{2}, -\frac{\sqrt{3}}{2})$
$\frac{2\pi}{3}$	$(-\frac{1}{2}, \frac{\sqrt{3}}{2})$
$\frac{4\pi}{3}$	$(-\frac{1}{2}, -\frac{\sqrt{3}}{2})$

49. $\cos \frac{2\pi}{3} = -\frac{1}{2}$ since $\frac{2\pi}{3}$ corresponds to $(-\frac{1}{2}, \frac{\sqrt{3}}{2})$.

53. $\sin \frac{5\pi}{6} = \frac{1}{2}$ since $\frac{5\pi}{6}$ corresponds to $(\frac{-\sqrt{3}}{2}, \frac{1}{2})$.

57. If $P(\frac{3}{8}, z)$ corresponds to arc length s on the unit circle, then $\cos s = \frac{3}{8}$ and $\sin s = z$.

61. If P(x,y) is on the unit circle, then $x^2 + y^2 = 1$. Hence, if $P(\frac{3}{5}, y)$, y > 0, is on the unit circle, we have
$$\frac{9}{25} + y^2 = 1$$
$$y^2 = \frac{16}{25}$$
$$y = \frac{4}{5}.$$

Hence, $\sin s = \frac{4}{5}$ and $\cos s = \frac{3}{5}$.

65. If $P(\frac{-1}{\sqrt{13}}, y)$, with $y > 0$, is on the

unit circle, then

$$\frac{1}{13} + y^2 = 1$$

$$y^2 = \frac{12}{13}$$

$$y = \frac{2\sqrt{3}}{\sqrt{13}}.$$

Hence, $\sin s = \frac{2\sqrt{3}}{\sqrt{13}} = \frac{2\sqrt{39}}{13}$, and

$$\cos s = \frac{-1}{\sqrt{13}} = \frac{-\sqrt{13}}{13}.$$

69. If $a < o$ and $x < o$, and if

$P(x, \frac{b}{\sqrt{a^2+b^2}})$ is on the unit circle,

then

$$x^2 + \frac{b^2}{a^2 + b^2} = 1$$

$$x^2 = 1 - \frac{b^2}{a^2 + b^2}$$

$$x^2 = \frac{a^2}{a^2 + b^2}$$

$$x = \frac{\pm\sqrt{a^2}}{\sqrt{a^2 + b^2}}$$

$$= \frac{a}{\sqrt{a^2 + b^2}},$$

since $a < o$ and we wish to have
$x < o$.   Hence,

$$\sin s = \frac{b}{\sqrt{a^2 + b^2}} \text{ and}$$

$$\cos s = \frac{a}{\sqrt{a^2 + b^2}}.$$

Section 6.2   Further Trigonometric Functions

Additional Examples

Example 1   Find (a) $\tan \pi/6$
(b) $\sec \pi/6$ (c) $\csc \pi/3$
(d) $\cot \pi/3$.

Solution   As we found in Example 1 in
the previous section, $\pi/6$ corresponds
to $P(\sqrt{3}/2, 1/2)$, with $x = \sqrt{3}/2$ and
$y = 1/2$. Using the definitions in
the text,

(a) $\tan \frac{\pi}{6} = \frac{y}{x} = \frac{1/2}{\sqrt{3}/2} = \frac{1}{\sqrt{3}} = \frac{\sqrt{3}}{3}$, and

(b) $\sec \frac{\pi}{6} = \frac{1}{x} = \frac{1}{\sqrt{3}/2} = \frac{2}{\sqrt{3}} = \frac{2\sqrt{3}}{3}$.

Also, from Example 1 in the previous
section, $\pi/3$ corresponds to
$(1/2, \sqrt{3}/2)$, with $x = 1/2$ and
$y = \sqrt{3}/2$. By definition,

(c) $\csc \frac{\pi}{3} = \frac{1}{y} = \frac{1}{\sqrt{3}/2} = \frac{2}{\sqrt{3}} = \frac{2\sqrt{3}}{3}$, and

(d) $\cot \frac{\pi}{3} = \frac{x}{y} = \frac{1/2}{\sqrt{3}/2} = \frac{1}{\sqrt{3}} = \frac{\sqrt{3}}{3}$.

Example 2   Suppose s terminates in
quadrant IV and $\cos s = 1/5$. Find
the values of the other trigonometric fractions.

Solution   Since $\cos s = x$, we have
$x = 1/5$. Find y from the equation
of a unit circle, $x^2 + y^2 = 1$.
This gives

$$x^2 + y^2 = 1$$

$$(\tfrac{1}{5})^2 + y^2 = 1$$

$$\frac{1}{25} + y^2 = 1$$

$$y^2 = \frac{24}{25}$$

$$y = \frac{\pm\sqrt{24}}{5} = \frac{\pm 2\sqrt{6}}{5}.$$

Since s is in quadrant IV, y must
be negative, with

$$y = \frac{-2\sqrt{6}}{5}.$$

Now using the definitions of the
trigonometric functions, we have

$$\sin s = y = \frac{-2\sqrt{6}}{5},$$

$$\tan s = \frac{y}{x} = \frac{-2\sqrt{6}/5}{1/5} = -2\sqrt{6},$$

$$\cot s = \frac{x}{y} = \frac{1/5}{-2\sqrt{6}/5} = -\frac{1}{2\sqrt{6}} = -\frac{\sqrt{6}}{12},$$

$$\sec s = \frac{1}{x} = \frac{1}{1/5} = 5,$$

$$\csc s = \frac{1}{y} = \frac{1}{-2\sqrt{6}/5} = \frac{5}{2\sqrt{6}} = \frac{5\sqrt{6}}{2 \cdot 6}$$

$$= -\frac{5\sqrt{6}}{12}.$$

Selected Solutions

1. If $\sin s = \frac{1}{2}$, $\cos s = \frac{\sqrt{3}}{2}$, then

$$\tan s = \frac{\sin s}{\cos s} = \frac{1/2}{\sqrt{3}/2} = \frac{1}{\sqrt{3}} = \frac{\sqrt{3}}{3},$$

$$\cot s = \frac{1}{\tan s} = \frac{3}{\sqrt{3}} = \sqrt{3},$$

$$\sec s = \frac{1}{\cos s} = \frac{1}{\sqrt{3}/2} = \frac{2}{\sqrt{3}} = \frac{2}{3}\sqrt{3}, \text{ and}$$

$$\csc s = \frac{1}{\sin s} = \frac{1}{1/2} = 2.$$

5. If $\sin s = \frac{-\sqrt{3}}{2}$, $\cos s = \frac{1}{2}$, then

$$\tan s = \frac{-\sqrt{3}/2}{1/2} = -\sqrt{3},$$

$$\cot s = \frac{1}{\tan s} = \frac{-\sqrt{3}}{3},$$

$$\sec s = 2, \text{ and}$$

$$\csc s = -\frac{2}{3}\sqrt{3}.$$

s	$\sin s$	$\cos s$	$\tan s$	$\cot s$	$\sec s$	$\csc s$
9. $\frac{3\pi}{4}$	$\frac{\sqrt{2}}{2}$	$\frac{-\sqrt{2}}{2}$	-1	-1	$-\sqrt{2}$	$\sqrt{2}$
13. $\frac{\pi}{6}$	$\frac{1}{2}$	$\frac{\sqrt{3}}{2}$	$\frac{\sqrt{3}}{3}$	$\sqrt{3}$	$\frac{2\sqrt{3}}{3}$	2
17. $\frac{7\pi}{6}$	$-\frac{1}{2}$	$\frac{-\sqrt{3}}{2}$	$\frac{\sqrt{3}}{3}$	$\sqrt{3}$	$\frac{-2\sqrt{3}}{3}$	-2

	Quadrant	sin	cos	tan	cot	sec	csc
19.	I	+	+	+	+	+	+
20.	II	+	−	−	−	−	+
21.	III	−	−	+	+	−	−
22.	IV	−	+	−	−	+	−

25. If $P(\frac{-3}{7}, y)$, $y > 0$, is on the unit

circle, then

$$\left(\frac{-3}{7}\right)^2 + y^2 = 1$$

$$\frac{9}{49} + y^2 = 1$$

$$y^2 = \frac{40}{49}$$

$$y = \frac{2\sqrt{10}}{7}.$$

We then have

$$\sin s = y = \frac{2\sqrt{10}}{7},$$

$$\cos s = x = \frac{-3}{7},$$

$$\tan s = \frac{y}{x} = \frac{-2\sqrt{10}}{3},$$

$$\cot s = \frac{x}{y} = \frac{-3}{2\sqrt{10}} = \frac{-3\sqrt{10}}{20},$$

$$\sec s = \frac{1}{x} = -7/3, \text{ and}$$

$$\csc s = \frac{1}{y} = \frac{7}{2\sqrt{10}} = \frac{7\sqrt{10}}{20} .$$

29. If $P(\frac{-1}{\sqrt{7}}, y)$, $y > 0$, is on the unit

circle, then $\frac{1}{7} + y^2 = 1$, or $y^2 = \frac{6}{7}$.

Hence, $y = \sqrt{\frac{6}{7}} = \frac{\sqrt{42}}{7}$, and we have

$$\sin s = y = \frac{\sqrt{42}}{7} ,$$

$$\cos s = x = \frac{-1}{\sqrt{7}} = \frac{-\sqrt{7}}{7},$$

$$\tan s = \frac{y}{x} = \frac{-\sqrt{42}}{\sqrt{7}} = -\sqrt{6},$$

$$\cot s = \frac{x}{y} = \frac{-\sqrt{7}}{\sqrt{42}} = \frac{-1}{\sqrt{6}} = -\frac{\sqrt{6}}{6} ,$$

$$\sec s = \frac{1}{x} = -\sqrt{7}, \text{ and}$$

$$\csc s = \frac{1}{y} = \frac{7}{\sqrt{42}} = \frac{7\sqrt{42}}{42} = \frac{\sqrt{42}}{6}.$$

33. If $P(x, q)$ is on the unit circle
and if $x < 0$ and $0 < q < 1$, then
$\sin s = q$ and

$$x^2 + q^2 = 1$$

$$x^2 = 1 - q^2$$

$$x = \pm\sqrt{1 - q^2}.$$

Since $x < 0$, we have $x = -\sqrt{1 - q^2}$

and hence $\cos s = -\sqrt{1 - q^2}$. Thus,

$\sin s = q$,

$\cos s = -\sqrt{1 - q^2}$,

$\tan s = \dfrac{y}{x} = \dfrac{-q}{\sqrt{1 - q^2}}$,

$\cot s = \dfrac{x}{y} = \dfrac{-\sqrt{1 - q^2}}{q}$,

$\sec s = \dfrac{1}{x} = \dfrac{-1}{\sqrt{1 - q^2}}$, and

$\csc s = \dfrac{1}{q}$.

37. The statement $\csc t = 2$ is possible. This would occur when $t = \pi/6$.

41. The statement $\sin t = \dfrac{1}{2}$ and $\csc t = 2$ is possible. This is true when $t = \pi/6$.

45. For all s we must have $-1 \le \sin s \le 1$. Hence, it is impossible to have $\sin s = 3.251924$.

49. If $\sec s < 0$ and $\csc s < 0$, then s must be in quadrant III.

53. If $\csc s < 0$, then s could terminate in either quadrant II or III.

57. If $\tan s = \dfrac{3}{2}$ and $\csc s = \dfrac{\sqrt{13}}{3}$, then s must terminate in quadrant I and

$\sin s = \dfrac{1}{\csc s} = \dfrac{3}{\sqrt{13}} = \dfrac{3\sqrt{13}}{13}$,

$\cos s = +\sqrt{1 - \sin^2 s} = \sqrt{1 - (\frac{9}{13})} = \sqrt{\frac{4}{13}}$,

or $\cos = \dfrac{2\sqrt{13}}{13}$. Since $\tan s = \dfrac{3}{2}$, then $\cot s = \dfrac{2}{3}$. Also, $\sec s = \dfrac{1}{\cos s} = \dfrac{\sqrt{13}}{2}$.

61. If $\tan s = \dfrac{3}{2}$, then $\cot s = \dfrac{2}{3}$. If $\csc s = \dfrac{\sqrt{13}}{3}$, then $\sin s = \dfrac{3\sqrt{13}}{13}$. Since $\cot s = \dfrac{\cos s}{\sin s}$,

$\cos s = \cot s \sin s = \dfrac{2}{3} \cdot \dfrac{3\sqrt{13}}{13} = \dfrac{2\sqrt{13}}{13}$

and hence, $\sec s = \dfrac{\sqrt{13}}{2}$.

65. If $\tan t = .642193$ and t is in quadrant III, then $\sin t < 0$ and $\cos t < 0$, so that $\csc t < 0$ and $\sec t < 0$. Also, $\cot t = \dfrac{1}{\tan t}$

$= \dfrac{1}{.642193} = 1.55716$, and using the identities $\sec^2 t = 1 + \tan^2 t$, and $\csc^2 t = 1 + \cot^2 t$, we have $\sec t = -\sqrt{1 + \tan^2 t} = -1.18845$, and $\csc t = -\sqrt{1 + \cot^2 t} = -1.85061$. Thus we can conclude that

$\cos t = \dfrac{1}{\sec t} = -.841433$ and

$\sin t = \dfrac{1}{\csc t} = -.540362$.

69. If $\cos s = -.428193$ and s is in quadrant II, then $\sin s > 0$ and $\tan s < 0$. Using $\sin^2 s + \cos^2 s = 1$, we have $\sin s = +\sqrt{1 - \cos^2 s}$ $= .903687$. Thus we can conclude that $\tan s = \dfrac{\sin s}{\cos s} = -2.11047$,

$\cot s = \dfrac{1}{\tan s} = -.473829$,

$\sec s = \dfrac{1}{\cos s} = -2.33540$, and

$\csc s = \dfrac{1}{\sin s} = 1.10658$.

73. We can prove the identity $\tan^2 s + 1 = \sec^2 s$ in two ways.

(a) Using $\sin^2 s + \cos^2 s = 1$, we can divide each term by $\cos^2 s$ and arrive at

$\dfrac{\sin^2 s}{\cos^2 s} + \dfrac{\cos^2 s}{\cos^2 s} = \dfrac{1}{\cos^2 s}$, or $\tan^2 s + 1 = \sec^2 s$.

(b) If $P(x,y)$ is a point on the unit circle, we have $\cos s = x$ and $\sin s = x$. Also,

$$x^2 + y^2 = 1$$
$$\dfrac{x^2}{x^2} + \dfrac{y^2}{x^2} = \dfrac{1}{x^2}$$
$$1 + \left(\dfrac{y}{x}\right)^2 = \left(\dfrac{1}{x}\right)^2.$$

Then, since $\dfrac{y}{x} = \tan s$ and $\dfrac{1}{x} = \sec s$,

$1 + \tan^2 s = \sec^2 s$.

77. We see that the length of OA is the x-component of point G and hence, $\overline{OA}$ = cos s.

81. We know that tan s = $\dfrac{\overline{AG}}{\overline{OA}}$. Also the triangles AOG and BOF are similar. Hence, $\dfrac{\overline{AG}}{\overline{OA}} = \dfrac{\overline{BF}}{\overline{OB}}$. Then, since $\overline{OB}$ = 1, we have $\overline{BF}$ = tan s.

85. For each positive integer n, the arc length s = nπ terminates on either the positive x=axis or the negative x-axis. Hence, the point on the unit circle is either (1,0) or (-1,0). If n is odd, then s = nπ corresponds to (-1,0), while n even implies s = nπ corresponds to (1,0). Since cos s = x, we conclude that cos nπ = $(-1)^n$ is correct.

Section 6.3 Angles and the Unit Circle

Additional Examples

Example 1   Convert to radians
     (a) 29° 40'   (b) 74.9162°.
Solution   (a) We know that
     40' = 40/60 = 2/3 of a degree.
     Thus, 29° 40' = $29\dfrac{2}{3}^{\circ}$

$= \dfrac{89^{\circ}}{3}$

$= \dfrac{89}{3}(\dfrac{\pi}{180})$ radians

29° 40' $= \dfrac{89\pi}{540}$ radians.

This answer is exact. If we now replace π with the approximation 3.14159, we get

29° 40' $\approx \dfrac{89(3.14159)}{540}$

29° 40' $\approx$ .518 radians.

(b) 74.9162° = $74.9162(\dfrac{\pi}{180})$ Multiply by π/180°

$\approx 74.9162(\dfrac{3.14159}{180})$

$\approx$ 1.30753 radians

Example 2   A belt runs a pulley of radius 6 cm at 80 revolutions per minute. Find the angular velocity of the pulley in radians per second.

Solution   In one minute, the pulley makes 80 revolutions. Each revolution is 2π radians, for a total of 80(2π) = 160π radians per minute. Since there are 60 seconds in a minute, ω, the angular velocity in radians per second, is given by

$\omega = \dfrac{160\pi}{60} = \dfrac{8\pi}{3}$ radians per second.

Selected Solutions

1. -40° corresponds to 360° + (-40°) = 320°.

5. 450° = 360° + 90° corresponds to 90°.

9. Use $\dfrac{\pi}{180}$ radians = 1°. Then we have
    60° = $60(\dfrac{\pi}{180}) = \dfrac{\pi}{3}$ radians.

13. We have 135° = $135(\dfrac{\pi}{180}) = \dfrac{3\pi}{4}$ radians.

17. 405° = $405(\dfrac{\pi}{180}) = \dfrac{9\pi}{4}$ radians.

21. Using the fact that π radians is 180°, we have
     $\dfrac{\pi}{3} = \dfrac{180°}{3} = 60°$.

25. $\dfrac{11\pi}{6} = \dfrac{11(180°)}{6} = 330°$.

29. 5π radians = 5(180°) = 900°.

33. We have $10' = (\frac{1}{6})°$, so that

$$139°10' = (139 + \frac{1}{6})° = (\frac{835}{6})°$$

$$= (\frac{835}{6})(\frac{\pi}{180}) \text{ radians}$$

$$\approx 2.4289 \text{ radians}.$$

37. We have $42' = (\frac{42}{60})° = (\frac{7}{10})°$ and

$36" = (\frac{36}{60})' = (\frac{6}{10})' = (\frac{6}{600})°$

$= (\frac{1}{100})°$. Hence,

$$-29°42'36" = -(29 + \frac{7}{10} + \frac{1}{100})°$$

$$= (\frac{-2971}{100})°$$

$$= (\frac{-2971}{100})(\frac{\pi}{180}) \text{ radians}$$

$$\approx -.5185 \text{ radians}.$$

41. $2 \text{ radians} = 2(\frac{180}{\pi}) \text{ degrees}$

$$= \frac{360}{\pi} \text{ degrees}$$

$$\approx 114.5916°, \text{ or } 114°35'$$

45. $.0912 \text{ radians} = .0912(\frac{180}{\pi}) \text{ radians}$

$$\approx 5.2254°, \text{ or } 5°14'$$

49. In radians, the central angle has measure $\frac{12}{8} = \frac{3}{2}$ radians.

53. The central angle has measure $\frac{5.98421}{1.93740} \approx 3.09309$ radians.

57. The difference in latitudes is
$41° + 12° = 53° = 53(\frac{\pi}{180}) = \frac{53\pi}{180}$
radians. Hence,
$t = (4000)(\frac{53\pi}{180}) = \frac{53,000\pi}{45}$ miles,
or $t \approx 3700$ miles.

61. If $r = 12.3$ cm and $\theta = \frac{2\pi}{3}$ radians,
then $s = (12.3)(\frac{2\pi}{3}) \approx 25.8$ cm.

65. We have $52.417° = (52.417)(\frac{\pi}{180})$
radians. Hence,
$s = (58.402)(\frac{52.417\pi}{180}) \approx 53.429$ meters.

69. If $\omega = \frac{\pi}{4}$ and $t = 5$, then
$\theta = \omega t = \frac{5\pi}{4}$ radians.

73. If $\theta = \frac{3\pi}{8}$ and $\omega = \frac{\pi}{24}$, then $\omega = \frac{\theta}{t}$
implies $t = \frac{\theta}{\omega}$, and we have
$t = (\frac{3\pi}{8})/(\frac{\pi}{24}) = \frac{3\pi}{8} \cdot \frac{24}{\pi} = 9$ min.

77. If $v = 18$ and $r = 3$, then $v = r\omega$
implies that $\omega = \frac{v}{r}$, and we have
$\omega = \frac{18 \text{ ft. per sec}}{3 \text{ ft.}}$,
$\omega = 6$ radians per sec.

81. Using $s = r\omega t$ with $r = 6$, $\omega = \pi/3$,
and $t = 9$, gives
$s = 6(\frac{\pi}{3})(9) = 18\pi$ cm.

85. If $s = r\omega t$, $s = \frac{3\pi}{4}$ km, $r = 2$, and
$t = 4$, then
$\omega = \frac{s}{rt} = \frac{(\frac{3\pi}{4})}{(2)(4)} = \frac{3\pi}{16}$ rad/sec.

89. In one hour the hour hand moves
1/12 of the way around the clock.
Thus, $\omega = (\frac{1}{12})(2\pi) = \frac{\pi}{6}$ radians per hour.

93. Using $s = r\omega t$, we are given
$s = \frac{8\pi}{9}$m, $r = \frac{4}{3}$m, and $t = 12$ sec,
and hence
$\omega = \frac{s}{rt} = \frac{(\frac{8\pi}{9})}{(\frac{4}{3})(12)} = \frac{8\pi}{9} \cdot \frac{1}{16}$

$\omega = \frac{\pi}{18}$ radians per sec.

Section 6.4 Trigonometric Functions
           of Angles

Additional Examples

Example 1   Find the values of the
   trigonometric functions for 60°.

Solution   To find those values, use
   the 30°-60° right triangle of the
   figure. The side of length $\sqrt{3}$ is
   the side opposite the 60° angle,
   while the side of length 1 is
   adjacent. Thus $\sin 60° = \frac{\sqrt{3}}{2}$,

   $\tan 60° = \sqrt{3}$, $\sec 60° = 2$,
   $\cos 60° = \frac{1}{2}$, $\cot 60° = \frac{\sqrt{3}}{3}$,
   $\csc 60° = \frac{2\sqrt{3}}{3}$.

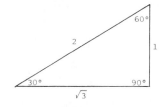

Example 2   Find the trigonometric functions of θ if the terminal side of
   θ passes through the point P(-3, -4).

Solution   As shown in the figure
   x = -3 and y = -4. Use the
   Pythagorean theorem to find that
   r = 5. (Remember r > 0.)
   Then we have

$\sin\theta = \frac{-4}{5} = -\frac{4}{5}$ $\cot\theta = \frac{-3}{-4} = \frac{3}{4}$

$\cos\theta = \frac{-3}{5} = -\frac{3}{5}$ $\sec\theta = \frac{5}{-3} = -\frac{5}{3}$

$\tan\theta = \frac{-4}{-3} = \frac{4}{3}$ $\csc\theta = \frac{5}{-4} = -\frac{5}{4}$

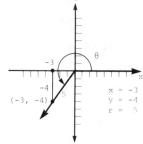

Selected Solutions

For problems 1-9, follow these steps.

(a) Draw the angle in standard position.

(b) Choose point P on the terminal
     side so that r = 2.

(c) Use the relationships to determine
     the function values.

(d) Note that 120°, 240°, and 420° each
     make a 60° reference angle to the
     x-axis.

	θ	sinθ	cosθ	tanθ	cotθ	secθ	cscθ
1.	120°	$\frac{\sqrt{3}}{2}$	$-\frac{1}{2}$	$-\sqrt{3}$	$-\frac{\sqrt{3}}{3}$	-2	$\frac{2\sqrt{3}}{3}$
5.	$\frac{4\pi}{3}$	$\frac{-\sqrt{3}}{2}$	$-\frac{1}{2}$	$\sqrt{3}$	$\frac{\sqrt{3}}{3}$	-2	$\frac{-2\sqrt{3}}{3}$
9.	420°	$\frac{\sqrt{3}}{2}$	$\frac{1}{2}$	$\sqrt{3}$	$\frac{\sqrt{3}}{3}$	2	$\frac{2\sqrt{3}}{3}$
13.	π	0	-1	0	unde-fined	-1	unde fined
17.	30°	$\frac{1}{2}$	$\frac{\sqrt{3}}{2}$	$\frac{1}{\sqrt{3}}$ $\frac{\sqrt{3}}{3}$	$\sqrt{3}$	$\frac{2\sqrt{3}}{3}$	2
21.	135°	$\frac{\sqrt{2}}{2}$	$\frac{-\sqrt{2}}{2}$	-1	-1	$-\sqrt{2}$	$\sqrt{2}$

25. For (-3,4) we have
     $r = \sqrt{(-3)^2+4^2} = \sqrt{9 + 16} = \sqrt{25} = 5$,
     so that

     $\sin\theta = \frac{y}{r} = \frac{4}{5}$,

     $\cos\theta = \frac{x}{r} = \frac{-3}{5}$,

     $\tan\theta = \frac{\sin\theta}{\cos\theta} = \frac{4}{-3} = -\frac{4}{3}$

     $\cot\theta = \frac{-3}{4}$,

     $\sec\theta = \frac{1}{\cos\theta} = \frac{5}{-3} = -\frac{5}{3}$, and

     $\csc\theta = \frac{1}{\sin\theta} = \frac{5}{4}$.

29. For (-12,-5), we have
     $r = \sqrt{144 + 25} = \sqrt{169} = 13$, and

$$\sin \theta = \frac{-5}{13}, \qquad \cos \theta = \frac{-12}{13},$$

$$\tan \theta = \frac{5}{12} \qquad \cot \theta = \frac{12}{5}$$

$$\sec \theta = \frac{-13}{12} \qquad \csc \theta = \frac{-13}{5}.$$

33.   For $P(2\sqrt{2}, -2\sqrt{2})$ we have
$r^2 = 8 + 8 = 16$, so that $r = 4$.
Hence,

$$\sin \theta = \frac{-2\sqrt{2}}{4} = \frac{-\sqrt{2}}{2},$$

$$\cos \theta = \frac{\sqrt{2}}{2},$$

$$\tan \theta = -1,$$

$$\cot \theta = -1,$$

$$\sec \theta = \frac{2}{\sqrt{2}} = \sqrt{2}, \text{ and}$$

$$\csc \theta = -\sqrt{2}.$$

37.   For $P(-\sqrt{13}, \sqrt{3})$ we have
$r^2 = 13 + 3 = 16$, so that $r = 4$.
Hence,

$$\sin \theta = \frac{\sqrt{3}}{4}, \quad \cos \theta = \frac{-\sqrt{13}}{4},$$

$$\tan \theta = \frac{-\sqrt{3}}{\sqrt{13}} = \frac{-\sqrt{39}}{13}, \cot \theta = -\frac{\sqrt{39}}{3},$$

$$\sec \theta = -\frac{4}{\sqrt{13}} = \frac{-4\sqrt{13}}{13}, \text{ and}$$

$$\csc \theta = \frac{4}{\sqrt{3}} = \frac{4\sqrt{3}}{3}.$$

41.   For $P(8.7691, -3.2473)$ we have
$r^2 = (8.7691)^2 + (-3.2473)^2$
$r^2 = 76.897115 + 10.544957$
$r^2 = 87.442072$, or
$r \approx 9.3510$.
Then we have

$$\sin \theta = \frac{y}{r} = -.34727$$

$$\cos \theta = \frac{x}{r} = .93777,$$

$$\tan \theta = \frac{y}{x} = -.37031,$$

$$\cot \theta = \frac{x}{y} = -2.70043,$$

$$\sec \theta = \frac{r}{x} = 1.06636,$$

$$\csc \theta = \frac{r}{y} = -2.8796.$$

45.   For $P(9.713\sqrt{12.4}, -8.765\sqrt{10.2})$ we
have
$r^2 = (9.713)^2(12.4) + (-8.765)^2(10.2)$
$r^2 = 1169.8454 + 783.6173$
$r^2 = 1953.4627.$
Hence $r \approx 44.198$, and we then have

$$\sin \theta = \frac{y}{r} \approx -.633,$$

$$\cos \theta = \frac{x}{r} \approx .774,$$

$$\tan \theta = \frac{y}{x} \approx -.318,$$

$$\cot \theta = \frac{x}{y} \approx -1.222,$$

$$\sec \theta = \frac{r}{x} \approx 1.292,$$

$$\csc \theta = \frac{r}{y} \approx -1.580.$$

49.   Using the given figure, we have

$$\sin \theta = \frac{\text{opposite}}{\text{hypotenuse}} = \frac{3}{5},$$

$$\cos \theta = \frac{\text{adjacent}}{\text{hyp}} = \frac{4}{5},$$

$$\tan \theta = \frac{\text{opp}}{\text{adj}} = \frac{3}{4},$$

$$\cot \theta = \frac{\text{adj}}{\text{opp}} = \frac{4}{3},$$

$$\sec \theta = \frac{\text{hyp}}{\text{adj}} = \frac{5}{4}, \text{ and}$$

$$\csc \theta = \frac{\text{hyp}}{\text{opp}} = \frac{5}{3}.$$

53.   Using the given figure, we have

$$\sin \theta = \frac{.897425}{1.181973} = .759260,$$

$$\cos \theta = \frac{.769213}{1.181973} = .650787, \text{ and}$$

$$\tan \theta = \frac{.897425}{.769213} = 1.16668.$$

57.   We have
$\tan 120° = -\tan 60° = -\sqrt{3},$
$\sin 150° = +\sin 30° = \frac{1}{2}, \text{ and}$
$\cos 180° = -1.$
Hence, we have
$2 \tan^2 120° + 3 \sin^2 150° - \cos^2 180°$
$$= 2(-\sqrt{3})^2 + 3(\tfrac{1}{2})^2 - (-1)^2$$
$$= 2(3) + 3(\tfrac{1}{4}) - 1$$
$$= 6 + \frac{3}{4} - 1 = \frac{23}{4}.$$

61. We have $\cos 60° = \frac{1}{2}$,

$$\sec 150° = -\sec 30° = \frac{-1}{\cos 30°} = -\frac{2}{\sqrt{3}},$$

and $\csc 210° = -\csc 30° = \frac{-1}{\sin 30°}$

$= -2$. Hence, we have

$\cos^2 60° + \sec^2 150° - \csc^2 210°$

$$= (\tfrac{1}{2})^2 + (\tfrac{-2}{\sqrt{3}})^2 - (-2)^2$$

$$= \frac{1}{4} + \frac{4}{3} - 4 = \frac{19}{12} - 4$$

$$= \frac{19 - 48}{12} = \frac{-29}{12}.$$

65. The answer is false since

$$\sin 30° + \sin 60° = \frac{1}{2} + \frac{\sqrt{3}}{2}$$

$$= \frac{1 + \sqrt{3}}{2} \approx 1.366,$$

and $\sin(30° + 60°) = \sin 90° = 1$.

69. The answer is false since

$$\sin 120° = +\sin 60° = \frac{\sqrt{3}}{2} \approx .866$$

and $\sin 150° - \sin 30° = \frac{1}{2} - \frac{1}{2} = 0$.

73. The identity

$\cos (A + B) = \cos A \cos B$
   $- \sin A \sin B$

with $A = 120°$ and $B = 30°$ gives

$\cos 150° = \cos 120° \cos 30°$
   $- \sin 120° \sin 30°$.

The formula is true. One can plug in the values to check the result numerically also. We see that

$\cos 150° = -\cos 30° = -\frac{\sqrt{3}}{2}$, while

$\cos 120° \cos 30° - \sin 120° \sin 30°$

$$= (-\tfrac{1}{2})(\tfrac{\sqrt{3}}{2}) - (\tfrac{\sqrt{3}}{2})(\tfrac{1}{2})$$

$$= \frac{-\sqrt{3}}{4} - \frac{\sqrt{3}}{4} = -\frac{\sqrt{3}}{2}.$$

77. Solve $\tan \theta = \sqrt{3}$ for $0 \le \theta < 360°$. Since $\tan 60° = \sqrt{3}$ and $\tan \theta > \theta$ in quadrants I and III, we see that

θ is in quadrants I and III and the reference angle is R = 60°. Hence, $\theta = 60°$ and $(180° + 60°)$, or $\theta = 60°$, 240°.

81. Solve $\sin \theta = \frac{-\sqrt{3}}{2}$, $0 \le \theta < 360°$.

We know that $\sin 60° = \frac{\sqrt{3}}{2}$ and that $\sin \theta < 0$ if θ is in quadrants III and IV. Hence, the solutions θ are angles in quadrants III and IV with a reference angle of R = 60°. The solutions are

$\theta = (180° + 60°)$ and $(360° - 60°)$,
$\theta = 240°$ and 300°.

85. If $\cot \theta$ is undefined, then $\tan \theta = 0$. Thus, $\theta = 0°$, 180°.

89. Using the figure we can see that $\sin 60° = \frac{6}{24}$, so that $b = 24 \sin 60°$

$= 24(\frac{\sqrt{3}}{2}) = 12\sqrt{3}$. Also, $\cos 60° = \frac{a}{24}$, so that $a = 24 \cos 60°$, or $a = 24(\frac{1}{2}) = 12$. Then, using the 45° angle, we have $\tan 45° = \frac{d}{b}$ or $d = b \tan 45°$, $d = (12\sqrt{3})(1) = 12\sqrt{3}$. Also, using the 45° angle, we have $\sin 45° = \frac{d}{c} = \frac{12\sqrt{3}}{c}$, or

$$c = \frac{12\sqrt{3}}{\sin 45°} = \frac{12\sqrt{3}}{\frac{\sqrt{2}}{2}} = 12\sqrt{6}.$$

Section 6.5 Values of Trigonometric
           Functions

Additional Examples

Example 1   Use Table 3 in the back of the book to find each of the following.

(a) $\sin 190° 10'$ (b) $\tan 305° 20'$
(c) $\cos 1045° 10'$ (d) $\cot 100° 50'$

Solution   (a) The figure shows the
        reference angle 10° 10'. An angle
        of 190° 10' is in quadrant III,
        where sine is negative. Thus,
            sin 190° 10' = -sin 10° 10'
                        = -.1765.

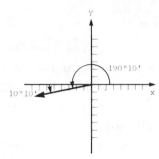

(b)   The reference angle is 54° 40'.
        (To subtract 305° 20' from 360°,
        first change 360° to 359° 60'.)
        Since 305° 20' is in quadrant IV,
        tangent is negative and
          tan 305° 20' = -tan 54° 40'
            = -1.411.
(c)   cos 1045° 10' = cos(1045°10'-720°)
                            Subtract 720° to
                            get an angle
                            between 0° and
                            360°.
                    = cos 325° 10'
        Since 325° 10' is in quadrant IV,
        its reference angle is
          360° - 325° 10' = 34° 50'.
        Finally, cos 1045° 10' = cos 34°50'
                            = .8208.
        (Why is the answer positive?)
(d)   cot 100° 50' = -cot 79° 10' = -.1914
Example 2   Use Table 3 to find a value
        of θ in the interval 0° ≤ θ ≤ 90°
        satisfying each of the following.
(a)   sin θ = .5807
(b)   tan θ = 2.699
Solution   (a) Use Table 3 and read
        the columns having sine at either
        the top or the bottom. Here we
        find .5807 in a column having sine
        at the top. Thus, we use the
        angles at the left.
                θ = 35° 30'

(b) Since 2.699 is in a column having
        tangent at the bottom, use the
        angles at the right.
                θ = 69° 40'

Selected Solutions
  1.   Since 215° = 180° + 35°, the
        reference angle is R = 35°.

  5.   The angle θ = -110° 10' is in
        quadrant III and hence the
        reference angle is R = 180° - 110°10'
          = 69° 50'.

  9.   Since 2π ≈ 6.2832 and $\frac{3\pi}{2}$ ≈ 4.7124,
        we conclude that 5.9690 is in
        quadrant IV. This implies that
        the reference angle is
        R = 2π - 5.9690 ≈ 6.2832 - 5.9690,
                or R ≈ .3142.

 13.   A calculator gives
          sin 39° 20' ≈ .63383.

 17.   We could use a calculator in degree
        mode and directly evaluate the
        result. However, note the following
        statements which allow the use of
        Table 3. We have
          cos(-124° 50') = -cos(55° 10'),
        since -124° 50' is in quadrant III
        and the reference angle is 55° 10'.
        Using a calculator gives
          cos(-124° 50') = -.57119.

 21.   First be sure that the calculator
        is in "Rad" mode. Placing the
        number 7.5835 in the calculator
        and pushing the "sin" button gives
          sin 7.5835 ≈ .96364.

25. Using table 3, we have the following.

$$10\left\{2\left\{\begin{array}{l}\tan 29°40' = .5696\\ \tan 29°42' = x\\ \tan 29"50' = .5735\end{array}\right\}d\right\}.0039$$

$$\frac{2}{10} = \frac{d}{.0039}$$

$$d = .0008$$

Hence, $\tan 29°42' = .5704$.

29. Using table 3, we have the following.

$$.0029\left\{.0006\left\{\begin{array}{l}\sin .1629 = .1622\\ \sin .1635 = x\\ \sin .1668 = .1650\end{array}\right\}d\right\}.0028$$

Then $\frac{6}{29} = \frac{d}{.0028}$,

or $d = .0006$.

Hence,

    $\sin .1635 = .1622 + .0006 = .1628$.

33. If $\sin \theta = .8480$ and $0° \le \theta \le 90°$, a calculator gives
$\theta = $ "inv sin" $(.8480) = 57.9948°$.
We could round this off to
$\theta = 58°00'$.

37. If $\sin \theta = .7214$ and $0° \le \theta \le 90°$, a calculator gives
    $\theta = $ "inv sin" $(.7214) = 46.1702°$,
or $\theta = 46°10'$.

41. Using radian measure, we have that if $\tan s = .2126$ and if $0 \le s \le 1.5708$ radians, then a calculator gives
$s = $ "inv tan" $(.2126)$,
$s \approx .2095$ radians.

45. Using radian measure, we have that if $\cot s = .0963$ and if $0 \le s \le 1.5708$ radians, then
$\tan s = \frac{1}{.0963} \approx 10.384216$
and $s \approx$ "inv tan" (10.384216),
or $s \approx 1.4748$.

49. If $\sin s = 0.4067$ and $0 \le s \le 1.5708 \approx \frac{\pi}{2}$,
then $s = $ "inv sin" $(0.4067) \approx 23.998°$ or $s = 24°$.

53. Using $t(x) = 60 - 30 \cos \frac{x\pi}{6}$, we have:

(a) January: $t(0) = 60 - 30 \cos 0$,
        $t(0) = 60 - 30(1) = 30°$.

(b) April: $t(3) = 60 - 30 \cos \frac{3\pi}{6}$,
        $t(3) = 60 - 0 = 60°$.

(c) May: $t(4) = 60 - 30 \cos \frac{4\pi}{6}$,
        $t(4) = 60 - 30(\frac{-1}{2}) = 75°$.

(d) June: $t(5) = 60 - 30 \cos \frac{5\pi}{6}$,
        $t(5) = 60 - 30(\frac{-\sqrt{3}}{2})$
            $\approx 85.7°$, or $86°$.

(e) August: $t(7) = 60 - 30 \cos \frac{7\pi}{6}$,
        $t(7) = 60 - 30(\frac{-\sqrt{3}}{2})$
            $\approx 85.7°$, or $86°$.

(f) October: $t(9) = 60 - 30 \cos \frac{9\pi}{6}$,
        $t(9) = 60 - 30(0) = 60°$.

57. Using $\cos x \approx 1 - \frac{x^2}{2!} + \frac{x^4}{4!}$, we have
    $\cos 1.4 \approx 1 - \frac{(1.4)^2}{2} + \frac{(1.4)^4}{24}$
    $\cos 1.4 \approx 1 - 0.98 + 0.1600677$
    $\cos 1.4 \approx 0.1800677$.
A calculator gives
    $\cos 1.4 \approx 0.169967$.

61. Using the given figure, we have
$\sin 36°20' = \frac{a}{964}$, so that
$a = (964) \sin(36.33°) \approx 571.15$ m.
Rounding off, $a \approx 571$ m. Also,
$\cos 36°20' = \frac{b}{964}$, or
$b = (964)(\cos 36.33°) \approx 776.58$ m.
Rounding off, $b \approx 777$ m. In addition
we could conclude that $B = 53°40'$.

65. Using the given figure, we see that

$\sin (42.0892°) = \dfrac{56.851}{c}$, or

$c = \dfrac{58.851}{\sin (42.0892°)} \approx 84.8159$, or

c = 84.816 cm. Also we have

$\tan (42.0892°) = \dfrac{56.851}{a}$, or

$a = \dfrac{56.851}{\tan (42.0892°)} \approx 62.942$.

In addition we have A = 47.9108°.

69. From the figure
     we see that

$\cos 49.74° = \dfrac{18.705}{s}$

$s = \dfrac{18.705}{\cos 49.74°}$

$s \approx 28.94$ in.

A = 49.74°
b = 18.705

73. Using the figure,
     which represents
     the smallest tri-
     angle in the fig-
     ure in the text,
     we then see that

$\sin 48° = \dfrac{h}{4.5}$, or   A = 180° - (94°+38°)

h = (4.5) sin 48°   A = 48°

$h \approx 3.34$ ft.

77. Using $\dfrac{c_1}{c_2} = \dfrac{\sin \theta_1}{\sin \theta_2}$, with

$c_1 = 3 \times 10^8$, $\theta_1 = 46°$, and $\theta_2 = 31°$,
we have

$c_2 = \dfrac{c_1 \sin \theta_2}{\sin \theta_1} = \dfrac{(3 \times 10^8) \sin 31°}{\sin 46°}$,

or $c_2 \approx 2.15 \times 10^8$, or $c_2 \approx 2 \times 10^8$.

81. Using $\dfrac{c_1}{c_2} = \dfrac{\sin \theta_1}{\sin \theta_2}$, with

$c_1 = 3 \times 10^8$, $c_2 = 2.254 \times 10^8$, and
$\theta_1 = 90°$,
     we have

$\sin \theta_2 = \dfrac{c_2 \sin \theta_1}{c_1} = \dfrac{2.254}{3} \approx .751333$,

$\theta_2 =$ "inv sin" (.751333) $\approx 48.7°$.

Section 6.6   Graphs of the Sine and
               Cosine Functions

Additional Examples

Example 1   Graph $y = \cos \frac{1}{4}x$.

Solution   For each x-value first find
     (1/4)x. Then find cos (1/4)x. The
     following table gives enough ordered
     pairs so that we can graph one
     complete period.

x	0	π	2π	3π	4π	5π	6π	8π
(1/4)x	0	π/4	π/2	3π/4	π	5π/4	3π/2	2π
cos(1/4)x	1	.7	0	-.7	-1	-.7	0	1

Use the first and last rows of the
table to get the ordered pairs
necessary for the graph. The final
graph is shown in the figure; the
graph shows that the period is 8π.

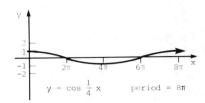

$y = \cos \frac{1}{4} x$ period = 8π

Example 2   Graph $y = 3 \cos (x + \frac{\pi}{4})$.

Solution   The amplitude is 3 and the
     period is 2π. To find the phase
     shift, set the argument equal to 0
     and solve for x. This gives

$x + \dfrac{\pi}{4} = 0$

or $x = -\dfrac{\pi}{4}$.

Since -π/4 is negative, the phase
shift is $|-\pi/4| = \pi/4$ to the left.
The graph is shown in the figure.

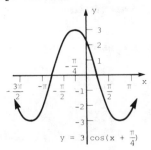

$y = 3 \cos(x + \frac{\pi}{4})$

Selected Solutions

1. For $y = 2 \cos x$, the amplitude is 2 and the period is 2π. Note that $\cos x = 0$ for $x = \frac{-3\pi}{2}, \frac{-\pi}{2}, \frac{\pi}{2}, \frac{3\pi}{2}$, and that $\cos(-2\pi) = \cos 0 = \cos 2\pi = 1$ while $\cos(-\pi) = \cos \pi = -1$. This would locate the maximum values, minimum values, and where the graph crosses the x-axis. See the graph in the answer section of the text.

5. For $y = -\cos x$, $-2\pi \le x \le 2\pi$, the same information given above in exercise 1 can be used to determine that the minimum values of the graph occur at $x = -2\pi, 0, 2\pi$; the maximum values occur at $x = -\pi, \pi$; and the graph crosses the x-axis at $x = \frac{-3\pi}{2}, \frac{-\pi}{2}, \frac{\pi}{2}$, and $\frac{3\pi}{2}$. See the graph in the text.

9. The graph of $y = \sin \frac{1}{2}x$ has period $\frac{2\pi}{1/2} = 4\pi$ and amplitude $= 1$. A two-period interval could be $[0, 8\pi]$ or $[-4\pi, 4\pi]$. See a graph over $[-4\pi, 4\pi]$ in the text.

13. The graph for $y = \sin 3x$ has period $= \frac{2\pi}{3}$ and amplitude 1. A two-period interval could be either $[0, \frac{4\pi}{3}]$ or $[\frac{-2\pi}{3}, \frac{2\pi}{3}]$. The graph in the text is over $[\frac{-2\pi}{3}, \frac{2\pi}{3}]$. Note that $\sin 3x = 0$ for $x = \frac{-2\pi}{3}, \frac{-\pi}{3}, 0, \frac{\pi}{3}$, and $\frac{2\pi}{3}$. Also, $\sin 3x = 1$ if $x = \frac{-\pi}{2}, \frac{\pi}{6}$, and $\sin 3x = -1$ if $\frac{-\pi}{6}, \frac{\pi}{2}$. See the graph in the text.

17. The graph for $y = -\sin 4x$ has period $= \frac{2\pi}{4} = \frac{\pi}{2}$ and amplitude $= |-1| = 1$.

A two-period interval is $[\frac{-\pi}{2}, \frac{\pi}{2}]$, and $y = 0$ when $x = 0, \pm\frac{\pi}{4}, \pm\frac{\pi}{2}$. We see that $y = -1$ when $\sin 4x = 1$, or $x = \frac{\pi}{8}, \frac{\pi}{8} - \frac{\pi}{2}$, which is $x = -\frac{3\pi}{8}, \frac{\pi}{8}$. Also, $y = +1$ where $\sin 4x = -1$, or $x = -\frac{\pi}{8}, \frac{3\pi}{8}$. See the graph in the text.

21. The graph for $y = -2 \cos 3x$ has period $= \frac{2\pi}{3}$ and amplitude $= |-2| = 2$. A two-period interval is $[\frac{-2\pi}{3}, \frac{2\pi}{3}]$ and the graph has $y = 0$ when $\cos 3x = 0$, or $x = \frac{-\pi}{2}, \frac{-\pi}{6}, \frac{\pi}{6}$, and $\frac{\pi}{2}$. We have $y = -2$ when $\cos 3x = 1$, or $x = \frac{-2\pi}{3}, 0, \frac{2\pi}{3}$, and we have $y = +2$ when $\cos 3x = -1$, or $x = \frac{-\pi}{3}$ and $\frac{\pi}{3}$. The graph is given in the text.

25. The graph of $y = 2 - \cos x$ is a vertical translation of the graph $y = -\cos x$ in exercise 5. The graph of $y = 2 - \cos x$ raises the graph of $y = -\cos 2x$ upward two units. See the graph in the text.

29. We can write $y = 1 - 2 \cos \frac{1}{2}x$ as $(y - 1) = -2 \cos \frac{1}{2}x$. The graph is then seen to be the graph of $y = -2 \cos \frac{1}{2}x$ raised upward one unit. The period of $-2 \cos \frac{1}{2}x$ is $\frac{2\pi}{1/2} = 4\pi$, and the amplitude is $|-2| = 2$. If we sketch the graph of $y = -2 \cos \frac{1}{2}x$ and raise this one unit upward, we have the graph shown in the answer section.

33. The graph for $y = \cos (x - \frac{\pi}{2})$ has period = 2π and amplitude 1. There is no vertical translation, but there is a phase shift of $\frac{\pi}{2}$ units to the right. See the graph in the text. Note that the graph of $y = \cos x$ has the table shown below.

x	0	$\pi/2$	π	$3\pi/2$	2π
$y = \cos x$	1	0	-1	0	1

If we shift this graph to the right $\frac{\pi}{2}$ units, we have the graph of $y = \cos (x - \frac{\pi}{2})$ for $\frac{\pi}{2} \leq x \leq \frac{5\pi}{2}$.

37. The graph of $y = 2 \cos (x - \frac{\pi}{3})$ has period = 2π and amplitude = $|2| = 2$. Also, the phase shift is $x - \frac{\pi}{3} = 0$, $x = \frac{\pi}{3}$, which give a phase shift of $\frac{\pi}{3}$ to right.
To sketch the graph:
(1) First determine where cos x crosses the x-axis ($x = \frac{\pi}{2}, \frac{3\pi}{2}$), where cos x reaches its maximum ($x = 0, 2\pi$), and where cos x reaches its minimum ($x = \pi$).
(2) Then move each of these points to the right $\frac{\pi}{3}$ units. See graph in text.

41. The graph for $y = -4 \sin (2x - \pi)$ has period $\frac{2\pi}{1} = \pi$ and amplitude $|4| = 4$. Phase shift is $2x - \pi = 0$, or $x = \frac{\pi}{2}$. There is a phase shift of the graph of $y = -4 \sin 2x$ of a $\frac{\pi}{2}$ shift to the right.
To sketch the graph:
(1) First determine where $y = \sin 2x$ crosses the x-axis $(0, \frac{\pi}{2}, \pi)$, where $-4 \sin 2x$ reaches its maximum

value ($x = \frac{3\pi}{4}$, since a < 0), where $-4 \sin 2x$ reaches its minimum value ($x = \frac{\pi}{4}$).
(2) Then move each of these to the right $\frac{\pi}{2}$ units. See graph in text.

43. $y = \frac{1}{2} \cos (\frac{1}{2}x - \frac{\pi}{4})$. See the graph in the text. The graph has period $= \frac{\pi}{1/2} = 4\pi$ and amplitude $= \left|\frac{1}{2}\right| = \frac{1}{2}$.
To find the phase shift:

$\frac{1}{2}x - \frac{\pi}{4} = 0$

$\frac{1}{2}x = \frac{\pi}{4}$

$x = \frac{\pi}{2}$

To sketch the graph first determine where:
(1) $\frac{1}{2} \cos \frac{1}{2}x$ crosses the x-axis $(\pi, 3\pi)$.
(2) $\frac{1}{2} \cos \frac{1}{2}x$ achieves its maximum value of $\frac{1}{2}$ $(0, 4\pi)$ and its minimum value of $-\frac{1}{2}$ (2π).
Then shift each point to the right $\frac{\pi}{2}$ units. See the final graph in the text.

45. The graph for $y = -3 + 2 \sin (x - \frac{\pi}{2})$ has both a vertical displacement (3 units downward) and a phase shift ($\frac{\pi}{2}$ units to the right) from the graph of $y = 2 \sin x$. See the final graph in the text.

49. Let $f(x) = \sin x$. We have $f(-x) = \sin (-x) = - \sin x = -f(x)$. Hence, sin x is an odd function.

53. The amplitude is 1 and the period is $\frac{4\pi}{3}$.

57. The amplitude is 2 hours.

61. (a) The amplitude is 5 and the period is $\frac{2\pi}{120\pi} = \frac{1}{60}$.

(b) There are 60 cycles completed in one second.

(c) $E(0) = 5 \cos 0 = 5$,

$E(.03) = 5 \cos (3.6\pi) \approx 1.545$,

$E(.06) = 5 \cos (7.2\pi) \approx -4.045$,

$E(.09) = 5 \cos (10.8\pi) \approx -4.045$,

$E(.12) = 5 \cos (14.4\pi) \approx 1.545$.

(d) See the graph in the text.

65. Consider this table:

x	0	$\frac{\pi}{2b}$	$\frac{\pi}{b}$	$\frac{3\pi}{2b}$	$\frac{2\pi}{b}$
sin bx	0	1	0	-1	0

The graph of $y = \sin bx$ goes through one period in $\frac{2\pi}{b}$ units.

69. We have $y = \sin^2 x = (\sin x)^2$. The graph will be periodic, and we can compare the points in the following table to the graph in the text:

x	0	$\frac{\pi}{4}$	$\frac{\pi}{2}$	$\frac{3\pi}{4}$	π
$y = \sin^2 x$	0	$\frac{1}{2}$	1	$\frac{1}{2}$	0

x	$\frac{5\pi}{4}$	$\frac{3\pi}{2}$	$\frac{7\pi}{4}$	2π
$y = \sin^2 x$	$\frac{1}{2}$	1	$\frac{1}{2}$	0

73. For $y = e^{-t} \sin t$ consider $0 \leq t \leq 2\pi$ and since $-1 \leq \sin t \leq 1$, we always have $-e^{-t} \leq e^{-t} \sin t \leq e^{-t}$. When $\sin t = 0$ ($t = 0$, π, 2π), we have $y = 0$. See the graph in the text.

Section 6.7   Graphs of the Other Trigonometric Functions

Additional Examples

Example 1   Graph $y = 2 \sec x$ for $-2\pi \leq x \leq 2\pi$.

Solution   The cosine and secant functions are reciprocal functions. Consider $y = 2 \cos x$. The period is 2π and the amplitude is 2. If we dot the graph of $y = 2 \cos x$ and note the zeros at $x = \frac{-3\pi}{2}$, $\frac{-\pi}{2}$, $\frac{\pi}{2}$, $\frac{3\pi}{2}$, then at these numbers x the graph of $y = 2 \sec x$ becomes undefined. Also, the secant graph seems to flip over. Note the graph below. The solid curves denote the graph of $y = 2 \sec x$.

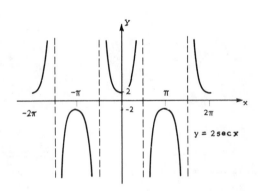

Example 2   Graph $y = \tan (2x + \frac{\pi}{2})$ for $-\frac{\pi}{2} \leq x \leq \frac{\pi}{2}$.

Solution   Find the phase shift just as with sine and cosine: Set the argument equal to 0. This gives

$2x + \frac{\pi}{2} = 0$

$2x = -\frac{\pi}{2}$

$x = -\frac{\pi}{4}$.

Since $\frac{-\pi}{4} < 0$, the phase shift is $\left|-\frac{\pi}{4}\right| = \frac{\pi}{4}$ to the left. The period $\frac{\pi}{2}$, so one complete cycle of the graph is compressed between points $\frac{\pi}{2}$ units apart. The usual origin point is translated to $\frac{-\pi}{4}$, with other x-intercepts every $\frac{\pi}{2}$ units. As shown in the figure, the asymptotes are $x = 0 + \frac{\pi k}{2}$, where k is any integer.

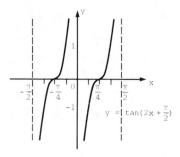

$y = \tan(2x + \frac{\pi}{2})$

Selected Solutions

1. The graph of $y = 2 \tan x$ has the same zeros and vertical asymptote lines as the graph of $y = \tan x$. We can note that the graph of $y = 2 \tan x$ seems to rise twice as rapidly as $y = \tan x$ in the sense that at $x = \frac{-\pi}{4}$, $2 \tan x = -2$ and $\tan x = -1$; at $x = 0$, $2 \tan x = \tan x = 0$; and at $x = \frac{\pi}{4}$, $\tan x = 1$ and $2 \tan x = 2$. See the graph in the text for $-2\pi \le x \le 2\pi$.

5. The graph of $y = 1 + \tan x$ is the graph of $y = \tan x$ shifted one unit upward. This is a vertical translation of one unit. See the graph in the text.

9. The graph of $y = 1 - \cot x$ is a vertical translation of the graph $y = -\cot x$ in exercise 3, shifted one unit upward. The graph for each of these can be seen in the answer section of the text.

13. The graph for $y = -\sec x$ can be determined by turning the graph of $y = \sec x$ "upside down." Note that the vertical asymptote lines are the same for both graphs. See the graph in the text.

17. The graph $y = \tan 2x$ has period $= \frac{\pi}{2}$, and with $-\pi \le x \le \pi$ the graph has vertical asymptotes of $x = \frac{-3\pi}{4}$, $\frac{-\pi}{4}$, $\frac{\pi}{4}$, $\frac{3\pi}{4}$. The graph has zeros (x-axis intercepts) when $x = -\pi$, $\frac{-\pi}{2}$, 0, $\frac{\pi}{2}$, π. See the graph over the two-period interval $[\frac{-\pi}{2}, \frac{\pi}{2}]$ in the answer section.

21. The graph of $y = \csc 4x$ has period $\frac{2\pi}{4} = \frac{\pi}{2}$. Over the two-period interval $\frac{-\pi}{2} \le x \le \frac{\pi}{2}$, the graph has vertical asymptote lines of $x = \frac{-\pi}{2}$, $\frac{-\pi}{4}$, 0, $\frac{\pi}{4}$, $\frac{\pi}{2}$. The graph has no zeros since $y = \csc 4x = \frac{1}{\sin 4x}$, and the numerator is never zero. We have $y = 1$ when $\sin 4x = 1$, or $x = \frac{-3\pi}{8}$, $\frac{\pi}{8}$, and $y = -1$ when $\sin 4x = -1$, or $x = \frac{-\pi}{8}$, $\frac{3\pi}{8}$. The graph consists of a "parabolic" shaped cup, horns upward U in the intervals for $\frac{-\pi}{2} < x < \frac{-\pi}{4}$ and $0 < x < \frac{\pi}{4}$, and cups downward ∩ for $\frac{-\pi}{4} < x < 0$ and $\frac{\pi}{4} < x < \frac{\pi}{2}$. See the graph in the text.

25. The graph of $y = \tan (x - \frac{\pi}{4})$ is the graph of $y = \tan x$ shifted horizontally to the right $\frac{\pi}{4}$ units. See the graph in the text.

29. The graph of $y = 3 \csc (x + \frac{3\pi}{2})$ has no points in the horizontal strip $-3 \leq y \leq 3$. The period is 2π and a two-period interval is $[\frac{-7\pi}{2}, \frac{\pi}{2}]$. The graph has vertical asymptotes of $x = \frac{-7\pi}{2}, \frac{-5\pi}{2}, \frac{-3\pi}{2}, \frac{-\pi}{2}$, and $\frac{\pi}{2}$. Also, the graph cups upward for $\frac{-7\pi}{2} < x < \frac{-5\pi}{2}$ and for $\frac{-3\pi}{2} < x < \frac{-\pi}{2}$. The graph cups downward for $\frac{-5\pi}{2} < x < \frac{-3\pi}{2}$ and for $\frac{-\pi}{2} < x < \frac{\pi}{2}$. See the graph in the text.

33. The graph of $y = 1 - \frac{1}{2} \csc (x - \frac{3\pi}{4})$ is the graph of $y = -\frac{1}{2} \csc x$ (see exercise 12) shifted horizontally to the right $\frac{3\pi}{4}$ units and upward one unit. The graph $y = \frac{-1}{2} \csc x$ has vertical asymptotes of $x = -2\pi, -\pi, 0, \pi, 2\pi$, so that $y = 1 - \frac{1}{2} \csc (x - \frac{3\pi}{4})$ has vertical asymptotes of $x = \frac{-5\pi}{4}, \frac{-\pi}{4}, \frac{3\pi}{4}, \frac{7\pi}{4}, \frac{11\pi}{4}$. Note that $I = [\frac{-5\pi}{4}, \frac{11\pi}{4}]$ is a two-period interval. The graph $y = -\frac{1}{2} \csc x$ has no points in the horizontal strip $-\frac{1}{2} \leq y \leq \frac{1}{2}$, so that $y = 1 - \frac{1}{2} \csc x$ has no points in the strip $\frac{1}{2} \leq y \leq \frac{3}{2}$.

The graph of $y = -\frac{1}{2} \csc x$ has downward cups $\cap$ for $-2\pi < x < -\pi$ and $0 < x < \pi$, and upward cups $\cup$ for $-\pi < x < 0$ and $\pi < x < 2\pi$. Hence, the graph of $y = 1 - \frac{1}{2} \csc (x - \frac{3\pi}{4})$

cups downward for $-\frac{5\pi}{4} < x < \frac{-\pi}{4}$ and $\frac{3\pi}{4} < x < \frac{7\pi}{4}$, and cups upward for $-\frac{\pi}{4} < x < \frac{3\pi}{4}$ and $\frac{7\pi}{4} < x < \frac{11\pi}{4}$. See the graph in the text.

37. If we dot the graphs of $f(x) = x$ and $g(x) = \cos x$ for $-2\pi \leq x \leq 2\pi$, and for each x let $y = f(x) + g(x)$, we have the graph of $y = x + \cos x$. If we consider the following table we can see some specific points

	$f(x) = x$	$g(x) = \cos x$	$x + \cos x$
-2π	-2π	1	$1 - 2\pi \approx -5.28$
$-\frac{3\pi}{2}$	$-\frac{3\pi}{2}$	0	$-\frac{3\pi}{2} \approx -4.71$
$-\pi$	$-\pi$	-1	$-\pi - 1 \approx 4.14$
$-\frac{\pi}{2}$	$-\frac{\pi}{2}$	0	$-\frac{\pi}{2} \approx -1.57$
0	0	1	1
$\frac{\pi}{2}$	$\frac{\pi}{2}$	0	$\frac{\pi}{2} \approx 1.57$
π	π	-1	$\pi - 1 \approx 2.14$
$\frac{3\pi}{2}$	$\frac{3\pi}{2}$	0	$\frac{3\pi}{2} \approx 4.71$
2π	2π	1	$1 + 2\pi \approx 7.28$

See the graph in the text.

41. We will graph $y = \sin x + \sin 2x$ over the interval $[0, 2\pi]$ since the graph will repeat over every interval of length 2π. Consider the table:

x	$\sin x$	$\sin 2x$	$y = \sin x + \sin 2x$
0	0	0	0
$\frac{\pi}{4}$	$\frac{\sqrt{2}}{2} \approx .707$	1	$1 + \frac{\sqrt{2}}{2} \approx 1.707$
$\frac{\pi}{2}$	1	0	1
$\frac{3\pi}{4}$	$\frac{\sqrt{2}}{2}$	-1	$-1 + \frac{\sqrt{2}}{2} \approx -.293$
π	0	0	0

x	sin x	sin 2 x	y = sin x + sin 2 x
$\frac{5\pi}{4}$	$-\frac{\sqrt{2}}{2}$	1	$1 - \frac{\sqrt{2}}{2} \approx .293$
$\frac{3\pi}{2}$	-1	0	-1
$\frac{7\pi}{4}$	$-\frac{\sqrt{2}}{2}$	-1	$-1 - \frac{\sqrt{2}}{2} \approx -1.707$
2π	0	0	0

See the graph in the text.

45. The graph of $y = 2 \cos x - \sec x$ has period 2π, and we will consider the graph over the interval $I = [-\pi, \pi]$. This graph has the same vertical asymptotes as the sec x, the vertical lines $x = \frac{-\pi}{2}$ and $x = \frac{\pi}{2}$. Consider the table:

x	2 cos x	sec x	y = 2cos x - sec x
$-\pi$	-2	-1	$-2 + 1 = -1$
$-\frac{3\pi}{4}$	$-\sqrt{2}$	$-\sqrt{2}$	0
$\frac{\pi}{2}$	0	$-$	undefined
$-\frac{\pi}{4}$	$\sqrt{2}$	$\sqrt{2}$	0
0	2	1	$2 - 1 = 1$
$\frac{\pi}{4}$	$\sqrt{2}$	$\sqrt{2}$	0
$\frac{\pi}{2}$	0	$-$	undefined
$\frac{3\pi}{4}$	$-\sqrt{2}$	$-\sqrt{2}$	0
π	-2	-1	$-2 + 1 = -1$

See the graph in the text.

49. Consider $y = -x + \sec x$ over the interval $[-2\pi, 2\pi]$. The graph will have vertical asymptotes for $x = \frac{-3\pi}{2}, \frac{-\pi}{2}, \frac{\pi}{2}, \frac{3\pi}{2}$. Consider the table: use $\pi \approx 3.14$

x	$-x$	sec x	y = -x + sec x
-2π	6.28	1	$1 + 2\pi \approx 7.28$
$-\frac{7\pi}{4}$	5.49	$\sqrt{2}$	6.91
$-\frac{3\pi}{2}$	4.71	$-$	undefined
$-\frac{5\pi}{4}$	3.93	$-\sqrt{2}$	2.52
$-\pi$	3.14	-1	2.14
$-\frac{3\pi}{4}$	2.36	$-\sqrt{2}$	0.95
$-\frac{\pi}{2}$	1.57	$-$	undefined
$-\frac{\pi}{4}$	.79	$\sqrt{2}$	2.10
0	0	1	1.00
$\frac{\pi}{4}$	$-.79$	$\sqrt{2}$	0.62
$\frac{\pi}{2}$	-1.57	$-$	undefined
$\frac{3\pi}{4}$	-2.36	$-\sqrt{2}$	-3.77
π	-3.14	-1	-4.14
$\frac{5\pi}{4}$	-3.93	$-\sqrt{2}$	-5.34
$\frac{3\pi}{2}$	-4.71	$-$	undefined
$\frac{7\pi}{4}$	-5.49	$\sqrt{2}$	-4.08
2π	-6.28	1	-5.28

See the graph in the text.

53. (a) Consider the shaded triangle. We have

$$\cot \theta = \frac{d}{h_2 - h_1},$$

or $d = (h_2 - h_1)\cot \theta$.

(b) If $h_2 = 55$ and $h_1 = 5$, then $d = 50 \cot \theta$. Using radian measure and considering $0 < \theta < \frac{\pi}{2}$, we have the table:

θ	$\cot \theta$	$d = 50 \cot \theta$
0	–	undefined
$\dfrac{\pi}{6}$	$\sqrt{3}$	86.5
$\dfrac{\pi}{4}$	1	50
$\dfrac{\pi}{3}$	$\dfrac{\sqrt{3}}{3}$	28.8
$\dfrac{\pi}{2}$	0	0

See the graph in the text.

57. For the graph of $y = 2^{-x} \sin x$ we use a calculator and consider the following table:

x	$y = 2^{-x} \sin x$
-2π	0
$-\dfrac{3\pi}{2}$	$2^{\frac{3\pi}{2}} \approx 26.2$
$-\pi$	0
$-\dfrac{\pi}{2}$	$-2^{\frac{\pi}{2}} \approx -2.97$
0	0
$\dfrac{\pi}{2}$	$2^{-\frac{\pi}{2}} \approx 0.34$
π	0
$\dfrac{3\pi}{2}$	$2^{-\frac{3\pi}{2}} \approx 0.04$
2π	0

The graph is not periodic. See the graph in the text.

Section 6.8   Inverse Trigonometric Functions

Additional Examples

Example 1   Find θ in degrees for each of the following.

(a) $\theta = \arccos \left(-\dfrac{1}{\sqrt{2}}\right)$

(b) $\theta = \arctan 1$

(c) $\theta = \text{arccot} \, (-.3541)$

Solution   (a) The values for arccos x are in quadrants I and II. (Why?) Since $-1/\sqrt{2}$ is negative, we are restricted to values in quadrant II. Write the equation as $\cos \theta = -1/\sqrt{2}$. In quadrant II, $\cos 135° = -1/\sqrt{2}$, so $\theta = 135°$.

(b) By writing the alternate equation, $\tan \theta = 1$, we see that $\theta = 45°$ Note that θ must be in quadrant I.

(c) From a calculator or Table 3, we see that $\cot 70°30' = .3541$. We need a second-quadrant angle. Thus, $\theta = 180° - 70°30' = 109°30'$.

Example 2   Evaluate each of the following without a calculator or tables.

(a) $\tan \left(\arccos \dfrac{-5}{13}\right)$

(b) $\cos (\arctan \sqrt{3} + \arcsin 1/3)$

Solution   (a) Let $y = \arccos (-5/13)$. Then $\cos y = -5/13$. Sketch y in quadrant II. (Why?) See the figure. From the triangle in the figure, $\tan \left(\arccos \dfrac{-5}{13}\right) = \tan y = -\dfrac{12}{5}$.

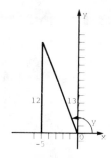

(b)   Let A = arctan $\sqrt{3}$ and B = arcsin 1/3.   Then tan A = $\sqrt{3}$ and sin B = 1/3.   Sketch both A and B in quadrant I, as shown in the figure.

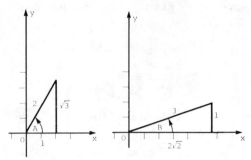

Now use the identity for cos (A + B).
cos (A + B) = cos A cos B - sin A sin B.
cos (arctan $\sqrt{3}$ + arcsin 1/3)
= cos (arctan $\sqrt{3}$) cos (arcsin 1/3)
- sin (arctan $\sqrt{3}$) sin (arcsin 1/3)
From the figure,
cos (arctan $\sqrt{3}$) = cos A = $\frac{1}{2}$,
sin (arctan $\sqrt{3}$) = sin A = $\frac{\sqrt{3}}{2}$,
cos (arcsin $\frac{1}{3}$) = cos B = $\frac{2\sqrt{2}}{3}$,
sin (arcsin $\frac{1}{3}$) = sin B = $\frac{1}{3}$.

Substitute these values into the equation to get
cos (arctan $\sqrt{3}$ + arcsin $\frac{1}{3}$)
= $\frac{1}{2} \cdot \frac{2\sqrt{2}}{3} - \frac{\sqrt{3}}{2} \cdot \frac{1}{3}$
= $\frac{2\sqrt{2}}{6} - \frac{\sqrt{3}}{6}$
= $\frac{2\sqrt{2} - \sqrt{3}}{6}$.

Selected Solutions

1. If y = $\sin^{-1}(-\frac{\sqrt{3}}{2})$, then
$\frac{-\pi}{2} \leq y \leq 0$, since $\frac{-\sqrt{3}}{2} < 0$.
The angle in that quadrant with a sine of $-\sqrt{3}/2$ is y = $-\pi/3$.

5. If y = $\sin^{-1}(-1)$, then
$-\frac{\pi}{2} \leq y \leq 0$ since $-1 \leq 0$.
Then we that y = $-\frac{\pi}{2}$.

9. If y = arccos $(\frac{-\sqrt{2}}{2})$, then
$\frac{\pi}{2} \leq y \leq \pi$, since $\frac{-\sqrt{2}}{2} < 0$.
Hence, y = $3\pi/4$.

13. If y = $\sin^{-1}(-.1334)$, then
$-90° \leq y \leq 0$, since $-.1334 < 0$,
and y = $-7°40'$.

17. If y = $\cos^{-1}(.9272)$, then
$0 \leq y \leq 90°$, since $.9272 > 0$,
and y = $22°00'$.

21. If y = arctan $(-.9217)$, then
$\frac{-\pi}{2} < y < 0$, since $-.9217 < 0$, and
y = $-42°40'$.

25. $\tan^{-1}(-4.114) = -1.332$

29. $\sin^{-1}(-0.443981) = -26°21'29''$

33. To find tan (arccos $\frac{3}{4}$), let
θ = arccos $\frac{3}{4}$, so that cos θ = $\frac{3}{4}$.
We have θ in quadrant I
and the figure gives
the fact that
tan θ = tan (arccos $\frac{3}{4}$) = $\frac{\sqrt{7}}{3}$.

37. Let θ = arcsin $(\frac{-2}{3})$.   Then sin θ = $\frac{-2}{3}$
and θ is in quadrant IV.   We complete the triangle and arrive at
cot θ = cot $\left(\arcsin(\frac{-2}{3})\right)$ = $\frac{-\sqrt{5}}{2}$.

41. Let $\theta = \arccos \frac{1}{2}$. Then $\cos \theta = \frac{1}{2}$ and we see that $\cos (\arccos \frac{1}{2}) = \cos \theta = \frac{1}{2}$.

45. Let $\theta = \sec^{-1} 2$. Then we have $\sec \theta = 2$ and conclude that $\sec (\sec^{-1} 2) = \sec \theta = 2$.

49. Let $\theta = \arcsin (\sin \frac{\pi}{3})$. Since $\sin \frac{\pi}{3} = \frac{\sqrt{3}}{2}$ we have $\theta = \arcsin \frac{\sqrt{3}}{2} = \frac{\pi}{3}$.

53. Let $\theta = \cos^{-1} (\cos \frac{5\pi}{4})$. Since $\cos \frac{5\pi}{4} = -\frac{\sqrt{2}}{2}$, we see that $\theta = \cos^{-1} (-\frac{\sqrt{2}}{2})$. Thus, θ is in quadrant II and $\cos \theta = \frac{-\sqrt{2}}{2}$. The reference angle is $\frac{\pi}{4}$, so that $\theta = \frac{3\pi}{4}$.

57. If we let $\theta = \arctan (.3)$ then θ is in quadrant I and we have the given figure. Then $c^2 = 1 + (.3)^2 = 1.09$, or $c = \sqrt{1.09}$. Then, $\cos \theta = \frac{1}{\sqrt{1.09}} \approx 0.957826$.

61. If $y = 4 \sin^{-1} x$, then
$$\frac{y}{4} = \sin^{-1} x$$
$$\sin (\frac{y}{4}) = x.$$

65. If $y = \sin^{-1} (x + 2)$, then
$$\sin y = x + 2, \text{ or}$$
$$x = -2 + \sin y.$$

69. Let $\theta = \cot^{-1} u$, so that $u = \cot \theta$. Then, solving the right triangle for the hypotenuse, we see that $\sec (\cot^{-1} u) = \sec \theta = \frac{1}{\cos \theta} = \frac{\sqrt{u^2 + 1}}{u}$.

73. Let $\theta = \sec^{-1} \frac{u}{2}$, so that $\sec \theta = \frac{u}{2}$. We complete the triangle and conclude that $\sin (\sec^{-1} \frac{u}{2}) = \sin \theta = \frac{\sqrt{u^2 - 4}}{4}$.

77. If we let $\theta = \text{arccot} \frac{\sqrt{4 - u^2}}{u}$, then $\cot \theta = \frac{\sqrt{4 - u^2}}{4}$ and we complete the triangle. Then we have $\sec \theta = \frac{2}{\sqrt{4 - u^2}}$.

81. If $y = \text{arcsec } x$, then $x = \sec y$. We can graph $y = \text{arcsec } x$ by considering the properties of the secant graph. If we have the graph of $y = \sec x$, for $0 \leq x < \frac{\pi}{2}$ and $\pi \leq x < \frac{3\pi}{2}$, and then we interchange the x- and y-axis we have the graph of $x = \sec y$, which is $y = \text{arcsec } x$. The graph $y = \text{arcsec } x$ has <u>horizontal</u> asymptote lines of $y = \frac{\pi}{2}$ and $y = \frac{3\pi}{2}$. If $f(x) = \text{arcsec } x$, we have dom $f = (-\infty, -1] \cup [1, \infty)$, and we see that Ran $f = [0, \frac{\pi}{2}] \cup [\pi, \frac{3\pi}{2})$. See the graph in the answer section of the text.

85. We have $\frac{\pi}{2} \approx 1.57029$, so that 1.74283 radians would represent a quadrant II angle. If $\theta = 1.74283$, then the reference angle in quadrant I is $R \approx 1.398763$. Thus, $\arcsin (\sin \theta) = R$.

89. The statement $2 \cos^{-1} x = \cos^{-1} 2x$ is false. Let $x = \frac{1}{2}$. We have $\cos^{-1} (\frac{1}{2}) = \frac{\pi}{3}$ so that $2 \cos^{-1} (\frac{1}{2}) = \frac{2\pi}{3}$, while $\cos^{-1} (1) = 0$.

93. The statement "$y = \sin^{-1} x$ is an even function" is <u>false</u>. This can be observed by letting $x = \frac{1}{2}$. We have $\arcsin(\frac{1}{2}) = \frac{\pi}{6}$, while $\arcsin(\frac{-1}{2}) = \frac{-\pi}{6}$.
Hence, it is not true that for all x, $f(-x) = f(x)$.

97. If $\alpha = 2 \arcsin \frac{1}{m}$, then;

(a) If $m = 1.2$, then
$$\alpha = 2 \arcsin \frac{1}{1.2} = 2 \arcsin \frac{5}{6}.$$
A calculator gives $\alpha \approx 112.885°$,
or $\alpha \approx 113°$.

(b) If $m = 1.5$, then
$$\alpha = 2 \arcsin \frac{1}{1.5} = 2 \arcsin \frac{3}{5}$$
$$\alpha \approx 84°.$$

(c) If $m = 2$, then
$$\alpha = 2 \arcsin \frac{1}{2} = (\frac{\pi}{6}) = \frac{\pi}{3},$$
or $\alpha \approx 60°$.

(d) If $\alpha = 2.5$, then
$$\alpha = 2 \arcsin \frac{1}{2.5} = \arcsin \frac{2}{5}$$
$$\alpha \approx 47°.$$

Chapter 6   Review Exercises

Selected Solutions

1. If $s = \frac{-\pi}{4}$, then the point P is in quadrant IV and
$$x = \cos(\frac{-\pi}{4}) = \frac{\sqrt{2}}{2},$$
$$y = \sin(\frac{-\pi}{4}) = \frac{-\sqrt{2}}{2}.$$
Hence, $P(\frac{\sqrt{2}}{2}, \frac{-\sqrt{2}}{2})$ is the point.

5. Since $\frac{5\pi}{4}$ is in quadrant III,
$$\sin \frac{5\pi}{4} = -\sin \frac{\pi}{4} = \frac{-\sqrt{2}}{2},$$
$$\cos \frac{5\pi}{4} = -\cos \frac{\pi}{4} = \frac{-\sqrt{2}}{2}, \text{ and}$$
$$\tan \frac{5\pi}{4} = +\tan \frac{\pi}{4} = 1.$$

9. Since $\cos s < 0$ and $\sin s > 0$, we must have s in quadrant II. This implies that $-s$ is in quadrant III and has the same reference angle as s. Thus, $-s$ corresponds to $P(\frac{-2}{3}, \frac{-\sqrt{5}}{3})$.

13. Since $\sin\theta > 0$ in quadrants I, II, and $\cos\theta < 0$ in quadrants II, III, we see that θ is in quadrant II.

17. If s terminates in quadrant I and if $\sin s = \frac{2}{3}$, then we complete the triangle and conclude that $\cos s = \frac{\sqrt{5}}{3}$,

$$\tan s = \frac{2}{\sqrt{5}} = \frac{2\sqrt{5}}{5}, \quad \cot s = \frac{\sqrt{5}}{2},$$
$$\sec s = \frac{3}{\sqrt{5}} = \frac{3\sqrt{5}}{5}, \text{ and } \csc s = \frac{3}{2}.$$

21. If the rotation is 320 rotations per minute, then using $\frac{2}{3}$ sec $= (\frac{2}{3})(\frac{1}{60})$ min $= \frac{1}{90}$ min, there are $320(\frac{1}{90}) = \frac{32}{9}$ rotations. Since each rotation is $360°$, the total degrees a point moves is $\frac{32}{9}(360°) = (32)(40) = 1280°$.

25. We see that $0.2983°$ can be changed to minutes by $\frac{2983}{10,000} = \frac{x}{60}$, or
$$x = \frac{(2983)(60)}{10,000} \text{ minutes} = 17.898',$$
and $0.898'$ can be changed to seconds

by $\frac{898}{1000} = \frac{x}{60}$, or $x = \frac{(898)(60)}{1000} = 53.88"$.
Hence, we conclude that
$74.2983° \approx 74°17'54"$.

29. We have $\frac{3\pi}{4} = \frac{3(180°)}{4} = 3(45)° = 135°$.

33. Since $180° = \pi$ radians, then
$270° = 270°(\frac{\pi}{180°}) = \frac{3\pi}{2}$ radians.

37. $\sin \frac{\pi}{3} = \frac{\sqrt{3}}{2}$

41. Since $900° = 2(360°) + 180°$, we
have $\sec 900° = \sec 180° = -1$.

45. A calculator gives $\tan 235° \approx 1.428$.
Note that $235°$ is in quadrant III
and the reference angle is $280 - 235$
$= 55°$. Hence, if a table is used,
we have
$\tan 235° = + \tan 55° \approx 1.428$.

49. Using a calculator gives
$\cos 58°4' = \cos (58.06667°) \approx 0.5289$.

53. If $\cos \theta = .9754$, then a calculator
gives $\theta = $ "inv cos" $.9754 \approx (12.735)°$,
and since $(.735)(60) = 44.1$,
$\theta \approx 12°44'$.

57. If $\sin s = 0.4924$, then a calculator
gives
$s = $ "inv sin" $(0.4924) \approx .5148$ radians.

61. If $A = 39.72°$ and $b = 38.97$, then
$\tan A = \frac{a}{b}$, or $a = b \tan A$. Hence,
$a = (38.97) \tan 39.72° \approx 32.38$m.
Then $c = \sqrt{a^2 + b^2} = \sqrt{(32.38)^2 + (38.97)^2}$,
$c \approx \sqrt{2567.1253} \approx 50.67$m.

65. If $\theta = \frac{2\pi}{5}$ radians and $t = 8$ seconds,
then $w = \frac{\theta}{t} = (\frac{2\pi}{5})(\frac{1}{8}) = \frac{\pi}{20}\frac{\text{radians}}{\text{sec}}$.

69. For $y = -\frac{1}{2} \cos 3x$ the period is $\frac{2\pi}{3}$,
the amplitude is $|-\frac{1}{2}| = \frac{1}{2}$, there
is no vertical translation, and no
phase shift.

73. The graph of $y = 3 \cos(x + \frac{\pi}{2})$ has
period $= 2\pi$, amplitude $= 3$, no
vertical translation, and a phase
shift of $\frac{-\pi}{2}$ (that is, $\frac{\pi}{2}$ units to
the left).

77. The graph for $y = 3 \sin x$ has period
2π and amplitude 3. The graph crosses
the x-axis when $\sin x = 0$, or $x = 0$,
π, 2π. The graph has $y = 3$ when
$\sin x = 1$, or $x = \frac{\pi}{2}$, and has $y = -3$
when $\sin x = -1$, or $x = \frac{3\pi}{2}$. See
the graph in the text.

81. The graph $y = 2 + \cot x$ is the graph
of $y = \cot x$ with a vertical translation of 2 units upward. The graph
has period π and has vertical asymp-
totes of $x = 0$, π. Since $\cot \frac{\pi}{2} = 0$,
the graph of $y = 2 + \cot x$ has
$y = 2$ at $x = \frac{\pi}{2}$. See the graph in
the text.

85. The graph for $y = 3 \cos 2x$ has
period $= \frac{2\pi}{2} = \pi$ and amplitude $= 3$.
The graph crosses the x-axis when
$\cos 2x = 0$, or $x = \frac{\pi}{4}$, $\frac{3\pi}{4}$. Note that
$\cos 0 = \cos 2(\pi) = 1$ while $\cos 2(\frac{\pi}{2})$
$= -1$. See the graph in the text.

89. The graph for $y = \sec(2x + \frac{\pi}{3})$ has period $= \frac{2\pi}{2} = \pi$. This graph has a a phase shift of $\frac{\pi}{3}$ units to the right of the graph $y = \sec 2x$. If $y = \sec 2x$ is graphed over $[\frac{-\pi}{2}, \frac{\pi}{2}]$, there are vertical asymptotoes of $x = \frac{-\pi}{4}$ and $x = \frac{\pi}{4}$. These asymptotes are shifted to $x = \frac{-\pi}{4} + \frac{\pi}{3} = \frac{\pi}{12}$ and $x = \frac{\pi}{4} + \frac{\pi}{3} = \frac{7\pi}{12}$. See the final graph in the text.

93. The graph of $y = 2 \sin \pi x$ has period $= \frac{2\pi}{\pi} = 2$ and amplitude $= 2$. Graphing over the interval $I = [0, 2]$, the graph crosses the x-axis when $\sin \pi x = 0$, or $x = 0, 1, 2$. We have $y = 2$ when $\sin \pi x = 1$, or $x = \frac{1}{2}$, and we have $y = -2$, when $x = \frac{3}{2}$. See the graph in the text.

97. Consider the table for $y = \tan x - x$ for $\frac{-\pi}{2} < x < \frac{\pi}{2}$.

x	tan x	-x	y = tan x - x
$\frac{-\pi}{2}$	$-$	$\frac{\pi}{2}$	undefined
$\frac{-\pi}{4}$	-1	$\frac{\pi}{4}$	$-1 + \frac{\pi}{4} \approx -.215$
0	0	0	0
$\frac{\pi}{4}$	1	$\frac{-\pi}{4}$	$1 - \frac{\pi}{4} \approx .215$
$\frac{\pi}{2}$	$-$	$\frac{-\pi}{2}$	undefined

See the graph in the text.

101. (a) The length of one period is approximately 20 years.
(b) The maximum population is $M \approx 150,000$, and the minimum is $M \approx 10,000$.

105. If $y = \tan^{-1}(-\sqrt{3})$, then $\tan y = -\sqrt{3}$. Hence, y is in quadrant IV and the reference angle is $\frac{\pi}{3}$. Hence, $y = \frac{-\pi}{3}$.

109. Let $\theta = \sin^{-1}(\frac{1}{2})$. We see that $\theta = \frac{\pi}{6}$. Then, $\sin(\sin^{-1}(\frac{1}{2})) = \sin \theta = \sin \frac{\pi}{6} = \frac{1}{2}$.

113. Since $\cos \frac{3\pi}{4} = -\frac{\sqrt{2}}{2}$, we have $\arccos(\cos \frac{3\pi}{4}) = \arccos(\frac{-\sqrt{2}}{2})$. Letting $\theta = \arccos(\frac{-\sqrt{2}}{2})$ we have θ in quadrant II and $\cos \theta = \frac{-\sqrt{2}}{2}$. Thus, $\theta = \frac{3\pi}{4}$. Hence, $\arccos(\cos \frac{3\pi}{4}) = \frac{3\pi}{4}$.

117. Let $\theta = \text{arcsec} \frac{\sqrt{u^2 + 1}}{u}$. Then $\sec \theta = \frac{\sqrt{u^2 + 1}}{u}$ and we can complete triangle and conclude that $\tan \theta = \frac{1}{u}$.

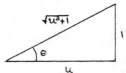

121. (a) If $e = E_{max} \sin 2\pi ft$, then
$$E_{max} = \sin 2\pi ft$$
$$2\pi ft = \arcsin(\frac{e}{E_{max}})$$
$$t = \frac{1}{2\pi c} \arcsin(\frac{e}{E_{max}}).$$

(b) If $E_{max} = 12$, $e = 5$, and $f = 100$, then
$$t = \frac{1}{200\pi} \arcsin(\frac{5}{12})$$
$$t \approx 0.000684, \text{ or } t \approx 0.0007.$$

Chapter 6   Test

1. Find the coordinates of the point on a unit circle corresponding to
    an arc length of 3.75π.

For each of the following arc lengths, find sin s and cos s.

2. -8.5π

3.   -3π/4

4. Find tan s and cot s if sin s = -3/5 and cos s = -4/5.

5. Decide on the quadrant where s must terminate if cos s < 0 and sec s < 0.

6. Find the values of the other trigonometric functions if sin t = 3/7
    and cos t = -2√10/7.

7. Find the angle of smallest possible positive measure coterminal with an
    angle of -477°.

8. Convert 450° to radians. Leave the answer as a multiple of π.

9. Convert 11π/15 radians to degrees.

10. A shaft is rotating 5000 times per minute. How many degrees does a point on
    the edge of the shaft rotate through in 8 seconds?

11. Find the distance in miles between cities of 25° N latitude and 9° S. Assume
    that the cities are on a north-south line and that the radius of the earth
    is 4000 miles.

12. Find the sine and cosine of an angle of 225°.

13. Find the six trigonometric function values of θ where P(8, 15) is on the
    terminal side of angle θ in standard position.

Find the reference angle for each of the following. Use 3.1416 as an approximation
for π.

14. 321° 50'

15. -1.3320

Find the values of the following.

16. tan 82° 30'

17. tan (-2.4027)

18. Use interpolation to find cos 82° 24'.

19. Find a value of θ in degrees if cos θ = 0.8616.

20. A kite string makes an angle of 59° 40' with the ground. The kite is 47.8 m
    above the ground. Assume that the string makes a straight line and find its
    length.

Graph one period of each of the following functions.

21. y = -5 cos 2x

22. y = 2 sin (x - $\frac{\pi}{2}$)

23. y = -tan 3x

24. y = -$\frac{1}{2}$ csc x

Give the value of y in radians without using tables or a calculator.

25. y = $\cos^{-1}\left(\frac{-\sqrt{3}}{2}\right)$

26. y = arccos (-1)

27. Give the value of $\tan^{-1}$ (-9.010) in degrees.

Give the value of each of the following without using tables or a calculator.

28. csc (arcsin $\frac{12}{13}$)

29. $\cos^{-1}$ (tan $\frac{\pi}{4}$)

30. Solve for x: y = 2 ($\cos^{-1}$ x) - 3.

    (Answers for this test are on page 362.)

Chapter 6   Trigonometric Functions

If you are using <u>Algebra</u> <u>and</u> <u>Trigonometry</u> --<u>An</u> <u>Alternate</u> <u>Approach</u>, follow Sections 6.1 through Section 6.4 here. Then turn back to Section 6.5 on page 179. Work until you get to the review exercises, when you will need to turn to the review exercises that begin on page 204.

Section 6.1   Angles
Additional Examples
Example 1   Given the two angles 38°16' and 72°49' of a triangle, find the third angle.
Solution   The sum of the three angles of a triangle is 180°. The sum of the two given angles is
38°16' + 72°49' = 110°65' = 111°5'.
Hence, the third angle is
180° - 111°5' = 68°55'.
Example 2   Convert the decimal angle 26.4211° into an angle in degrees, minutes, and seconds.
Solution   The conversion needed is to change 0.4211° into minutes and seconds. Using ratios we see that
$\frac{4211}{10,000}$ degrees $\cdot \frac{60 \text{ min}}{1 \text{ degree}}$ = x minutes.
That is (.4211)(60) = x. This gives
x = 25.266. Thus, 0.4211° = 25.226'.
Now we need to convert 0.266' into seconds. Using the same reasoning, we have
0.266' = (0.266)(60) seconds
0.266' = 15.96" or ≈ 16".
Hence,
26.4211° ≈ 26°25'16".

Selected Solutions
1.   The angle of smallest possible <u>posi</u>-<u>tive</u> measure coterminal with -40° is θ = -40° + 360° = 320°.

5.   The angle 450° is coterminal with θ = 450° - 360° = 90°.

9.   The angle 850° is coterminal with θ = 850° - 2(360°) = 850° - 720° = 130°.

13.   Two angles coterminal with 75° are
θ_1 = 75° + 360° = 435°, and
θ_2 = 75° - 360° = -285°. These angles are in quadrant I.

17.   Two angles coterminal with 234° are
θ_1 = 234° + 360° = 594°, and
θ_2 = 234° - 360° = -126°. These angles are in quadrant III.

21.   Two angles coterminal with 438° are
θ_1 = 438° - 360° = 78° (positive), and
θ_2 = 438° - 2(360°) = 438° - 720°
     = -282° (negative).
These angles are in quadrant I.

25.   Two angles coterminal with -52° are
θ_1 = -52° + 360° = 308°, and
θ_2 = -52° - 360° = -412°. These angles are in quadrant IV.

29.   The point P(-3, -3) is in quadrant III, and the ray from the origin through P makes a 45° angle in quadrant III. Hence, the angle is
θ_1 = 180° + 45° = 225°, or
θ_2 = -180° + 45° = -135°.

33.   The point P(-2, $2\sqrt{3}$) lies in quadrant II, and the ray from the origin through P makes a 120° angle from the positive x-axis.

37.   We have
(5k + 5)+(3k + 5) = 90
         8k + 10 = 90
              8k = 80
               k = 10.
The angles are 55° and 35°.

41. We have

$$
\begin{array}{r}
75°15' \\
+83°32' \\
\hline
158°47'.
\end{array}
$$

45. We have

$$
\begin{array}{r}
90°00' = 89°60' \\
-51°28' = -51°28' \\
\hline
38°32'.
\end{array}
$$

49. Since 90° = 89°60' = 89°59'60",
     we have

$$
\begin{array}{r}
90° \qquad = 89°59'60" \\
-36°18'47" = -36°18'47" \\
\hline
53°41'13".
\end{array}
$$

53. The sum of the angles 74°15' +
     83°57', = 157°72', or 158°12'.
     Hence, the third angle is
     θ = 180° - 158°12' = 21°48'.

57. The sum of the angles
     74°12'59" + 80°58'05" is
     154°70'64" = 154°71'4",
                = 155°11'4".
     The third angle is
     θ = 180° - 155°11'4" = 24°48'56".

61. We have 35' = $\left(\frac{35}{60}\right)^\circ$ = 0.58333°,

     and 54" = $\left(\frac{54}{60}\right)' = \left(\frac{9}{10}\right)'$

     $= \left(\frac{9}{10} \cdot \frac{1}{60}\right)^\circ = \left(\frac{3}{200}\right)^\circ$,

     or 54" = 0.015°. Hence,
     91°35'54" = (91 + .5833 + .015)°,
               = 91.5983°.

65. We have
     0.4296° = (.4296)(60) minutes
             = 25.776',
     and
     0.776' = (.776)(60) seconds
            = 46.56", or ≈ 47".
     Hence,
     31.4296° ≈ 31°25'47".

69. We have
     0.5994° = (.5994)(60) minutes
             = 35.964',
     and 0.964' = (.964)(60) seconds
                = 57.84", or ≈ 58".
     Hence,
     178.5994° = 178°35'58".

73. The pulley rotates
     (75)(60) = 4500° in one hour,

     or $\frac{4500}{360} = \frac{50}{4}$ = 12.5 rotations

     in one hour.

Section 6.2   The Trigonometric
               Functions

Additional Examples

Example 1   Find the six trigonometric
             functions for the angle in standard
             position having P(2, -2√3) on the
             terminal side.

Solution   We complete
            the triangle with
            $r^2 = 2^2 + (-2\sqrt{3})^2$
            $r^2 = 4 + 12 = 16$.
            Hence, r = 4.
            Then we have

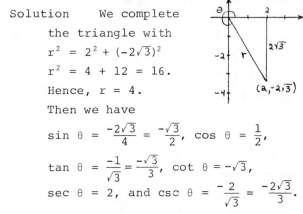

$\sin \theta = \frac{-2\sqrt{3}}{4} = \frac{-\sqrt{3}}{2}$, $\cos \theta = \frac{1}{2}$,

$\tan \theta = \frac{-1}{\sqrt{3}} = \frac{-\sqrt{3}}{3}$, $\cot \theta = -\sqrt{3}$,

$\sec \theta = 2$, and $\csc \theta = \frac{-2}{\sqrt{3}} = \frac{-2\sqrt{3}}{3}$.

Example 2   Find sec θ if tan θ = $\frac{2}{3}$

             and θ is in quadrant III.

Solution   Start with the Pythagorean
            identity $\tan^2 \theta + 1 = \sec^2 \theta$ and
            replace tan θ with $\frac{2}{3}$. This gives

$\sec^2 \theta = \left(\frac{2}{3}\right)^2 + 1 = \frac{4}{9} + 1 = \frac{13}{9}$,

and hence, sec $\theta = \pm\frac{\sqrt{13}}{3}$. Since θ
is in quadrant III, we have
sec $\theta < 0$. Hence,
sec $\theta = \frac{-\sqrt{13}}{3}$.

Selected Solutions

1. Since cos 90° = 0 and sin 270° = -1,
    we have
    cos 90° + 3 sin 270° = 0 + 3(-1) = -3.

5. We have tan 360° = tan 0° = 0,
    sin 180° = 0, and cos 180° = -1.
    Hence, tan 360° + 4 sin 180° +
    5 cos^2 180° = 0 + 4(0) + 5(-1)^2 = 5.

9. We have sec 180° = -1, sin 360° = 0,
    and cos 180° = -1. Hence,
    sec^2 180° - 3 sin^2 360° + 2 cos 180°
    = (-1)^2 - 3(0)^2 + 2(-1) = 1 - 2 = -1.

13. We have sin 90° = 1, cos 180° = -1,
    and csc 270° = -1. Hence,
    -4|sin 90°|+3|cos 180°|+2|csc 270°|
    = -4|1|+3|-1|+2|-1|
    = -4(1) + 3(1) + 2(1)
    = -4 + 3 + 2
    = 1.

17. For P(5, -12) we have x = 5, y = -12,
    and hence r = $\sqrt{25 + 144}$ = $\sqrt{169}$ = 13.
    This gives sin $\theta = \frac{-12}{13}$, cos $\theta = \frac{5}{13}$,
    tan $\theta = \frac{-12}{5}$, cot $\theta = -\frac{5}{12}$, sec $\theta = \frac{13}{5}$,
    and csc $\theta = \frac{-13}{12}$.

21. For P(8, 0) we have x = 8, y = 0,
    so that r = $\sqrt{64 + 0}$ = 8. Hence,
    we have sin $\theta = \frac{0}{8} = 0$, cos $\theta = \frac{8}{8} = 1$,
    tan $\theta = 0$, cot θ is undefined,
    sec $\theta = 1$, and csc θ is undefined.

25. For P($5\sqrt{3}$, - 5) we have x = $5\sqrt{3}$,
    y = -5, so that r = $\sqrt{75 + 25}$ = 10.
    Hence, sin $\theta = \frac{-5}{10} = -\frac{1}{2}$,
    cos $\theta = \frac{5\sqrt{3}}{10} = \frac{\sqrt{3}}{2}$,
    tan $\theta = -\frac{5}{5\sqrt{3}} = \frac{-\sqrt{3}}{3}$,
    cot $\theta = -\sqrt{3}$, sec $\theta = \frac{2}{\sqrt{3}} = \frac{2\sqrt{3}}{3}$,
    and csc $\theta = -2$.

29. For P($\sqrt{5}$, -2) we have x = $\sqrt{5}$, y = -2,
    and r = $\sqrt{5 + 4}$ = 3. Hence,
    sin $\theta = \frac{-2}{3}$, cos $\theta = \frac{\sqrt{5}}{3}$,
    tan $\theta = \frac{-2}{\sqrt{5}} = \frac{-2\sqrt{5}}{5}$, cot $\theta = \frac{-\sqrt{5}}{2}$,
    sec $\theta = \frac{3}{\sqrt{5}} = \frac{3\sqrt{5}}{5}$, and csc $\theta = \frac{-3}{2}$.

33. For P($\sqrt{15}$, - $\sqrt{10}$) we have x = $\sqrt{15}$,
    y = -$\sqrt{10}$, and r = $\sqrt{15 + 10}$ = 5.
    Hence, sin $\theta = \frac{-\sqrt{10}}{5}$, cos $\theta = \frac{\sqrt{15}}{5}$,
    tan $\theta = \frac{-\sqrt{10}}{\sqrt{15}} = \frac{-\sqrt{150}}{15} = \frac{-5\sqrt{6}}{15} = \frac{-\sqrt{6}}{3}$,
    cot $\theta = \frac{-3}{\sqrt{6}} = \frac{-3\sqrt{6}}{6} = \frac{-\sqrt{6}}{2}$,
    sec $\theta = \frac{5}{\sqrt{15}} = \frac{\sqrt{15}}{3}$, and
    csc $\theta = \frac{-5}{\sqrt{10}} = \frac{-\sqrt{10}}{2}$.

37. For P(-.04716, -.03219) we have
    x = -.04716, y = -.03219, and
    r = $\sqrt{(-.04716)^2 + (-.03219)^2}$ ≈ 0.05710.
    Hence, sin $\theta = \frac{y}{r}$ ≈ -.5638,
    cos $\theta = \frac{x}{r}$ ≈ -.8259,
    tan $\theta = \frac{y}{x}$ ≈ .6826,
    cot $\theta = \frac{x}{y}$ ≈ 1.465,
    sec $\theta = \frac{r}{x}$ ≈ -1.211, and
    csc $\theta = \frac{y}{r}$ ≈ -1.774.

41. If $\csc \theta = 3$, then $\sin \theta = \frac{1}{3}$.

45. If $\sin \alpha = \frac{\sqrt{2}}{4}$, then $\csc \alpha = \frac{4}{\sqrt{2}} = 2\sqrt{2}$.

49. If $\csc \theta = 1.42716$, then
    $\sin \theta = 0.700692$.

53. We have $\sin \alpha > 0$ in quadrants I and II and $\cos \alpha < 0$ in quadrants II and III. Hence, α is in quadrant II.

57. We have $\sin B < 0$ in quadrants III and IV and $\cos B > 0$ in quadrants I and IV. Hence, B is in quadrant IV.

61. If $\sin \alpha > 0$, then α is in either quadrant I or II.

65. If $\sin \theta = \frac{2}{3}$ and θ in quadrant II, then we use $\sin^2 \theta + \cos^2 \theta = 1$ to conclude that $(\frac{2}{3})^2 + \cos^2 \theta = 1$, or $\cos^2 \theta = 1 - \frac{4}{9} = \frac{5}{9}$. Hence, $\cos \theta = \pm \frac{\sqrt{5}}{3}$. Since $\cos \theta < 0$ in quadrant II, we have $\cos \theta = \frac{-\sqrt{5}}{3}$.

69. If $\tan \theta = \frac{\sqrt{7}}{3}$ and θ is quadrant III, then we use $\tan^2 \theta + 1 = \sec^2 \theta$ to conclude that $(\frac{\sqrt{7}}{3})^2 + 1 = \frac{7}{9} + 1 = \frac{16}{9} = \sec^2 \theta$. Hence, $\sec \theta = \pm \frac{4}{3}$. Since $\sec \theta < 0$ in quadrant III, we have $\sec \theta = \frac{-4}{3}$.

73. If $\cos \alpha = \frac{-3}{5}$ and α is in quadrant III, then we use $\sin^2 \alpha + \cos^2 \alpha = 1$ to conclude that $\sin^2 \alpha = 1 - (\frac{-3}{5})^2 = 1 - \frac{9}{25}$, $\sin^2 \alpha = \frac{16}{25}$. Thus,

$\sin \alpha = \pm \frac{4}{5}$. Since $\sin \alpha < 0$ in quadrant III, $\sin \alpha = \frac{-4}{5}$. Then, $\tan \alpha = \frac{\sin \alpha}{\cos \alpha} = \frac{-4/5}{-3/5} = \frac{4}{3}$, $\cot \alpha = \frac{3}{4}$, $\sec \alpha = -\frac{5}{3}$, and $\csc \alpha = \frac{-5}{4}$.

77. If $\csc \theta = 2$ and θ is in quadrant II, then we use $1 + \cot^2 \theta = \csc^2 \theta$ to conclude that $1 + \cot^2 \theta = 4$, $\cot^2 \theta = 3$, or $\cot \theta = \pm \sqrt{3}$. Since θ is in quadrant II, $\cot \theta < 0$, so that $\cot \theta = -\sqrt{3}$. Then, $\sin \theta = \frac{1}{\csc \theta} = \frac{1}{2}$, and $\tan \theta = \frac{-1}{\sqrt{3}} = \frac{-\sqrt{3}}{3}$. Also, $\cos \theta = (\sin \theta)(\cot \theta) = (\frac{1}{2})(-\sqrt{3}) = \frac{-\sqrt{3}}{2}$. Then, $\sec \theta = \frac{-2}{\sqrt{3}} = \frac{-2\sqrt{3}}{3}$.

81. If $\sin \theta = \frac{-5}{6}$, then $\sin^2 \theta + \cos^2 \theta = 1$ gives $\frac{25}{36} + \cos^2 \theta = 1$, $\cos^2 \theta = \frac{11}{36}$, or $\cos \theta = \frac{\sqrt{11}}{6}$ since we are given $\cos \theta > 0$. Then $\tan \theta = \frac{\sin \theta}{\cos \theta} = \frac{-5}{\sqrt{11}} = \frac{-5\sqrt{11}}{11}$, $\cot \theta = \frac{-\sqrt{11}}{5}$, $\sec \theta = \frac{6\sqrt{11}}{11}$, and $\csc \theta = \frac{-6}{5}$.

85. If $\csc \theta = \frac{\sqrt{13}}{3}$, then $\sin \theta = \frac{3}{\sqrt{13}} = \frac{3\sqrt{13}}{13}$. If $\tan \theta = \frac{3}{2}$, then $\cot \theta = \frac{2}{3}$. Also θ must be in quadrant I since these four trigonometric functions are positive. We have $\cot \theta = \frac{\cos \theta}{\sin \theta}$, so that
$\cos \theta = \sin \theta \cot \theta$
$\cos \theta = \frac{3\sqrt{13}}{13} \cdot \frac{2}{3} = \frac{2\sqrt{13}}{13}$.
Then we have $\sec \theta = \frac{\sqrt{13}}{2}$.

89. If γ is in quadrant III, then
     $\tan \gamma > 0$, $\cot \gamma > 0$, and the other
     four are negative. Using
     $\sec^2 \gamma = 1 + \tan^2 \gamma$ with
     $\tan \gamma = .642193$, we have
     $\sec^2 \gamma = 1 + .412412$, or
     $\sec \gamma = -\sqrt{1.412412} \approx -1.18845$.
     Then,

     $\cos \gamma = \dfrac{1}{\sec \gamma} \approx -.841433$.

     We use
     $\tan \gamma = \dfrac{\sin \gamma}{\cos \gamma}$ to

     conclude that
     $\sin \gamma = \cos \gamma \cdot \tan \gamma \approx -.540362$.
     Also,
     $\cot \gamma = \dfrac{1}{\tan \gamma} \approx 1.55716$, and

     $\csc \gamma \quad \dfrac{1}{\sin \gamma} \approx -1.85061$.

93. We use the fact that if $P(x_1 y)$ is
     any point on the terminal side of
     the angle and if $r = \sqrt{x^2 + y^2}$, then
     $\sin \theta = \dfrac{y}{r}$, $\cos \theta = \dfrac{x}{r}$, and $\tan \theta = \dfrac{y}{x}$.

     Then, $\dfrac{\sin \theta}{\cos \theta} = \dfrac{y/r}{x/r} = \dfrac{y}{r} \cdot \dfrac{r}{x}$

     $\qquad\qquad = \dfrac{y}{x} = \tan \theta$.

Section 6.3   Trigonometric Functions
               of Special Angles

Additional Examples
Example 1   Find the values of the
             trigonometric functions for 60°.
Solution   To find those values, use
            the 30°-60° right triangle of the
            figure. The side of length $\sqrt{3}$ is
            the side opposite the 60° angle,
            while the side of length 1 is
            adjacent. Thus,

$\sin 60° = \dfrac{\sqrt{3}}{2}, \qquad \tan 60° = \sqrt{3},$

$\sec 60° = 2, \qquad \cos 60° = \dfrac{1}{2},$

$\cot 60° = \dfrac{\sqrt{3}}{3}, \qquad \csc 60° = \dfrac{2\sqrt{3}}{3}.$

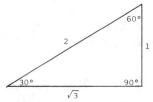

Example 2   Find the trigronometric
             functions of θ if the terminal side
             of θ passes through the point
             $P(-3, 4)$.
Solution   We have $r = \sqrt{9 + 16} = 5$.
            Then we have

$\sin \theta = \dfrac{-4}{5} = -\dfrac{4}{5}, \qquad \cot \theta = \dfrac{-3}{-4} = \dfrac{3}{4},$

$\cos \theta = \dfrac{-3}{5} = -\dfrac{3}{5}, \qquad \sec \theta = \dfrac{5}{-3} = -\dfrac{5}{3},$

$\tan \theta = \dfrac{-4}{-3} = \dfrac{4}{3}, \qquad \csc \theta = \dfrac{5}{-4} = -\dfrac{5}{4}.$

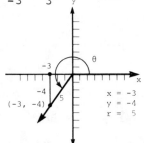

Selected Solutions
1. Using the text's figure, we have
    $\sin A = \dfrac{3}{5}$, $\cos A = \dfrac{4}{5}$, $\tan A = \dfrac{3}{4}$,
    $\cot A = \dfrac{4}{3}$, $\sec A = \dfrac{5}{4}$, and $\csc A = \dfrac{5}{3}$.

5. We have $\sin A = \dfrac{.8974}{1.1819} \approx .75960$,

    $\cos A = \dfrac{.7692}{1.1819} \approx .650787$,

    $\tan A = \dfrac{.8974}{.7692} \approx 1.16668$,

    $\cot A \approx .857133$, $\sec A = 1.53660$,
    $\csc A = 1.31707$.

9. The angle $\theta = 150°$ is in quadrant II, with a reference angle of 30°. Thus,

$\sin 150° = \frac{1}{2}$,　　$\cos 150° = \frac{-\sqrt{3}}{2}$,

$\tan 150° = \frac{-\sqrt{3}}{3}$,　$\cot 150° = -\sqrt{3}$,

$\sec 150° = \frac{-2\sqrt{3}}{3}$,　$\csc 150° = 2$.

13. The angle $\theta = 330°$ is in quadrant IV, with a reference angle of $R = 30°$. Thus,

$\sin 330° = \frac{-1}{2}$,　　$\cos 330° = \frac{\sqrt{3}}{2}$,

$\tan 330° = \frac{-\sqrt{3}}{3}$,　$\cot 330° = -\sqrt{3}$,

$\sec 330° = \frac{2\sqrt{3}}{3}$,　$\csc 330° = -2$.

17. The angle $\theta = 510° = 360° + 150°$ is in quadrant II and has a reference angle of 30°. Hence,

$\sin 510° = \frac{1}{2}$,　　　$\cos 510° = \frac{-\sqrt{3}}{2}$,

$\tan 510° - \frac{-\sqrt{3}}{3}$,　$\cot \theta = -\sqrt{3}$,

$\sec \theta = \frac{-2\sqrt{3}}{3}$, and $\csc \theta = 2$.

21. The angle $\theta = 1500° = 4(360°) + 60°$ is in quadrant I, with a reference angle of $R = 60°$. Hence,

$\sin \theta = \frac{\sqrt{3}}{2}$,　　　$\cos \theta = \frac{1}{2}$,

$\tan \theta = \sqrt{3}$,　　$\cot \theta = \frac{\sqrt{3}}{3}$,

$\sec \theta = 2$, and　$\csc \theta = \frac{2\sqrt{3}}{3}$.

25. The angle $\theta = -1020° = -3(360°) + 60°$ has terminal ray in quandrant I, with a reference angle $R = 60°$. Hence,

$\sin (-1020°) = \frac{\sqrt{3}}{2}$,

$\cos (-1020°) = \frac{1}{2}$,

$\tan (-1020°) = \sqrt{3}$,

$\cot (-1020°) = \frac{\sqrt{3}}{3}$,

$\sec (-1020°) = 2$, and

$\csc (-1020°) = \frac{2\sqrt{3}}{3}$.

29. The missing blanks are $\sin 60° = \frac{\sqrt{3}}{2}$, $\cot 60° = \frac{\sqrt{3}}{3}$, and $\csc 60° = \frac{2\sqrt{3}}{3}$.

33. The angle $\theta = 210° = 180° + 30°$ is in quadrant III, and the reference angle is $R = 30°$. The missing blanks are $\cos 210° = \frac{-\sqrt{3}}{2}$ and $\sec 210° = \frac{-2\sqrt{3}}{3}$.

37. Since $\tan 120° = -\tan 60° = -\sqrt{3}$,

$\sin 150° = \sin 30° = \frac{1}{2}$,

and $\cos 180° = -1$, we have

$2 \tan^2 120° + 3 \sin^2 150° - \cos^2 180°$

$= 2(-\sqrt{3})^2 + 3(\frac{1}{2})^2 - (-1)^2$

$= 2(3) + 3(\frac{1}{4}) - 1$

$= 5 + \frac{3}{4}$

$= \frac{23}{4}$.

41. Since $\cos 60° = \frac{1}{2}$,

$\sec 150° = -\sec 30° = \frac{-1}{\cos 30°} = \frac{-2}{\sqrt{3}}$

and

$\csc 210° = -\csc 30° = \frac{-1}{\sin 30°} = -2$,

we have

$\cos^2 60° + \sec^2 150° - \csc^2 210°$

$= (\frac{1}{2})^2 + (\frac{-2}{\sqrt{3}})^2 - (-2)^2$

$= \frac{1}{4} + \frac{4}{3} - 4$

$= \frac{3 + 16 - 48}{12}$

$= \frac{-29}{12}$.

45. We have $\sin 30° = \frac{1}{2}$, $\sin 60° = \frac{\sqrt{3}}{2}$,
and $\sin (30° + 60°) = \sin 90° = 1$.
Since $\frac{1}{2} + \frac{\sqrt{3}}{2} \neq 1$, the statement is
<u>false</u>.

49. We have $\cos 60° = \frac{1}{2}$ and $2 \cos 30° = 2(\frac{\sqrt{3}}{2}) = \sqrt{3}$.   Hence, the statement
is false.

53. We have $\cos 150° = -\cos 30° = \frac{-\sqrt{3}}{2}$,
and $\cos 120° \cos 30° -$
    $\quad \sin 120° \sin 30°$
  $= (-\cos 60°) \cdot \cos 30° -$
    $\quad (\sin 60°) \sin 30°$
  $= (-\frac{1}{2}) \frac{\sqrt{3}}{2} - (\frac{\sqrt{3}}{2})(\frac{1}{2})$
  $= \frac{-\sqrt{3}}{4} - \frac{\sqrt{3}}{4} = \frac{-\sqrt{3}}{2}$.

Hence, the statement is true.

57. If $\tan \theta = \sqrt{3}$ and $0° \leq \theta \leq 360°$,
then θ is in quadrants I and III
with a reference angle R = 60°.
Hence, $\theta = 60°$ or $\theta = 180° + 60° = 240°$.

61. If $\sin \theta = \frac{-\sqrt{3}}{2}$ and $0° \leq \theta \leq 360°$,
then θ is in quadrants III and IV
with a reference angle of R = 60°.
Hence, $\theta = 180° + 60 = 240°$, or
$\theta = 360° - 60 = 300°$.

65. If $\cot \theta$ is undefined, then
$\tan \theta = 0$, and $\theta = 0°$ or $\theta = 180°$.

69. Using the triangle with hypotenuse
of 24, we have $\cos 60° = \frac{a}{24}$, or
$a = 24 \cos 60° = 24(\frac{1}{2}) = 12$, and
then $\sin 60° = \frac{b}{24}$, or $b = 24 \sin 60°$
$= 24(\frac{\sqrt{3}}{2}) = 12\sqrt{3}$.   Then, using the
triangle with hypotenuse of c, we
have $\cos 45° = \frac{b}{c}$, or

$c = \frac{b}{\cos 45°} = \sqrt{2}$ $b = \sqrt{2}(12\sqrt{3}) = 12\sqrt{6}$,

and then $\sin 45° = \frac{d}{c}$, or

$d = c \sin 45° = 12\sqrt{6}(\frac{1}{\sqrt{2}}) = 12\sqrt{3}$.

Section 6.4   Radian Measure and
               Circular Functions

Additional Examples
Example 1   Convert to radians
    (a) 29° 40'   (b) 74.9162°.
Solution   (a) We know that
    40' = 40/60 = 2/3 of a degree. Thus,
        $29° \ 40' = 29\frac{2}{3}°$
                  $= \frac{89°}{3}$
                  $= \frac{89}{3}(\frac{\pi}{180})$ radians
        $29° \ 40' = \frac{89\pi}{540}$ radians.

This answer is exact. If we now
replace π with the approximation
3.14159, we get
    $29° \ 40' \approx \frac{89(3.14159)}{540}$
    $29° \ 40' \approx .518$ radians.

(b) $74.9162° = 74.9162(\frac{\pi}{180})$ Multiply
                                    by $\pi/180°$

    $\approx 74.9162(\frac{3.14159}{180})$

    ≈ 1.30753 radians

Example 2   A belt runs a pully of
radius 6 cm at 80 revolutions per
minute. Find the angular velocity
of the pulley in radians per
second.
Solution   In one minute, the pulley
makes 80 revolutions. Each revolution is 2π radians, for a total of
$80(2\pi) = 160\pi$ radians per minute.
Since there are 60 seconds in a
minute, ω, the angular velocity

in radians per second, is given by

$$\omega = \frac{160}{60} = \frac{8\pi}{3} \text{ radians per second.}$$

Also, $42' = \left(\frac{42}{60}\right)^\circ = \left(\frac{7}{10}\right)^\circ = .7^\circ.$

Hence,

$$-29°42'36'' = -29.71°$$

$$= (-29.71)\left(\frac{\pi}{180}\right) \text{ radians}$$

$$\approx -0.518537 \text{ radians.}$$

Selected Solutions

1. We have

$$150° = 150\left(\frac{\pi}{180}\right) \text{ radians}$$

$$= \frac{5\pi}{6} \text{ radians.}$$

5. We have

$$300° = 300\left(\frac{\pi}{180}\right) \text{ radians}$$

$$= \frac{5\pi}{3} \text{ radians.}$$

9. We have

$$20° = 20\left(\frac{\pi}{180}\right) \text{ radians}$$

$$= \frac{\pi}{9} \text{ radians.}$$

13. We have

$$39° = 39\left(\frac{\pi}{180}\right) \text{ radians}$$

$$= \frac{39}{180} \cdot \pi \text{ radians}$$

$$\approx .68 \text{ radians}$$

17. We have

$$139°10' \approx 139.1667°, \text{ and hence,}$$

$$139°10' \approx (139.1667)\left(\frac{\pi}{180}\right) \text{ radians}$$

$$\approx 2.43 \text{ radians.}$$

21. We have

$$56°25' \approx 56.4166°, \text{ and hence,}$$

$$56°25' \approx (56.4166)\left(\frac{\pi}{180}\right) \text{ radians}$$

$$\approx 0.9847 \text{ radians.}$$

25. We have $36'' = \left(\frac{36}{60}\right)' = \left(\frac{6}{10}\right)' = .6',$ and

$$(.6)' = \left(\frac{.6}{60}\right)^\circ = \left(\frac{1}{100}\right)^\circ = .01°.$$

29. We have

$$\frac{11\pi}{6} \text{ radians} = \frac{11(180°)}{6} = 11(30°) = 330°.$$

33. We have

$$\frac{8\pi}{5} \text{ radians} = \frac{8(180°)}{5} = 8(36°) = 288°.$$

37. We have

$$\frac{7\pi}{20} \text{ radians} = \frac{7(180°)}{20} = 7(9°) = 63°.$$

41. We have the fact that

$$2 \text{ radians} = 2\left(\frac{180°}{\pi}\right) = \left(\frac{360°}{\pi}\right)$$

$$\approx 114.5916°, \text{ or}$$

$$\approx 114°35'.$$

45. We have

$$0.0912 \text{ radians} = \frac{(0.0912)(180)}{\pi} \text{ radians}$$

$$\approx 5.2254°, \text{ or}$$

$$\approx 5°14'.$$

49. We have

$$(-3.47189) \text{ radians} = \frac{(-3.47189)(180)}{\pi} \text{ degrees}$$

$$\approx -198.925°, \text{ or}$$

$$\approx -192°55'.$$

53. Since $\frac{\pi}{3}$ radians $= 60°$, we have

$$\sin \frac{\pi}{3} = \frac{\sqrt{3}}{2}.$$

57. Since $\frac{\pi}{6}$ radians $= 30°$, we have

$$\sec \frac{\pi}{6} = \frac{1}{\cos \frac{\pi}{6}} = \frac{1}{\frac{\sqrt{3}}{2}} = \frac{2\sqrt{3}}{3}.$$

61. Since $\frac{2\pi}{3}$ radians = 120°, we have

$\tan \frac{2\pi}{3} = - \tan \frac{\pi}{3} = -\sqrt{3}$.

65. Since $\frac{-\pi}{6}$ radians = -60°, we have

$\tan \left(\frac{-\pi}{3}\right) = - \tan \frac{\pi}{3} = -\sqrt{3}$.

69. If we begin at 30° and proceed counterclockwise, we have

$30° = \frac{\pi}{6}$, $45° = \frac{\pi}{4}$, $60° = \frac{\pi}{3}$, $90° = \frac{\pi}{2}$,

$120° = \frac{2\pi}{3}$, $135° = \frac{3\pi}{4}$, $150° = \frac{5\pi}{6}$,

$180° = \pi$, $210° = \frac{7\pi}{6}$, $225° = \frac{5\pi}{4}$,

$240° = \frac{4\pi}{3}$, $270° = \frac{3\pi}{2}$, $300° = \frac{5\pi}{3}$,

$315° = \frac{7\pi}{4}$, $330° = \frac{11\pi}{6}$.

73. If r = 12.3 cm and $\theta = \frac{2\pi}{3}$, then

$s = r\theta = 12.3\left(\frac{2\pi}{3}\right) = 8.2\pi \approx 25.8$ cm.

77. We have $\theta = 60° = \frac{\pi}{3}$ radians, so that $s = r\theta = 4.82\left(\frac{\pi}{3}\right) \approx 5.05$ m.

81. The angular measure between the cities is $\theta = 44° - 30° = 14° = \frac{14\pi}{180}$ radians. Then, the distance between the cities is

$d = r\theta = 6400\left(\frac{14\pi}{180}\right) \approx 1600$ km, if we round to the nearest hundred.

85. The angular measure is
$\theta = 105° - 40° = 65°$, or
$\theta = \frac{65\pi}{180} = \frac{13\pi}{36}$ radians. Hence, the distance is
$d = 6400\left(\frac{13\pi}{36}\right) \approx 7300$ km.

89. If $\omega = \frac{\theta}{t}$, with $\omega = \frac{\pi}{4}$ and t = 5, then $\theta = \omega t = \frac{5\pi}{4}$ radians.

93. If $\omega = \frac{\theta}{t}$, with $\theta = \frac{3\pi}{8}$ and $\omega = \frac{\pi}{24}$, then

$t = \frac{\theta}{\omega} = \frac{\frac{3\pi}{8}}{\frac{\pi}{24}} = \frac{3\pi}{8} \cdot \frac{24}{\pi} = 9$ min.

97. One revolution on the clock is 2π radians. One second is $\frac{1}{60}$ of a revolution. Hence,

$\omega = \frac{\pi}{30}$ radians per second.

101. If the radius is r = 1.5 m and the circle is rotating through $\omega = \frac{2\pi}{5}$ radians per second, then a point on the edge moves $d = \frac{12\pi}{5}$ m in [d = rωt]

$t = \frac{d}{r\omega}$ seconds. Then we have

$t = \frac{\frac{12\pi}{5}}{(1.5)\left(\frac{2\pi}{5}\right)}$ seconds

$t = \frac{12\pi}{5} \cdot \frac{5}{(1.5)2\pi} = \frac{6}{1.5} = 4$ sec.

Chapter 6   Review Exercises

Selected Solutions

1. Using the figure, we have

$\sin A = \frac{60}{61}$, $\cos A = \frac{11}{61}$, $\tan A = \frac{60}{11}$,

$\cot A = \frac{11}{60}$, $\sec A = \frac{61}{11}$, and

$\cot A = \frac{11}{60}$.

5. The angle $300° = 360° - 60°$ is in quadrant IV, with a reference angle of R = 60°. Hence,

$$\sin 300° = \frac{\sqrt{3}}{2}, \qquad \cos 300° = \frac{1}{2},$$

$$\tan 300° = -\sqrt{3}, \qquad \cot 300° = \frac{-\sqrt{3}}{3},$$

$$\sec 300° = 2, \text{ and } \csc 300° = \frac{-2\sqrt{3}}{2}.$$

9. We have $\sin 360° = \sin 0° = 0$, $\cos 180° = -1$, and $\sin 270° = -1$. Hence,

$$5 \sin^2 360^0 + 5 \cos^3 180° + 2\left|\sin 270°\right|$$
$$= 5(0)^2 + 5(-1)^3 + 2\left|-1\right|$$
$$= -5 + 2 = -3.$$

13. We have $\cot 300° = - \cot 60° = \frac{-1}{\sqrt{3}}$,

$$\cos 120° = - \cos 60° = \frac{-1}{2}, \text{ and}$$

$$\sin 240° = - \sin 60° = \frac{-\sqrt{3}}{2}. \quad \text{Hence,}$$

$$\cot^2 300° + \cos^2 120° - 3 \sin^2 240°$$

$$= (\frac{-1}{\sqrt{3}})^2 + (\frac{-1}{2})^2 - 3(\frac{-\sqrt{3}}{2})^2$$

$$= \frac{1}{3} + \frac{1}{4} - 3(\frac{3}{4})$$

$$= \frac{1}{3} - \frac{8}{4} = \frac{1}{3} - 2 = \frac{-5}{3}.$$

17. If α is in quadrant III, then if P(x,y) is on the terminal side then $x < 0$ and $y < 0$. Using $\tan \alpha = 2$ $= \frac{y}{x}$, we can choose $y = -2$ and $x = -1$. Then $r = \sqrt{x^2 + y^2}$, or $r = \sqrt{5}$. Then we have $\sin \alpha = \frac{-2}{\sqrt{5}} = \frac{-2\sqrt{5}}{5}$,

$$\cos \alpha = \frac{-\sqrt{5}}{5}, \quad \tan \alpha = 2,$$

$$\cot \alpha = \frac{1}{2}, \quad \sec \alpha = -\sqrt{5},$$

$$\text{and } \csc \alpha = \frac{-\sqrt{5}}{2}.$$

Turn back to page 192 for Exercises 21 - 121 of the Chapter 6 Review Exercises. Then take the chapter test on page 195.

CHAPTER 7   Trigonometric Identities and Equations

Section 7.1   Fundamental Identities

Additional Examples

Example 1   Use the fundamental identities to find the other five trigonometric identities given $\sin \theta = 2/3$ and θ is in quadrant II.

Solution   Since $\sin \theta = 2/3$ and

$\csc \theta = 1/\sin \theta,$

$$\csc \theta = \frac{1}{2/3} = \frac{3}{2}.$$

Also, from

$\sin^2 \theta + \cos^2 \theta = 1,$

$$\left(\frac{2}{3}\right)^2 + \cos^2 \theta = 1$$

$$\frac{4}{9} + \cos^2 \theta = 1$$

$$\cos^2 \theta = \frac{5}{9}$$

$$\cos \theta = \frac{\pm\sqrt{5}}{3}.$$

Because θ is in quadrant II, where cosine is negative,

$$\cos \theta = \frac{-\sqrt{5}}{3}.$$

Using the reciprocal identity,

$$\sec \theta = \frac{1}{\cos \theta} = \frac{1}{-\sqrt{5}/3} = -\frac{3}{\sqrt{5}}.$$

Rationalizing the denominator gives

$$\sec \theta = \frac{-3\sqrt{5}}{5}.$$

Then $\tan \theta = \dfrac{\sin \theta}{\cos \theta} = \dfrac{2/3}{-\sqrt{5}/3}$

$$= \frac{2}{3} \cdot \frac{-3}{\sqrt{5}} = \frac{-2}{\sqrt{5}} = \frac{-2\sqrt{5}}{5},$$

and $\cot \theta = \dfrac{1}{\tan \theta} = \dfrac{1}{-2/\sqrt{5}} = \dfrac{-\sqrt{5}}{2}.$

Example 2   Given $\dfrac{\sec x + \csc x}{\tan x + \cot x},$ use the fundamental identities to express it using only $\sin x$ and $\cos x$ and simplify the result.

Solution

$$\frac{\sec x + \csc x}{\tan x + \cot x} = \frac{\dfrac{1}{\cos x} + \dfrac{1}{\sin x}}{\dfrac{\sin x}{\cos s} + \dfrac{\cos x}{\sin x}}$$

$$= \frac{\dfrac{\sin x + \cos x}{\cos x \sin x}}{\dfrac{\sin^2 x + \cos^2 x}{\cos x \sin x}}$$

$$= \frac{\sin x + \cos x}{\cos x \sin x} \cdot \frac{\cos x \sin x}{1}$$

$$= \sin x + \cos x$$

Selected Solutions

1. If $\cos s = \dfrac{3}{4}$ and s is in quadrant I, then the other five trigonometric functions are positive, and

$$\sin^2 s + \cos^2 s = 1$$

$$\sin^2 s + \frac{9}{16} = 1$$

$$\sin^2 s = \frac{7}{16}$$

$$\sin s = \frac{\sqrt{7}}{4}.$$

5. If $\cos \theta = \dfrac{-2}{5}$ and $\sin \theta < 0$, then

$$\sin^2 \theta + \cos^2 \theta = 1$$

$$\sin^2 \theta = 1 - \left(\frac{-2}{5}\right)^2$$

$$\sin^2 \theta = 1 - \frac{4}{25} = \frac{21}{25}$$

$$\sin \theta = \pm\frac{\sqrt{21}}{5}$$

so that $\sin \theta = \dfrac{-\sqrt{21}}{5}.$

Hence,

$$\tan \theta = \frac{\sin \theta}{\cos \theta} = \frac{\dfrac{-\sqrt{21}}{5}}{\dfrac{-2}{5}} = \frac{\sqrt{21}}{2}.$$

9. If $\tan (-\theta) = \dfrac{1}{4}$, then $\tan \theta = \dfrac{-1}{4}$, and then $\cot \theta = \dfrac{1}{\tan \theta} = -4$. Then

$$\sec^2 \theta = 1 + \tan^2 \theta = 1 + \frac{1}{16} = \frac{17}{16},$$

so that $\sec \theta = \pm \dfrac{\sqrt{17}}{4}$. Since θ is in quadrant V, only $\sec \theta$ and $\cos \theta$ are positive. Thus,

$\sec \theta = \dfrac{\sqrt{17}}{4}$, and $\cos \theta = \dfrac{1}{\sec \theta} = \dfrac{4\sqrt{17}}{17}$.

Since $\tan \theta = \dfrac{\sin \theta}{\cos \theta}$, we have

$$\sin \theta = \tan \theta \cos \theta$$
$$= \frac{-1}{4} \cdot \frac{4\sqrt{17}}{17} = \frac{-\sqrt{17}}{17}.$$

Then, $\csc \theta = \dfrac{1}{\sin \theta} = -\sqrt{17}$

13. If $\cot \theta = \dfrac{4}{3}$, then $\tan \theta = \dfrac{3}{4}$. If $\sin \theta > 0$, then θ must be in quadrant I. Also, $\sec^2 \theta = 1 + \tan^2 \theta$
$= 1 + \dfrac{9}{16} = \dfrac{25}{16}$, so that $\sec \theta = \dfrac{5}{4}$.
Then $\cos \theta = \dfrac{4}{5}$. Also, $\tan \theta = \dfrac{\sin \theta}{\cos \theta}$ gives $\sin \theta = \tan \theta \cos \theta$
$= \dfrac{3}{4} \cdot \dfrac{4}{5} = \dfrac{3}{5}$, and then $\csc \theta = \dfrac{5}{3}$.

17. We have $\dfrac{\cos x}{\sin x} = \cot x$. The answer is (b).

21. Since $\sin^2 x + \cos^2 x = 1$ for all x, the answer is (a).

25. $\csc^2 x - \cot^2 x + \sin^2 x$
$= \dfrac{1}{\sin^2 x} - \dfrac{\cos^2 x}{\sin^2 x} + \sin^2 x$
$= \dfrac{1 - \cos^2 x}{\sin^2 x} + \sin^2 x$
$= \dfrac{\sin^2 x}{\sin^2 x} + \sin^2 x$
$= 1 + \sin^2 x$
The answer is (d).

29. $\tan (-\alpha) \cos (-\alpha) = \dfrac{\sin (-\alpha)}{\cos (-\alpha)} \cdot \cos (-\alpha)$
$= \sin (-\alpha)$
$= -\sin \alpha.$

33. $\sec \theta + \tan \theta = \dfrac{1}{\cos \theta} + \dfrac{\sin \theta}{\cos \theta}$
$= \dfrac{1 + \sin \theta}{\cos \theta}.$

37. $\cot^2 \beta - \csc^2 \beta = \dfrac{\cos^2 \beta}{\sin^2 \beta} - \dfrac{1}{\sin^2 \beta}$
$= \dfrac{\cos^2 \beta - 1}{\sin^2 \beta}$
$= \dfrac{-\sin^2 \beta}{\sin^2 \beta}$
$= -1,$
using $\sin^2 \beta + \cos^2 \beta = 1$.

41. $\cot^2 B \sin^2 B + \tan^2 B \cos^2 B$
$= \dfrac{\cos^2 B}{\sin^2 B} \cdot \sin^2 B + \dfrac{\sin^2 B}{\cos^2 B} \cdot \cos^2 B$
$= \cos^2 B + \sin^2 B$
$= 1.$

45. $1 - \cot^4 s$
$= 1 - \dfrac{\cos^4 s}{\sin^4 s}$
$= \dfrac{\sin^4 s - \cos^4 s}{\sin^4 s}$
$= \dfrac{(\sin^2 s - \cos^2 s)(\sin^2 s + \cos^2 s)}{\sin^4 s}$
$= \dfrac{\sin^2 s - \cos^2 s}{\sin^4 s}.$

49. We have $\tan \theta = \dfrac{\sin \theta}{\cos \theta}$. Also, $\sin^2 \theta + \cos^2 \theta = 1$ gives
$$\cos \theta = \pm\sqrt{1 - \sin^2 \theta}.$$
Hence, $\tan \theta = \dfrac{\pm\sin \theta}{\sqrt{1 - \sin^2 \theta}}.$
Also, $\tan \theta = \dfrac{\sin \theta}{\cos \theta} = \dfrac{\pm\sqrt{1 - \cos^2 \theta}}{\cos \theta}.$
Using $1 + \tan^2 \theta = \sec^2 \theta$, we have
$$\tan \theta = \pm\sqrt{\sec^2 \theta - 1}.$$
Then using $1 + \cot^2 \theta = \csc^2 \theta$, we have $\cot \theta = \pm\sqrt{\csc^2 \theta - 1}$
and hence $\tan \theta = \pm\dfrac{1}{\sqrt{\csc^2 \theta - 1}},$
or $\tan \theta = \dfrac{\pm\sqrt{\csc^2 \theta - 1}}{\csc^2 \theta - 1}.$

53. Is $\cos \theta = \dfrac{x}{x + 1}$, then we can use

$\sin^2 \theta + \cos^2 \theta = 1$ to get

$$\sin^2 \theta = 1 - \cos^2 \theta$$

$$\sin^2 \theta = 1 - \frac{x^2}{(x + 1)^2}$$

$$\sin^2 \theta = \frac{(x + 1)^2 - x^2}{(x + 1)^2}$$

$$\sin^2 \theta = \frac{2x + 1}{(x + 1)^2}$$

and hence, $\sin \theta = \dfrac{\pm\sqrt{2x + 1}}{x + 1}$.

57. If we let $s = \dfrac{\pi}{6}$, we have

$$2 \sin s = 2 \sin \frac{\pi}{6} = 2\left(\frac{1}{2}\right) = 1,$$

but $\sin 2s = \sin \dfrac{\pi}{3} = \dfrac{\sqrt{3}}{2}$.

61. If we let $x = \dfrac{4}{3} \tan \theta$, then

$$9x^2 = 16 \tan^2 \theta, \text{ and}$$

$$\sqrt{16 + 9x^2} = \sqrt{16 + 16 \tan^2 \theta}$$

$$= 4\sqrt{1 + \tan^2 \theta}$$

$$= 4\sqrt{\sec^2 \theta}$$

$$= 4 \sec \theta.$$

We can then conclude that

$$\sec \theta = \frac{\sqrt{16 + 9x^2}}{4}, \text{ and hence}$$

$$\cos \theta = \frac{4}{\sqrt{16 + 9x^2}} = \frac{4\sqrt{16 + 9x^2}}{16 + 9x^2}.$$

Using $\tan \theta = \dfrac{\sin \theta}{\cos \theta}$, we have

$$\sin \theta = \tan \theta \cos \theta$$

$$\sin \theta = \frac{3x}{4} \cdot \frac{4\sqrt{16 + 9x^2}}{16 + 9x^2}$$

$$\sin \theta = \frac{3x\sqrt{16 + 9x^2}}{16 + 9x^2}.$$

65. If $x = \dfrac{1}{4} \tan \theta$, then $\tan \theta = 4x$ and

$\tan^2 \theta = 16x^2$. Hence,

$$\sqrt{1 + 16x^2} = \sqrt{1 + \tan^2 \theta}$$

$$\sqrt{1 + 16x^2} = \sqrt{\sec^2 \theta}$$

$$\sqrt{1 + 16x^2} = \sec \theta.$$

We can conclude that

$$x^2\sqrt{1 + 16x^2} = \frac{1}{16} \tan^2 \theta \sec \theta.$$

Also, $\cos \theta = \dfrac{1}{\sec \theta} = \dfrac{\sqrt{1 + 16x^2}}{1 + 16x^2}$

and since $\tan \theta = \dfrac{\sin \theta}{\cos \theta}$,

then $\sin \theta = \tan \theta \cos \theta$,

or $\sin \theta = \dfrac{4x \cdot \sqrt{1 + 16x^2}}{1 + 16x^2}$.

69. Since $\log \dfrac{1}{u} = \log 1 - \log u$, and

$\log 1 = 0$, we have $\log \dfrac{1}{u} = -\log u$.

Then, using $u = \sin x = \dfrac{1}{\csc x}$, we

have $\log \sin s = \log \left(\dfrac{1}{\csc s}\right)$

$= -\log \csc s$.

Section 7.2   Verifying Trigonometric
              Identities

Additional Examples

Example 1   Perform the indicated oper-
             ations and simplify the result for

$\tan \theta + \dfrac{\cos \theta}{1 + \sin \theta}$.

Solution

$$\tan \theta + \frac{\cos \theta}{1 + \sin \theta}$$

$$= \frac{\sin \theta}{\cos \theta} + \frac{\cos \theta}{1 + \sin \theta}$$

$$= \frac{(\sin \theta)(1 + \sin \theta) + \cos^2 \theta}{\cos \theta(1 + \sin \theta)}$$

$$= \frac{\sin \theta + \sin^2 \theta + \cos^2 \theta}{\cos \theta(1 + \sin \theta)}$$

$$= \frac{\sin \theta + 1}{\cos \theta(1 + \sin \theta)}$$

$$= \frac{1}{\cos \theta} = \sec \theta.$$

Example   Factor each expression.
   (a) $\sin^2 s + 3 \sin s + 2$
   (b) $\cos^2 s - 2 \sin s \cos s$
   (c) $\sec^2 t - \cos^2 t$

Solution
   (a) $\sin^2 s + 3 \sin s + 2$
       $= (\sin s + 1)(\sin s + 2)$
   (b) $\cos^2 s - 2 \sin \cos s$
       $= \cos s(1 - 2 \sin s)$

(c) $\sec^2 t - \cos^2 t$

$\qquad = (\sec t + \cos t)(\sec t - \cos t)$

Example 3 Verify

$\qquad \sec^2 t \csc^2 t = \sec^2 t + \csc^2 t.$

Solution   We'll work on the right side, to convert it to the left side.

$$\sec^2 t \csc^2 t = \sec^2 t + \csc^2 t$$

$$= \frac{1}{\cos^2 t} + \frac{1}{\sin^2 t}$$

$$= \frac{\sin^2 t + \cos^2 t}{\cos^2 t \sin^2 t}$$

$$= \frac{1}{\cos^2 t \sin^2 t}$$

$$= \frac{1}{\cos^2 t} \cdot \frac{1}{\sin^2 t}$$

$$= \sec^2 t \csc^2 t.$$

Selected Solutions

1. $\tan \theta + \dfrac{1}{\tan \theta} = \tan \theta + \cot \theta$

$$= \frac{\sin \theta}{\cos \theta} + \frac{\cos \theta}{\sin \theta}$$

$$= \frac{\sin^2 \theta + \cos^2 \theta}{\sin \theta \cos \theta}$$

$$= \frac{1}{\sin \theta \cos \theta}$$

$$= \frac{1}{\sin \theta} \cdot \frac{1}{\cos \theta}$$

$$= \csc \theta \sec \theta.$$

5. $\dfrac{1}{\csc^2 \theta} + \dfrac{1}{\sec^2 \theta} = \sin^2 \theta + \cos^2 \theta$

$$= 1.$$

9. $(1 + \sin t)^2 + \cos^2 t$

$= 1 + 2 \sin t + \sin^2 t + \cos^2 t$

$= 1 + 2 \sin t + 1$

$= 2(1 + \sin t)$

13. If we let $a = \sin x + 1$ and $b = \sin x - 1$ and use the formula $a^2 - b^2 = (a - b)(a + b)$, we have

$(\sin x + 1)^2 - (\sin x - 1)^2$

$= a^2 - b^2$

$= [(\sin x + 1) - (\sin x - 1)] \cdot$

$\quad [(\sin x + 1) + (\sin x - 1)]$

$= [2][2 \sin x]$

$= 4 \sin x.$

17. We have

$4 \sec^2 x + 3 \sec\ x - 1$

$= (4 \sec x - 1)(\sec x + 1).$

21. We have $\tan \theta \cdot \cos \theta = \dfrac{\sin \theta}{\cos \theta} \cdot \cos \theta$

$$= \sin \theta.$$

25. We have

$\dfrac{\sin \beta \tan \beta}{\cos \beta} = \dfrac{\sin \beta}{\cos} \cdot \tan \beta$

$$= \tan \beta \cdot \tan \beta$$

$$= \tan^2 \beta.$$

29. $\dfrac{\sin^2 x}{\cos^2 x} + \sin x \csc x$

$$= \frac{\sin^2 x}{\cos^2 x} + \sin x \cdot \frac{1}{\sin x}$$

$$= \frac{\sin^2 x}{\cos^2 x} + 1$$

$$= \frac{\sin^2 x + \cos^2 x}{\cos^2 x}$$

$$= \frac{1}{\cos^2 x}$$

$$= \sec^2 x.$$

33. Working with the right side, we have

$$\frac{\sin^2 \theta}{\cos^2 \theta} = \sec^2 \theta - 1$$

$$= \frac{1}{\cos^2 \theta} - 1$$

$$= \frac{1 - \cos^2 \theta}{\cos^2 \theta}$$

$$= \frac{\sin^2 \theta}{\cos^2 \theta}.$$

37. We have

$$\frac{\sin^2 \gamma}{\cos \gamma} = \frac{1 - \cos^2 \gamma}{\cos \gamma}$$

$$= \frac{1}{\cos \gamma} - \cos \gamma$$

$$= \sec \gamma - \cos \gamma, \quad \text{since}$$

$\sin^2 \gamma = 1 - \cos^2 \gamma.$

41. $\dfrac{\cos \alpha}{\sin \alpha \cot \alpha} = \dfrac{\cos \alpha}{\sin \alpha} \cdot \dfrac{1}{\cot \alpha}$

$\qquad\qquad\qquad = \dfrac{\cos \alpha}{\sin \alpha} \cdot \tan \alpha$

$\qquad\qquad\qquad = \dfrac{\cos \alpha}{\sin \alpha} \cdot \dfrac{\sin \alpha}{\cos \alpha}$

$\qquad\qquad\qquad = 1.$

45. $\dfrac{(\sec \theta - \tan \theta)^2 + 1}{\sec \theta \csc \theta - \tan \theta \csc \theta}$

$= \dfrac{\sec^2 \theta - 2 \sec \theta \tan \theta + \tan^2 \theta + 1}{\csc \theta (\sec \theta - \tan \theta)}$

$= \dfrac{\sec^2 \theta - 2 \sec \theta \tan \theta + \sec^2 \theta}{\csc \theta (\sec \theta - \tan \theta)}$

$= \dfrac{2 \sec^2 \theta - 2 \sec \theta \tan \theta}{\csc \theta (\sec \theta - \tan \theta)}$

$= \dfrac{2 \sec \theta (\sec \theta - \tan \theta)}{\csc \theta (\sec \theta - \tan \theta)}$

$= \dfrac{2 \sec \theta}{\csc \theta} = 2 \dfrac{\dfrac{1}{\cos \theta}}{1/\sin \theta}$

$= 2 \dfrac{\sin \theta}{\cos \theta} = 2 \tan \theta.$

49. Working with the right side gives

$(\cot x - \csc x)^2$

$= \left(\dfrac{\cos x}{\sin x} - \dfrac{1}{\sin x}\right)^2$

$= \left(\dfrac{\cos x - 1}{\sin x}\right)^2$

$= \dfrac{(\cos x - 1)^2}{\sin^2 x}$

$= \dfrac{(\cos x - 1)^2}{1 - \cos^2 x}$

$= \dfrac{(\cos x - 1)(\cos x - 1)}{(1 - \cos x)(1 + \cos x)}$

$= \dfrac{-(\cos x - 1)}{1 + \cos x}$

$= \dfrac{1 - \cos x}{1 + \cos x},$

which is the left side.

53. $\dfrac{\csc \theta + \cot \theta}{\tan \theta + \sin \theta}$

$= \dfrac{\dfrac{1}{\sin \theta} + \dfrac{\cos \theta}{\sin \theta}}{\dfrac{\sin \theta}{\cos \theta} + \dfrac{\sin \theta}{1}}$

$= \dfrac{\dfrac{1 + \cos \theta}{\sin \theta}}{\dfrac{\sin \theta + \sin \theta \cos \theta}{\cos \theta}}$

$= \dfrac{1 + \cos \theta}{\sin \theta} \cdot \dfrac{\cos \theta}{\sin \theta (1 + \cos \theta)}$

$= \dfrac{\cos \theta}{\sin \theta} \cdot \dfrac{1}{\sin \theta}$

$= \cot \theta \csc \theta.$

57. Working with the right side,

$\dfrac{\sin \theta}{1 - \dfrac{\cos \theta}{\sin \theta}} + \dfrac{\cos \theta}{1 - \dfrac{\sin \theta}{\cos \theta}}$

$= \dfrac{\sin \theta}{\dfrac{\sin \theta - \cos \theta}{\sin \theta}} + \dfrac{\cos \theta}{\dfrac{\cos \theta - \sin \theta}{\cos \theta}}$

$= \dfrac{\sin^2 \theta}{\sin \theta - \cos \theta} + \dfrac{\cos^2 \theta}{\cos \theta - \sin \theta}$

$= \dfrac{\sin^2 \theta}{\sin \theta - \cos \theta} - \dfrac{\cos^2 \theta}{\sin \theta - \cos \theta}$

$= \dfrac{\sin^2 \theta - \cos^2 \theta}{\sin \theta - \cos \theta}$

$= \dfrac{(\sin \theta - \cos \theta)(\sin \theta + \cos \theta)}{\sin \theta - \cos \theta}$

$= \sin \theta + \cos \theta.$

61. Working with the right side gives

$\dfrac{\tan t - \cot t}{\tan t + \cot t} = \dfrac{\tan t - 1/\tan t}{\tan t + 1/\tan t}$

$\qquad\qquad = \dfrac{\dfrac{\tan^2 t - 1}{\tan t}}{\dfrac{\tan^2 t + 1}{\tan t}}$

$\qquad\qquad = \dfrac{\tan^2 t - 1}{\tan t} \cdot \dfrac{\tan t}{1 + \tan^2 t}$

$\qquad\qquad = \dfrac{\tan^2 t - 1}{\sec^2 t},$

since $\sec^2 t = 1 + \tan^2 t.$

65. $\dfrac{1 + \cos x}{1 - \cos x} - \dfrac{1 - \cos x}{1 + \cos x}$

$= \dfrac{(1 + \cos x)^2 - (1 - \cos x)^2}{1 - \cos^2 x}$

$= \dfrac{1 + 2 \cos x + \cos^2 x - (1 - 2 \cos x + \cos^2 x)}{\sin^2 x}$

$= \dfrac{4 \cos x}{\sin^2 x}$

$= 4 \dfrac{\cos x}{\sin x} \cdot \dfrac{1}{\sin x}$

$= 4 \cot x \csc x.$

69. $\dfrac{\cot^2 x + \sec^2 x + 1}{\cot^2 x}$

$= \dfrac{\sec^2 x + (\cot^2 x + 1)}{\cot^2 x}$

$= \dfrac{\sec^2 x + \csc^2 x}{\cot^2 x}$

$= \dfrac{\dfrac{1}{\cos^2 x} + \dfrac{1}{\sin^2 x}}{\dfrac{\cos^2 x}{\sin^2 x}}$

$= \dfrac{\sin^2 x + \cos^2 x}{\sin^2 x \cos^2 x} \cdot \dfrac{\sin^2 x}{\cos^2 x}$

$= \dfrac{1}{\cos^4 x}$

$= \sec^4 x.$

73. Since $\dfrac{1}{\sec x + \tan x}$

$= \dfrac{1}{\dfrac{1}{\cos x} + \dfrac{\sin x}{\cos x}} = \dfrac{\cos x}{1 + \sin x}$

$= \dfrac{\cos x}{1 + \sin x} \cdot \dfrac{1 - \sin x}{1 - \sin x}$

$= \dfrac{\cos x(1 - \sin x)}{1 - \sin^2 x}$

$= \dfrac{\cos x(1 - \sin x)}{\cos^2 x} = \dfrac{1 - \sin x}{\cos x}$

$= \dfrac{1}{\cos x} - \dfrac{\sin x}{\cos x} = \sec x - \tan x,$

we have

$\ln |\sec x - \tan x|$

$= \ln \left| \dfrac{1}{\sec x + \tan x} \right|$

$= -\ln |\sec x + \tan x|.$

77. $\dfrac{\tan s - \cot s}{\tan s + \cot s}$

$= \dfrac{\dfrac{\sin s}{\cos s} - \dfrac{\cos s}{\sin s}}{\dfrac{\sin s}{\cos s} + \dfrac{\cos s}{\sin s}}$

$= \dfrac{\dfrac{\sin^2 s - \cos^2 s}{\sin s \cos s}}{\dfrac{\sin^2 s + \cos^2 s}{\sin s \cos s}}$

$= \dfrac{\sin^2 s - \cos^2 s}{\sin s \cos s} \cdot \dfrac{\sin s \cos s}{1}$

$= \sin^2 s - \cos^2 s$

$= \sin^2 s - (1 - \sin^2 s)$

$= 2 \sin^2 s - 1,$

not $2 \sin^2 s$. The statement in the text is not an identity. We can

substitute $s = \dfrac{\pi}{4}$ and arrive at

$\dfrac{\tan \dfrac{\pi}{4} - \cot \dfrac{\pi}{4}}{\tan \dfrac{\pi}{4} + \cot \dfrac{\pi}{4}} = \dfrac{1 - 1}{1 + 1} = 0,$

while $2 \sin^2 \left(\dfrac{\pi}{4}\right) = 2 \left(\dfrac{\sqrt{2}}{2}\right)^2 = 1.$

81. Since $\sin^2 s + \cos^2 s = 1$ for all s, and if $s = \dfrac{\pi}{8}$, we have

$\dfrac{1}{2}(1 - \cos 4 s) = \dfrac{1}{2}\left(1 - \cos \dfrac{\pi}{2}\right)$

$= \dfrac{1}{2}(1 - 0) = \dfrac{1}{2}.$

The statement in the text is not an identity.

85. If we let $t = \dfrac{-\pi}{4}$, then

$\csc t = \dfrac{1}{\sin t} = \dfrac{1}{-\dfrac{\sqrt{2}}{2}} = -\sqrt{2},$

and $\cot t = -1$, but

$\sqrt{1 + \cot^2 t} = \sqrt{1 + (-1)^2} = \sqrt{2}.$

Section 7.3   Sum and Difference Identities for Cosine

Additional Examples

Example 1   Write cot 72° in terms of its cofunction.

Solution   The cofunction of cotangent is tangent.

cot 72° = tan(90° – 72°)

= tan 18°

Example 2   Use a sum or difference identity to find
cos 14° cos 16° – sin 14° sin 16°.

Solution

cos 14° cos 16° – sin 14° sin 16°

= cos (14° + 16°)

= cos 30°

$= \dfrac{\sqrt{3}}{2}.$

Example 3   Find cos (s − t) given cos s = 1/3 and sin t = −2/3, where s and t are in quadrant IV.

Solution   To use the difference identity, we first need to find sin s and cos t. Since

$$\cos^2 s + \sin^2 s = 1$$

$$\frac{1}{9} + \sin^2 s = 1$$

$$\sin^2 s = \frac{8}{9}$$

$$\sin s = \frac{-2\sqrt{2}}{3}.$$

We chose the negative square root because s is in quadrant IV. Also,

$$\cos^2 t + \sin^2 t = 1$$

$$\cos^2 t + \frac{4}{9} = 1$$

$$\cos^2 t = \frac{5}{9}$$

$$\cos t = \frac{\sqrt{5}}{3},$$

where cos t is positive, since t is in quadrant IV. Then

$$\cos (s - t) = \cos s \cos t + \sin s \ \sin t$$

$$= \frac{1}{3} \cdot \frac{\sqrt{5}}{3} + \frac{-2\sqrt{2}}{3} \cdot \frac{-2}{3}$$

$$= \frac{\sqrt{5} + 4\sqrt{2}}{9}.$$

Selected Solutions

1. tan 87° = cot (90° − 87°) = cot 3°.

5. csc (−14°27') = sec [90° − (−14°27°)]
$$= 104°27'.$$

9. sec 146°42' = csc (90° − 146°42')
$$= csc (−56°42').$$

13. Using cot θ = tan $\left(\frac{\pi}{2} - \theta\right)$, we have
$$\cot \frac{\pi}{3} = \tan \frac{\pi}{6}.$$

17. Since cos 70° = sin (90° − 70°)
$$= \sin 20°,$$
and since sin 20° = $\frac{1}{\csc 20°}$,

we have   cos 70° = $\frac{1}{\csc 20°}$.

21. We see that 74° = 60° + 14° and we have
cos 74° = cos (60° + 14°)
$$= \cos 60° \cos 14° -$$
$$\sin 60° \sin 14°,$$
<u>not</u> cos 60° cos 14° + sin 60° sin 14°. The statement is false.

25. Since cos A cos B − sin A sin B
= cos (A + B), we have that
cos 70° cos 20° − sin 70° sin 20°
$$= \cos (70° + 20°)$$
$$= \cos 90°$$
$$= 0.$$
The statement is true.

29. Since sec θ = csc (90° − θ) we see that the equation becomes

$$\sec \theta = \csc \left(\frac{\theta}{2} + 20°\right)$$

$$\csc (90° - \theta) = \csc \left(\frac{\theta}{2} + 20°\right)$$

$$90° - \theta = \frac{\theta}{2} + 20°$$

$$70° = \frac{3\theta}{2}$$

$$\theta = \left(\frac{140}{3}\right)°,$$

or $\theta = 46°20'.$

33. We have 285° = 225° + 60°, so that
$$\cos 285° = \cos (225° + 60°)$$
$$= \cos 225° \cos 60° -$$
$$\sin 225° \sin 60°.$$
Then, 225° is in quadrant III, with a reference angle R = 45°. Hence,
$$\cos 225° = \frac{-\sqrt{2}}{2} \text{ and } \sin 225° = \frac{-\sqrt{2}}{2}.$$
Then we have
$$\cos 285° = \left(\frac{-\sqrt{2}}{2}\right)\left(\frac{1}{2}\right) - \left(\frac{-\sqrt{2}}{2}\right)\left(\frac{\sqrt{3}}{2}\right)$$

$$= \frac{-\sqrt{2}}{4} + \frac{\sqrt{6}}{4} = \frac{\sqrt{6} - \sqrt{2}}{4}.$$

37. Since $\frac{\pi}{4} + \frac{\pi}{3} = \frac{7\pi}{12}$, we have

$$\cos \frac{7\pi}{12} = \cos \left(\frac{\pi}{4} + \frac{\pi}{3}\right)$$

$$= \cos \frac{\pi}{4} \cos \frac{\pi}{3} - \sin \frac{\pi}{4} \sin \frac{\pi}{3}$$

$$= \frac{\sqrt{2}}{2} \cdot \frac{1}{2} - \frac{\sqrt{2}}{2} \cdot \frac{\sqrt{3}}{2}$$

$$= \frac{\sqrt{2} - \sqrt{6}}{4}.$$

41. Since $\cos A \cos B + \sin A \sin B$
$= \cos (A - B)$, we have
$\cos (-10°) \cos 35° +$
$\sin (-10°) \sin 35°$
$= \cos [(-10°) - 35°]$
$= \cos (-45°)$
$= \cos 45°$
$= \frac{\sqrt{2}}{2}.$

45. We have

$\cos \frac{2\pi}{5} \cos \frac{\pi}{10} - \sin \frac{2\pi}{5} \sin \frac{\pi}{10}$

$= \cos \left(\frac{2\pi}{5} + \frac{\pi}{10}\right)$

$= \cos \left(\frac{4\pi}{10} + \frac{\pi}{10}\right)$

$= \cos \frac{\pi}{2}$

$= 0.$

49. We have

$\cos (60° + \theta) = \cos 60° \cos \theta -$
$\qquad\qquad\qquad \sin 60° \sin \theta$

$\qquad = \frac{1}{2} \cos \theta - \frac{\sqrt{3}}{2} \sin \theta.$

53. If $\cos s = \frac{-1}{5}$ and $\sin t = \frac{3}{5}$, and
if both s and t are in quadrant II,
then we can complete the triangles
below.

$\quad y^2 + 1 = 25 \qquad\qquad x^2 + 9 = 25$

$\qquad\quad y = \sqrt{24} \qquad\qquad x = -\sqrt{16} = -4$

Then $\sin s = \frac{\sqrt{24}}{5}$ and $\cos t = \frac{-4}{5}$.
Hence,

$\cos (s + t) = \cos s \cos t - \sin s \sin t$

$\cos (s + t) = \left(\frac{-1}{5}\right) \left(\frac{-4}{5}\right) - \left(\frac{\sqrt{24}}{5}\right) \left(\frac{3}{5}\right)$

$\cos (s + t) = \frac{4 - 6\sqrt{6}}{25},$ and

$\cos (s - t) = \cos s \cos t + \sin s \sin t$

$\qquad = \frac{4 + 6\sqrt{6}}{25}.$

Another way to find sin s if

$\cos s = \frac{-1}{5}$ and s in quadrant II is

by

$\sin^2 s + \cos^2 s = 1$

$\quad \sin^2 s + \frac{1}{25} = 1$

$\qquad \sin^2 s = \frac{24}{25}$

$\qquad\quad \sin s = \pm \frac{2\sqrt{6}}{5}.$

57. If $\cos s = \frac{-15}{17}$ and s in quadrant II,
then
$\sin^2 s + \cos^2 s = 1$

$\quad \sin^2 s + \frac{225}{289} = 1$

$\qquad \sin^2 s = \frac{64}{289}$

$\qquad\quad \sin s = \pm \frac{8}{17},$

so $\sin s = \frac{8}{17}$. Also, if $\sin t = \frac{4}{5}$
and if t is in quadrant I, then
$\sin^2 t + \cos^2 t = 1$

$\quad \cos^2 t = 1 - \frac{16}{25} = \frac{9}{25}$

$\qquad \cos\ t = \pm \frac{3}{5},$

so that $\cos t = \frac{3}{5}$. Then, we have

$\cos (s + t) = \cos s \cos t -$
$\qquad\qquad\qquad \sin s \sin t$

$\qquad = \left(\frac{-15}{17}\right) \left(\frac{3}{5}\right) - \left(\frac{8}{17}\right) \left(\frac{4}{5}\right)$

$\qquad = \frac{-45 - 32}{85} = \frac{-77}{85}.$

Also,

$\cos (s - t) = \frac{-45 + 32}{85} = \frac{-13}{85}.$

61. We have

$$\cos\left(\frac{\pi}{2} + x\right) = \cos\frac{\pi}{2}\cos x - \sin\frac{\pi}{2}\sin x$$

$$= (0)\cos x - (1)\sin x$$

$$= -\sin x.$$

65. We have

$$\cos(\alpha - \theta) = \cos\alpha\cos\theta + \sin\alpha\sin\theta, \text{ and}$$

$$\cos(\alpha + \theta) = \cos\alpha\cos\theta - \sin\alpha\sin\theta, \text{ so that}$$

so that

$$\frac{\cos(\alpha - \theta) - \cos(\alpha + \theta)}{\cos(\alpha - \theta) + \cos(\alpha + \theta)}$$

$$= \frac{2\sin\alpha\sin\theta}{2\cos\alpha\cos\theta}$$

$$= \frac{\sin\alpha}{\cos\alpha}\frac{\sin\theta}{\cos\theta}$$

$$= \tan\alpha \cdot \tan\theta.$$

69. We have

$$\cos(\alpha + \beta)\cos(\alpha - \beta)$$

$$= (\cos\alpha\cos\beta - \sin\alpha\sin\beta)$$
$$\quad(\cos\alpha\cos\beta + \sin\alpha\sin\beta)$$

$$= \cos^2\alpha\cos^2\beta - \sin^2\alpha\sin^2\beta$$

$$= (1 - \sin^2\alpha)(1 - \sin^2\beta) - \sin^2\alpha\sin^2\beta$$

$$= 1 - \sin^2\beta - \sin^2\beta + \sin^2\alpha\sin^2\beta - \sin^2\alpha\sin^2\beta$$

$$= 1 - \sin^2\alpha - \sin^2\beta.$$

73. (a) We have

$$\cot\left(\frac{\pi}{2} - t\right) = \frac{\cos\left(\frac{\pi}{2} - t\right)}{\sin\left(\frac{\pi}{2} - t\right)}$$

$$= \frac{\cos\frac{\pi}{2}\cos t + \sin\frac{\pi}{2}\sin t}{\sin\frac{\pi}{2}\cos t - \cos\frac{\pi}{2}\sin t}$$

$$= \frac{(0)\cos t + (1)\sin t}{(1)\cos t - (0)\sin t}$$

$$= \frac{\sin t}{\cos t} = \tan t.$$

(b) Since $\cos\left(\frac{\pi}{2} - t\right) = \sin t$, (see part a) we take reciprocals to arrive at $\sec\left(\frac{\pi}{2} - t\right) = \csc t$.

75. Let $A = \sin^{-1}\frac{8}{17}$ and $B = \tan^{-1}\frac{3}{4}$.

Then $\sin A = \frac{8}{17}$ and $\tan B = \frac{3}{4}$, with A and B in quadrant I.

$$\begin{array}{ll} x^2 + 64 = 289 & r^2 = 16 + 9 \\ x^2 = 225 & r^2 = 25 \\ x = 15 & r = 5 \end{array}$$

We see that by completing triangles that we have

$$\cos(A + B) = \cos A\cos B - \sin A\sin B$$

$$= \left(\frac{15}{17}\right)\left(\frac{4}{5}\right) - \left(\frac{8}{17}\right)\left(\frac{3}{5}\right)$$

$$= \frac{60 - 24}{85}$$

$$= \frac{36}{85}.$$

77. Let $A = \cos^{-1}\frac{1}{4}$ and $B = \tan^{-1}\frac{5}{8}$.

Then $\cos A = \frac{1}{4}$ and we have

$\sin A = \frac{\sqrt{15}}{4}$. Also, $\tan B = \frac{5}{8}$

implies that $\sin B = \frac{5}{\sqrt{89}}$ and

$\cos B = \frac{8}{\sqrt{89}}$. We use the identity

$$\cos(A + B) = \cos A\cos B - \sin A\sin B$$

$$= \frac{1}{4} \cdot \frac{8}{\sqrt{89}} - \frac{\sqrt{15}}{4} \cdot \frac{5}{\sqrt{89}}$$

$$= \frac{8 - 5\sqrt{15}}{\sqrt{89}}.$$

Section 7.4   Sum and Difference Identities for Sine and Tangent

Additional Examples

Example 1   Use identities to find $\tan 225°$.

Solution   Since $255° = 225° + 30°$,

$$\tan 255° = \tan(225° + 30°)$$

$$= \frac{\tan 225° + \tan 30°}{1 - \tan 225° \tan 30°}$$

$$= \frac{1 + (1/\sqrt{3})}{1 - (1)(1/\sqrt{3})}$$

$$= \frac{\dfrac{3+1}{\sqrt{3}}}{\dfrac{\sqrt{3}-1}{\sqrt{3}}} = \frac{\sqrt{3}+1}{\sqrt{3}-1}.$$

Rationalizing the denominator gives

$$\frac{\sqrt{3}+1}{\sqrt{3}-1} \cdot \frac{\sqrt{3}+1}{\sqrt{3}+1} = \frac{3+2\sqrt{3}+1}{3-1}$$

$$= \frac{4+2\sqrt{3}}{2} = 2 + \sqrt{3}.$$

Example 2   Verify

$$\frac{\tan (\alpha + \beta)}{\cot (\alpha - \beta)} = \frac{\tan^2 \alpha - \tan^2 \beta}{1 - \tan^2 \alpha \tan^2 \beta}$$

Solution   We'll work on the left side.

$$\frac{\tan (\alpha + \beta)}{\cot (\alpha - \beta)} = \frac{\tan (\alpha + \beta)}{\dfrac{1}{\tan (\alpha - \beta)}}$$

$$= \tan (\alpha + \beta) \tan (\alpha - \beta)$$

$$= \frac{\tan \alpha + \tan \beta}{1 - \tan \alpha \tan \beta} \cdot$$

$$\frac{\tan \alpha - \tan \beta}{1 + \tan \alpha \tan \beta}$$

$$= \frac{\tan^2 \alpha - \tan^2 \beta}{1 - \tan^2 \alpha \tan^2 \beta}$$

Example 3   Use the reduction identity to simplify $12 \sin \theta + 5 \cos \theta$ for any angles between 0° and 360°. Choose the smallest possible value of θ.

Solution   Here a = 12 and b = 5, so that, by the reduction identity,

$12 \sin \theta + 5 \cos \theta$

$= \sqrt{144 + 25} \sin (\theta + \alpha)$

$= 13 \sin (\theta + \alpha)$.

For any angle α,

$$\sin \alpha = \frac{b}{\sqrt{a^2 + b^2}} = \frac{5}{13} \approx .3846 \text{ and}$$

$$\cos \alpha = \frac{a}{\sqrt{a^2 + b^2}} = \frac{12}{13} \approx .9231.$$

From Table 3 or a calculator, the smallest value of α which satisfies both of these conditions is $\alpha = 23°$ (to the nearest degree).

Selected Solutions

1. $\sin 15° = \sin (60° - 45°)$

$= \sin 60° \cos 45° -$

$\cos 60° \sin 45°$

$= (\frac{\sqrt{3}}{2})(\frac{\sqrt{2}}{2}) - (\frac{1}{2})(\frac{\sqrt{2}}{2})$

$= \frac{\sqrt{6} - \sqrt{2}}{4}$.

5. $\sin (-105°) = \sin (45° - 150°)$

$= \sin 45° \cos 150° -$

$\cos 45° \sin 150°$

$= (\frac{\sqrt{2}}{2})(\frac{-\sqrt{3}}{2}) - (\frac{\sqrt{2}}{2})(\frac{1}{2})$

$= \frac{-\sqrt{6} - \sqrt{2}}{4}$.

9. $\sin 76° \cos 31° - \cos 76° \sin 31°$

$= \sin (76° - 31°)$

$= \sin 45°$

$= \frac{\sqrt{2}}{2}$.

13. $\dfrac{\tan 100° + \tan 80°}{1 - \tan 100° \tan 80°} = \tan (100° + 80°)$

$= \tan 180°$

$= 0$.

17. With A = 79.802° and B = 100.198°, we have A + B = 180°, and

$\sin A \cos B + \cos A \sin B = \sin (A + B)$

$= \sin 180°$

$= 0$.

21. We have

$\sin (45° + \theta) = \sin 45° \cos \theta +$

$\cos 45° \sin \theta$

$= \frac{\sqrt{2}}{2} \cos \theta + \frac{\sqrt{2}}{2} \sin \theta$

$= \frac{\sqrt{2}}{2} (\cos \theta + \sin \theta)$.

25. $\tan (\frac{\pi}{4} + s) = \dfrac{\tan \frac{\pi}{4} + \tan s}{1 - \tan \frac{\pi}{4} \tan s}$

$= \dfrac{1 + \tan s}{1 - \tan s}$.

29. $\tan(180° + \theta) = \dfrac{\tan 180° + \tan\theta}{1 - \tan 180° \tan\theta}$

$= \dfrac{0 + \tan\theta}{1 - (0)(\tan\theta)}$

$= \tan\theta.$

33. We can complete the following triangles.

$9 + y^2 = 25$ $x^2 + 25 = 169$

$\quad y = 4$ $\quad x = 12$

Then we have

  (i) $\sin(s + t)$

    $= \sin s \cos t + \cos s \sin t$

    $= \dfrac{4}{5}\cdot\dfrac{12}{13} + \dfrac{3}{5}\cdot\dfrac{5}{13} = \dfrac{63}{65},$

  (ii) $\sin(s - t)$

    $= \dfrac{4}{5}\cdot\dfrac{12}{13} - \dfrac{3}{5}\cdot\dfrac{5}{13} = \dfrac{33}{65},$

  (iii) $\tan(s + t)$

    $= \dfrac{\tan s + \tan t}{1 - \tan s \tan t}$

    $= \dfrac{\dfrac{4}{3} + \dfrac{5}{12}}{1 - \dfrac{4}{3}\cdot\dfrac{5}{12}} = \dfrac{\dfrac{21}{12}}{1 - \dfrac{5}{9}}$

    $= \dfrac{\dfrac{21}{12}}{\dfrac{4}{9}} = \dfrac{21}{12}\cdot\dfrac{9}{4} = \dfrac{63}{16},$

  and

  (iv) $\tan(s - t)$

    $= \dfrac{\dfrac{4}{3} - \dfrac{5}{12}}{1 + \dfrac{5}{9}} = \dfrac{\dfrac{11}{12}}{\dfrac{14}{9}}$

    $= \dfrac{11}{12}\cdot\dfrac{9}{14} = \dfrac{33}{56}.$

37. Given that s and t are in quadrant III, we complete the triangle for y using $x^2 + y^2 = r^2$.

$\sin s = \dfrac{-15}{17}$ $\sin t = \dfrac{-4}{5}$

$\cos s = \dfrac{-8}{17}$ $\cos t = \dfrac{-3}{5}$

$\tan s = \dfrac{15}{8}$ $\tan t = \dfrac{4}{3}$

Hence,

  (i) $\sin(s + t)$

    $= \sin s \cos t + \cos s \sin t$

    $= \left(\dfrac{-15}{17}\right)\left(\dfrac{-3}{5}\right) + \left(\dfrac{-8}{17}\right)\left(\dfrac{-4}{5}\right)$

    $= \dfrac{45 + 32}{85} = \dfrac{77}{85}$

  (ii) $\sin(s - t)$

    $= \sin s \cos t - \cos s \sin t$

    $= \left(\dfrac{-15}{17}\right)\left(\dfrac{-3}{5}\right) - \left(\dfrac{-8}{17}\right)\left(\dfrac{-4}{5}\right)$

    $\dfrac{45 - 32}{85} = \dfrac{13}{85}$

  (iii) $\tan(s + t)$

    $= \dfrac{\tan s + \tan t}{1 - \tan s \tan t}$

    $= \dfrac{\dfrac{15}{8} + \dfrac{4}{3}}{1 - \left(\dfrac{15}{8}\right)\left(\dfrac{4}{3}\right)}$

    $= \dfrac{\dfrac{45 + 32}{24}}{1 - \dfrac{60}{24}}$

    $= \dfrac{77}{24}\cdot\left(\dfrac{-24}{36}\right)$

    $= \dfrac{-77}{36}$

  (iv) $\tan(s - t)$

    $= \dfrac{\tan s - \tan t}{1 + \tan s \tan t}$

    $= \dfrac{\dfrac{15}{8} - \dfrac{4}{3}}{1 + \left(\dfrac{15}{8}\right)\left(\dfrac{4}{3}\right)}$

    $= \dfrac{\dfrac{45 - 32}{24}}{1 + \dfrac{60}{24}}$

    $= \dfrac{13}{24}\cdot\dfrac{24}{84}$

    $= \dfrac{13}{84}$

41. Here we will use identities rather than completing triangles as in #37. Either method can be used.

If $\sin s = \frac{-8}{17}$, s is in quadrant III, then

$$\cos s = -\sqrt{1 - (\frac{-8}{17})^2} \quad \text{since s is in QIII}$$

$$\cos s = -\frac{15}{17}.$$

Also, $\tan s = \frac{8}{15}$.

If $\cos t = \frac{-8}{17}$,

t is in quadrant III, then

$$\sin t = -\sqrt{1 - (\frac{-8}{17})^2} \quad \text{since t is in QIII}$$

$$\sin t = -\frac{15}{17}.$$

Also, $\tan t = \frac{15}{8}$. Hence we have

(i) $\sin (s + t)$

$= \sin s \cos t + \cos s \sin t$

$= (-\frac{8}{17})(-\frac{8}{17}) + (-\frac{15}{17})(-\frac{15}{17})$

$= \frac{64 + 225}{289}$

$= \frac{289}{289}$

$= 1,$

(ii) $\sin (s - t)$

$= \sin s \cos t - \cos s \sin t$

$= (-\frac{8}{17})(-\frac{8}{17}) - (-\frac{15}{17})(-\frac{15}{17})$

$= \frac{64 - 225}{289}$

$= \frac{-161}{289},$

(iii) $\tan (s + t)$

$= \frac{\tan s + \tan t}{1 - \tan s \tan t}$

$= \frac{\frac{8}{15} + \frac{15}{8}}{1 - (\frac{8}{15})(\frac{15}{8})}$

$= \frac{\frac{8}{15} + \frac{15}{8}}{1 - 1}$

$= \frac{64 + 225}{0}$, undefinded,

(iv) $\tan (s - t)$

$= \frac{\tan s - \tan t}{1 + \tan s \tan t}$

$= \frac{\frac{8}{15} - \frac{15}{8}}{1 + (\frac{8}{15})(\frac{15}{8})}$

$= \frac{\frac{8}{15} - \frac{15}{8}}{1 + 1}$

$= \frac{\frac{64 - 225}{120}}{2}$

$= \frac{-161}{120} \cdot \frac{1}{2}$

$= \frac{-161}{240}.$

45. We cannot use the tan (A + B) formula since $\tan \frac{\pi}{2}$ is undefined. Hence, we use the fact that $\tan \theta = \frac{\sin \theta}{\cos \theta}$. This gives

$\tan (\frac{\pi}{2} + x)$

$= \frac{\sin (\frac{\pi}{2} + x)}{\cos (\frac{\pi}{2} + x)}$

$= \frac{\sin \frac{\pi}{2} \cos x + \cos \frac{\pi}{2} \sin x}{\cos \frac{\pi}{2} \cos x - \sin \frac{\pi}{2} \sin x}$

$= \frac{(1) \cos x + (0) \sin x}{(0) \cos x - (1) \sin x}$

$= -\frac{\cos x}{\sin x}$

$= - \cot x.$

49. $\tan (x - y) - \tan (y - x)$

$= \frac{\tan x - \tan y}{1 + \tan x \tan y} - \frac{\tan y - \tan x}{1 + \tan x \tan y}$

$= \frac{\tan x - \tan y - \tan y + \tan x}{1 + \tan x \tan y}$

$= \frac{2(\tan x - \tan y)}{1 + \tan x \tan y}$

53. $\frac{\sin (x - y)}{\sin (x + y)}$

$= \frac{\sin x \cos y - \cos x \sin y}{\sin x \cos y + \cos x \sin y}$

$$= \frac{\dfrac{\sin x \cos y - \cos x \sin y}{\cos x \quad \cos y}}{\dfrac{\sin x \cos y + \cos x \sin y}{\cos x \cos y}}$$

$$= \frac{\dfrac{\sin x}{\cos x} - \dfrac{\sin y}{\cos y}}{\dfrac{\sin x}{\cos x} + \dfrac{\sin y}{\cos y}}$$

$$= \frac{\tan x - \tan y}{\tan x + \tan y}$$

57. We have the identity
$\sin 2 s = \sin (s + s)$
$\qquad = \sin s \cos s + \cos s \sin s$
$\qquad = 2 \sin s \cos s.$
Also, if $\sin s = 0.599832$ and s is
in quadrant II, then
$\sin^2 s + \cos^2 s = 1$
$\qquad \cos^2 s = 1 - \sin^2 s$
$\qquad \cos^2 s = 0.6402016$
$\qquad \cos s = -0.800126,$
since s is in quadrant II.
Hence, we have
$\sin 2 s = 2(0.599832)(-0.800126)$
$\sin 2 s = -.9598823.$

61. We use the reduction identity that
$a \sin x + b \cos x$
$= \sqrt{a^2 + b^2} \sin (x + \alpha)$, where
$\sin \alpha = \dfrac{b}{\sqrt{a^2 + b^2}}$ and $\cos \alpha = \dfrac{a}{\sqrt{a^2 + b^2}}$.
This gives
$12 \sin A + 5 \cos A$
$= \sqrt{144 + 25} \sin (A + \alpha)$
$= 13 \sin (A + \alpha),$
where $\sin \alpha = \dfrac{5}{13}$ and $\cos \alpha = \dfrac{12}{13}$.
a calculator gives $\alpha \approx 22.62°$, or
$\alpha \approx 23°$. The solution is
$13 \sin (A + 23°).$

65. Using the reduction identity,
$-7 \sin t + 24 \cos t$
$= \sqrt{49 + 576} \sin (t + \alpha)$
$= 25 \sin (t + \alpha)$, where
$\sin \alpha = \dfrac{24}{25}$ and $\cos \alpha = \dfrac{-7}{25}$. This

implies that α is in quadrant II,
with a reference angle
$R = \sin^{-1} \dfrac{24}{25} \approx 73.44°.$
Hence, $\alpha \approx 106°$. The answer is
$25 \sin (t + 106°).$

69. Using the reduction identity we have
$y = \sin x - \sqrt{3} \cos x = \sqrt{1 + 3}$
$\qquad\qquad\qquad\qquad \sin (x + \alpha)$
$\qquad\qquad\qquad = 2 \sin (x + \alpha),$
where $\sin \alpha = \dfrac{-\sqrt{3}}{2}$ and $\cos \alpha = \dfrac{1}{2}$.
This implies α is in quadrant IV,
with a reference angle $R = \dfrac{\pi}{3}$. Thus,
$\alpha = \dfrac{-\pi}{3}$. The graph is
$y = 2 \sin (x - \dfrac{\pi}{3}) \cdot$ [or $y = 2 \sin (x + \dfrac{5\pi}{3})$].
The amplitude is 2, the period is
2π, and there is a phase shift of
$\dfrac{\pi}{3}$ units to the right. See the graph
in the text.

73. The result is undefined since use of
$\tan (A + B) = \dfrac{\tan A + \tan B}{1 - \tan A \tan B}$ with
$A = 65.902°$ and $B = 24.098°$ gives
$\tan (A + B) = \tan 90°$, which is
undefined.

77. According to the figure we have
$\tan \alpha = m_1$ and $\tan \beta = m_2$. The
three angles interior to the triangle
are α, θ, and $\pi - \beta$. These add to
π radians. That is
$\alpha + \theta + (\pi - \beta) = \pi$, or
$\qquad\qquad \theta = \beta - \alpha.$
Then,
$\tan \theta = \tan(\beta - \alpha) = \dfrac{\tan \beta - \tan \alpha}{1 + \tan \beta \tan \alpha}$
$\qquad = \dfrac{m_2 - m_1}{1 + m_2 m_1}.$

81. Let $A = \sin^{-1} \frac{2}{3}$ and $B = \tan^{-1} \frac{1}{4}$.

Then A and B are in quadrant I, and

$\sin A = \frac{2}{3}$ and $\tan B = \frac{1}{4}$. We complete the triangles below.

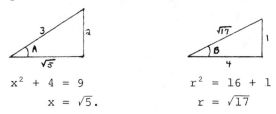

$x^2 + 4 = 9$ $r^2 = 16 + 1$

$\quad x = \sqrt{5}.$ $\quad r = \sqrt{17}$

Then we have

$\sin (A + B) = \sin A \cos B + \cos A \sin B$

$= \frac{2}{3} \cdot \frac{4}{\sqrt{17}} + \frac{\sqrt{5}}{3} \cdot \frac{1}{\sqrt{17}}$

$= \frac{8 + \sqrt{5}}{3\sqrt{17}} \cdot \frac{\sqrt{17}}{\sqrt{17}}$

$= \frac{8\sqrt{17} + \sqrt{85}}{51}.$

84. (a) Exercise 29 shows this part.

(b) Since $\cot A = \frac{1}{\tan A}$, and by

exercise 29, $\tan (180° + x) = \tan x$,

we have

$\cot (x + 180°) = \frac{1}{\tan (x + 180°)}$

$= \frac{1}{\tan x} = \cot x.$

Hence, the period of cotangent is

$180° = \pi$ radians.

Section 7.5   Multiple-Angle Identities

Additional Examples

Example 1   Find tan x if $\sin 2x = \frac{-4}{5}$

and $180° \leq 2x \leq 270°$.

Solution   Using the first of the three

formulas for tan s/2, we have

$\tan x = \pm \sqrt{\frac{1 - \cos 2x}{1 + \cos 2x}}.$

To find cos 2x, use the fact that

$\cos^2 2x = 1 - \sin^2 2x = 1 - \frac{16}{25} = \frac{9}{25},$

so that $\cos 2x = \frac{-3}{5}.$ Use a

negative sign, since 2x is in quadrant III. Then

$\tan x = \pm \sqrt{\frac{1 - (-3/5)}{1 + (-3/5)}} = \pm \sqrt{\frac{8/5}{2/5}}$

$= \pm \sqrt{4} = \pm 2.$

Since $180° \leq 2x \leq 270°$

$\qquad 90° \leq x \leq 135°,$

$\tan x = -2.$

Example 2   Find values of the six

trigonometric functions of 2θ, given

$\sin \theta = \frac{-1}{4}$ and $\cos \theta > 0.$

Solution   Since $\sin \theta < 0$ and $\cos \theta > 0$,

θ is in quadrant IV. Also

$\cos^2 \theta = 1 - \sin^2 \theta = 1 - \frac{1}{16} = \frac{15}{16},$

so that $\cos \theta = \frac{\sqrt{15}}{4},$ from which

$\tan \theta = \frac{\sin \theta}{\cos \theta} = \frac{-\sqrt{15}}{15}.$ Using

the identities given in this section,

$\sin 2\theta = 2 \sin \theta \cos \theta$

$= 2 (-\frac{1}{4}) (\frac{\sqrt{15}}{4})$

$= \frac{-2\sqrt{15}}{16}$

$= \frac{-\sqrt{15}}{8},$

$\cos 2\theta = \cos^2 \theta - \sin^2 \theta$

$= \frac{15}{16} - \frac{1}{16} = \frac{14}{16} = \frac{7}{8},$

$\tan 2\theta = \frac{2 \tan \theta}{1 - \tan^2 \theta}$

$= \frac{2 (-\frac{\sqrt{15}}{15})}{1 - \frac{15}{225}}$

$= \frac{\frac{-2\sqrt{15}}{15}}{\frac{210}{225}}$

$= \frac{-2\sqrt{15}}{15} \cdot \frac{225}{210} = \frac{-\sqrt{15}}{7}.$

By the reciprocal identities,

$\csc 2\theta = \frac{-8}{\sqrt{15}} = \frac{-8\sqrt{15}}{15},$

$\sec 2\theta = \frac{8}{7},$

$$\cot 2\theta = \frac{-7}{\sqrt{15}}$$

$$= \frac{-7 \cdot \sqrt{15}}{\sqrt{15} \cdot \sqrt{15}}$$

$$= \frac{-7\sqrt{15}}{15}.$$

Example 3   Verify

$$\frac{1 - \sin 2s}{\cos 2s} = \frac{1 - \tan s}{1 + \tan s}.$$

Solution $\dfrac{1 - \tan s}{1 + \tan s}$

$$= \frac{1 - \dfrac{\sin s}{\cos s}}{1 + \dfrac{\sin s}{\cos s}}$$

$$= \frac{\dfrac{\cos s - \sin s}{\cos s}}{\dfrac{\cos s + \sin s}{\cos s}}$$

$$= \frac{\cos s - \sin s}{\cos s + \sin s}$$

Now multiply top and bottom by cos s - sin s.

$$= \frac{\cos^2 s - 2 \sin s \cos s + \sin^2 s}{\cos^2 s - \sin^2 s}$$

$$= \frac{1 - \sin 2s}{\cos 2s}$$

Selected Solutions

1. We have $\sqrt{\dfrac{1 - \cos \alpha}{2}} = \sin \dfrac{\alpha}{2}$, so

that $\sqrt{\dfrac{1 - \cos 40°}{2}} = \sin 20°.$

5. Using the formula

$\tan \dfrac{x}{2} = \dfrac{1 - \cos x}{\sin x}$, we have

$$\frac{1 - \cos 59.74°}{\sin 59.74°} = \tan \left(\frac{59.74}{2}\right)°$$

$$= \tan 29.87°.$$

9. Using the formula

$\tan \dfrac{x}{2} = \pm\sqrt{\dfrac{1 - \cos x}{1 + \cos x}}$, we have

$$\pm\sqrt{\frac{1 - \cos 8\theta}{1 + \cos 8\theta}} = \tan 4\theta.$$

13. Using the formula

$\cos 2\theta = 1 - 2 \sin^2 \theta$, we have

$1 - 2 \sin^2 15° = \cos 30° = \dfrac{\sqrt{3}}{2}.$

17. Using the formula

$\sin 2x = 2 \sin x \cos x$, we have

$\sin \dfrac{\pi}{8} \cos \dfrac{\pi}{8} = \dfrac{1}{2} \sin \dfrac{\pi}{4}$

$$= \frac{1}{2} \frac{\sqrt{2}}{2}$$

$$= \frac{\sqrt{2}}{4}.$$

21. Using $\sin 2\theta = 2 \sin \theta \cos \theta$, we have

$\dfrac{1}{8} \sin 29.5° \cos 29.5° = \dfrac{1}{16} \sin 59°.$

25. Since 195° is in quandrant III and the sine is negative in quadrant III, the negative sign should be selected.

29. Using the formula

$\sin \dfrac{x}{2} = \pm\sqrt{\dfrac{1 - \cos x}{2}}$, we have

$\sin 22.5° = \sqrt{\dfrac{1 - \cos 45°}{2}}$ + since 22.5° in QI

$\sin 22.5° = \sqrt{\dfrac{1 - \dfrac{\sqrt{2}}{2}}{2}}$

$$= \sqrt{\frac{2 - \sqrt{2}}{4}} = \frac{\sqrt{2 - \sqrt{2}}}{2}.$$

Also

$\cos 22.5° = +\sqrt{\dfrac{1 + \cos 45°}{2}} = \sqrt{\dfrac{2 + \sqrt{2}}{4}}$

$$= \frac{\sqrt{2 + \sqrt{2}}}{2},$$

and using

$\tan \dfrac{x}{2} = \dfrac{1 - \cos x}{\sin x}$, we have

$\tan 22.5° = \dfrac{1 - \cos 45°}{\sin 45°} = \dfrac{1 - \dfrac{\sqrt{2}}{2}}{\dfrac{\sqrt{2}}{2}}$

$$= \frac{2 - \sqrt{2}}{\sqrt{2}} \cdot \frac{\sqrt{2}}{\sqrt{2}} = \frac{2\sqrt{2} - 2}{2}$$

$\tan 22.5° = \sqrt{2} - 1.$

The text gives $\sqrt{3 - 2\sqrt{2}}$, which is the same answer but the formula

$\tan \dfrac{x}{2} = \sqrt{\dfrac{1 - \cos x}{1 + \cos x}}$ was used.

33. We know $\sin \frac{5\pi}{2} = \sin (\frac{\pi}{2} + 2\pi) = 1$

and $\cos \frac{5\pi}{2} = \cos (\frac{\pi}{2} + 2\pi) = 0$.

Hence, $\tan \frac{5\pi}{2}$ is undefined. Also,

we could use the formula

$$\sin \frac{5\pi}{2} = + \sqrt{\frac{1 - \cos 5\pi}{2}}$$

$$= \sqrt{\frac{1 + 1}{2}} \qquad \text{since } \cos 5\pi = -1$$

$$= 1,$$

and so on.

37. $3 - 3 \cos 4\theta = 6(\frac{1 - \cos 4\theta}{2})$

$$= 6 \sin^2 2\theta$$

Hence,

$$k = 6$$

and

$$t = 2.$$

41. If $\pi < \alpha < \frac{3\pi}{2}$, then $\frac{\pi}{2} < \frac{\alpha}{2} < \frac{3\pi}{4}$,

so that α is in quadrant II. Hence,

$\cos \frac{\alpha}{2}$ is negative. We then have

$$\cos \frac{\alpha}{2} = - \sqrt{\frac{1 + \cos \alpha}{2}} = \sqrt{\frac{1 + (-\frac{1}{4})}{2}}$$

$$\cos \frac{\alpha}{2} = - \sqrt{\frac{3}{8}} = \frac{-\sqrt{6}}{4}.$$

45. If $\sin \theta = \frac{2}{5}$ and $\cos \theta < 0$, then θ

is in quadrant II and

$$\cos^2 \theta + \sin^2 \theta = 1$$

$$\cos^2 \theta = 1 - \frac{4}{25} = \frac{21}{25}$$

$$\cos \theta = - \frac{\sqrt{21}}{5}.$$

Then we have

(1) $\sin 2\theta = 2 \sin \theta \cos \theta = \frac{-4\sqrt{21}}{25}$,

(2) $\cos 2\theta = \cos^2 \theta - \sin^2 \theta$

$$= \frac{21}{25} - \frac{4}{25} = \frac{17}{25},$$

(3) $\tan 2\theta = \frac{\sin 2\theta}{\cos 2\theta} = \frac{-4\sqrt{21}}{17}$,

(4) $\cot 2\theta = \frac{1}{\tan 2\theta} = \frac{-17}{4\sqrt{21}} = \frac{-17\sqrt{21}}{84}$,

(5) $\sec 2\theta = \frac{1}{\cos 2\theta} = \frac{25}{17}$, and

(6) $\csc 2\theta = \frac{1}{\sin 2\theta} + \frac{-25}{4\sqrt{21}} = \frac{-25\sqrt{21}}{84}$.

49. If $\cos \alpha = \frac{1}{3}$ and $\sin \alpha < 0$, then α

is in quadrant IV, or $\frac{3\pi}{2} < \alpha < 2\pi$.

Then $\frac{3\pi}{4} < \frac{\alpha}{2} < \pi$, so that $\frac{\alpha}{2}$ is in

quadrant II.

Hence, we have

(1) $\sin \frac{\alpha}{2} = + \sqrt{\frac{1 - \cos \alpha}{2}}$

$$= \sqrt{\frac{1 - \frac{1}{3}}{2}} = \frac{\sqrt{3}}{3},$$

(2) $\cos \frac{\alpha}{2} = - \sqrt{\frac{1 + \cos \alpha}{2}}$

$$= - \sqrt{\frac{1 + \frac{1}{3}}{2}} = \frac{-\sqrt{6}}{3},$$

(3) $\tan \frac{\alpha}{2} = \frac{\sin \frac{\alpha}{2}}{\cos \frac{\alpha}{2}} = \frac{\frac{\sqrt{3}}{3}}{\frac{-\sqrt{6}}{3}}$

$$= - \frac{\sqrt{3}}{\sqrt{6}} = \frac{-\sqrt{2}}{2},$$

(4) $\cot \frac{\alpha}{2} = \frac{1}{\tan \frac{\alpha}{2}} = -\sqrt{2}$,

(5) $\sec \frac{\alpha}{2} = \frac{1}{\cos \frac{\alpha}{2}} = \frac{-3}{\sqrt{6}} = \frac{-\sqrt{6}}{2}$, and

(6) $\csc \frac{\alpha}{2} = \frac{1}{\sin \frac{\alpha}{2}} = \sqrt{3}$.

53. We have

$$\frac{\sec^2 x + \sec^4 x}{2 + \sec^2 x - \sec^4 x}$$

$$= \frac{\frac{1}{\cos^2 x} + \frac{1}{\cos^4 x}}{2 + \frac{1}{\cos^2 x} - \frac{1}{\cos^4 x}}$$

$$= \frac{\frac{\cos^2 x + 1}{\cos^4 x}}{\frac{2 \cos^4 x + \cos^2 x - 1}{\cos^4 x}}$$

$$= \frac{\cos^2 x + 1}{(2 \cos^2 x - 1)(\cos^2 x + 1)}$$

$$= \frac{1}{2 \cos^2 x - 1} = \frac{1}{\cos^2 2x} = \sec 2x.$$

57. We have

$$\sec^2 \frac{x}{2} = \frac{1}{\cos^2 \frac{x}{2}} \; ; \qquad \text{use } \cos x = 2 \cos^2 \frac{x}{2} - 1$$

$$= \frac{1}{\frac{1 + \cos x}{2}}$$

$$= \frac{2}{1 + \cos x}.$$

61. Since $\tan \frac{x}{2} = \frac{\sin x}{1 + \cos x}$ we have

$$\frac{2}{1 + \cos x} - \tan^2 \frac{x}{2}$$

$$= \frac{2}{1 + \cos x} - \frac{\sin^2 x}{(1 + \cos x)^2}$$

$$= \frac{2(1 + \cos x) - \sin^2 x}{(1 + \cos x)^2}$$

$$= \frac{2 + 2 \cos x - (1 - \cos^2 x)}{(1 + \cos x)^2}$$

$$= \frac{1 + 2 \cos x + \cos^2 x}{(1 + \cos x)^2}$$

$$= \frac{(1 + \cos x)^2}{(1 + \cos x)^2}$$

$$= 1.$$

65. Since $\sec^2 \theta = 1 + \tan^2 \theta$, we have

$$\frac{2 \tan \theta}{\sec^2 \theta - 2} = \frac{2 \tan \theta}{\tan^2 \theta - 1}$$

$$= -\frac{\tan \theta + \tan \theta}{1 - \tan^2 \theta}$$

$$= -\tan (\theta + \theta)$$

$$= -\tan 2\theta.$$

69. We have the formulas that

$$\tan \frac{x}{2} = \frac{1 - \cos x}{\sin x} = \frac{\sin x}{1 + \cos x}.$$

Hence we will use

$$\tan x = \frac{1 - \cos x}{\sin x} \text{ and }$$

$$\cot \frac{x}{2} = \frac{1}{\tan \frac{x}{2}} = \frac{1 + \cos x}{\sin x} \text{ to get}$$

$$\frac{\tan \frac{x}{2} + \cot \frac{x}{2}}{\cot \frac{x}{2} - \tan \frac{x}{2}}$$

$$= \frac{\frac{1 - \cos x}{\sin x} + \frac{1 + \cos x}{\sin x}}{\frac{1 + \cos x}{\sin x} - \frac{1 - \cos x}{\sin x}}$$

$$= \frac{\frac{1 - \cos x + 1 + \cos x}{\sin x}}{\frac{1 + \cos x - 1 + \cos x}{\sin x}}$$

$$= \frac{2}{\sin x} \cdot \frac{\sin x}{2 \cos x} = \frac{1}{\cos x} = \sec x.$$

73. Since $\tan 2x = \frac{2 \tan x}{1 + \tan^2 x}$, then

$$\tan^2 2x = \left(\frac{2 \tan x}{1 + \tan^2 x}\right)^2$$

$$= \frac{4 \tan^2 x}{1 + 2 \tan^2 x + \tan^4 x}.$$

77. We have

$$\cos 4x = 2 \cos^2 2x - 1$$

and $\cos 2x = 2 \cos^2 x - 1$, so that

$$\cos 4x = 2(2 \cos^2 x - 1)^2 - 1$$

$$= 8 \cos^4 x - 8 \cos^2 x + 1.$$

81. If $m = 2$, then

$\sin \frac{\alpha}{2} = \frac{1}{2}$, so that

$\frac{\alpha}{2} = 30°$, which implies $\alpha = 60°$.

85. If $\frac{7\pi}{4} < s < 2\pi$, then $\frac{7\pi}{2} < 2s < 4\pi$, so that $2s$ is in quadrant IV. We are given $\sin s = -0.48113$, so that

$$\sin^2 s + \cos^2 s = 1$$

$$\cos^2 s = 1 - (-0.48113)^2$$

$$\cos^2 s = 0.768514$$

$$\cos s = +0.87665.$$

Then,

$$\sin 2s = 2 \sin s \cos s$$

$$= 2(-0.48113)(0.87665)$$

$$= -0.84357.$$

89. Using exercise 85, we have found $\cos s = 0.87665$. Hence,

$$\tan s = \frac{\sin s}{\cos s} = \frac{-0.48113}{0.87665}$$

$$\tan s = -0.54883.$$

Then we can write

$$\tan 2s = \frac{2 \tan s}{1 - \tan^2 s}$$

$$= \frac{2(-.54883)}{1 - (0.30121)} = -1.57081.$$

93. If $\pi < s < \frac{3\pi}{2}$, then $\frac{\pi}{2} < \frac{s}{2} < \frac{3\pi}{4}$, so that $\frac{s}{2}$ is in quadrant II. Thus, $\tan \frac{s}{2} < 0$. We can use the formula

$$\tan \frac{s}{2} = -\sqrt{\frac{1 - \cos s}{1 + \cos s}}$$

$$= -\sqrt{\frac{1 + .592147}{1 - .592147}}$$

$$= -\sqrt{\frac{1.592147}{0.407853}}$$

$$= -1.975785.$$

97. $\sin^2 2x + \cos^2 2x = 1$ for all x.

Section 7.6   Sum and Product Identities

Additional Examples

Example 1   Write $\cos 24° \sin 100°$ as a sum or difference of trigonometric functions.

Solution   Use the second identity of this section to get

$\cos 24° \sin 100°$

$= \frac{1}{2} [\sin (24° + 100°) - \sin (24° - 100°)]$

$= \frac{1}{2} \sin 124° - \frac{1}{2} \sin (-76°)$

$= \frac{1}{2} \sin 124° + \frac{1}{2} \sin 76°.$

Example 2   Write $\cos 3x - \cos x$ as a product of trigonometric functions.

Solution $\cos 3x - \cos x$

$= -2 \sin (\frac{3x + x}{2}) \sin (\frac{3x - x}{2})$

$= -2 \sin 2x \sin x.$

Selected Solutions

1. $\cos 35° \sin 25°$

$= \frac{1}{2} (\sin (25° + 35°) + \sin (25° - 35°))$

$= \frac{1}{2} (\sin 60° - \sin 10°)$

$= \frac{1}{2}(\frac{\sqrt{3}}{2} - \sin 10°).$

5. $\sin (-\theta) \sin (-3\theta)$

$= \frac{1}{2} [\cos (-\theta - (-3\theta)) - \cos (-\theta - 3\theta)]$

$= \frac{1}{2} [\cos 2\theta - \cos (-4\theta)]$

$\frac{1}{2} [\cos 2\theta - \cos 4\theta].$

9. $\sin 60° - \sin 30°$

$= 2 \sin (\frac{60° - 30°}{2}) \cos (\frac{60° + 30°}{2})$

$= 2 \sin 15° \cos 45°.$

13. $\sin 12\beta - \sin 3\beta$

$= 2 \sin (\frac{12\beta - 3\beta}{2}) \cos (\frac{12\beta + 3\beta}{2})$

$= 2 \sin \frac{9}{2}\beta \cos \frac{15}{2}\beta$

17. $\tan x = \frac{\sin 3x - \sin x}{\cos 3x + \cos x}$

Proof: $\frac{\sin 3x - \sin x}{\cos 3x + \cos x}$

$= \frac{2 \sin \frac{3x - x}{2} \cos \frac{3x + x}{2}}{2 \cos \frac{3x + x}{2} \cos \frac{3x + x}{2}}$

$= \frac{\sin x}{\cos x}$

$= \tan x$

21. $\frac{1}{\tan 2s} = \frac{\sin 3s - \sin s}{\cos s - \cos 3s}$

Proof: $\frac{\sin 3s - \sin s}{\cos s - \cos 3s}$

$= \frac{2 \sin s \cos 2s}{2 \sin \frac{s + 3s}{2} \sin \frac{3s - s}{2}}$

$= \frac{\cos 2s}{\sin 2s}$

$= \cot 2s$

$= \frac{1}{\tan 2s}.$

25. $\sin^2 u - \sin^2 v = \sin (u + v) \sin (u - v)$

Proof: $\sin^2 u - \sin^2 v$

$= (\sin u + \sin v)(\sin u - \sin v)$

$= (2 \sin \frac{u + v}{2} \cos \frac{u - v}{2}) \cdot$

$(2 \sin \frac{u - v}{2} \cos \frac{u + v}{2})$

$$= 2 \sin \frac{u + v}{2} \cos \frac{u + v}{2} \cdot$$

$$2 \sin \frac{u - v}{2} \cos \frac{u - v}{2}$$

$$= \sin (u + v) \cdot \sin (u - v)$$

27. sin s cos t

$$= \frac{1}{2} [\sin (s + t) + \sin (s - t)]$$

Let s = t:

sin t cos t

$$= \frac{1}{2} [\sin (2t) + \sin (0)]$$

$$= \frac{1}{2} \sin 2t$$

From this, sin 2t = 2 sin t cos t.

Section 7.7   Trigonometric Equations

Additional Examples

Example 1   Solve cos x − $\sqrt{3}$ sin x = 1
in the interval [0, 2π).

Solution   cos x − $\sqrt{3}$ sin x = 1

$$\cos x = 1 + \sqrt{3} \sin x$$

Square both sides.

$$\cos^2 x = 1 + 2\sqrt{3} \sin x + 3 \sin^2 x$$
$$1 - \sin^2 x = 1 + 2\sqrt{3} \sin x + 3 \sin^2 x$$
$$0 = 2\sqrt{3} \sin x + 4 \sin^2 x$$
$$0 = \sqrt{3} \sin x + 2 \sin^2 x$$
$$0 = \sin x \, (\sqrt{3} + 2 \sin x)$$

sin x = 0 or

$\sqrt{3}$ + 2 sin x = 0

$$\sin x = -\frac{\sqrt{3}}{2}$$

The possible values of x are 0, π,
$\frac{4\pi}{3}$, $\frac{5\pi}{3}$. These values must be
checked in the original equation.
Verify that the only solutions are
0 and $\frac{4\pi}{3}$.

Example 2   Solve 2 $\cos^2 \frac{x}{2}$ = $\cos^2$ x
for x in [0°, 360°).

Solution   Use the identity $\cos^2 \frac{x}{2}$ =
$\frac{1 + \cos x}{2}$ and substitute. This gives

$$2 \cos^2 \frac{x}{2} = \cos^2 x$$

$$2 \left(\frac{1 + \cos x}{2} \right) = \cos^2 x$$

$$1 + \cos x = \cos^2 x$$

$$0 = \cos^2 x - \cos x - 1.$$

Now use the quadratic theorem with
cos x as the variable and a = 1,
b = −1, c = −1.

$$\cos x = \frac{1 \pm \sqrt{1 + 4}}{2} = \frac{1 \pm \sqrt{5}}{2}$$

This gives cos x = 1.6180 or cos x
= −.6180, which leads to x = 231°50'
or x = 128°10' to the nearest 10
minutes. Since cosine cannot be
greater than 1, there are no solutions from cos x = 1.6180.

Example 3   Solve $\sin^{-1}$ x + $\tan^{-1} \frac{3}{4}$ = $\frac{\pi}{4}$.

Solution   Let $\tan^{-1} \frac{3}{4}$ = A, so that
tan A = $\frac{3}{4}$. Subtract $\tan^{-1} \frac{3}{4}$ on
both sides of the equation to get

$$\sin^{-1} x = \frac{\pi}{4} - \tan^{-1} \frac{3}{4}$$

$$\sin \left(\frac{\pi}{4} - \tan^{-1} \frac{3}{4} \right) = x$$

$$\sin \left(\frac{\pi}{4} - A \right) = x$$

$$\sin \frac{\pi}{4} \cos A - \cos \frac{\pi}{4} \sin A = x. \quad (1)$$

Sketch a right triangle in which
tan A = $\frac{3}{4}$. Use it to find cos A = $\frac{4}{5}$
and sin A = $\frac{3}{5}$. Then substitute into
equation (1) along with the values
for sin $\frac{\pi}{4}$ and cos $\frac{\pi}{4}$.

$$\frac{\sqrt{2}}{2} \cdot \frac{4}{5} - \frac{\sqrt{2}}{2} \cdot \frac{3}{5} = x,$$

or $x = \frac{\sqrt{2}}{10}$

Verify that this is correct by
substitution into the original
equation. Use a calculator or
Table 3 to check.

Selected Solutions

1. $3 \tan x + 5 = 2$

$3 \tan x = -3$

$\tan x = -1$

$x = \dfrac{3\pi}{4}, \dfrac{7\pi}{4}$

The solution set is $\{\dfrac{3\pi}{4}, \dfrac{7\pi}{4}\}$.

5. $(\cot x - \sqrt{3})(2 \sin x + \sqrt{3}) = 0$

$\cot x = \sqrt{3} \qquad$ or $\quad \sin x = \dfrac{-\sqrt{3}}{2}$

$\tan x = \dfrac{1}{\sqrt{3}} \qquad$ or $\quad \sin x = \dfrac{-\sqrt{3}}{2}$

$x = \dfrac{\pi}{6}, \dfrac{7\pi}{6} \qquad\qquad x = \dfrac{4\pi}{3}, \dfrac{5\pi}{3}$

The solution set is $\{\dfrac{\pi}{6} \quad \dfrac{7\pi}{6} \quad \dfrac{4\pi}{3} \quad \dfrac{5\pi}{3}\}$.

9. $\cos^2 x + 2 \cos x + 1 = 0$

$(\cos x + 1)^2 = 0$

$\cos x = -1$

$x = \pi$

The solution set is $\{\pi\}$.

13. $\cos^2 x - \sin^2 x = 0$

$\cos x = \sin x \qquad$ or $\qquad \cos x = -\sin x$

$x = \dfrac{\pi}{4}, \dfrac{5\pi}{4} \qquad\qquad x = \dfrac{3\pi}{4}, \dfrac{7\pi}{4}$

The solution set is $\{\dfrac{\pi}{4}, \dfrac{3\pi}{4}, \dfrac{5\pi}{4}, \dfrac{7\pi}{4}\}$.

17. $3 \tan 2x = \sqrt{3}$

$\tan 2x \quad \dfrac{\sqrt{3}}{3}$

If $0 \le x < 2\pi$, then $0 \le 2x < 4\pi$.

Thus $2x = \dfrac{\pi}{6}, \dfrac{13\pi}{6}, \dfrac{7\pi}{6}, \dfrac{19\pi}{6}$,

or $\quad x = \dfrac{\pi}{12}, \dfrac{13\pi}{12}, \dfrac{7\pi}{12}, \dfrac{19\pi}{12}$.

21. $\sin \dfrac{x}{2} = \sqrt{2} - \sin \dfrac{x}{2}$

If $0 \le x < 2\pi$, then $0 \le \dfrac{x}{2} < \pi$.

Hence, $2 \sin \dfrac{x}{2} = \sqrt{2}$ gives

$\sin \dfrac{x}{2} = \dfrac{\sqrt{2}}{2}$, so that

$\dfrac{x}{2} = \dfrac{\pi}{4}, \dfrac{3\pi}{4}$,

or $x = \dfrac{\pi}{2}, \dfrac{3\pi}{2}$.

The solution set $\{\dfrac{\pi}{2}, \dfrac{3\pi}{2}\}$.

25. If $\tan \theta + 6 \cot \theta = 5$, then

$\tan \theta + \dfrac{6}{\tan \theta} - 5 = 0$

$\tan^2 \theta - 5 \tan \theta + 6 = 0$

$(\tan \theta - 2)(\tan \theta - 3) = 0$

$\tan \theta = 2 \quad$ or $\quad \tan \theta = 3$.

Hence, we have θ in quadrants I and III, and

$\theta = \arctan 2 \approx 63°30'$ and $243°30'$,

or $\theta = \arctan 3 \approx 71°30'$ and $251°30'$.

The solution set is $\{63°30', 71°30', 243°30', 251°30'\}$.

29. If $5 \sec^2 \theta = 6 \sec \theta$, then

$\sec \theta (5 \sec \theta - 6) = 0$

$\sec \theta = 0 \quad$ or $\quad \sec \theta = \dfrac{6}{5}$.

However, $\sec \theta = 0$ is impossible; this would imply $\cos \theta$ is undefined.

If $\sec \theta = \dfrac{6}{5}$, then $\cos \theta = \dfrac{5}{6}$.

θ is in quadrants I and IV, and

$\theta = \cos^{-1}(\dfrac{5}{6}) \approx 33°30'$ and $326°30'$.

The solution set is $\{33°30', 326°30'\}$.

33. If $\sin^2 \theta \cos^2 \theta = 0$, then

$\sin \theta = 0 \quad$ or $\quad \cos \theta = 0$

$\theta = 0°, 180° \quad$ or $\quad \theta = 90°, 270°$.

The solution set is $\{0°, 90°, 180°, 270°\}$.

37. If $\cos \dfrac{\theta}{2} = 1$, then

$\dfrac{\theta}{2} = 0°$ or any angle coterminal to $0° (-360°, 360°$, etc.). Hence, $\theta = 0°$, and this is the only solution in $[0°, 360°)$.

The solution set is $\{0°\}$.

41. Using $\cos 2\theta = 1 - 2 \sin^2 \theta$, we have
$$2 \sin \theta = 2 \cos 2\theta$$
$$2 \sin \theta = 2 - 4 \sin^2 \theta$$
$$4 \sin^2 \theta + 2 \sin \theta - 2 = 0$$
$$2(2 \sin \theta - 1)(\sin \theta + 1) = 0$$
$$2 \sin \theta - 1 = 0 \quad \text{or} \quad \sin \theta + 1 = 0$$
$$\sin \theta = \frac{1}{2} \quad \text{or} \quad \sin \theta = -1$$
$$\theta = 30°, 150° \quad \text{or} \quad \theta = 270°.$$
The solution set is $\{30°, 150°, 270°\}$.

45. Using $\cos 2A = 1 - 2 \sin^2 A$, with $A = \frac{\theta}{2}$, we have
$$\cos \theta = \sin^2 \frac{\theta}{2}$$
$$\cos \theta = \frac{1}{2} - \frac{1}{2} \cos \theta$$
$$\frac{3}{2} \cos \theta = \frac{1}{2}$$
$$\cos \theta = \frac{1}{3}.$$
Hence, θ is in quadrants I and II, and $\theta = \cos^{-1} \left(\frac{1}{3}\right) \approx 70°31', 289°30'$.
The solution set is $\{70°30', 278°30'\}$.

49. If $\sin x - \cos x = 1$, then we have
$$\sin x = 1 + \cos x$$
$$\sin^2 x = (1 + \cos x)^2 = 1 + 2 \cos x + \cos^2 x$$
$$1 - \cos^2 x = 1 + 2 \cos x + \cos^2 x$$
$$2 \cos^2 x + 2 \cos x = 0$$
$$2 \cos x (\cos x + 1) = 0$$
$$\cos x = 0 \quad \text{or} \quad \cos x = -1$$
$$x = 90° + 360n, \quad \text{or} \quad x = 180° + 360n$$
$$x = 270° + 360n,$$
where n is any integer.
However, 270° does not check since $\sin 270° = -1$. The solution set is $\{90° + 360n°, 180° + 360n°; n \text{ is any integer}\}$.

53. If $\tan^2 x + 2 \tan x - 3 = 0$, then
$$(\tan x + 3)(\tan x - 1) = 0$$
$$\tan x = -3 \quad \text{or} \quad \tan x = 1$$
$$x \approx 108.5° + 180°n \quad \text{or} \quad x = 45° + 180n°,$$
where n is any integer.
The solution set is
$$\{45° + 180°, 108.5° + 180n°;$$
$$n \text{ is any integer}\}.$$

57. If $9 \sin^2 x - 6 \sin x - 1 = 0$, then the quadratic formula must be used, with $a = 9$, $b = -6$, and $c = -1$, to arrive at
$$\sin x = \frac{6 \pm \sqrt{36 + 36}}{18}$$
$$\sin x = \frac{6 \pm 6\sqrt{2}}{18}$$
$$\sin x = \frac{1 \pm \sqrt{2}}{3}.$$
Hence,
$$\sin x = \frac{1 + \sqrt{2}}{3} \text{ or } \sin x = \frac{1 - \sqrt{2}}{3}$$
$$\sin x \approx 0.804738 \text{ or } \sin x \approx -0.1380712$$
$$x \approx 53.6° \quad \text{or} \quad x \approx 187.9°$$
$$\text{and } x \approx 126.4° \quad \text{and} \quad x = 352.1°$$
The solution set is
$$\{53.6°, 126.4°, 187.9°, 352.1°\}.$$

61. If $\sin^2 x - 2 \sin x + 3 = 0$, then we must use the quadratic formula since the equation will not factor. Using $a = 1$, $b = -2$, and $c = 3$, we have
$$\sin x = \frac{2 \pm \sqrt{4 - 4(1)(3)}}{2}$$
$$\sin x = \frac{2 \pm \sqrt{-8}}{2}.$$
Since $\sqrt{-8}$ is not a real number, the equation has no solutions. The solution set is $\emptyset$.

65.
$$\sin x + \sin 3x = \cos x$$
$$2 \sin \frac{x + 3x}{2} \cos \frac{3x - x}{2} = \cos x$$
$$2 \sin 2x \cos x = \cos x$$
$$(2 \sin 2x - 1) \cos x = 0$$
$$\cos x = 0 \quad \text{or} \quad \sin 2x = \frac{1}{2}$$

If $0 \leq x < 2\pi$, then $0 \leq 2x < 4\pi$.

$x = \dfrac{\pi}{2}, \dfrac{3\pi}{2}$ or $2x = \dfrac{\pi}{6}, \dfrac{13\pi}{6}, \dfrac{5\pi}{6}, \dfrac{17\pi}{6}$

$$x = \dfrac{\pi}{12}, \dfrac{13\pi}{12}, \dfrac{5\pi}{12}, \dfrac{17\pi}{12}$$

The solution set is

$\{\dfrac{\pi}{12}, \dfrac{13\pi}{12}, \dfrac{5\pi}{12}, \dfrac{17\pi}{12}, \dfrac{\pi}{2}, \dfrac{3\pi}{2}\}$.

69. $\sin 4x + \sin 2x = 2 \cos x$

$2 \sin \dfrac{4x + 2x}{2} \cos \dfrac{4x - 2x}{2} = 2 \cos x$

$2 \sin 3x \cos x = 2 \cos x$

If $0 \leq x \leq 2\pi$, then $0 \leq 3x < 6\pi$.

$\cos x = 0$ or $\sin 3x = 1$

$x = \dfrac{\pi}{2}, \dfrac{3\pi}{2}$ or $3x = \dfrac{\pi}{2}, \dfrac{5\pi}{2}, \dfrac{9\pi}{2}$

$x = \dfrac{\pi}{6}, \dfrac{5\pi}{6}, \dfrac{3\pi}{6}$

The solution set is

$\{\dfrac{\pi}{6}, \dfrac{5\pi}{6}, \dfrac{\pi}{2}, \dfrac{3\pi}{2}\}$.

73. If $20 \sin \left(\dfrac{\pi t}{4} - \dfrac{\pi}{2}\right) = 0$,

then $\dfrac{\pi t}{4} - \dfrac{\pi}{2} = 0$

$\dfrac{\pi t}{4} = \dfrac{\pi}{2}$

$t = 2$.

The answer is 2 sec.

77. (a) We set L = 6074 and solve,

$6074 = 6077 - 31 \cos 2\theta$

$31 \cos 2\theta = 3$

$\cos 2\theta = \dfrac{3}{31} \approx 0.0967742$,

$2\theta \approx 84.45° + 360n$,   or

$276.55° + 360n$,

$\theta = 42.22°, 137.82°,$

$222.22°, 317.82°$

(b) If L = 6108, then

$6108 = 6077 - 31 \cos 2\theta$

$\cos 2\theta = \dfrac{-31}{31} = -1$

$2\theta = 180° + 360n°$

$\theta = 90°, 270°.$

(c) If L = 6080.2 we have

$6080.2 = 6077 - 31 \cos 2\theta$

$31 \cos 2\theta = -3.2$

$\cos 2\theta = \dfrac{-3.2}{31} \approx -0.103226$

$2\theta = \cos^{-1} (-0.103226)$, so

that 2θ is in quandrant II or III.

$2\theta \approx 95.925° + 360n°$, or

$2\theta \approx 264.075 + 360n$. Then

$\theta \approx 47.963° + 180n$, or

$\theta \approx 132.037° + 180n$.

Letting n = 0 and 1, and rounding to

the nearest degree, we have

$\theta = 48°, 132°, 228°, 312°$.

81. If $\arccos x = \arcsin \dfrac{3}{5}$, let

$A = \arcsin \dfrac{3}{5}$. Then we have

$\arccos x = A$

$x = \cos A$,

and $\cos A = \dfrac{4}{5}$.

The solution set is $\{\dfrac{4}{5}\}$.

85. Let $A = \sin^{-1} \dfrac{\sqrt{3}}{2}$. Then $\sin A = \dfrac{\sqrt{3}}{2}$

and $A = \dfrac{\pi}{3}$. The equation becomes

$\cos^{-1} x + 2 \sin^{-1} \dfrac{\sqrt{3}}{2} = \pi$

$\cos^{-1} x + 2\left(\dfrac{\pi}{3}\right) = \pi$

$\cos^{-1} x = \pi - \dfrac{2\pi}{3}$

$\cos^{-1} x = \dfrac{\pi}{3}$

$x = \cos \dfrac{\pi}{3}$

$x = \dfrac{1}{2}$.

The solution set is $\{\dfrac{1}{2}\}$.

89. Let $A = \cos^{-1} x$ and $B = \tan^{-1} x$.

Then we have $\cos A = x$ and $\tan B = x$.

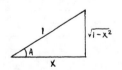 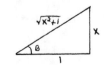

The equation becomes

$$A + B = \frac{\pi}{2},$$

and we can take the cosine of both sides to arrive at

$$\cos (A + B) = \cos \frac{\pi}{2}$$

$$\cos A \cos B - \sin A \sin B = 0$$

$$x \left(\frac{1}{\sqrt{x^2+1}}\right) - \left(\sqrt{1-x^2}\right)\left(\frac{x}{\sqrt{x^2+1}}\right) = 0$$

$$\frac{x - x\sqrt{1-x^2}}{\sqrt{1+x^2}} = 0$$

$$x(1 - \sqrt{1-x^2}) = 0$$

$$x = 0 \qquad \text{or} \qquad \sqrt{1-x^2} = 1$$

$$1 - x^2 = 1$$

$$x^2 = 0$$

$$x = 0.$$

The only solution is $x = 0$.

Chapter 7   Review Exercises

Selected Solutions

1. If $\cos x = \frac{3}{5}$ and x is in quadrant IV, then

    $$\sin x = \frac{-4}{5}$$

    $$\tan x = \frac{-4}{3}$$

    $$\cot x = \frac{-3}{4}$$

    $$\sec x = \frac{5}{3}$$

    $$\csc x = \frac{-5}{4}$$

5. For $x = \frac{\pi}{8}$, we have

    $$\sin \frac{\pi}{8} = \sin \frac{1}{2} \cdot \frac{\pi}{4} = \sqrt{\frac{1 - \cos \frac{\pi}{4}}{2}}$$

    $$= \frac{\sqrt{2 - \sqrt{2}}}{2},$$

    $$\cos \frac{\pi}{8} = \cos \frac{1}{2} \cdot \frac{\pi}{4} = \sqrt{\frac{1 + \cos \frac{\pi}{4}}{2}}$$

    $$= \frac{\sqrt{2 + \sqrt{2}}}{2}, \text{ and}$$

$$\tan \frac{\pi}{8} = \frac{\sqrt{2 - \sqrt{2}}}{\sqrt{2 + \sqrt{2}}}.$$

Alternatively, $\tan \frac{\pi}{8} = \sqrt{3 - 2\sqrt{2}}$.

9. $\cos 75° = \cos \frac{1}{2} \cdot 150°$

    $$= \sqrt{\frac{1 + \cos 150°}{2}}$$

    The match is (c)

13. $\csc x = \frac{1}{\sin x}$

     Use (a).

17. $\tan^2 x + 1 = \sec^2 x$

     $$= \frac{1}{\cos^2 x}$$

     Use (e).

21. $\tan^2 \theta (1 + \cot^2 \theta)$

     $$= \tan^2 \theta + \tan^2 \theta \cot^2 \theta$$

     $$= \tan^2 \theta + 1$$

     $$= \frac{\sin^2 \theta}{\cos^2 \theta} + 1$$

     $$= \frac{\sin^2 \theta + \cos^2 \theta}{\cos^2 \theta}$$

     $$= \frac{1}{\cos^2 \theta},$$

     which can simplify to

     $$= \sec^2 \theta$$

25. $\dfrac{\sin 2x}{\sin x} = \dfrac{2}{\sec x}$

     Proof: $\dfrac{\sin 2x}{\sin x} = \dfrac{2 \sin x \cos x}{\sin x}$

     $$= 2 \cos x$$

     $$= 2 \cdot \frac{1}{\sec x}$$

27. $\dfrac{2 \tan B}{\sin 2B} = \sec^2 B$

     Proof: $\dfrac{2 \tan B}{\sin 2B} \qquad \dfrac{2 \sin B}{\sin 2B \cos B}$

     $$= \frac{2 \sin B}{2 \sin B \cos B \cdot \cos B}$$

     $$= \frac{1}{\cos^2 B}$$

     $$= \sec^2 B$$

29. $1 + \tan^2 \alpha = 2 \tan \alpha \csc 2\alpha$

Proof: $2 \tan \alpha \csc 2\alpha$

$= \dfrac{2 \tan \alpha}{\sin 2\alpha}$

$= \sec^2 \alpha$, from exercise 27,

$= 1 + \tan^2 \alpha$

31. $\dfrac{\sin t}{1 - \cos t} = \cot \dfrac{t}{2}$

Proof:

$\cos \dfrac{t}{2} = \dfrac{\cos \dfrac{t}{2}}{\sin \dfrac{t}{2}} = \dfrac{\sqrt{\dfrac{1 + \cos t}{2}}}{\sqrt{\dfrac{1 - \cos t}{2}}}$

$\qquad = \dfrac{\sqrt{1 + \cos t}}{\sqrt{1 - \cos t}} \cdot \dfrac{\sqrt{1 - \cos t}}{\sqrt{1 - \cos t}}$

$\qquad = \dfrac{\sqrt{1 - \cos^2 t}}{1 - \cos t}$

$\qquad = \dfrac{\sin t}{1 - \cos t}$

33. $\dfrac{2 \cot x}{\tan 2x} = \csc^2 x - 2$

Proof: $\dfrac{2 \cot x}{\tan 2x} = \dfrac{2 \dfrac{\cos x}{\sin x}}{\dfrac{\sin 2x}{\cos 2x}}$

$\qquad = \dfrac{2 \cos x}{\sin x} \cdot \dfrac{\cos 2x}{\sin 2x}$

$\qquad = \dfrac{2 \cos x \cos 2x}{2 \sin^2 x \cos x}$

$\qquad = \dfrac{\cos 2x}{\sin^2 x}$

$\qquad = \dfrac{1 - 2 \sin^2 x}{\sin^2 x}$

$\qquad = \dfrac{1}{\sin^2 x} - \dfrac{2 \sin^2 x}{\sin^2 x}$

$\qquad = \csc^2 x - 2$

37. $2 \tan x \csc 2x - \tan^2 x = 1$

Proof: $2 \tan x \csc 2x - \tan^2 x$

$= \dfrac{2 \sin x}{\cos x \sin 2x} - \dfrac{\sin^2 x}{\cos^2 x}$

$= \dfrac{2 \sin x}{2 \sin x \cos^2 x} - \dfrac{\sin^2 x}{\cos^2 x}$

$= \dfrac{1}{\cos^2 x} - \dfrac{\sin^2 x}{\cos^2 x}$

$= \dfrac{1 - \sin^2 x}{\cos^2 x} = \dfrac{\cos^2 x}{\cos^2 x}$

$= 1$

41. Using the identity

$\cos^2 A = 2 \cos^2 A - 1$, which gives

$\cos^2 A = \dfrac{1}{2} + \dfrac{1}{2} \cos 2A$, we have

$\cos^4 \theta = (\cos^2 \theta)^2$

$\qquad = (\dfrac{1}{2} + \dfrac{1}{2} \cos 2\theta)^2$

$\qquad = \dfrac{1}{4} + \dfrac{1}{2} \cos 2\theta + \dfrac{1}{4} \cos^2 2\theta$

$\qquad = \dfrac{1}{4} + \dfrac{1}{2} \cos 2\theta + \dfrac{1}{4}(\dfrac{1}{2} + \dfrac{1}{2} \cos 4\theta)$

$\qquad = \dfrac{1}{4} + \dfrac{1}{2} \cos 2\theta + \dfrac{1}{8} + \dfrac{1}{8} \cos 4\theta$

$\qquad = \dfrac{3}{8} + \dfrac{1}{2} \cos 2\theta + \dfrac{1}{8} \cos 4\theta.$

45. $\tan 8k - \tan 8k \cdot \tan^2 4k = 2 \tan 4k$

Proof: $\tan 8k - \tan 8k \cdot \tan^2 4k$

$= \tan 8k(1 - \tan^2 4k)$

$= \tan (2 \cdot 4k)(1 - \tan^2 4k)$

$= \dfrac{2 \tan 4k}{1 - \tan^2 4k} \cdot (1 - \tan^2 4k)$

$= 2 \tan 4k.$

49. To prove $\tan 2\beta - \sec 2\beta = \dfrac{\tan \beta - 1}{\tan \beta + 1}$,

we note that

$\sec 2\beta = \dfrac{1}{\cos 2\beta} = \dfrac{1}{\cos^2 \beta - \sin^2 \beta}$

$\qquad = \dfrac{1}{\cos^2 \beta (1 - \dfrac{\sin^2 \beta}{\cos^2 \beta})}$

$\qquad = \dfrac{\sec^2 \beta}{1 - \tan^2 \beta}$

$\qquad = \dfrac{1 + \tan^2 \beta}{1 - \tan^2 \beta}.$

Then, we can see that

$\tan 2\beta - \sec 2\beta = \dfrac{2 \tan \beta}{1 - \tan^2 \beta} - \dfrac{1 + \tan^2 \beta}{1 - \tan^2 \beta}$

$\qquad = \dfrac{-(\tan^2 \beta - 2 \tan \beta + 1)}{1 - \tan^2 \beta}$

$\qquad = \dfrac{\tan^2 \beta - 2 \tan \beta + 1}{\tan^2 \beta - 1}$

$\qquad = \dfrac{(\tan \beta - 1)^2}{(\tan \beta - 1)(\tan \beta + 1)}$

$\qquad = \dfrac{\tan \beta - 1}{\tan \beta + 1}$

53. $\sin^2 x = 1$, $0 \le x < 2\pi$

$\sin x = 1$ or $\sin x = -1$

$x = \dfrac{\pi}{2}, \dfrac{3\pi}{2}$

The solution set is $\{\dfrac{\pi}{2}, \dfrac{3\pi}{2}\}$.

57. $\sec^4 2x = 4$

If $0 \le x < 2\pi$, then $0 \le 2x < 4\pi$,
and $\sec^2 2x = 2$ or $\sec^2 2x = -2$

$1 + \tan^2 2x = 2$ not possible

$\tan^2 2x = 1$

$\tan 2x = 1$ or $\tan 2x = -1$.

Hence,

$2x = \dfrac{\pi}{4}, \dfrac{5\pi}{4}, \dfrac{9\pi}{4}, \dfrac{13\pi}{4}$

$2x = \dfrac{3\pi}{4}, \dfrac{7\pi}{4}, \dfrac{11\pi}{4}, \dfrac{15\pi}{4}$, or

$x = \dfrac{\pi}{8}, \dfrac{5\pi}{8}, \dfrac{9\pi}{8}, \dfrac{13\pi}{8}, \dfrac{3\pi}{8}, \dfrac{7\pi}{8}, \dfrac{11\pi}{8}, \dfrac{15\pi}{8}$

The solution set is

$\{\dfrac{\pi}{8}, \dfrac{5\pi}{8}, \dfrac{9\pi}{8}, \dfrac{13\pi}{8}, \dfrac{3\pi}{8}, \dfrac{7\pi}{8}, \dfrac{11\pi}{8}, \dfrac{15\pi}{8}\}$.

61. If $\cos 2x + \cos x = 0$, then

$2\cos^2 x - 1 + \cos x = 0$

$2\cos^2 x + \cos x - 1 = 0$

$(2\cos x - 1)(\cos x + 1) = 0$

$\cos x = \dfrac{1}{2}$ or $\cos x = -1$

$x = \dfrac{\pi}{3}, \dfrac{5\pi}{3}$ or $x = \pi$.

The solution set is $\{\dfrac{\pi}{3}, \pi, \dfrac{5\pi}{3}\}$.

65. If $\sin^2 \theta + 3\sin \theta + 2 = 0$, then

$(\sin \theta + 1)(\sin \theta + 2) = 0$

$\sin \theta = -1$ or $\sin \theta = 2$

$\theta = 270°$ not possible.

The solution set is $\{270°\}$.

69. (a) If $\dfrac{c_1}{c_2} = .752$ and $\theta_2 = 90°$,

then the "critical angle" θ, is
found by

$\dfrac{\sin \theta_1}{\sin 90°} = .752$

$\sin \theta_1 = .752$

$\theta_1 = \sin^{-1} (.752)$

$\theta_1 \approx 48.8°$.

(b) The light beam remains completely
under water.

73. We can see from the figure in the
text, considering the triangle ACD,
that

(A) $\tan 15° = \dfrac{AC}{CD} = \dfrac{1}{2 + \sqrt{3}}$.

Using the same triangle, ACD, and
labeling the angle DAB = α,

$\tan (60° + \alpha) = \dfrac{CD}{AC} = 2 + \sqrt{3}$

$\dfrac{\tan 60° + \tan \alpha}{1 - \tan 60° \tan \alpha} = 2 + \sqrt{3}$

$\dfrac{\sqrt{3} + \tan \alpha}{1 - \sqrt{3} \tan \alpha} = 2 + \sqrt{3}$

$\sqrt{3} + \tan \alpha = (2 + \sqrt{3})(1 - \sqrt{3} \tan \alpha)$

$\sqrt{3} + \tan \alpha = (2 + \sqrt{3}) - (2 + \sqrt{3})\sqrt{3} \tan \alpha$

$\tan \alpha + (2\sqrt{3} + 3) \tan \alpha = (2 + \sqrt{3}) - \sqrt{3}$

$\tan \alpha (4 + 2\sqrt{3}) = 2$

$\tan \alpha = \dfrac{2}{4 + 2\sqrt{3}}$

(B) $\tan \alpha = \dfrac{1}{2 + \sqrt{3}}$.

Comparing this with (A) above and
realizing that $0 < A < 90°$, we have
$\tan \alpha = \tan 15°$, and hence, $\alpha = 15°$.

77. We know that length EC is $2 - \sqrt{3}$
and that triangle AEC is a right
triangle. Also, the length AC is
1 so that, letting length AE = r, we
have

$r^2 = 1^2 + (2 - \sqrt{3})^2$

$r^2 = 1 + 4 - 4\sqrt{3} + 3$

(A) $r^2 = 8 - 4\sqrt{3} = 4(2 - \sqrt{3})$

$r = 2\sqrt{2 - \sqrt{3}}$,

and this is $\sqrt{6} - \sqrt{2}$. The fact that
$r = 2\sqrt{2 - \sqrt{3}} = \sqrt{6} - \sqrt{2}$ can be seen
from $(\sqrt{6} - \sqrt{2})^2 = 6 - 2\sqrt{12} + 2$

$= 8 - 4\sqrt{3} = r^2$ in (A).

81. (a) Let α and β be numbers with

$$\sin(\alpha + \beta) = \sin(\alpha - \beta)$$

$$\sin\alpha\cos\beta + \cos\alpha\sin\beta$$
$$= \sin\alpha\cos\beta -$$
$$\cos\alpha\sin\beta$$

$$2\cos\alpha\sin\beta = 0$$

$$\cos\alpha = 0 \quad\text{or}\quad \sin\beta = 0$$

$$\alpha = \frac{\pi}{2} + 2n\pi \quad\text{or}\quad \beta = 0 + n\pi,$$

$$\alpha = \frac{3\pi}{2} + 2n\pi \qquad n \text{ an integer}$$

n an integer.

Hence, either α is an odd multiple of $\frac{\pi}{2}$ or β is a multiple of π, or both.

(b) If $\cos(\alpha + \beta) = \cos(\alpha - \beta)$, then

$$\cos\alpha\cos\beta - \sin\alpha\sin\beta$$
$$= \cos\alpha\cos\beta + \sin\alpha\sin\beta$$
$$2\sin\alpha\sin\beta = 0$$

$$\sin\alpha = 0 \quad\text{or}\quad \sin\beta = 0$$

$$\alpha = n\pi \quad\text{or}\quad \beta = n\pi.$$

Hence, either α is a multiple of or π is a multiple of π, or both.

(c) If $\tan(\alpha + \beta) = \tan(\alpha - \beta)$, then

$$\frac{\tan\alpha + \tan\beta}{1 - \tan\alpha\tan\beta} = \frac{\tan\alpha - \tan\beta}{1 + \tan\alpha\tan\beta}$$

$$(\tan\alpha + \tan\beta)(1 + \tan\alpha\tan\beta)$$
$$= (\tan\alpha - \tan\beta)(1 - \tan\alpha\tan\beta)$$

$$\tan\alpha + \tan\beta + \tan^2\alpha\tan\beta +$$
$$\tan\alpha\tan^2\beta$$

$$= \tan\alpha - \tan\beta - \tan^2\alpha\tan\beta +$$
$$\tan\alpha\tan^2\beta$$

$$2\tan\beta + 2\tan^2\alpha\tan\beta = 0$$

$$2\tan\beta(1 + \tan^2\alpha) = 0$$

$$\tan\beta = 0 \quad\text{or}\quad 1 + \tan^2\alpha = 0$$

$$\beta = 0 + n\pi \quad\text{or}\quad \text{impossible}$$

n any integer.

Hence, β is a multiple of π.

Chapter 7 Test

1. Find sin s if tan s = 2, with s in quadrant III.

2. Find cos t if sin t = -3/8 and sec t > 0.

Use the fundamental identities to find the values of the remaining functions for the following.

3. $\cos \theta = 1/5$, θ in quadrant I   4. $\tan \theta = -1/4$, θ in quadrant IV

For the following, get an equivalent expression with only sines and cosines, and then simplify it.

5. $\sec^2 t - \tan^2 t$ 6. $\csc^2 \gamma + \sec^2 \gamma$

7. $\cot^2 \alpha - \csc^2 \alpha$ 8. $1 - \cot^4 s$

9. Write sin s in terms of cot s.

Verify each identity.

10. $\dfrac{(\sec \theta - \tan \theta)^2 + 1}{\sec \theta \csc \theta - \tan \theta \csc \theta} = 2 \tan \theta$ 11. $\dfrac{\cos \beta + 1}{\tan^2 \beta} = \dfrac{\cos \beta}{\sec \beta - 1}$

12. $\dfrac{\csc \theta + \cot \theta}{\tan \theta + \sin \theta} = \cot \theta \csc \theta$ 13. $\dfrac{\tan^2 \theta}{\cos^2 \alpha} - \dfrac{\tan^2 \alpha}{\cos^2 \theta} = \dfrac{\sin^2 \theta - \sin^2 \alpha}{\cos^2 \alpha \cos^2 \theta}$

Write each of the following in terms of the cofunction of a complementary angle.

14. $\cos 50°43'$ 15. $\cot \pi/4$

Use sum and difference identities for cosine to find the following without using tables or a calculator.

16. $\cos 105°$ 17. $\cos 5\pi/12$ 18. $\cos -7\pi/12$

For each of the following, find cos (s + t) and cos (s - t).

19. sin s = 4/5 and cos t = 12/13,   20.   sin s = -8/17 and cos t = -8/17,
     s in quadrant IV and t in I   s and t in quadrant III

For each of the following, find sin (s + t) and tan (s - t).

21. sin s = -4/5 and cos t = 12/13,   22.   sin s = -8/17 and cos t = -8/17,
     s in quadrant III and t in IV   s and t in quadrant III

Use the reduction identity to simplify each of the following for angles between 0° and 360°. Find angles to the nearest degree.

23. -8 sin x + 15 cos x   24.   -4 sin x + 3 cos x

Find each of the following.

25. sin x, given cos 2x = 1/2 and x in quadrant I

26. tan $\alpha/2$, given sin α = 1/4 and $\pi/2 < \alpha < \pi$

Use the identities for the double or half angles to find the sine for the following angles.

27. $22\frac{1}{2}°$ 28. $13\pi/12$

Find the values of the six trigonometric functions for the following.

29. θ, given cos 2θ = 3/5 and $0 < \theta < \pi/2$

30.   t/2, given cos t = -5/9 and tan t > 0

Find all solutions for the following equations.   Give only solutions in the interval [0, 2π).

31.   sin 2x = 1

32.   sin x = sin 2x

33. $2 \cos^2 x + \cos x = 0$

34. $2 \cos^4 x = \cos^2 x$

35. $\sqrt{3} \cot^2 x = \cot x$

36.   sin x = cos x/2

Give all solutions in degrees for the following equations.

37. $15 \sin^2 x - 4 \sin x = 3$

38.   sin x/2 = cos x/2

39. $2 \cos^2 x - \sin x = 1$

40.   tan x = sec x

(Answers for this test are on page 363.)

CHAPTER 8   Applications; De Moivre's
            Theorem

Section 8.1 Right-Triangle Applications

Additional Examples

Example 1 At a point 45-feet from the
    bottom of a tree, the angle of
    elevation to the top of the tree is
    32°. How tall is the tree?
Solution As shown in the sketch,

$$\tan 32° = \frac{x}{45}$$
$$x = 45 \tan 32°$$
$$= 45(.6249)$$
$$\approx 28.$$

The tree is 28 feet tall, to two
significant figures.

Example 2 A small plane travels on a
    bearing of 48° for 210 miles. The
    plane then turns on a bearing of
    138° and travels awhile. Finally
    it turns again and travels on a
    bearing of 279° until it reaches the
    starting point. How far was the
    entire trip?
Solution

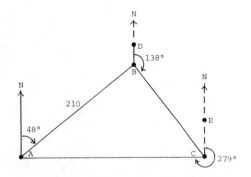

The sketch shows the given information, with point A as the starting
point. We must find lengths BC and

and AC. Since angle ABD is
180° - 48° = 132°, angle
ABC = 360° - 138° - 132° = 90°.
Also, angle BCE = 180° - 138° = 42°,
so angle ACB = 360° - 42° - 279° = 39°.
Then

$$\sin 39° = \frac{210}{AC}$$
$$AC = \frac{210}{\sin 39°} = 334,$$

and $\tan 39° = \dfrac{210}{BC}$

$$BC = \frac{210}{\tan 39°} = 259.$$

The length of the entire trip was
210 + 334 + 259 = 803 miles

Selected Solutions

1. If B = 73° and C = 90°, then A = 17°,
    Then,

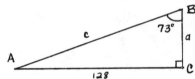

$$\sin 73° = \frac{128}{c}$$
$$c = \frac{128}{\sin 73°}$$
$$c \approx 133.85 \text{ or } c = 134.$$

Also,

$$\sin A = \frac{a}{c},$$
$$\sin 17° = \frac{a}{134},$$
$$a = 134 \sin 17°$$
$$a \approx 39.2, \text{ or } a = 39.$$

Hence, A = 17°, C = 90°, a = 39,
and c = 134.

5. If a = 18.9, c = 46.3, and C = 90°,
    then $a^2 + b^2 = c^2$, or $b^2 = c^2 - a^2$,
    gives

$$b^2 = (46.3)^2 - (18.9)^2$$
$$= 2143.69 - 357.21$$

$b^2 = 1786.48$

$b = 42.2667$, or $b = 42.3$.

Then $\sin A = \dfrac{a}{c}$ gives

$$\sin A = \frac{18.9}{46.3} = 0.4082$$

$$A = \sin^{-1}(0.4082)$$

$$= 24.0923°$$

or $A = 24°6'$.

Since $A + B = 90°$, we have

$B = 65°54'$.

Note: If we round to the nearest

10 minutes, we let $A = 24°10'$ and

$B = 65°50'$.

9. If $B = 39°09'$ and $C = 90°$, then

$A = 50°51'$.

We have

$$\sin B = \frac{b}{c},$$

with $c = .6231$,

$b = .6231 \sin 39°09'$

$b = .6231 \sin 39.15°$

$b \approx .393396$, or $b = .3934$ meters.

also,

$\sin A = \dfrac{a}{c}$, so that

$a = .6231 \sin 50°51'$

$a = .6231 \sin 50.85°$

$a \approx .4832114$, or

$a = .4832$ meters.

13. If $B = 42.432°$ and $C = 90°$, then

$A = 47.568°$.

Given $a = 157.49$ m, we have

$$c = \frac{157.49}{\sin 47.568°}$$

$c = 213.37835$, or

$c = 213.38$ meters.

Also,

$\tan A = \dfrac{a}{b}$ gives $b = \dfrac{a}{\tan A}$,

$$b = \frac{157.49}{\tan 47.568°}$$

$b = 143.97$ meters.

17. Let $C = 90°$. If $b = 173.921$ and

$c = 208.543$, then $a^2 + b^2 = c^2$ gives

$$a^2 = (208.543)^2 - (173.921)^2$$

$$a^2 = 43{,}490.183 - 30{,}248.514$$

$$a^2 = 13{,}241.669$$

$$a \approx 115.072 \text{ meters.}$$

Also, we have

$$\sin B = \frac{b}{c}$$

$$b = c \sin B$$

$$\sin B = \frac{b}{c} = \frac{173.921}{208.543}$$

$$\sin B = .8339815$$

$$B = 56.5099°.$$

Then $A = 90° - B = 43.4901°$.

21. The angle θ is given by

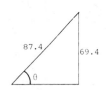

$$\theta = \sin^{-1}\frac{69.4}{87.4}$$

$$\theta = 52°30'.$$

25.

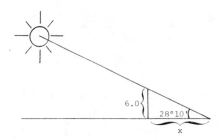

The length of the shadow is

$x = 6.0/\tan 28°10' \approx 11$ feet.

29. The angle of depression α equals

the angle of elevation α shown in

the figure.

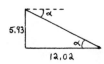

Hence,

$$\tan \alpha = \frac{5.93}{12.02}$$

$$\tan \alpha = .4933444$$

$$\alpha \simeq 26.25917°$$

or $\alpha \simeq 26°16'$.

We round this to $\alpha = 26°20'$.

33.

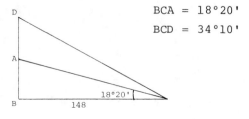

$$BCA = 18°20'$$
$$BCD = 34°10'$$

$$\frac{AB}{148} = \tan 18°20' \quad \text{and} \quad \frac{DB}{148} = \tan 34°10'$$

height: $DA = DB - AB$

$$= 148(\tan 34°10' - \tan 18°20')$$

height = 51.4 meters.

37.

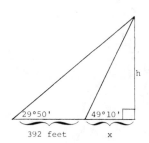

$$h = x \tan 49°10'$$

$$h = (x + 392)\tan 29°50'$$

$$x \tan 49°10' = x \tan 29°50' + 392 \tan 29°50'$$

$$x = \frac{392 \tan 29°50'}{\tan 49°10' - \tan 29°50'}$$

$$x = \frac{392(.5735)}{1.157 - .5735} = 385$$

$$h = x \tan 49°10' = 385(1.157)$$
$$= 446 \text{ feet.}$$

39.

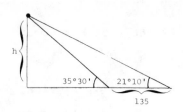

$$h = \frac{135}{\cot 21°10' - \cot 35°30'} = 114 \text{ feet.}$$

41.

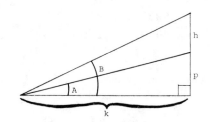

$$h = 28.0 \tan 18°10'$$

$$x + h = 28.0 \tan 27°10'$$

$$x = 28.0(\tan 27°10' - \tan 18°10')$$

$$x = 5.18 \text{ meters.}$$

43.

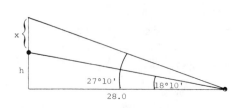

$$p = k \tan A$$

$$h + p = k \tan B$$

$$h = k(\tan B - \tan A).$$

45. We have

$$d_1 = 20.0 \text{ mph} \times 5 \text{ hours} = 100 \text{ miles.}$$

and $d_2 = 24.0 \text{ mph} \times 5 \text{ hours} = 120 \text{ miles.}$

The angle between $28°10'$ and $118°10'$ is $90°$.

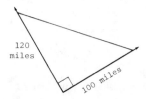

The distance is

$$d = \sqrt{120^2 + 100^2} = 10\sqrt{244}$$

$$= 20\sqrt{61} \text{ miles or } d \approx 156 \text{ miles.}$$

47.

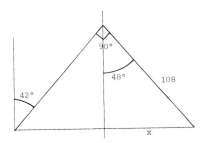

$$d = \sqrt{60^2 + 108^2} = 12\sqrt{106},$$

$$\text{or } d \approx 124 \text{ miles.}$$

(or 120 miles, to two significant digits)

49.

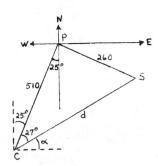

If we consider the triange PSC, it is a right triangle with $P = 90°$. We also have $\tan C = \dfrac{260}{510}$

$$\tan C = .5098$$

$$C = 27°.$$

Hence, $25° + 27° + \alpha = 90°$, or $\alpha = 38°$

53. We have $\tan A = \dfrac{\text{face diagonal}}{\text{cell edge}}$

$$\tan A = \dfrac{4.24 \times 10^{-8}}{3.00 \times 10^{-8}}$$

$$\tan A = 1.413333$$

$$A \approx 54.72°, \text{ or}$$

$$A \approx 54°43'.$$

57. Let $\theta = \cos^{-1} 1/4$.
Then $\cos \theta = 1/4$.
Completing the tri-
angle gives $\sin \theta = \dfrac{\sqrt{15}}{4}$.

Section 8.2   Oblique Triangles and the
Law of Sines

Additional Examples

Example 1 Solve triangle ABC given
c = 31.5, b = 50.8, and C = 33°10'.
Solution Begin by using the law of
sines to find angle B.

$$\frac{b}{\sin B} = \frac{c}{\sin C}$$

$$\frac{50.8}{\sin B} = \frac{31.5}{\sin 33°10'}$$

$$\sin B = \frac{50.8 \sin 33°10'}{31.5}$$

$$\sin B = 0.8823$$

$$B = 62°00' \text{ (to the nearest ten minutes)}$$

However, another triangle is possible, with sin B = .8823 and B = 180° - 62° = 118°00'. Let $B_1 = 62°00'$ and $B_2 = 118°00'$.

Since B_2 is larger, find A_2 next:

$$A_2 = 180° - 118°00' - 33°10' = 28°50'.$$

Now find a_2.

$$\frac{a_2}{\sin A_2} = \frac{c}{\sin C}$$

$$\frac{a_2}{\sin 28°50'} = \frac{31.5}{\sin 33°10'}$$

$$a_2 = \frac{31.5 \sin 28°50'}{\sin 33°10'}$$

$$a_2 = 27.8$$

Now solve triangle $A_1 B_1 C$.

$$A_1 = 180° - 62°00' - 33°10'$$

$$= 84°50'$$

$$\frac{a_1}{\sin A_1} = \frac{c}{\sin C}$$

$$\frac{a_1}{\sin 84°50'} = \frac{31.5}{\sin 33°10'}$$

$$a_1 = 57.3$$

Example 2   A surveyor wishes to measure the distance between points M and N, which cannot be measured directly because of a large rocky outcropping. From point M she walks 160 meters at an angle of 52°20' with the line MN to a point P. She then walks 130 meters to point N. Find the required distance.

Solution   See the sketch. We first

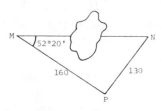

find angle N, then angle P, and then MN, using the law of sines twice.

$$\frac{\sin N}{160} = \frac{\sin 52°20'}{130}$$

$$\sin N = .9743$$

$$N = 77°00'$$

$$P = 180° - M - N$$

$$= 180° - 52°20' - 77°00'$$

$$= 50°40'.$$

$$\frac{MN}{\sin P} = \frac{130}{\sin 52°20'}$$

$$\frac{MN}{\sin 50°40'} = \frac{130}{\sin 52°20'}$$

$$MN = 127$$

The required distance is 127 meters.

Example 3   Find the area of a triangle with A = 27°15', b = 41.27 m, c = 16.53 m.

Solution   Use the area formula,

$$K = \frac{1}{2} bc \sin A$$

$$K = \frac{1}{2}(41.27)(16.53)\sin 27°15'$$

$$K \approx 156.2 \text{ square meters}$$

Selected Solutions

1.   If A = 46°30' and B = 52°50', then C = 80°40'.

Using $\frac{b}{\sin B} = \frac{a}{\sin A}$, with b = 87.3, we have

$$a = \frac{b \sin A}{\sin B} = \frac{87.3 \sin 46.5°}{\sin 52.833°}$$

$$a \approx 79.5 \text{ mm}.$$

also,

$$\frac{c}{\sin C} = \frac{b}{\sin B} \text{ gives}$$

$$c = \frac{87.3 \sin 80.667°}{\sin 52.833°}$$

$$c \approx 108.1 \text{ mm}.$$

5.   If A = 68.41° and B = 54.23°, then C = 57.36°.

Using $\frac{b}{\sin B} = \frac{a}{\sin A}$, with a = 12.75, we have

$$b = \frac{12.75 \sin 54.23°}{\sin 68.41°}$$

$$b \approx 11.13 \text{ ft}.$$

Also, $\frac{c}{\sin C} = \frac{a}{\sin A}$,

$$c = \frac{12.75 \sin 57.36°}{\sin 68.41°},$$

$$c \approx 11.55 \text{ ft}.$$

9.   If B = 20°50' and C = 103°10', then A = 56°00'. Since AC is the side opposite angle B, let b = AC = 132. Then we have (using a = BC)

$$\frac{a}{\sin A} = \frac{b}{\sin B}$$

$$a = \frac{b \sin A}{\sin B} = \frac{132 \sin 56°}{\sin 20.833°}$$

$$a \approx 307.7, \text{ or } a \approx 308 \text{ ft}.$$

Also,

$$\frac{c}{\sin C} = \frac{b}{\sin B}$$

$$c = \frac{b \sin C}{\sin B} = \frac{132 \sin 103.167°}{\sin 20.833°}$$

$$\approx 361 \text{ ft}.$$

13. If $B = 42.88°$ and $C = 102.40°$, then $A = 34.72°$. Given $b = 3974$ ft, we have

$$\frac{a}{\sin A} = \frac{b}{\sin B}$$

$$a = \frac{b \sin A}{\sin B} = \frac{3974 \sin 34.72°}{\sin 42.88°}$$

$$a \approx 3326.34, \text{ or } a \approx 3326 \text{ ft.}$$

Also,

$$\frac{c}{\sin C} = \frac{b}{\sin B}$$

$$c = \frac{b \sin C}{\sin B} = \frac{3974 \sin 102.40°}{\sin 42.88°}$$

$$c \approx 5704 \text{ ft.}$$

17. Using $\frac{a}{\sin A} = \frac{b}{\sin B}$, we have

$$\sin B = \frac{b \sin A}{a}$$

$$= \frac{41.5 \sin 29.7°}{27.2}$$

$$\sin B \approx 0.7559388$$

$$B = \sin^{-1}(.7559388),$$

so that

$$B_1 = 40.1° \text{ or } \qquad B_2 = 139.9°,$$

then

$$C_1 = 101.2°, \text{ while } C_2 = 19.4°.$$

Note that $b > a$ and $a > b \sin A$ since $\frac{b \sin A}{a} < 1$. This implies two solutions.

21. If we try to use the law of sines we have

$$\frac{b}{\sin B} = \frac{a}{\sin A}$$

$$\sin A = \frac{a \sin B}{b} = \frac{859 \sin 74.3°}{783}$$

$$\sin A = 1.0561331.$$

It is impossible to have the $\sin A > 1$. Hence, there is no such triangle.

25. Using $\frac{c}{\sin C} = \frac{a}{\sin A}$ we have

$$\sin A = \frac{a \sin C}{c}$$

$$= \frac{372.9 \sin 129°18'}{416.7}$$

$$\sin A = 0.6925006.$$

Since $c > a$, there is one solution.

Hence, $A = \sin^{-1}(.6925006) \approx 43°50'$.

Then we have $B = 180° - (A + C)$

$$\approx 6°52'.$$

29. Using $\frac{b}{\sin B} = \frac{c}{\sin C}$ we have

$$\sin C = \frac{c \sin B}{b} = \frac{145 \sin 72.2°}{78.3}$$

$$\approx 1.7632.$$

This is impossible. There are no solutions.

33. Using $\frac{b}{\sin B} = \frac{a}{\sin A}$, we have

$$\sin A = \frac{a \sin B}{b}$$

$$= \frac{7540 \sin 32° 50'}{5180}$$

$$\sin A = 0.7892142.$$

This is true for $A_1 = 52.112°$ and for $A_2 = 127.888°$, or $A_1 \approx 52°10'$ $A_2 = 127°50'$. There are two triangles since $a > b$.

We have $C_1 = 180° - (A_1 + B) = 95°00'$, and using $\frac{c_1}{\sin C_1} = \frac{b}{\sin B}$ gives

$$c_1 = \frac{b \sin C_1}{\sin B} = \frac{5180 \sin 95°}{\sin 32.833°},$$

or $c_1 \approx 9517.5$ or $c_1 \approx 9520$ m.

In the second triangle we have $C_2 = 180° - (A_2 + B) = 19°20'$ and

$$\frac{c_2}{\sin C_2} = \frac{b}{\sin B} \text{ gives}$$

$$c_2 = \frac{b \sin C_2}{\sin B} = \frac{5180 \sin 19.333°}{\sin 32.833°}$$

$$c_2 = 3162.86, \text{ or } c_2 \approx 3160 \text{ cm.}$$

37. Given B, b, and a with a > b,
    implies there will be two triangles.
    Using

    $\dfrac{b}{\sin B} = \dfrac{a}{\sin A}$ gives

    $\sin A = \dfrac{a \sin B}{b} = \dfrac{29.81 \sin 39.68°}{23.76}$

    $\sin A = 0.80108,$
    and hence,

    $A_1 = 53.23°$ and $A_2 = 126.77°.$

    Thus, we have

    $C_1 = 180° - (A_1 + B)$ and $C_2 = 180° - (A_2 + B)$

    $C_1 = 87.09°$ and $C_2 = 13.55°$

    Also, we have

    $\dfrac{c_1}{\sin C_1} = \dfrac{b}{\sin B}$ and $\dfrac{c_2}{\sin C_2} = \dfrac{b}{\sin B}$

    $c_1 = \sin C_1 \left(\dfrac{b}{\sin B}\right)$ and $c_2 = \sin C_2 \left(\dfrac{b}{\sin B}\right)$

    $c_1 \approx 37.16$ m   and $c_2 \approx 8.72$ m.

41.

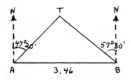

    We see that in the triangle ABT
    that A = 42°40', B = 32°30', and
    Hence T = 104°50'. Then, letting b
    be the distance from A to the
    transmitter T, we have

    $\dfrac{b}{\sin B} = \dfrac{3.46}{\sin T}$

    $b = \dfrac{3.46 \sin 32.5°}{\sin 104.833°}$

    $b \approx 1.92314,$ or 1.92 miles.

45.

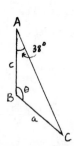

    From the figure in the text we
    can see that c = 1.6 + 2.7 = 4.3

and that a = 1.6 + 3.6 = 5.2.
Hence,

$\dfrac{a}{\sin A} = \dfrac{c}{\sin C}$

$\sin C = \dfrac{c \sin A}{a} = \dfrac{4.3 \sin 38°}{5.2}$

$\sin C \approx 0.5091047,$
and since 0° < C < 90°,
    C ≈ 30.6°. Hence
    θ = 180° - (A + C), or
    θ ≈ 180° - 68.6°
    θ ≈ 111.4°, or θ = 111°,
rounded to the nearest degree.

49.

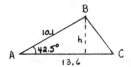

We can find the area of the triangle
by the formula A = $\frac{1}{2}$ (base)(height).
Using base = AC = 13.6 and height = h,
we see that sin A = $\dfrac{h}{10.1}$, or

h = 10.1 sin 42.5°. Hence,
h ≈ 6.82346, or h ≈ 6.82. Thus,
A = $\frac{1}{2}$(13.6)(6.82) = 46.376,
or
A = 46.4 m^2.

53. We use A = $\frac{1}{2}$ (base)(height), where
    base = 32.67 and height = h = 52.89
    sin 56.8° as in exercise 49. Hence,
    A = $\frac{1}{2}$(32.67)(52.89) sin 56.80°
    A ≈ 722.92935 in^2, or
    A ≈ 722.93 in^2.

57. We use A = $\frac{1}{2}$bh, with b = 16.1 and
    h = 15.2 sin 125°. Hence,
    A = $\frac{1}{2}$(16.1)(15.2) sin 125°
    A ≈ 100.2314, or
    A ≈ 100 m^2.

59. $\dfrac{a + b}{b} = \dfrac{\sin A + \sin B}{\sin B}$

Proof: $\dfrac{a}{\sin A} = \dfrac{b}{\sin B}$

or $\qquad \dfrac{a}{b} = \dfrac{\sin A}{\sin A}$

$\qquad \dfrac{a}{b} + 1 = \dfrac{\sin A}{\sin B} + 1$

$\qquad \dfrac{a + b}{b} = \dfrac{\sin A + \sin B}{\sin B}$

60. $\dfrac{a - b}{a + b} = \dfrac{\sin A - \sin B}{\sin A + \sin B}$

Proof: $\dfrac{a}{\sin A} = \dfrac{b}{\sin B}$

$\qquad \dfrac{a}{b} = \dfrac{\sin A}{\sin B}$

$\qquad \dfrac{a}{b} - 1 = \dfrac{\sin A}{\sin B} - 1$

$\qquad \dfrac{a - b}{b} = \dfrac{\sin A - \sin B}{\sin B}$

Therefore, $\dfrac{a - b}{a + b} = \dfrac{\dfrac{a - b}{b}}{\dfrac{a + b}{b}}$

$\qquad = \dfrac{\dfrac{\sin A - \sin B}{\sin B}}{\dfrac{\sin A + \sin B}{\sin B}}$

$\qquad = \dfrac{\sin A - \sin B}{\sin A + \sin B}.$

61. $\dfrac{a + b}{c} = \dfrac{\cos \frac{1}{2}(A - B)}{\sin \frac{1}{2} C}$

Proof: $\dfrac{a}{c} = \dfrac{\sin A}{\sin C}$ and $\dfrac{b}{c} = \dfrac{\sin B}{\sin C}$

$\dfrac{a + b}{c} = \dfrac{\sin A + \sin B}{\sin C}$

$\qquad = \dfrac{2 \sin \left(\frac{A + B}{2}\right) \cos \left(\frac{A - B}{2}\right)}{\sin(180° - (A + B))}$

$\qquad = \dfrac{2 \sin \left(\frac{A + B}{2}\right) \cos \left(\frac{A - B}{2}\right)}{\sin(A + B)}$

$\qquad$ since $0° < A + B < 180°$

$\qquad = \dfrac{2 \sin \left(\frac{A + B}{2}\right) \cos \left(\frac{A - B}{2}\right)}{2 \sin \left(\frac{A + B}{2}\right) \cos \left(\frac{A + B}{2}\right)}$

$\qquad = \dfrac{\cos \left(\frac{A - B}{2}\right)}{\cos \left(\frac{A + B}{2}\right)}$

$\qquad = \dfrac{\cos \left(\frac{A - B}{2}\right)}{\sin \left(90° - \frac{A + B}{2}\right)}$

$\qquad = \dfrac{\cos \frac{A - B}{2}}{\sin \frac{1}{2}(180 - (A + B))}$

$\qquad = \dfrac{\cos \frac{1}{2}(A - B)}{\sin \frac{1}{2}C}.$

63. If $a + b > c$, then
$\sin A + \sin B > \sin (A + B)$ for any
two angles of a triangle.

Proof:

$1 < \dfrac{a}{c} + \dfrac{b}{c} = \dfrac{\sin A}{\sin C} + \dfrac{\sin B}{\sin C}$

$\qquad = \dfrac{\sin A + \sin B}{\sin C}$

Therefore, $\sin C < \sin A + \sin B$,

but $\sin C = \sin (180° - (A + B))$

$\qquad = \sin (A + B)$

$\qquad$ since $0° < A + B < 180°$.

Therefore, $\sin (A + B) < \sin A + \sin B$.

64.

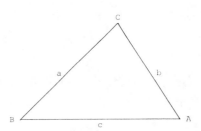

show the area $= \dfrac{a^2 \sin B \sin C}{2 \sin A}.$

Proof: $\quad$ area $= \dfrac{1}{2} ab \sin C$

but $\qquad \dfrac{b}{\sin B} = \dfrac{a}{\sin A}$, so

$\dfrac{1}{2} ab \sin C = \dfrac{1}{2} \cdot a \cdot \dfrac{a \sin B}{\sin A} \sin C$

$\qquad = \dfrac{1}{2} a^2 \dfrac{\sin B \sin C}{\sin A}$

65.

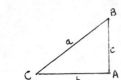

Consider the triangle ABC where
A = 90°.   We have sin A = sin 90°
= 1.   Using the right triangle we
have

$$\sin C = \frac{c}{a}$$

$$a = \frac{c}{\sin C}, \text{ and}$$

(I) $\dfrac{a}{\sin A} = \dfrac{c}{\sin C}$, since sin A = 1.
Also, we have

$$\sin B = \frac{b}{a}$$

$$a = \frac{b}{\sin B}, \text{ and}$$

(II) $\dfrac{a}{\sin A} = \dfrac{b}{\sin B}$.

Thus, we have from (I) and (II),

$$\frac{a}{\sin A} = \frac{b}{\sin B} = \frac{c}{\sin C}.$$

Section 8.3   The Law of Cosines

Additional Examples

Example 1   Find all angles to the
   nearest ten minutes in a triangle
   ABC with sides a = 3.9 ft,
   b = 6.2 ft, and c = 4.8 ft.
Solution   Use the law of cosines.
   Find the largest angle, B, first.

$$\cos B = \frac{a^2 + c^2 - b^2}{2ac}$$

$$= \frac{(3.9)^2 + (4.8)^2 - (6.2)^2}{2(3.9)(4.8)}$$

$$\approx -.1900$$

$$B \approx 101°00'$$

Now use the law of sines to find C.

$$\frac{c}{\sin C} = \frac{b}{\sin B}$$

$$\frac{4.8}{\sin C} = \frac{6.2}{\sin 101°00'}$$

$$\sin C \approx \frac{4.8 \sin 101°00'}{6.2}$$

$$C \approx 49°30'$$

Finally,

$$A = 180° - 101°00' - 49°30'$$

$$= 29°30'.$$

Example 2   Two motorists leave a city
   on roads with an angle of 65°00'
   between them.   One motorist travels
   to a small town 142 miles away.
   The other motorist travels to a
   lake 193 miles away.   How far is
   the lake from the small town?
Solution   See the sketch.

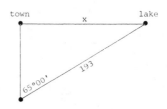

Use the law of cosines.

$$x^2 = 142^2 + 193^2 - 2(142)(193)\cos 65°00'$$

$$= 20,164 + 37,249 - 23,165$$

$$= 34,248$$

$$x \approx 185$$

The lake is 185 miles from the town.

Example 3   The sides of a triangular
   plot are 47.3, 82.1, and 65.7 ft.
   respectively.   Find the area.
Solution   Use the formula

$$K = \sqrt{s(s-a)(s-b)(s-c)}, \text{ with}$$

$$s = \frac{1}{2}(47.3 + 82.1 + 65.7) = 97.55$$

$$s - a = 97.55 - 47.3 = 50.25$$

$$s - b = 97.55 - 82.1 = 15.45$$

$$s - c = 97.55 - 65.7 = 31.85$$

$$K = \sqrt{97.55(50.25)(15.45)(31.85)}$$

$$= 1553.$$

The area is 1550 square feet.

Selected Solutions

1. If $C = 28.3°$, $a = 4.21$, and $b = 5.71$, we can use the law of cosines to find c:

$$c^2 = a^2 + b^2 - 2ab \cos C,$$

$$c^2 = (4.21)^2 + (5.71)^2 - 2(4.21)(5.71) \cos 28.3°$$

$$c^2 = 17.7241 + 32.6041 - 42.3318$$

$$c^2 = 8.0447, \text{ so that}$$

$$c \approx 2.8363, \text{ or } c \approx 2.84 \text{ in.}$$

We can then use the law of sines to get

$$\frac{c}{\sin C} = \frac{a}{\sin A}$$

$$\sin A = \frac{a \sin C}{c} = \frac{4.21 \sin 28.3°}{2.84}$$

$$\sin A = 0.705269, \text{ so that}$$

$$A \approx 44.85°, \text{ or } A \approx 44.9°.$$

Then,

$$B = 180 - (A + C) = 106.8°.$$

5. If $A = 80°40' = 80.667°$, $b = 143$, and $c = 89.6$, then

$$a^2 = b^2 + c^2 - 2bc \cos A$$

$$a^2 = (143)^2 + (89.6)^2 - 2(143)(89.6) \cos 80.667°$$

$$a^2 = 28,477.16 - 4155.76$$

$$a^2 = 24,321.4, \text{ so that}$$

$$a \approx 155.953, \text{ or } a \approx 156 \text{ cm.}$$

Using the law of sines gives

$$\frac{a}{\sin A} = \frac{b}{\sin B}$$

$$\sin B = \frac{b \sin A}{a} = \frac{143 \sin 80.667°}{156}$$

$$\sin B = 0.9045323, \text{ so that}$$

$$B \approx 64.76°, \text{ or } B \approx 64°50'.$$

Then,

$$C = 180° - (A + B) = 34°30'.$$

9. If $A = 112.8°$, $b = 6.28$, and $c = 12.2$, then

$$a^2 = b^2 + c^2 - 2bc \cos A$$

$$a^2 = (6.28)^2 + (12.2)^2 - 2(6.28)(12.2) \cos 112.8°$$

$$a^2 = 188.2784 - (-59.379788)$$

$$a^2 = 247.65819, \text{ so that}$$

$$a \approx 15.74 \text{ m.}$$

Using the law of sines gives

$$\frac{a}{\sin A} = \frac{b}{\sin B}$$

$$\sin B = \frac{b \sin A}{a} = \frac{6.28 \sin 112.8°}{15.74}$$

$$\sin B = 0.3678082, \text{ so that}$$

$$B \approx 21.58°, \text{ or } B \approx 21.6°.$$

then,

$$C = 180° - (A + B) = 45.6°.$$

13. If $a = 3.0$, $b = 5.0$, and $c = 6.0$, then

$$a^2 = b^2 + c^2 - 2bc \cos A \text{ gives}$$

$$\cos A = \frac{b^2 + c^2 - a^2}{2bc} = \frac{25 + 36 - 9}{60}$$

$$\cos A = \frac{52}{60} = 0.86666..., \text{ so that}$$

$$A \approx 29.926°, \text{ or } A = 30°$$

if we round to the nearest degree. Then we can use the law of sines to arrive at

$$\frac{a}{\sin A} = \frac{b}{\sin B}$$

$$\sin B = \frac{b \sin A}{a} = \frac{5\left(\frac{1}{2}\right)}{3}$$

$$\sin B = \frac{5}{6} = 0.8333..., \text{ so that}$$

$$B \approx 56.44°, \text{ or } B = 56°.$$

Then we have

$$C = 180° - (A + B) = 94°.$$

17. If $a = 42.9$, $b = 37.6$ and $c = 62.7$, then

$$a^2 = b^2 + c^2 - 2bc \cos A \text{ gives}$$

$$\cos A = \frac{b^2 + c^2 - a^2}{2bc} = \frac{3504.64}{4662.4}$$

$$\cos A = 0.74329, \text{ so that}$$

$$A \approx 41.9876°, \text{ or } A \approx 42°00'.$$

The law of sines gives

$$\frac{a}{\sin A} = \frac{b}{\sin B}$$

$$\sin B = \frac{b \sin A}{a} = \frac{37.6 \sin 42°}{42.9}$$

$\sin B = 0.586464$, so that

$B \approx 35.9°$, or $35°50'$.

Then,

$C = 180° - (A + b) = 102°10'$.

21. If $a = 12.54$, $b = 16.83$, and
$c = 21.62$, then

$$\cos A = \frac{b^2 + c^2 - a^2}{2bc} = \frac{593.4217}{727.7292}$$

$\cos A = 0.815443$, so that

$A \approx 35.3688° = 35°22'$.

The law of sines gives

$$\frac{a}{\sin A} = \frac{b}{\sin B}$$

$$\sin B = \frac{b \sin A}{a} = \frac{16.83 \sin 35°22'}{12.54}$$

$\sin B = 0.77686$, so that

$B \approx 50.974° = 50°58'$.

Then

$C = 180° - (A + B) = 93°40'$.

25. The law of cosines gives

$$(AB)^2 = 350^2 + 286^2 - 2(350)(286) \cos 46.8°$$

$$(AB)^2 = 204,296 - 137046.33$$

$$(AB)^2 = 67,249.669, \text{ so that}$$

$AB \approx 259.325$, or 259 m.

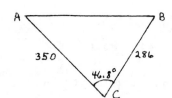

29. We have

$$x^2 = 25^2 + 25^2 - 2(25)(25) \cos 52°$$

$$x^2 = 625 + 625 - 2(625) \cos 52°$$

$$x^2 = 625[2 - 2 \cos 52°]$$

$$x^2 = 625(0.768677) = 480.42316$$

$x \approx 21.9186$, or $x \approx 22$ feet.

33.

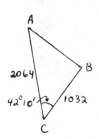

If sound travels at 344 m per sec,
then
$AC = (344)(6) = 2064$ m, and
$BC = (344)(3) = 1032$ m.
Then,

$$(AB)^2 = (AC)^2 + (BC)^2 - 2(AC)(BC) \cos 42.1667°$$

$$(AB)^2 = 4,260,096 + 1,065,204 - 3,157,561.3$$

$$(AB)^2 = 2,167,558.7, \text{ so that}$$

$AB \approx 1472.26$, or $AB \approx 1472$ m.

37. $(BC)^2 = (AB)^2 + (AC)^2 - \\ \cdot 2(AB)(AC) \cos A,$

$$(BC)^2 = (22.47928)^2 + (28.14276)^2 - 1265.258 \cos 58.5698°$$

$$(BC)^2 = 637.55224, \text{ so that}$$

$BC \approx 25.2498$.

41. If $a = 15$, $b = 19$, and $c = 24$, then
$s = \frac{1}{2}(a + b + c) = \frac{1}{2}(58) = 29$, and
the area of K is given by
$$K = \sqrt{s(s - a)(s - b)(s - c)}$$
$$K = \sqrt{29(14)(10)(5)} = \sqrt{20300},$$
or
$K \approx 142.478$ in^2.
The answer in the text is rounded
to $K = 140$ in^2.

45. If a = 76.3, b = 109, and c = 98.8, then

$$s = \frac{1}{2}(a + b + c) = \frac{76.3 + 109 + 98.8}{2}$$

s = 142.05, or s = 142.

Then

$$K = \sqrt{s(s - a)(s - b)(s - c)}$$

$$K = \sqrt{142(65.7)(33)(43.2)}$$

$$K = \sqrt{13,299,993}$$

$K \approx 3646.9155$, or $K \approx 3650 \text{ ft}^2$.

49. We have $S = \frac{1}{2}(75 + 68 + 85)$, or

s = 114.   Then the area K is given as

$$K = \sqrt{s(s - a)(s - b)(s - c)}$$

$$K = \sqrt{114(39)(46)(29)}$$

$$K \approx 2435.3571$$

If each can covers 75 m^2, then the number n of cans of paint necessary are

$$n = (\text{greatest integer in } \frac{2435.357}{75}) + 1$$

n = (greatest integer in 32.47) + 1

n = 32 + 1 = 33 cans of paint.

51.

$$1 + \cos A = 1 + \frac{b^2 + c^2 - a^2}{2bc}$$

$$= \frac{b^2 + 2bc + c^2 - a^2}{2bc}$$

$$= \frac{(b + c)^2 - a^2}{2bc}$$

$$= \frac{[(b + c) - a][b + c + a]}{2bc}$$

53.

$$\cos \frac{A}{2} = \sqrt{\frac{s(s - a)}{bc}}$$

Proof:

$$\cos \frac{A}{2} = \sqrt{\frac{1 + \cos A}{2}}$$

$$= \sqrt{\frac{1}{2}(\frac{(b + c - a)(b + c + a)}{2bc})}$$

from 49

$$= \sqrt{\frac{1}{bc} \cdot \frac{b + c - a}{2} \cdot \frac{b + c + a}{2}}$$

But, $s = \frac{b + c + a}{2}$

and $s - a = \frac{b + c - a}{2}$

so $\cos \frac{A}{2} = \sqrt{\frac{s(s - a)}{bc}}$,

55. area $= \frac{1}{2} bc \sin A$

Show that

$$\text{area} = \sqrt{\frac{1}{2}bc(1 + \cos A) \cdot \frac{1}{2}bc(1 - \cos A)}.$$

Proof: $\frac{1}{2} bc \sin A$

$$= \frac{1}{2} bc\sqrt{1 - \cos^2 A}$$

$$= \sqrt{(\frac{1}{2} bc)^2 (1 - \cos^2 A)}$$

$$= \sqrt{(\frac{1}{2} bc)^2 (1 - \cos A)(1 + \cos A)}$$

$$= \sqrt{\frac{1}{2} bc(1 + \cos A) \cdot \frac{1}{2} bc(1 - \cos A)}$$

56. Heron's formula:

$$\text{area} = \sqrt{s(s - a)(s - b)(s - c)}$$

Proof:

$$= \sqrt{\frac{1}{2}bc(1 + \cos A)\frac{1}{2}bc(1 - \cos A)}$$

from 53

$$= \sqrt{\frac{1}{2}bc \cdot \frac{(b+c+a)(b+c-a)}{2bc} \cdot \frac{1}{2}bc \cdot \frac{(a-b+c)(a+b-c)}{2bc}}$$

from 49 and 50

$$= \sqrt{\frac{b + c + a}{2} \cdot \frac{b + c - a}{2} \cdot \frac{a - b + c}{2} \cdot \frac{a + b - c}{2}}$$

$$= \sqrt{s(s - a)(s - b)(s - c)}$$

57. Suppose in a triangle that a = b.

Prove $c^2 = 2a^2(1 - \cos C)$.

Proof:

By the law of cosines,

$$c^2 = a^2 + b^2 - 2ab \cos C.$$

Since a = b, $a^2 = b^2$, and the law of cosines becomes

$$c^2 = 2a^2 - 2a^2 \cos C = 2a^2(1 - \cos C).$$

56.   Show $\frac{x}{c - x} = \frac{b}{a}$.

Use the law of sines

For triangle ADC: $x = \frac{y \sin \frac{C}{2}}{\sin A}$.

For triangle BDC: $c - x = \dfrac{y \sin \frac{C}{2}}{\sin B}$.

Thus, $\dfrac{x}{c - x} = \dfrac{y \sin \frac{C}{2}}{\sin A} \cdot \dfrac{\sin B}{y \sin \frac{C}{2}}$

$$= \frac{\sin B}{\sin A}.$$

Also, by the law of sines,

$\dfrac{\sin B}{b} = \dfrac{\sin A}{a}$ or $\dfrac{\sin B}{\sin A} = \dfrac{b}{a} = \dfrac{x}{c - x}$.

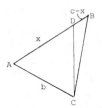

Section 8.4   Vectors and Applications

Additional Examples

Example 1   Write each vector in the
   form $\langle a, b \rangle$, and in the form
   $ai + bj$.
   (a) A vector of length 10, making
an angle of 120° with the positive
x-axis.   (See the figure.)

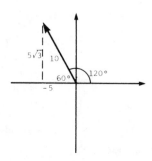

   (b) A vector ending at (0, 4).
Solution   (a) Use your knowledge of
   30°–60° right triangles to get the
   numbers shown in the sketch.   Then
   write the vector as
   $\langle -5, 5\sqrt{3} \rangle$, or $-5i + 5\sqrt{3}j$.

   (b) Write the vector as $\langle 0, 4 \rangle$, or
   $0i + 4j$.
Example 2   Find the magnitude of the
   vector $\langle -7, 8 \rangle$.
Solution   From the formula

$$|\langle a, b \rangle| = \sqrt{a^2 + b^2},$$

   the magnitude is

$$\sqrt{(-7)^2 + 8^2} = \sqrt{49 + 64} = \sqrt{113}.$$

Selected Solutions

1. Vectors are equal if they have the
    same <u>direction</u> and the same
    <u>magnitude</u>.   Thus, n and r appear
    to be equal, and m and p appear
    to be equal.

5. See the answer section of the text
    for a good sketch.

9. See the answer section of the test.

13. See the answer section of the text.

17. See the answer section of the text.

21. If $u = \langle -2, 5 \rangle$ and $v = \langle 3, -2 \rangle$, then
    $u + v = \langle -2 + 3, 5 + (-2) \rangle = \langle 1, 3 \rangle$.

25. If $\theta = 45°$ and $|v| = 20$, then
    $x = |v| \cos \theta = 20 \cos 45° = 10\sqrt{2}$,
    and $y = |v| \sin \theta = 20 \sin 45° = 10\sqrt{2}$,
    since $\sin 45° = \cos 45° = \dfrac{\sqrt{2}}{2}$.

29. If $\theta = 128°30'$ and $|v| = 198$, then
    $x = 198 \cos 128.5° = -123.26$,
    $y = 198 \sin 128.5° = 154.96$.
    Rounding off we have
    $\langle x, y \rangle = \langle -123, 155 \rangle$.

33. For the vector u = <1, 1>, we have
$|u| = r = \sqrt{1^2 + 1^2} = \sqrt{2}$, and Θ is
defined by $\sin \Theta = \frac{x}{r} = \frac{1}{\sqrt{2}} = \frac{\sqrt{2}}{2}$,
and $\cos \Theta = \frac{y}{r} = \frac{\sqrt{2}}{2}$. This means Θ
is in quadrant I and $\Theta = 45°$. The
magnitude is $r = \sqrt{2}$ and the
direction angle is $\Theta = 45°$.

37. If u = <15, -8>, then
$r = \sqrt{225 + 64} = \sqrt{289} = 17$, and Θ
is defined by $\sin \Theta = \frac{-8}{17}$ and
$\cos \Theta = \frac{15}{17}$. This implies that Θ
is in quadrant IV and the reference
angle R is
$$R = \cos^{-1}\left(\frac{15}{17}\right) = \sin^{-1}\left(\frac{+8}{17}\right)$$
$$\approx 28.07°,$$
or $R \approx 28°$.
Hence,
$\Theta = 332°$.

41. Using <a, b> = ai + bj, we have
<-5, 8> = -5i + 8j.

45. If $\Theta = 45°$ and r = 8, then
$x = 8 \cos 45° = 8\left(\frac{\sqrt{2}}{2}\right) = 4\sqrt{2}$, and
$y = 8 \sin 45° = 4\sqrt{2}$. The vector is
$4\sqrt{2}i + 4\sqrt{2}j$.

49.

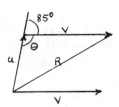

We can use the law of cosines to
find the magnitude $|R|$ of the
resultant vector R by noting in
the figure that $\Theta = 180° - 85° = 95°$.

We have
$$|R|^2 = (250)^2 + (450)^2 -$$
$$2(250)(450) \cos 95°$$
$$|R|^2 = 265,000 - (-19,610.042)$$
$$|R|^2 = 284,610.042$$
$$|R| = 533.49, \text{ or } |R| = 530 \text{ newtons}$$
if we round to the nearest 10
newtons.

53. Using the law of cosines, with
$\Theta = 180° - 140°50' = 39°10'$
$$|R|^2 = 116^2 + 139^2 -$$
$$2(116)(139) \cos 39°10'$$
$$|R|^2 = 32777 - (25002.251)$$
$$|R|^2 = 7774.749, \text{ so that}$$
$$|R| \approx 88.17, \text{ or } |R| \approx 88.2 \text{ lb.}$$

57.

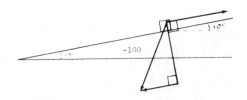

The force is $-100 \cos (90° + 10°)$
= 17.4 lb.

59.

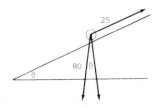

The equation for Θ is
$$25 = -80 \cos (90° + \Theta)$$
$$\frac{-25}{80} = \cos(90° + \Theta)$$
$$\Theta = \cos^{-1}\left(\frac{-25}{80}\right) - 90°$$
$$\Theta \approx 108.2° - 90° \text{ or}$$
$$\Theta \approx 18°.$$

61.

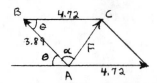

Set the 4.72-lb force on horizontal
axis with the dish at the origin.
Then the magnitude of the
equilibrium force F can be found
by the law of cosines.

$|F|^2 = 3.89^2 + 4.72^2 -$
$\qquad 2(3.89)(4.72) \cos 37.2°$

$|F|^2 = 37.4105 - 29.2499 = 8.16065$

$|F| \approx 2.8567$, or $|F| \cong 2.86$ lb.

We can then find angle B by the
law of sines:

$\dfrac{\sin B}{3.89} = \dfrac{\sin 37.2°}{2.86}$

$\sin B = \dfrac{3.89 \sin 37.2°}{2.86}$

$\sin B = 0.82234$

$\qquad B = 55.3°$

The angle that the equlibrium
force F makes with the 4.72 lb
force is 55.3°.

65.

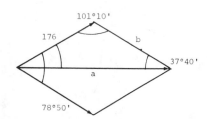

Using the law of sines, we have

$\dfrac{a}{\sin 101°10'} = \dfrac{176}{\sin 37°40'}$

$\begin{array}{l} \text{magnitude of} \\ \text{resultant a} \end{array} = \dfrac{176 \sin 101°10'}{\sin 37°40'}$

$\qquad\qquad = 283$ lb

Also,

$\begin{array}{l} \text{magnitude of} \\ \text{second force b} \end{array} = \dfrac{176 \sin 41°10'}{\sin 37°40'}$

$\qquad\qquad = 190$ lb.

69. The resultant force has magnitude x.

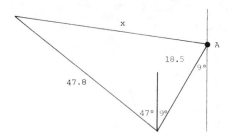

Use the law of cosines to find x.
We have

$x^2 = 47.8^2 + 18.5^2 -$
$\qquad 2(47.8)(18.5) \cos 52°$

$x^2 = 2627.09 - 1088.8589$

$x^2 = 1538.2311$, or

$\quad x \approx 39.2$ km.

The ship is approximately 39.2 km
from point A.

73.

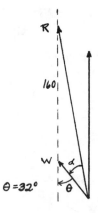

To travel 400 mi in 2.5 hours the
resultant vector R must have
magnitude 160(mi/hr). The wind
vector w has magnitude 11 and a
direction 328°. Hence the angle
at w is 180° - θ or 180° - 32° = 148°.
Then the magnitude of R is given by

$|R|^2 = 160^2 + 11^2 -$
$\qquad 2(160)(11) \cos 148°$

$|R|^2 = 25721 - (-2985.13)$

$|R|^2 = 28697.13$

$|R| = 169.4$ miles per hour.

We find the angle of α by the law of sines, and then the bearing of the plane is 328° + α.

$$\frac{|R|}{\sin 148°} = \frac{160}{\sin \alpha}$$

$$\sin \alpha = \frac{160 \sin 148°}{169.4}$$

$$\sin \alpha = .5005141$$

$$\alpha \simeq 30.03°, \text{ or } 30°.$$

Hence, the heading of the plane should be 358°.

77. $u + v = v + u$

Proof:

$u + v = \langle a_1, b_1 \rangle + \langle a_2, b_2 \rangle$

$\qquad = \langle a_1 + a_2, b_1 + b_2 \rangle$

$\qquad = \langle a_2 + a_1, b_2 + b_1 \rangle$

$\qquad = \langle a_2, b_2 \rangle + \langle a_1, b_1 \rangle$

$\qquad = v + u$

81. Prove $u + 0 = u$.

Proof:

We have $u = \langle a_1, b_1 \rangle$ and $0 = \langle 0, 0 \rangle$.

According to the definition of addition of vectors,

$u + 0 = \langle a_1, b_1 \rangle + \langle 0, 0 \rangle$

$\qquad = \langle a_1 + 0, b_1 + 0 \rangle$

$\qquad = \langle a_1, b_1 \rangle$

$\qquad = u.$

85. If $u = \langle -6, 8 \rangle$ and $v = \langle 3, -4 \rangle$, then

$u \cdot v = (-6)(3) + (8)(-4)$

$u \cdot v = -18 - 32$

$u \cdot v = -50.$

87. Prove $u \cdot v = |u||v| \cos \alpha$.

Proof:

Let $u = \langle a_1, b_1 \rangle$, $v = \langle a_2, b_2 \rangle$.

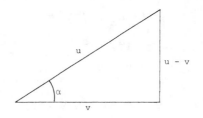

We see that

$$\cos \alpha = \frac{|u|^2 + |v|^2 - |u - v|^2}{2|u||v|}$$

from the law of cosines

$$= \frac{(a_1^2 + b_1^2) + (a_2^2 + b_2^2) - ((a_1 - a_2)^2 + (b_1 - b_2)^2)}{2|u||v|}$$

$$= \frac{a_1^2 + b_1^2 + a_2^2 + b_2^2 - (a_1^2 - 2a_1 a_2 + b_1^2 - 2b_1 b_2 + b_2^2)}{2|u||v|}$$

$$= \frac{2(a_1 a_2 + b_1 b_2)}{2|u||v|} = \frac{u \cdot v}{|u||v|}.$$

Thus, $u \cdot v = |u||v| \cos \alpha$.

89. We have $u = \langle 1, 8 \rangle$, $v = \langle 2, -5 \rangle$, and

$$\cos \alpha = \frac{u \cdot v}{|u||v|} = \frac{2 - 40}{\sqrt{1 + 64}\ \sqrt{4 + 25}}$$

$$\cos \alpha = \frac{-38}{\sqrt{65}\ \sqrt{29}} \simeq -0.8752415$$

$$\alpha = \cos^{-1}(-0.8752415)$$

$$\alpha \simeq 151.07° \text{ or } \alpha = 151°.$$

91. $\quad u = \langle a_1, b_1 \rangle$, $v = \langle a_2, b_2 \rangle$

$u \cdot v = a_1 a_2 + b_1 b_2$

$\qquad = a_2 a_1 + b_2 b_1$

$\qquad = v \cdot u$

92. $u \cdot u = a_1^2 + b_1^2 = |u|^2$

93. Prove $u \cdot (v + w) = u \cdot v + u \cdot w$.

Proof:

Let $u = \langle a_1, b_1 \rangle$, $v = \langle a_2, b_2 \rangle$,

and $w = \langle a_3, b_3 \rangle$.   Then

$$u \cdot (v + w) = u \cdot \langle a_2 + a_3, \ b_2 + b_3 \rangle$$
$$= a_1(a_2 + a_3) + b_1(b_2 + b_3)$$
$$= a_1 a_2 + a_1 a_3 + b_1 b_2 + b_1 b_3$$
$$= (a_1 a_2 + b_1 b_2) +$$
$$(a_1 a_3 + b_1 b_3)$$
$$= u \cdot v + u \cdot w.$$

95. If $u \neq 0$, $v \neq 0$, and $u \cdot v = 0$, then u and v are perpendicular.

Proof:

Let $u = \langle a_1, b_1 \rangle$, $v = \langle a_2, b_2 \rangle$.

Let α be the angle between u and v. Then by problem 87,

$$\cos \alpha = \frac{u \cdot v}{|u||v|} = 0.$$

Thus, $\alpha = 90°$, so u and v are perpendicular.

96. Prove that if u and v are perpendicular then $u \cdot v = 0$.

Proof:

The angle between u and v is $90°$ if they are perpendicular and, by problem 87,

$$u \cdot v = |u||v| \cos \alpha = 0.$$

Section 8.5   Trigonometric Form of Complex Numbers

Additional Examples

Example 1   Write $6(\cos 120° + i \sin 120°)$ in standard form.

Solution   Since $\cos 120° = -1/2$ and $\sin 120° = \sqrt{3}/2$,

$$6(\cos 120° + i \sin 120°)$$
$$= 6\left(-\frac{1}{2} + i\frac{\sqrt{3}}{2}\right)$$
$$= -3 + 3\sqrt{3}i.$$

Example 2   Write $2\sqrt{3} - 2i$ in trigonometric form.

Solution   Here $x = 2\sqrt{3}$ and $y = -2$.

Using the right hand formulas in the text for r and θ, we have

$$r = \sqrt{(2\sqrt{3})^2 + (-2)^2} = \sqrt{12 + 4}$$
$$= \sqrt{16} = 4,$$

and $\theta = \tan^{-1} \dfrac{-2}{2\sqrt{3}} = \tan^{-1} -\dfrac{\sqrt{3}}{3}$.

Since θ is in quadrant IV,

$$\theta = 330°$$

and $2\sqrt{3} - 2i = 4(\cos 330° + i \sin 330°)$.

Selected Solutions

1. The graph is shown in the answer section of the text.

5. The graph is in the answer section of the text.

9. The graph is in the answer section of the text.

13. $(-5 + 6i) + (3 - 4i)$
$$= (-5 + 3) + (6 - 4)i$$
$$= -2 + 2i$$

17. $(2 + 6i) + (-2i) = (2 + 0) + (6 - 2)i$
$$= 2 + 4i$$

21. Since $\cos 45° = \sin 45° = \dfrac{\sqrt{2}}{2}$, we

have $2(\cos 45° + i \sin 45°)$
$$= 2\left(\frac{\sqrt{2}}{2} + i\frac{\sqrt{2}}{2}\right)$$
$$= \sqrt{2} + i\sqrt{2}.$$

25. The angle $\theta = 240°$ is in quadrant III, with a reference angle of 60°. Hence, $\cos 240° = -\cos 60° = -\frac{1}{2}$ and $\sin 240° = \frac{-\sqrt{3}}{2}$.

Thus,

$4(\cos 240° + i \sin 240°)$

$= 4(\frac{-1}{2} - i\frac{\sqrt{3}}{2})$

$= -2 - 2i\sqrt{3}$.

29. The angle 300° is in quadrant IV, with a reference angle of 60°. Hence,

$\cos 300° = \frac{1}{2}$ and $\sin 300° = \frac{-\sqrt{3}}{2}$.

Thus

$5(\cos 300° + i \sin 300°)$

$= 5(\frac{1}{2} - i\frac{\sqrt{3}}{2})$

$= \frac{5}{2} - i\frac{5\sqrt{3}}{2}$.

33. We have for $2 + 3i$

$r = \sqrt{2^2 + 3^2} = \sqrt{4 + 9} = \sqrt{13}$, and

$\tan \theta = \frac{y}{x} = \frac{3}{2}$, with θ in quadrant I,

$\theta = \tan^{-1}(\frac{3}{2}) \approx 56.31° \approx 56°20'$.

The reason θ is in quadrant I is that $x = 2$ and $y = 3$ are both positive.
Hence,

$2 + 3i = \sqrt{13}(\cos 56°20' + i \sin 56°20')$.

37. For $-1.8794 + .6840i$, we have

$r = \sqrt{3.5321444 + .467856} \approx \sqrt{4} = 2$,

and $x < 0$, $y > 0$ implies θ is in quadrant II, with

$\tan \theta = -\frac{.6840}{1.8794} \approx 160°$.

The answer is

$2(\cos 160° + i \sin 160°)$.

41. For $3 - 3i$, we have $r = \sqrt{9 + 9} = 3\sqrt{2}$ and θ is in quadrant IV with $\tan \theta = -1$. Hence, $\theta = 315°$, and we have $3 - 3i = 3\sqrt{2}(\cos 315° + i \sin 315°)$.

45. For $\sqrt{3} - i$, we have $r = \sqrt{3 + 1} = 2$ and θ is in quadrant IV with $\tan \theta = \frac{-1}{\sqrt{3}}$. Hence, $\theta = 360° - 30° = 330°$, and we have $\sqrt{3} - i = 2(\cos 330° + i \sin 330°)$.

49. For $2 + 2i$, we have $r = \sqrt{4 + 4} = 2\sqrt{2}$ and θ is in quadrant I with $\tan \theta = 1$. Hence, $\theta = 45°$, and we have

$2 + 2i = 2\sqrt{2}(\cos 45° + i \sin 45°0)$.

53. $3(\cos 60° + \sin 60°) \cdot$
$2(\cos 90° + i \sin 90°)$

$= 6[\cos (60° + 90°)] + i \sin (60° + 90°)]$

$= 6(\cos 150° + i \sin 150°)$

$= 6(\frac{-\sqrt{3}}{2} + \frac{i}{2})$

$= -3\sqrt{3} + 3i$

57. $4(\cos 60° + i \sin 60°) \cdot$
$6(\cos 330° + i \sin 330°)$

$= 24[\cos (390°) + i \sin (390°)]$

$= 24(\cos 30° + i \sin 30°)$

$= 24(\frac{\sqrt{3}}{2} + \frac{i}{2})$

$= 12\sqrt{3} + 12i$

61. $\sqrt{3}(\cos 45° + i \sin 45°) \cdot$
$\sqrt{3}(\cos 225° + i \sin 225°)$

$= 3(\cos 270 + i \sin 270°)$

$= 3(0 - i) = -3i$

65. $\dfrac{16(\cos 300° + i \sin 300°)}{8(\cos 60° + i \sin 60°)}$

$= 2(\cos 240° + i \sin 240°)$

$= 2(-\dfrac{1}{2} - \dfrac{i\sqrt{3}}{2})$

$= -1 - i\sqrt{3}$

69. $\dfrac{8}{\sqrt{3} + i} = \dfrac{8}{\sqrt{3} + i} \cdot \dfrac{\sqrt{3} - i}{\sqrt{3} - i}$

$= \dfrac{8\sqrt{3} - 8i}{3 + 1} = \dfrac{8\sqrt{3} - 8i}{4}$

$= 2\sqrt{3} - 2i$

73. $\dfrac{2\sqrt{6} - 2i\sqrt{2}}{\sqrt{2} - i\sqrt{6}} \cdot \dfrac{\sqrt{2} + i\sqrt{6}}{\sqrt{2} + i\sqrt{6}}$

$= \dfrac{2\sqrt{12} - 4i + 2\sqrt{36}i - 2i^2\sqrt{12}}{2 + 6}$

$= \dfrac{(4\sqrt{3} + 4\sqrt{3}) + i(12 - 4)}{8}$

$= \dfrac{8\sqrt{3} + 8i}{8} = \sqrt{3} + i$

77. If $E = 8(\cos 20° + i \sin 20°)$ and
$Z = R + X_L i$ with $R = 6$ and $X_L = 3$
(so that $Z = 6 + 3i$), then using
$I = \dfrac{E}{Z}$, we have

$I = \dfrac{8(\cos 20° + i \sin 20°)}{6 + 3i}$,

and $6 + 3i = r(\cos \theta + i \sin \theta)$
with $r = \sqrt{36 + 9} = \sqrt{45}$ and
$\theta = \tan^{-1} \dfrac{3}{6} \approx 26.565°$.

Hence,

$I = \dfrac{8}{\sqrt{45}}[\cos (20° - 20.565°) +$

$i \sin (20° - 20.565°)]$

$I = \dfrac{8}{\sqrt{45}}[\cos (.565°) = i \sin (.565°)]$

since $\cos (-\theta)$
$= \cos \theta$ and $\sin (-\theta)$
$= \sin \theta$

$I = (1.19257)[0.99995 - i(.00986)]$

$I \approx 1.19 - 0.1176i$.

81. $\dfrac{45.3(\cos 127°25' + i \sin 127°25')}{12.8(\cos 43°32' + i \sin 43°32')}$

$= \dfrac{45.3}{12.8}(\cos 83°53' + i \sin 83°53')$

since $127°25' -$
$43°32' = 83°53'$
$= 83.883°$

$\approx .377 + 3.52i$

85. If $c = x + iy$ and if the real part of
c is 1, then the graph is $x = 1$.
See the graph in the answer section
of the text.

89. Prove that if
$z_1 = r_1(\cos \theta_1 + i \sin \theta_1)$
and if $z_2 = r_2(\cos \theta_2 + i \sin \theta_2)$,
then
$z_1 z_2 = r_1 r_2[\cos (\theta_1 + \theta_2) + i \sin (\theta_1 + \theta_2)]$.

Proof: Using ordinary multiplication,

$z_1 z_2 = r_1(\cos \theta_1 + i \sin \theta_1)$
$r_2(\cos \theta_2 + i \sin \theta_2)$

$= r_1 r_2 [\cos \theta_1 \cos \theta_2 +$
$i \sin \theta_1 \cos \theta_2 +$
$i \cos \theta_1 \sin \theta_2 +$
$i^2 \sin \theta_1 \sin \theta_2]$

$= r_1 r_2[(\cos \theta_1 \cos \theta_2 -$
$\sin \theta_1 \sin \theta_2) +$
$i(\sin \theta_1 \cos \theta_2 +$
$\cos \theta_1 \sin \theta_2)]$

$= r_1 r_2 [\cos (\theta_1 + \theta_2) +$
$i \sin (\theta_1 + \theta_2)]$

Section 8.6 De Moivre's Theorem and
           Nth Roots

Additional Examples

Example 1   Find $(2\sqrt{3} - 2i)^6$.
Solution   From example 2 in the
    previous section of this Study
    Guide,
    $2\sqrt{3} - 2i = 4(\cos 330° + i \sin 330°)$.
    Now use De Moivre's theorem,
    $(2\sqrt{3} - 2i)^6 = [4(\cos 330° + i \sin 330°)]^6$

$$= 4^6[\cos(6 \cdot 330°) + i \sin(6 \cdot 330°)]$$

$$= 4^6(\cos 1980° + i \sin 1980°)$$

$$= 4^6(\cos 180° + i \sin 180°)$$

$$= 4^6(-1 + 0)$$

$$= -4^6$$

$$= -4096.$$

Example 2   Find all fifth roots of i.
Solution   Write i in trigonometric
    form as
    $i = 0 + i$
    $i = 1(\cos 90° + i \sin 90°)$.

    The modulus of the fifth roots is
    $1^{1/5} = 1$, with the arguments given
    by
    $\dfrac{90° + 360° \cdot k}{5}$, k = 0, 1, 2, 3, or 4.
    Replacing k, in turn, with 0, 1, 2,
    3, and 4, gives angles of
    $\dfrac{90° + 360° \cdot 0}{5} = \dfrac{90°}{5} = 18°$,

    $\dfrac{90° + 360° \cdot 1}{5} = \dfrac{450°}{5} = 90°$,

    then 162°, 234°, and 306°. The
    fifth roots are
    $1(\cos 18° + i \sin 18°)$,
    $1(\cos 90° + i \sin 90°)$,
    $1(\cos 162° + i \sin 162°)$,
    $1(\cos 234° + i \sin 234°)$, and
    $1(\cos 306° + i \sin 306°)$.

These roots would be equally spaced
around a unit circle.

Selected Solutions
1. $[2(\cos 60° + i \sin 60°)]^3$
    $= 2^3(\cos 180° + i \sin 180°)$
    $= 8(-1 + 0i)$
    $= -8.$

5. $[3(\cos 100° + i \sin 100°)]^3$
    $= 27(\cos 300° + i \sin 300°)$
    $= 27(\dfrac{1}{2} - i\dfrac{\sqrt{3}}{2})$
    $= \dfrac{27}{2} - i\dfrac{27\sqrt{3}}{2}.$

9. For $2 - 2i\sqrt{3}$, we have
    $r = \sqrt{4 + 12} = \sqrt{16} = 4$, and since
    $x > 0$, $y < 0$, θ is in quadrant IV,
    with $\tan \theta = \dfrac{y}{x} = \dfrac{-2\sqrt{3}}{2} = -\sqrt{3}$. Hence,
    $\theta = 300°$. Then, we have
    $(2 - 2i\sqrt{3})^4 = [4(\cos 300° + i \sin 300°)]^4$
    $= 4^4(\cos 1200° + i \sin 1200°)$
    $= 265(\cos 120° + i \sin 120°)$
    $= 256(-\dfrac{1}{2} + i\dfrac{\sqrt{3}}{2})$
    $= -128 + 128i\sqrt{3}.$

13. For $-.4283 + .5172$ we have
    $r = \sqrt{(-.4283)^2 + (.5172)^2}$
    $= \sqrt{0.4509367}$,
    or $r \approx .6715182$. We see that θ is in
    quadrant II, with $\tan \theta = -\dfrac{.5172}{.4283}$
    ≈ -1.2076, so that $\theta \approx 129.63°$.
    Then
    $(-.4283 + .5172i)^4$
    $= r^4(\cos 518.5° + i \sin 518.5°)$
    $\approx .203344(\cos 158.5° + i \sin 158.5°)$
    $\approx -.1892 + .0745i.$

17. Note that $\cos 0° + i \sin 0° = 1$.
We are to find the cube roots of 1.
If $z = r(\cos \theta + i \sin \theta)$ is a cube
root of 1, then $z^3 = 1$, or

$r^3(\cos 3\theta + i \sin 3\theta)$

$= \cos 0° + i \sin 0°$.

Hence $r^3 = 1$, or $r = 1$, and
$3\theta = 0° + 360°k$, $k = 0, 1, 2$, or
$\theta = 120°k$, $k = 0, 1, 2$.
This gives angles $0°$, $120°$, and
$240°$. The solutions are
$1(\cos 0° + i \sin 0°)$

$= 1$,

$1(\cos 120° + i \sin 120°)$

$= -\dfrac{1}{2} + i\dfrac{\sqrt{3}}{2}$,   and

$1(\cos 240° + i \sin 240°)$

$= -\dfrac{1}{2} - i\dfrac{\sqrt{3}}{2}$.

21. $-8i = 8(\cos 270° + i \sin 270°)$
The modulus of the cube roots is
$8^{1/3} = 2$, and the arguments are as
follows.

If $k = 0$: $\dfrac{270° + 360°\cdot 0}{3} = 90°$,

if $k = 1$: $\dfrac{270° + 360°\cdot 1}{3} = 210°$,

if $k = 2$: $\dfrac{270° + 360°\cdot 2}{3} = 330°$.

So the cube roots are
$2(\cos 90° + i \sin 90°)$ $= 2i$,
$2(\cos 210° + i \sin 210°) = -\sqrt{3} - i$,
and $2(\cos 330° + i \sin 330°) = \sqrt{3} - i$.
See the graph in the text.

23. -64 is $64(\cos 180° + i \sin 180°)$
in trigonometric form.
The cube roots of this number have
modulus $64^{1/3} = 4$ and arguments
given as follows

$k = 0$: $\dfrac{180° + 360°(0)}{3}$ $= 60°$

$k = 1$: $\dfrac{180° + 360°(1)}{3}$ $= 180°$

$k = 2$: $\dfrac{180° + 360°(2)}{3}$ $= 300°$

So the cube roots of -64 are
$4(\cos 60° + i \sin 60°) = 2 + 2i\sqrt{3}$,
$4(\cos 180° + i \sin 180°) = -4$,
and $4(\cos 300° + i \sin 300°) = 2 - 2i\sqrt{3}$
See the graph in the text.

25. For $1 + i\sqrt{3}$ we have
$r = \sqrt{1 + 3} = 2$ and $\tan \theta = \sqrt{3}$
so that $\theta = 60°$. Thus,
$1 + i\sqrt{3} = 2(\cos 60° + i \sin 60°)$.
The cube roots of $1 + i\sqrt{3}$ have

modules $2^{1/3} = \sqrt[3]{2}$, and the arguments
are as follows.

If $k = 0$: $\dfrac{60° + 360(0)}{3} = 20°$,

if $k = 1$: $\dfrac{60° + 360(1)}{3} = 140°$,

if $k = 2$: $\dfrac{60° + 360(2)}{3} = 260°$.

Hence, the cube roots of $1 + i\sqrt{3}$
are
$\sqrt[3]{2}(\cos 20° + i \sin 20°)$,
$\sqrt[3]{2}(\cos 140° + i \sin 140°)$,
 and $\sqrt[3]{2}(\cos 260° + i \sin 260°)$.
See the graph in the text.

29. To find the square roots of 1 we
write
$1 = 1 + 0i$
$1 = 1(\cos 0° + 1 \sin 0°)$.
The square roots of this number have
modulus $1^{1/2} = 1$ and arguments
given as follows.

$k = 0$: $\dfrac{0° + 360°\cdot 0}{2} = 0°$

$k = 1$: $\dfrac{0° + 360°\cdot 1}{2} = 180°$

So the square roots of 1 are
$\cos 0° + i \sin 0° = 1$,
and $\cos 180° + i \sin 180° = -1$.
See the graph in the text.

33. To find the second roots of i we write

$i = 0 + 1i$

$i = 1(\cos 90° + i \sin 90°)$.

The second roots of i have modulus $1^{1/2} = 1$ and arguments given as follows.

$k = 0$: $\dfrac{90° + 0 \cdot 360°}{2} = 45°$

$k = 1$: $\dfrac{90° + 1 \cdot 360°}{2} = 225°$

So, the second roots of i are

$\cos 45° + i \sin 45° = \dfrac{\sqrt{2}}{2} + i\dfrac{\sqrt{2}}{2}$,

and $\cos 225° + i \sin 225° = \dfrac{-\sqrt{2}}{2} - i\dfrac{\sqrt{2}}{2}$.

See the graph in the text.

35. If $x^3 - 1 = 0$, then $x^3 = 1$. Hence, x is a cube root of 1. We write

$1 = 1 + oi$

$1 = 1(\cos 0° + i \sin 0°)$.

The cube roots of 1 have modulus $1^{1/3} = 1$ and arguments given as follows.

$k = 0$: $\dfrac{0° + 360°(0)}{3} = 0°$

$k = 1$: $\dfrac{0° + (360)(1)}{3} = 120°$

$k = 2$: $\dfrac{0° + 360(2)}{3} = 240°$

So the cube roots of 1 are

$\cos 0° + i \sin 0°$

$= 1$,

$\cos 120° + i \sin 120°$

$= -\dfrac{1}{2} + i\dfrac{\sqrt{3}}{2}$,

and $\cos 240° + i \sin 240°$

$= -\dfrac{1}{2} - i\dfrac{\sqrt{3}}{2}$.

37. If $x^3 + i = 0$, then $x^3 = -i$.
We have $-i = 1(\cos 270° + i \sin 270°)$.
The cube roots of -i have modulus $1^{1/3} = 1$ and arguments as follows.

$k = 0$: $\dfrac{270° + 360° \cdot 0}{3} = 90°$

$k = 1$: $\dfrac{270° + 360° \cdot 1}{3} = 210°$

$k = 2$: $\dfrac{270° + 360° \cdot 2}{3} = 330°$

Hence, the cube roots of -i are

$1(\cos 90° + i \sin 90°) = i$

$1(\cos 210° + i \sin 210°) = \dfrac{-\sqrt{3}}{2} - \dfrac{1}{2}i$,

and $1(\cos 330° + i \sin 330°) = \dfrac{\sqrt{3}}{2} - \dfrac{1}{2}i$.

41. If $x^4 + 1 = 0$, then $x^4 = -1$ and x is a fourth root of -1. We write

$-1 = -1 + 0i$

$-1 = \cos 180° + i \sin 180°$,

The modulus of the fourth roots of -1 is $1^{1/4} = 1$, and the arguments are found as follows

$k = 0$: $\dfrac{180° + 0 \cdot 360°}{4} = 45°$

$k = 1$: $\dfrac{180° + 1 \cdot 360°}{4} = 135°$

$k = 2$: $\dfrac{180° + 2 \cdot 360°}{4} = 225°$

$k = 3$: $\dfrac{180° + 3 \cdot 360°}{4} = 315°$

The fourth roots are

$\cos 45° + i \sin 45° = \dfrac{\sqrt{2}}{2} + i\dfrac{\sqrt{2}}{2}$,

$\cos 135° + i \sin 135° = -\dfrac{\sqrt{2}}{2} + i\dfrac{\sqrt{2}}{2}$,

$\cos 225° + i \sin 225° = \dfrac{-\sqrt{2}}{2} - i\dfrac{\sqrt{2}}{2}$,

and $\cos 315° + i \sin 315° = \dfrac{\sqrt{2}}{2} - i\dfrac{\sqrt{2}}{2}$.

45. We have $x^3 = 4 + 4i\sqrt{3}$, and we write

$4 + 4i\sqrt{3} = 8(\cos 60° + i \sin 60°)$

since $r = \sqrt{16 + 48} = 8$ and $\tan \theta = \sqrt{3}$. The cube roots of $4 + 4i\sqrt{3}$ have modulus $8^{1/3} = 2$, and the arguments are as follows.

$k = 0$: $\dfrac{60° + 360° \cdot 0}{3} = 20°$

$k = 1$: $\dfrac{60° + 360° \cdot 1}{3} = 140°$

$k = 2$: $\dfrac{60° + 360° \cdot 2}{3} = 260°$

Hence, the cube roots are

2(cos 20° + i sin 20°),

2(cos 140° + i sin 140°),

and 2(cos 260° + i sin 260°).

49. We have $x^2 = -3.72 - 8.24i$, and we write $-3.72 - 8.24$ in trigonometric form we have

$$r = \sqrt{(-3.72)^2 + (-8.24)^2} = \sqrt{81.736}$$
$$\approx 9.041,$$

and θ is in quadrant III with

$$\tan \theta = \frac{-8.24}{-3.72} \approx 2.21505$$
$$\theta \approx 245.7°.$$

Hence, $-3.72 - 8.24i$

$\approx 9.04(\cos 245.7° + i \sin 245.7°)$.

The modulus of the square roots is $\sqrt{9.04} \approx 3$, and the arguments are as follows.

$$k = 0: \frac{245.7° + 360°\cdot 0}{2} = 122.85°$$

$$k = 1: \frac{245.7° + 360°\cdot 1}{2} = 302.85°$$

The square roots are

3(cos 122.85° + i sin 122.85°)

$= -1.627 + 2.52i$,

and

3(cos 302.85° + i sin 302.85°)

$= 1.627 - 2.52i$.

53. We write

$3 - 3i = 3\sqrt{2}(\cos 315° + i \sin 315°)$

since $r = \sqrt{9 + 9} = 3\sqrt{2}$ and $x > 0$, $y < 0$ implies θ is in quadrant IV with $\tan \theta = -1$. Thus, $\theta = 315°$. The modulus of the square roots of $3 - 3i$ is $\sqrt{3\sqrt{2}}$, or $\sqrt[4]{18}$. The arguments are given by

$$k = 0: \frac{315° + 360°\cdot 0}{2} = 157.5°, \text{ and}$$

$$k = 1: \frac{315° + 360\cdot 1}{2} = 337.5°.$$

Hence, the solutions to $z^2 = 3 - 3i$ are

$\sqrt[4]{18}(\cos 157.5° + i \sin 157.5°)$ and

$\sqrt[4]{18}(\cos 337.5° + i \sin 337.5°)$. In standard form these numbers are

$-1.903 + .788i$ and $1.903 - .788i$.

Section 8.7 Polar Equations

Additional Examples

Example 1   Convert $r = 2 \cos \theta$ to rectangular coordinates.

Solution   Multiply both sides by r to get $r^2 = 2r \cos \theta$. Since $x = r \cos \theta$ and $r^2 = x^2 + y^2$, we have

$$x^2 + y^2 = 2x$$
$$x^2 - 2x + y^2 = 0$$
$$x^2 - 2x + 1 + y^2 = 1$$
$$(x - 1)^2 + y^2 = 1.$$

This is a circle with center $C(1, 0)$ and radius of 1.

Example 2   Convert $r = \frac{2}{1 + \cos \theta}$ to rectangular coordinates.

Solution   Multiply by $1 + \cos \theta$ to get

$$r(1 + \cos \theta) = 2$$
$$r + r\cos \theta = 2.$$

Use the formulas from the text to get

$$\sqrt{x^2 + y^2} + x = 2, \quad \text{since } x = r \cos \theta$$

or $\sqrt{x^2 + y^2} = 2 - x$.

Square both sides to get

$$x^2 + y^2 = 4 - 4x + x^2,$$

or $y^2 = 4 - 4x,$

the equation of a parabola.

Selected Solutions

1. See the graph in the answer section of the text.

5. See the graph in the answer section of the text.

9. See the graph in the answer section of the text.

13. Let $r = 2 + 2 \cos \theta$, and consider the following table.

θ	$\cos \theta$	$r = 2 + 2 \cos \theta$
0°	1	$2 + 2 = 4$
30°	$\sqrt{3}/2$	$2 + \sqrt{3} \simeq 3.732$
45°	$\sqrt{2}/2$	$2 + \sqrt{2} \simeq 3.414$
60°	1/2	$2 + 1 = 3$
90°	0	$2 + 0 = 2$
120°	-1/2	$2 - 1 = 1$
135°	$-\sqrt{2}/2$	$2 - \sqrt{2} \simeq .586$
150°	$-\sqrt{3}/2$	$2 - \sqrt{3} \simeq .268$
180°	-1	$2 - 2 = 0$

See the graph in the text.
Note that since $\cos(-\theta) = \cos \theta$, the graph is symmetric with respect to the x-axis.

17. The graph $r = \sin 2\theta$ has symmetry with respect to the y-axis since $\sin(-2\theta) = -\sin 2\theta$, We will consider $0 \leq \theta \leq 90°$ and $270° \leq \theta \leq 360°$ in the table.

θ	2θ	$r = \sin 2\theta$
0°	0	0
15°	30°	$1/2 = .5$
30°	60	$\sqrt{3}/2 \simeq .86$
45°	90°	1
60°	120°	$\sqrt{3}/2 \simeq .86$
75°	150°	$1/2 = .5$
90°	180°	0
270°	540°	$\sin 180° = 0$
285°	570	$\sin 210° = -.5$
300°	600°	$\sin 240° \simeq -.86$
315°	630°	$\sin 270° = -1$
330°	660°	$\sin 300° \simeq -.86$
345°	690°	$\sin 330° = -.5$
360°	720°	0

See the graph in the answer section of the text.

21. Let $r = 4(1 - \cos \theta)$, and consider the table that follows.

θ	$\cos \theta$	$r = 4(1 - \cos \theta$
0°	1	$4 - 4 = 0$
30°	$\sqrt{3}/2$	$4 - 2\sqrt{3} \simeq .536$
45°	$\sqrt{2}/2$	$4 - 2\sqrt{2} \simeq 1.172$
60°	1/2	$4 - 2 = 2$
90°	0	$4 - 0 = 4$
120°	-1/2	$4 + 2 = 6$
135°	$-\sqrt{2}/2$	$4 + 2\sqrt{2} \simeq 6.828$
150°	$-\sqrt{3}/2$	$4 + 2\sqrt{3} \simeq 7.464$
180°	-1	$4 + 4 = 8$

See the graph in the text, and note the summetry with respect to the x-axis due to the cosine function.

25. Let $r = \dfrac{3}{2 + \sin \theta}$ and note the table below.

θ	$\sin \theta$	$r = \dfrac{3}{2 + \sin \theta}$
0°	0	$\dfrac{3}{2} = 1.5$
30°	1/2	$\dfrac{3}{5/2} = \dfrac{6}{5} = 1.2$
45°	$\sqrt{2}/2$	$\dfrac{6}{4 + \sqrt{2}} \simeq 1.108$
60°	$\sqrt{3}/2$	$\dfrac{6}{4 + \sqrt{3}} \simeq 1.047$
90°	1	$\dfrac{3}{3} = 1$
120°	$\sqrt{3}/2$	$\dfrac{6}{4 + \sqrt{3}} \simeq 1.047$
135°	$\sqrt{2}/2$	$\dfrac{6}{4 + \sqrt{2}} \simeq 1.108$
150°	1/2	$\dfrac{6}{5} = 1.2$
180°	0	$\dfrac{3}{2} = 1.5$

There is symmetry with respect to the y-axis due to the sine function. See the graph in the text.

We could also note that if we change to rectangular form, we have

$$r(2 + \sin \theta) = 3$$
$$2r = 3 - r \sin \theta$$
$$2\sqrt{x^2 + y^2} = 3 - y$$
$$4(x^2 + y^2) = 9 - 6y + y^2$$
$$4x^2 + 3y^2 + 6y = 9$$
$$4x^2 + 3(y^2 + 2y + 1) = 9 + 3$$
$$4x^2 + 3(y + 1)^2 = 12.$$

This is an ellipse with center at $(0, -1)$.

29. If $r\theta = \pi$, then $r = \frac{\pi}{\theta}$ and we have the following table for θ measured in radians and $-\pi \le \theta \le \pi$.

θ	$r = \frac{\pi}{\theta}$
$-\pi$	-1
$\frac{-5\pi}{6}$	$\frac{-6}{5}$
$\frac{-3\pi}{4}$	$\frac{-4}{3}$
$\frac{-2\pi}{3}$	$\frac{-3}{2}$
$\frac{-\pi}{2}$	-2
$\frac{-\pi}{3}$	-3
$\frac{-\pi}{4}$	-4
$\frac{-\pi}{6}$	-6
0	undefined
$\frac{\pi}{6}$	6
$\frac{\pi}{4}$	4
$\frac{\pi}{3}$	3
$\frac{\pi}{2}$	2
$\frac{2\pi}{3}$	$\frac{3}{2}$
$\frac{3\pi}{4}$	$\frac{4}{3}$
$\frac{5\pi}{6}$	$\frac{6}{5}$
π	1

Note that in order to plot a point like $(-1, -\pi)$, we look in the direction of $-\pi$ (out the negative horizontal axis) and move backward 1 unit. Note that if $\theta = \frac{\pi}{10,000}$, then $r = 10,000$, while $\theta = \frac{-\pi}{10,000}$ corresponds to $r = -10,000$. See the graph in the answer section of the text.

33. If $r = 2 \sin \theta$, then we can multiply by r and arrive at

$$r^2 = 2r \sin \theta$$
$$x^2 + y^2 = 2y$$
$$x^2 + y^2 - 2y = 0$$
$$x^2 + y^2 - 2y + 1 = 1$$
$$x^2 + (y - 1)^2 = 1.$$

This is a circle with center at $(0, 1)$ and radius 1. See the graph in the text.

37. If $r = 2 \cos \theta - 2 \sin \theta$, then

$$r^2 = 2r \cos \theta - 2r \sin \theta$$
$$x^2 + y^2 = 2x - 2y$$
$$x^2 - 2x + y^2 + 2y = 0$$
$$(x^2 - 2x + 1) + (y^2 + 2y + 1) = 2$$
$$(x - 1)^2 + (y - 1)^2 = 2.$$

This is a circle with center at the point $(1, -1)$ and radius $\sqrt{2}$. See the graph in the text.

41. If $r(\cos \theta + \sin \theta) = 2$, then

$$r \cos \theta + r \sin \theta = 2$$
$$x + y = 2.$$

This is a line. See the graph in the text.

45. If x + y = 4, then

   r cos θ + r sin θ = 4

   r(cos θ + sin θ) = 4.

49. If y = 2, then r sin θ = 2,

   or $r = \dfrac{2}{\csc \theta}$.

53. If $x^2 + 9y^2 = 36$, then

   $x^2 + y^2 + 8y^2 = 36$.

   We use $x^2 + y^2 = r^2$ and $y = r \sin \theta$
   to arrive at

   $r^2 + 8r^2 \sin^2 \theta = 36$.

   $r^2(1 + 8 \sin^2 \theta) = 36$.

   Alternatively, we could use
   $x = r \cos \theta$ and $y = r \sin \theta$ to
   arrive at

   $$x^2 + 9y^2 = 36$$

   $$r^2 \cos^2 \theta + 9r^2 \sin^2 \theta = 36$$

   $$r^2(\cos^2 \theta + 9 \sin^2 \theta) = 36.$$

Chapter 8   Review Exercises

Selected Solutions

1. If C is the right angle and if we are
   given A = 47°20' = 47.333° and
   b = 39.6 cm, then

   $\cos A = \dfrac{b}{c}$, so that

   $$c = \frac{b}{\cos A} = \cos \frac{39.6}{47.333°} \approx 58.4 \text{ cm.}$$

   Also, $\sin B = \dfrac{b}{c} = \dfrac{39.6}{58.4}$, and hence,

   $$B = \sin^{-1}\left(\frac{39.6}{58.4}\right) \approx 42°40',$$

   rounding to the nearest ten degrees.

5. If C = 90°, B = 88°20', and
   b = 402 feet, then

   $B = \dfrac{b}{c}$, so that

   $$c = \frac{b}{\sin B} = \frac{402}{\sin 88.333°},$$

   c ≈ 402.17, or c = 402

   Also,

   $\tan B = \dfrac{b}{a}$, so that

   $$a = \frac{b}{\tan B} = \frac{402}{\tan 88.333°}$$

   a ≈ 11.7 feet.

9.

We wish to find y. We have two
equations involving x and y.
They are

1) $\tan 18° = \dfrac{y}{x + 2000}$, and

2) $\tan 21°10' = \dfrac{y}{x}$.

1) gives $x + 2000 = \dfrac{y}{\tan 18°}$, and

2) gives $x = \dfrac{y}{\tan 21°10'}$:

Hence,

$$2000 = \frac{y}{\tan 18°} - x$$

$$2000 = \frac{y}{\tan 18°} - \frac{y}{\tan 21°10'}$$

$$y\left(\frac{1}{\tan 18°} - \frac{1}{\tan 21°10'}\right) = 2000$$

$$y = \frac{2000 \tan 18° \tan 21° 10'}{\tan 21°10' - \tan 18°},$$

or y ≈ 4040 feet, rounding to the
nearest ten feet.

13. Given B = 39°50', b = 268 m,
    a = 430 m, we can use the law
    of sines to find A as follows:

    $$\frac{b}{\sin B} = \frac{a}{\sin A}$$

    $$\sin A = \frac{a \sin B}{b}$$

    $$\sin A = \frac{430 \sin 39.833°}{268}$$

    $\sin A = 1.02775.$
    However, we cannot have sin A > 1.
    There is no solution.

17.

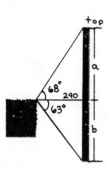

    The height of the second cliff is
    a + b. We note that

    $$\tan 68° = \frac{a}{290},$$

    and $\tan 63° = \dfrac{b}{290}$

    Thus, a = 290 tan 68°
        $a \approx 717.78$
    and   b = 290 tan 63°
        $b \approx 569.16.$
    We have a + b ≈ 1286.94 so we
    report the answer as a + b ≈ 1300
    feet, rounding to the nearest
    100 feet.

21. If A = 129°40', a = 127 ft,
    b = 69.8 feet, then we use the
    law of sines to arrive at

    $$\frac{a}{\sin A} = \frac{b}{\sin B}$$

    $$\sin B = \frac{b \sin A}{a}$$

    $$\sin B = \frac{69.8 \sin 129.667°}{127}$$

    $\sin B \approx 0.423069$

$B = \sin^{-1} (.423069)$, so that
$B \approx 25.0285$, or $B \approx 25°00'.$

25. Given A = 46°10', b = 18.4, c = 19.2,
    we use the law of cosines to arrive
    at

    $$a^2 = b^2 + c^2 - 2bc \cos A$$

    $$a^2 = (18.4)^2 + (19.2)^2 -$$
    $$2(18.4)(19.2) \cos 46.167°$$

    $$a^2 \approx 707.2 - 489.34$$

    $$a^2 \approx 217.86, \text{ so that}$$

    $a \approx 14.76$ or a = 14.8 m.

29.

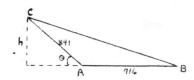

    From the figure we see that

    $$\sin \theta = \frac{h}{841}$$

    $h = 841 \sin 30.5°.$
    Hence, the area is given by

    $$A = \frac{1}{2} \text{ (base) (height)}$$

    $$A = \frac{1}{2} (716)(841) \sin 30.5°$$

    $$A \approx 152808.64,$$
    or $A = 153,000 \text{ m}^2$
    rounded to the nearest thousand.

33. See the graph in the answer section
    of the text.

37. If α = 75° and the magnitude is 69.2,
    then x = 69.2 cos 75°
        $x \approx 17.9,$
    and y = 69.2 sin 75°
        $y \approx 66.8.$

41. If $\theta = 210°$ and $|v| = 8$, then

$x = 8 \cos 210° = 8\left(\frac{-\sqrt{3}}{2}\right)$

$x = -4\sqrt{3}$,

and

$y = 8 \sin 210° = 8\left(\frac{-1}{2}\right)$

$y = -4$.

45. For the vector $<0, -2>$, the magnitude is

$r = \sqrt{0 + (-2)^2} = \sqrt{4} = 2$.   The direction angle θ is obviously 270° since the point $(0, -2)$ is on the negative y-axis.

49. If $\theta = 30°$ and $r = 20$, then

$x = r \cos \theta = 20 \cos 30°$

$x = 20\left(\frac{\sqrt{3}}{2}\right) = 10\sqrt{3}$,

and $y = 20 \sin \theta = 20 \sin 30°$

$y = 20\left(\frac{1}{2}\right) = 10$.

The vector is $10\sqrt{3}i + 10j$.

53. If $u = 5i = 5i + oj$ and

$v = 2i + 3j$, then

$u \cdot v = 5(2) + 0(3) = 10$.

57. If $u = <2\sqrt{3}, 2>$ and $v = <5, 5\sqrt{3}>$, then

$|u| = \sqrt{12 + 4} = 4$,

$|v| = \sqrt{25 + 75} = 10$, and

$u \cdot v = (2\sqrt{3})(5) + (2)(5\sqrt{3}) = 20\sqrt{3}$.

Using the formula

$\cos \theta = \frac{u \cdot v}{|u||v|}$ gives

$\cos \theta = \frac{20\sqrt{3}}{4 \ 10} = \frac{\sqrt{3}}{2}$.

Hence $\theta = 30°$.

61.

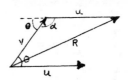

We use the law of cosines to find $|R|$.   The angle α is $180° - 58°20' = 121°40'$.   Hence

$|R|^2 = (85.2)^2 + (69.4)^2 - 2(85.2)(69.4) \cos 121°40'$

$|R|^2 \approx 12075.4 - (-6208.31)$

$|R|^2 \approx 18,283.71$, so that

$|R| \approx 135.22$, or $|R| \approx 135$ newtons.

65.

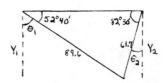

The y_1 and y_2 components are in lbs. The answer is $y_1 + y_2 - 10$, since the box weighs 10 lbs.   We have

$\cos \theta_1 = \frac{y_1}{89.6}$

$y_1 = 89.6 \cos 37.33°$

$y_1 \approx 71.25$,

and $\cos \theta_2 = \frac{y_2}{61.7}$

$y_2 = 61.7 \cos 7°30'$

$y_2 \approx 61.17$.

We have $y_1 + y_2 - 10 \approx 122.42$, or approximately 122 lbs.

69. The resultant is

$(7 + 3i) + (-2 + i) = 5 + 4i$.

73. See the graph in the answer section of the text.

77. Since $\cos 225° = \frac{-\sqrt{2}}{2}$ and

$\sin 225° = \frac{-\sqrt{2}}{2}$, we have

$2(\cos 225° + i \sin 225°)$

$= -\sqrt{2} - \sqrt{2}i.$

81. The number -4i lies on the negative
y - axis, so that $\theta = 270°$.
Also -4i = 0 - 4i so the magnitude
is $r = \sqrt{0^2 + (-4)^2} = \sqrt{16} = \sqrt{4}.$
Hence, the trigonometric form is
$-4i = 4(\cos 270° + i \sin 270°).$

85. $\dfrac{2(\cos 60° + i \sin 60°)}{8(\cos 300° + i \sin 300°)}$

$= \frac{1}{4}[\cos(-240°) + i \sin(-240°)]$

$= \frac{1}{4}(\cos 120° + i \sin 120°)$

since 120° and - 240°
are coterminal

$= \frac{1}{4}(\frac{-1}{2} + \frac{\sqrt{3}}{2}i)$

$= \frac{-1}{8} + \frac{\sqrt{3}}{8}i$

89. $(\cos 100° + i \sin 100°)$

$= \cos 600° + i \sin 600°$

$= \cos 240° + i \sin 240°$

$= -\frac{1}{2} - \frac{\sqrt{3}}{2}i$

93. In trigonometric form
$1 = 1(\cos 0° + i \sin 0°).$
The sixth roots of 1 have matnitude
$1^{1/6} = 1$, and the arguments are

k = 0: $\dfrac{0° + 360°·0}{6} = 0°,$

k = 1: $\dfrac{0° + 360°·1}{6} = 60°,$

k = 2: $\dfrac{0° + 360·2}{60} = 120°,$

k = 3: $\dfrac{0° + 360·3}{6} = 180°,$

k = 4: $\dfrac{0° + 360°·4}{6} = 240°,$ and

k = 5: $\dfrac{0° + 360°·5}{6} = 300°.$

Hence, the sixth roots of 1 are
$\cos 0° + i \sin 0° = 1,$
$\cos 60° + i \sin 60° = \frac{1}{2} + \frac{\sqrt{3}}{2}i,$
$\cos 120° + i \sin 120° = -\frac{1}{2} + \frac{\sqrt{3}}{2}i,$
$\cos 180° + i \sin 180° = -1,$
$\cos 240° + i \sin 240° = -\frac{1}{2} - \frac{\sqrt{3}}{2}i,$
and $\cos 300° + i \sin 300° = \frac{1}{2} - \frac{\sqrt{3}}{2}i.$

97. The graph $r = \dfrac{3}{1 + \cos \theta}$ has
symmetry with respect to the x-axis
since only $\cos \theta$ is involved.
Consider the following table.

θ	$\cos \theta$	$r = \dfrac{3}{1 + \cos \theta}$
0°	1	$\frac{3}{2} = 1.5$
30°	$\frac{\sqrt{3}}{2}$	$\dfrac{6}{2 + \sqrt{3}} \approx 1.608$
45°	$\frac{\sqrt{2}}{2}$	$\dfrac{6}{2 + \sqrt{2}} \approx 1.757$
60°	$\frac{1}{2}$	$\dfrac{6}{2 + 1} = 2.0$
90°	0	3.0
120°	$\frac{-1}{2}$	$\dfrac{6}{2 - 1} = 6$
135°	$\frac{-\sqrt{2}}{2}$	$\dfrac{6}{2 - \sqrt{2}} \approx 10.246$
150°	$\frac{-\sqrt{3}}{2}$	$\dfrac{6}{2 - \sqrt{3}} \approx 22.392$
180°	-1	undefined

See the final graph in the answer
section of the text.

101. If x = -3, then $r \cos \theta = -3$, or
$r = \dfrac{-3}{\sec \theta}$, whichever is desired.

105. In every triangle ABC the sum of the angles is 180°. That is, A + B + c = 180°. We then have A + B = 180° - C, or $\frac{1}{2}$(A + B) = 90° - $\frac{1}{2}$C. Using the formula sin (90° - α) = cos α, we have the formula

$$\sin \tfrac{1}{2}(A + B) = \sin (90° - \tfrac{1}{2}C),$$

or

(I) $\sin(\frac{A + B}{2}) = \cos \frac{C}{2}.$

The law of sines gives

$$\frac{a}{\sin A} = \frac{b}{\sin b}, \text{ or}$$

$$\frac{a}{b} = \frac{\sin A}{\sin B}$$

$$\frac{a}{b} + 1 = \frac{\sin A}{\sin B} + 1$$

(II) $\quad \frac{a + b}{b} = \frac{\sin A + \sin B}{\sin B}.$

also,

$$\frac{b}{\sin B} = \frac{c}{\sin C}, \text{ or}$$

(III) $\quad \frac{b}{c} = \frac{\sin B}{\sin C}.$

Multiplying (II) and (III) gives

$$\frac{a + b}{b}\,\frac{b}{c} = \frac{\sin A + \sin B}{\sin B} \cdot \frac{\sin B}{\sin C}$$

(IV) $\quad \frac{a + b}{c} = \frac{\sin A + \sin B}{\sin C}.$

Use the identity

sin C = 2 sin $\frac{C}{2}$ cos $\frac{C}{2}$ and the

factor identity sin A + sin B

= 2 sin $(\frac{A + B}{2})$ cos $(\frac{A - B}{2})$.

Substituting these in (IV) gives

$$\frac{a + b}{c} = \frac{2 \sin (\frac{A + B}{2}) \cos (\frac{A - B}{2})}{2 \sin \frac{C}{2} \cos \frac{C}{2}}.$$

However, using (I),

cos $\frac{C}{2}$ = sin $(\frac{A + B}{2})$, we cancel

2 and sin $(\frac{A + B}{2})$ and arrive at

$$\frac{a + b}{c} = \frac{\cos (\frac{A - B}{2})}{\sin \frac{C}{2}},$$

Newton's formula.

107.

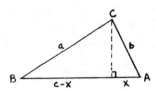

Let ABC be any given triangle and drop a perpendicular from C to side AB. Label x as in the figure. Then we have

cos A = $\frac{x}{b}$, so that   x = b cos A.

also, cos B = $\frac{c - x}{a}$, or c - x = a cos B.

addition gives   c = a cos B + b cos A, , which is the desired result.

108. Using c = a cos B + b cos A from exercise 107, we have

$$\frac{\sin C}{c}\,c = \frac{\sin C}{c} \cdot a \cos B + \frac{\sin C}{c}\,b \cdot \cos A$$

$$\sin C = \frac{\sin A}{a} \cdot a \cos B + \frac{\sin B}{b} \cdot b \cos A$$

since $\frac{\sin C}{c} = \frac{\sin A}{a}$ and $\frac{\sin C}{c} = \frac{\sin B}{b}$.

Therefore,

sin C = sin A cos B + sin B cos A.

110. We have sin (A + B) = sin C from exercise 109, and exercise 108 gives sin C = sin A cos B + sin B cos A. Hence, we conclude that

sin (A + B) = sin A cos B + sin B cos A.

113. We know that $\tan 180° = 0$. If
$A + B + C = 180°$, then
$0 = \tan 180° = \tan(A + B + C)$
$0 = \tan[(A + B) + C]$
$$0 = \frac{\tan(A + B) + \tan C}{1 - \tan(A+B)\,\tan C}.$$
However, a fraction is zero only
when the numerator is zero. Hence,
$\tan(A + B) + \tan C = 0$.
This implies that
$$\frac{\tan A + \tan B}{1 - \tan A \tan B} + \tan C = 0$$
$\tan A + \tan B + \tan C\,(1 - \tan A \tan B) = 0$
$\tan A + \tan B + \tan C - \tan A \tan B \tan C = 0$,
or $\tan A + \tan B + \tan C =$
$\tan A \tan B \tan C$.

117. Using the fact that $|z|^2 = z\bar{z}$,
we have
$$|z_1 + z_2|^2 = (z_1 + z_2)(\overline{z_1 + z_2})$$
$$= (z_1 + z_2)(\bar{z}_1 + \bar{z}_2)$$
$$= z_1\bar{z}_1 + z_2\bar{z}_1 + z_1\bar{z}_2 +$$
$$z_2\bar{z}_2$$
$$= |z_1|^2 + |z_2|^2 +$$
$$z_1\bar{z}_2 + \bar{z}_1 z_2 .$$
However, $\overline{(z_1\bar{z}_2)} = \bar{z}_1\bar{z}_2 = \bar{z}_1 z_2$.
Hence $z_1\bar{z}_2 + \bar{z}_1 z_2 = 2R(z_1\bar{z}_2)$.
Then we have
$$|z_1 + z_2|^2 = |z_1|^2 + |z_2|^2 + 2R(z_1\bar{z}_2).$$

Chapter 8 Test
Solve each of the following right triangles. Angle C is the right angle.
1. A = 48°20', b = 78.9 m   2. B = 10°10', b = 23.5 in

3. An airplane is flying at an altitude of 10,000 feet. The angle of depression
    from the plane to a tree is 13°50'. How far horizontally must the plane fly
    to be directly over the tree?

4. The angle of elevation to the top of a mountain from a point 140,000 feet from a
    point directly below the top of the mountain is 8°10'. The point from which
    the observation is made is at an altitude of 4000 feet. Find the height of the
    mountain.

Solve each of the following triangles that exist.
5. A = 27°10', C = 115° 30', c = 76.3 ft

6. B = 38°40', a = 19.7 cm, C = 91°40'

Find the missing angles in each of the following triangles.
7. A = 41°20', a = 25.9 m, c = 38.4 m

8. A = 38°40', a = 9.72 m, b = 11.8 m

Solve each triangle.
9. A = 67°20', b = 37.9 m, c = 40.8 m

10. B = 168°10', a = 15.1 cm, c = 19.2 cm

11. Find all angles in a triangle having a = 28 m, b = 47 m, and c = 58 m.
    Round to the nearest ten minutes.

12. The longest diagonal of a parallelogram is 15.7 m in length. The angle opposite
    this diagonal is 104°30'. One side of the parallelogram has a length of 8.91 m.
    Find the length of the side adjacent to this side.

Find the area of each triangle.
13. A = 29°10', b = 11.9 m, c = 14.7 m

14. a = 56.1 m, b = 22.5 m, c = 44.2 m

Let u = <7, -1>, v = <3, -5>, and w = <-2, 5>. Find each of the following.

15. 2v - 3w   16. -u + 4w

Find the x- and y- components of the vectors having the following direction angle and magnitude.

17. $\theta = 27°30'$, $|v| = 15.4$ 18. $\theta = 59°40'$, $|v| = 78.9$

Find the magnitude and direction angle for the following vectors.

19. $<\sqrt{3},\ -1>$ 20. $<6\sqrt{2},\ -6\sqrt{2}>$

21. $3i - 4j$ 22. $-5i\sqrt{3} + 5j$

Find the dot product for the following vectors.

23. $u = -3i + 9j$, $v = i + 6j$ 24. $u = <8,\ -3>$ and $v = <-1,\ 0>$

25. Find the angle between vectors $3i + 2j$ and $5i - j$.

26. Two forces of 31.5 lb and 22.9 lb act on a point. The resultant force is 36.7 lb. Find the angle between the forces.

27. Find the force required to keep a 25,000-lb. truck parked on a hill that makes an angle of 5°10' with the horizontal.

28. Person A pulls on a rope with a force of 38.9 lb. This rope is attached to a heavy object. Person B pulls on a rope attached to the same object, with a force of 47.2 lb. The angle between the ropes is 142°50'. Find the direction and magnitude of the equilibrant.

Find the polar coordinates of the following complex numbers.

29. $2 + 2i\sqrt{3}$ 30. $2 - i\sqrt{2}$

Express in standard form the complex numbers whose polar coordinates are given.

31. $(4,\ 120°)$ 32. $(9,\ 270°)$

Write the following as complex numbers in standard form.

33. $3(\cos 450° + i \sin 450°)$ 34. $5(\cos 300° + i \sin 300°)$

Find the following powers. Write the result in standard form.

35. $(1 + i\sqrt{3})^4$ 36. $(5\sqrt{2} - 5i\sqrt{2})^3$

Find all cube roots of the following complex numbers.

37. 1   38. $2 + 2i\sqrt{3}$

Graph each of the following.

39. $r = 4 \sin \theta$ 40. $r(1 - \cos \theta) = 6$

41. $r = 2 \sin \theta + 2$ 42. $r^2 = 4 \cos 2\theta$

43. $r = 4$ 44. $r = \dfrac{\pi}{\theta}$

   (Answers for this test are on page 363.)

CHAPTER 9   Systems of Equations and Inequalities

Section 9.1   Linear Systems

Additional Examples

Example 1   Solve $2x - 3y + z = 4$
$$3x + 2y - 2z = 2.$$

Solution   We could try some manipulations to have the coefficient of x in the first equation as 1 without introducing fractions (such as subtracting equation one from equation two, and then interchanging equations), but with only two equations we will leave the equations in their given order and plunge ahead. Thus, change equation one by multiplying by $\frac{1}{2}$. This gives

(1) $x - \frac{3}{2}y + \frac{1}{2}z = 2$

(2) $3x + 2y - 2z = 2.$

Then we eliminate x in (2) by replacing equation (2) by the sum of equation (2) and -3 times equation (1). This gives

(1) $x - \frac{3}{2}y + \frac{1}{2}z = 2$

(2) $\frac{13}{2}y - \frac{7}{2}z = -4.$

We want the coefficient of y in equation (2) to be one, so we multiply equation (2) by $\frac{2}{13}$. This gives

(1) $x - \frac{3}{2}y + \frac{1}{2}z = 2$

(2) $y - \frac{7}{13}z = \frac{-8}{13}.$

We cannot eliminate the z-variable since there are only two equations. Hence, we solve for x and y in terms of z. This gives

(2) $y = \frac{7}{13}z - \frac{8}{13}$

and (1) $x = \frac{3}{2}y - \frac{1}{2}z + 2,$

or $x = \frac{3}{2}(\frac{7}{13}z - \frac{8}{13}) - \frac{1}{2}z + 2$

substituting the y in (2)

$x = \frac{21}{26}z - \frac{12}{13} - \frac{1}{2}z + 2$

$x = (\frac{21 - 13}{26})z - (\frac{12 - 26}{13})$

$x = \frac{4}{13}z + \frac{14}{13}.$

There are infinitely many solutions to this system. If we let z be any arbitrary number k, then

$x = \frac{4}{13}k + \frac{14}{13},$ $y = \frac{7}{13}k - \frac{8}{13},$

and z = k is a solution. For example, k = 0 gives $x = \frac{14}{13}$, $y = \frac{-8}{13}$, and z = 0. Substitution shows that these numbers check. Also, letting k = 3 gives x = 2, y = 1, and z = 3, which check; k = -10 gives x = -2, y = -6, and z = -10, and so on.

Example 2   A hose and a water pipe running at the same time can fill a swimming pool in 5 hours. If the pipe and hose are run for 2 hours and the hose is shut off, it takes 6 more hours to fill the pool. How long will it take for each to fill the pool alone?

Solution   Let x be the number of hours it will take to fill the pool if only the water pipe is used, and let y be the number of hours using the hose alone. In 1 hour the pipe fills $\frac{1}{x}$ of the pool and the hose fills $\frac{1}{y}$ of the pool. Since the pool is filled in 5 hours' if they are running at the same time, we have $\frac{5}{x} + \frac{5}{y} = 1$. The second statement says that if both are run for 2 hours ($\frac{2}{x} + \frac{2}{y}$) and the pipe then runs for 6 hours ($\frac{6}{x}$), the pool is filled. That is,

$$\frac{8}{x} + \frac{2}{y} = 1.$$

This gives the system

(1) $\dfrac{5}{x} + \dfrac{5}{y} = 1$

(2) $\dfrac{8}{x} + \dfrac{2}{y} = 1.$

Dividing equation (1) by 5 gives

(1) $\dfrac{1}{x} + \dfrac{1}{y} = \dfrac{1}{5}$

(2) $\dfrac{8}{x} + \dfrac{2}{y} = 1.$

Replacing equation (2) by the sum of equation (2) and -8 times equation (1) gives

(1) $\dfrac{1}{x} + \dfrac{1}{y} = \dfrac{1}{5}$

(2) $-\dfrac{6}{y} = -\dfrac{3}{5},$ or $\dfrac{1}{y} = \dfrac{1}{10}.$

Solving equation (2) for y gives y = 10. Substituting y = 10 into equation (1) gives

$$\frac{1}{x} + \frac{1}{10} = \frac{1}{5}$$

$$\frac{1}{x} = \frac{1}{5} - \frac{1}{10} = \frac{1}{10},$$

or   x = 10.

Hence, both the hose and the pipe can fill the pool in 10 hours working alone.

Selected Solutions

1. Given the system

      x - 5y = 8
          x = 4y,

we substitute x = 4y into the first equation and arrive at

4y - 5y = 8
    -y = 8
     y = 8.

Then using x = 4y, we have x = -32.
The solution is x = -32, y = -8.
The solution set is {(-32, -8)}.

5. Given   7x - y = -10
            3y - x = 10,

the first equation gives y = 7x + 10. Substituting into the second equation gives

3(7x + 10) - x = 10
   21x + 30 - x = 10
            20x = -20
              x = -1.

Then y = 7(-1) + 10 = 3. The solution set is the set containing one point, s = {(-1, 3)}.

9. We can write this system as

  x - 2y + z = 0   (1)
 3x + y - 3z = 19   (2)
 2x - y + 4z = -1.   (3)

Leave equation (1) unchanged. Change equation (2) by adding to equation (2) -3 times equation (1). Change equation (3) by adding to equation (3) -2 times equation (1). This gives the new equations,

 x - 2y + z = 0   (1)
     7y - 6z = 19   (2)
     3y + 2z = -1.   (3)

We can solve equations (2) and (3) for y and z. If we multiply equation (3) by 3 and add to equation (2), we eliminate z and arrive at

16y = 16,   or
  y = 1.

Substituting y = 1 in 3y + 2z = -1 gives

3(1) + 2z = -1
       2z = -4
        z = -2.

Then, substituting y = 1, z = -2 in equation (1) gives

x - 2(1) + (-2) = 0
              x = 4.

The solution set is {(4, 1, -2)}.

13. If $3x + 2y = -6$
         $5x - 2y = -10$,
   we can add the two equations and
   arrive at $8x = -16$. Thus, $x = -2$,
   and we can substitute into the
   first equation and get
   $3(-2) + 2y = -6$
            $2y = 0$
             $y = 0$.
   The solution set is $\{(-2, 0)\}$.

17. Given $5x + 7y = 6$ (1)
           $10x - 3y = 46$,   (2)
   we multiply equation (1) by -2 and
   arrive at
   $-10x - 14y = -12$ (1)
    $10x - 3y = 46$.   (2)
   Adding gives
         $-17y = 34$
            $y = -2$.
   Substituting $y = -2$ into equation
   (2) gives
   $10x - 3(-2) = 46$
         $10x = 40$
           $x = 4$.
   The solution set is $\{(4, -2)\}$.

21. Given $\dfrac{x}{2} + \dfrac{y}{3} = 8$ (1)
           $\dfrac{2x}{3} + \dfrac{3y}{2} = 17$,   (2)
   we can clear fractions if we multi-
   ply both equations by 6. This
   gives
   $3x + 2y = 48$ (1)
   $4x + 9y = 102$.   (2)
   To eliminate x, multiply (1) by 4
   and (2) by -3. This gives
    $12x + 8y = 172$ (1)
   $-12x - 27y = -306$.   (2)
   Adding equations gives $-19y = -114$,
   or $y = 6$. Substituting $y = 6$ back
   into the original equation (1)
   gives

$\dfrac{x}{2} + \dfrac{6}{3} = 8$

$\dfrac{x}{2} = 6$

$x = 12$.
The solution set is $\{(12, 6)\}$.

25. Given the system
   $0.05x - 0.02y = -0.18$ (1)
   $0.04x + 0.06y = -0.22$,   (2)
   multiply (1) and (2) by 100. This
   gives
   $5x - 2y = -18$ (1)
   $4x + 6y = -22$.   (2)
   Now, multiply (1) by 3:
   $15x - 6y = -54$ (1')
    $4x + 6y = -22$.   (2)
   Add to eliminate y:
   $19x = -76$
     $x = -4$.
   Substituting $x = -4$ in $5x - 2y = -18$
   gives
   $-20 - 2y = -18$
       $-2y = 2$
          $y = -1$.
   Thus, $x = -4$ and $y = -1$.
   The solution set is $\{(-4, -1)\}$.

29. Given the system
      $1.9x - 4.8y = 11.2$ (1)
   $-4.37x + 11.04y = -7.6$ (2)
   Since $\dfrac{4.37}{1.9} = 2.3$, multiply (1) by 2.3:
    $4.37x - 11.04y = 25.76$ (1')
   $-4.37x + 11.04y = -7.6$.   (2)
   Adding these equations gives:
    $0 \cdot x + 0 \cdot y = 18.16$.
   This is impossible, so the system
   has no solutions. The solution
   set is $\emptyset$.

33. Given the system
    $x + y + z = 2$ (1)
   $2x + y - z = 5$ (2)
    $x - y + z = -2$,   (3)

add (1) and (2): $3x + 2y = 7$; and
add (2) and (3): $3x \qquad = 3$.
The last equation gives $x = 1$, and
substituting $x = 1$ into $3x + 2y = 7$
gives $y = 2$. Then we can find
$z = -1$. The solution set is
$\{(1, 2, -1\}$.

37. Given the system

$x + 2y + 3z = 8$ (1)
$3x - y + 2z = 5$ (2)
$-2x - 4y - 6z = 5$,   (3)

multiply (1) by 2 to get

$2x + 4y + 6z = 16$ (1')
$3x - y + 2z = 5$ (2')
$-2x - 4y - 6z = 15$.   (3')

Add (1') and (3') to get

$$0 = 21.$$

No solution. The solution set is $\emptyset$.

41. Given the system

$5.3x - 4.7y + 5.9z = 1.14$ (1)
$-2.5x + 3.2y - 1.4z = 7.22$ (2)
$2.25x - 2.88y + 1.26z = 4.88$,   (3)

we can multiply equation (2) by
0.9 and arrive at

$-2.25x + 2.88y - 1.26z = 6.498$.   (2)

writing equation (3),

$2.25x - 2.88y + 1.26z = 4.88$,   (3)

and subtracting gives

$$0 = 1.618.$$

This is impossible, so the solution
set is $\emptyset$.

45. Given the system

$\dfrac{2}{x} + \dfrac{1}{y} = 11$ (1)

$\dfrac{3}{x} - \dfrac{5}{y} = 10$ (2)

we let $\dfrac{1}{x} = t$ and $\dfrac{1}{y} = u$ to arrive at

$2t + u = 11$ (1)
$3t - 5u = 10$.   (2)

Multiplying equation (1) by 5 gives
the system

$10t + 5u = 55$ (1)
$3t - 5u = 10$,   (2)

and adding gives $13t = 65$, or $t = 5$.
Substituting $t = 5$ into $3t - 5u = 10$
gives

$15 - 5u = 10$
$5 = 5u$
$u = 1$.

If $t = 5$, then $\dfrac{1}{x} = 5$, or $x = \dfrac{1}{5}$.

If $u = 1$, then $\dfrac{1}{y} = 1$, or $y = 1$.

The solution set is $\{(\dfrac{1}{5}, 1)\}$.

49. If we let $\dfrac{1}{x} = t$, $\dfrac{1}{y} = u$, and $\dfrac{1}{z} = s$,

then the system becomes

$2t + 3u - 2s = -1$ (1)
$8t - 12u + 5s = 5$ (2)
$6t + 3u - s = 1$.   (3)

If we multiply equation (1) by -3
and add to equation (3), we have

$-6t - 9u + 6s = 3$ (1)
$6t + 3u - s = 1$ (3)
_____
$-6u + 5s = 4$.   (A)

Multiplying equation (1) by -4 and
adding to equation (2) gives

$-8t - 12u + 8s = 4$ (1)
$8t - 12u + 5s = 5$ (2)
_____
$-24u + 13s = 9$.   (B)

We can then multiply equation (A)
by -4 and add to equation (B) to get

$24u - 20s = -16$
$-24u + 13s = 9$
_____
$-7s = -7$,
$s = 1$.

Then, substituting $s = 1$ into
$-6u + 5s = 4$ gives $-6u + 5(1) = 4$,
or $-6u = -1$, so that $u = \dfrac{1}{6}$. We

can then substitute $s = 1$ and $u = \dfrac{1}{6}$

into the equation (2) $8t - 12u + 5s = 5$
and arrive at

$$8t - 12\left(\frac{1}{6}\right) + 5(1) = 5$$
$$8t - 2 \quad + 5 \quad = 5$$
$$8t = 2$$
$$t = \frac{1}{4}.$$

Then we have $x = \frac{1}{t} = 4$, $y = \frac{1}{u} = 6$,

and $z = \frac{1}{s} = 1$. The solution set
is $\{(4, 6, 1)\}$.

53. Given the system of equations
$$5x + 4y + z = 0 \qquad (1)$$
$$x + y \qquad = 0 \qquad (2)$$
$$-10x + 8y - 2z = 0, \qquad (3)$$
we can see that if we multiply
equation (1) by -2 we have exactly
equation (3). This implies that
equation (3) (or equation (1)) may
be omitted and the solution set is
the same. We can, for convenience,
write the systems as
$$x + y \qquad = 0$$
$$5x - 4y + z = 0,$$
and if we multiply the first by -5
and add, we have
$$x + y \qquad = 0$$
$$-9y + z = 0,$$
or
$$x + y \qquad = 0$$
$$y \qquad = \frac{1}{9}z.$$

If we subtract the second from the
first, we have the system
$$x = -\frac{1}{9}z$$
$$y = \frac{1}{9}z.$$

Hence, by arbitrarily choosing any
number k and letting z = k, we have
a solution $x = -\frac{k}{9}$, $y = \frac{k}{9}$, and z = k.
There are infinitely many solutions,
one for each choice of k. We could
remove the fractional appearance by
the notation: Let t be any arbitrarily chosen real number and let

z = 9t. Then x = -t, y = t, and
z = 9t is a solution. The solution
set is $\{(-t, t, 9t): t \in R\}$.

57. Let g = the cost of one goat and
let s = the cost of one sheep. Then
we have
$$6g + 5s = 305$$
$$2g + 9s = 285.$$
Solving by elimination gives
$$6g + 5s = 305$$
$$-6g - 27s = -855$$
$$\overline{\qquad\qquad\qquad}$$
$$- 22s = -550,$$
or $\qquad$ s = \$25.
Substituting s = 25 in the equation
6g + 5s = 305 gives g = \$30.

61. Let x = liters of 70% solution and
let y = liters of 20% solution. Then
x + y = 30. Making an equation that
describes the amount of alcohol
present, we have .7x + .2y = .5(30),
or .7x + .2y = 15. This gives the
system of equations
$$.7x + .2y = 15 \qquad (1)$$
$$x + y = 30, \qquad (2)$$
and we multiply (1) by 10 and (2)
by -2. This gives
$$7x + 2y = 150$$
$$-2x - 2y = -60$$
$$\overline{\qquad\qquad\qquad}$$
$$5x \qquad = 90$$
$$x = 18.$$
Substitution of x = 18 into x + y = 30
gives y = 12. The solution is x = 18
liters of 70% solution and y = 12
liters of 20% solution.

65. Let x = amount invested at 8%. Then
Mr. Caminiti has 3x dollars invested
at 12%. If the annual income is
\$2200, we have the equation

$$.08x + .12(3x) = 2200$$
$$8x + 12(3x) = 220,000 \quad \text{multiply by 100}$$
$$44x = 220,000$$
$$x = 5000.$$

Mr. Caminiti invested %5000 at 8% and $15,000 at 12%.

67.   Let x = amount of 4.5% butterfat. Then we have
$$.045x = .02(250 + x)$$
$$.045x = 5 + .02x$$
$$.025x = 5, \text{ or}$$
$$x = 200 \text{ gallons.}$$

69.   Let x = rate of car 1, and then x + 20 = rate of car 2. Consider the table below.

	t	r	d = rt
car 1	4	x	4x
car 2	4	x + 20	4(x + 20)

Then we have
$$4x + 4(x + 20) = 656$$
$$8x + 80 = 656$$
$$8x = 576, \text{ or}$$
$$x = 72 \text{ kph,}$$
and   x + 20 = 92 kph.

71.   Let x = length of shortest side,
        2x = length of medium side, and
    2x + 3 = length of longest side.

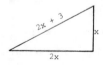

Then $x + 2x + (2x + 3) = 33$
$$5x = 30$$
$$x = 6.$$
The lengths are 6, 12, and 15.

73.   Let x be the "second" number. Then, x + 2 is the "first" number, and $(\frac{2}{3})x$ is the "third" number.

Also,
$$x + (x + 2) + (\tfrac{2}{3}x) = 50$$
$$2x + \tfrac{2}{3}x = 48$$
$$\tfrac{8}{3}x = 48$$
so that $x = 48 \left(\tfrac{3}{8}\right) = 18.$

Hence, the second number is 18. The first is x + 2 = 20, and the third is $\frac{2}{3}x = 12.$

77.   If $s(t) = at^2 + bt + c$ and if s(0) = 5, s(1) = 23, and s(2) = 37, then
$$s(0) = 5 = a(0) + b(0) + c, \text{ implies } c = 5,$$
$$s(1) = 23 = a + b + c, \text{ or } a + b = 18,$$
$$s(2) = 37 = 4a + 2b + c, \text{ or } 4a + 2b = 32.$$
We multiply the equation a + b = 18 by -2 and add to the other equation. This gives
$$-2a - 2b = -36$$
$$\underline{4a + 2b = 32}$$
$$2a = -4$$
$$a = -2.$$
Substitution of a = -2 into a + b = 18 gives b = 20. Hence,
$s(t) = -2t^2 + 20t + 5.$ Then we have
$$s(8) = -2(64) + 20(8) + 5$$
$$= -128 + 160 + 5$$
$$= 37.$$

Section 9.2   Matrix Solution of Linear Systems

Additional Examples

Example 1   Use the Gaussian reduction method to solve the system
$$x + 4y - 2z = 5$$
$$3x - 2y + z = -6$$
$$x - 10y + 5z = -16.$$

Solution   Writing the augmented matrix and using Gaussian reduction, we have

$$\begin{bmatrix} 1 & 4 & -2 & 5 \\ 3 & -2 & 1 & -6 \\ 1 & -10 & 5 & -16 \end{bmatrix}$$

$$\sim \begin{bmatrix} 1 & 4 & -2 & 5 \\ 0 & -14 & 7 & -21 \\ 0 & -14 & -7 & -21 \end{bmatrix} \begin{matrix} \\ r_2' = r_2 - 3r_1 \\ r_3' = r_3 - r_1 \end{matrix}$$

$$\sim \begin{bmatrix} 1 & 4 & -2 & 5 \\ 0 & 1 & -\frac{1}{2} & \frac{3}{2} \\ 0 & 0 & 0 & 0 \end{bmatrix} \begin{matrix} \\ r_2'' = \frac{-1}{14}\, r_2' \\ r_3'' = r_3' - r_2' \end{matrix}$$

This matrix is in echelon form, and the conclusions can now be drawn. However, one further step could help in making the conclusions. Use row 2 and place a zero above the 1 in the a_{22} position. Multiplying row 2 by -4 and adding to row 1 gives

$$\sim \begin{bmatrix} 1 & 0 & 0 & -1 \\ 0 & 1 & -\frac{1}{2} & \frac{3}{2} \\ 0 & 0 & 0 & 0 \end{bmatrix} \begin{matrix} r_1''' = r_1'' - 4r_2'' \\ \\ \end{matrix}.$$

Now, the conclusions are that

$x = -1$ and $y - \frac{1}{2}z = \frac{3}{2}$, or

$$y = \frac{1}{2}z + \frac{3}{2}.$$

Hence, there are infinitely many solutions. If we arbitrarily choose any real number k and let $z = k$, then $x = -1$ and

$y = \frac{k}{2} + \frac{3}{2}$.

The solution set is

$\{(-1, \frac{k+3}{2}, k), k$ is any real number$\}$.

Some solutions are $(-1, 1, -1)$

$(-1, 2, 1)$, and $(-1, \frac{3}{2}, 0)$.

Example 2   Solve the system

$2x - y + 4z = 5$
$x + y - z = 7$
$4x - 2y + 8z = 9$.

Solution   Using Gaussian reduction we have

$$\begin{bmatrix} 2 & -1 & 4 & 5 \\ 1 & 1 & -1 & 7 \\ 4 & -2 & 8 & 9 \end{bmatrix}$$

$$\sim \begin{bmatrix} 1 & 1 & -1 & 7 \\ 2 & -1 & 4 & 5 \\ 4 & -2 & 8 & 9 \end{bmatrix} \begin{matrix} r_1' = r_2 \\ r_2' = r_1 \\ \end{matrix}$$

$$\sim \begin{bmatrix} 1 & 1 & -1 & 7 \\ 0 & -3 & 6 & -9 \\ 0 & -6 & 12 & -19 \end{bmatrix} \begin{matrix} \\ r_2'' = r_2' - 2r_1' \\ r_3'' = r_3' - 4r_1' \end{matrix}$$

$$\sim \begin{bmatrix} 1 & 1 & -1 & 7 \\ 0 & -3 & 6 & -9 \\ 0 & 0 & 0 & -1 \end{bmatrix} \begin{matrix} \\ \\ r_3''' = r_3'' - 2r_2''. \end{matrix}$$

Hence, the original system is equivalent to the system in this last matrix. Note the last equation is $0 \cdot x + 0 \cdot y + 0 \cdot z = 1$, which cannot have a solution. We conclude that the given system has no solutions.

Example 3   The sum of three numbers is 1. The first number subracted from 3 times the third number gives 25. Find the three numbers.

Solution   Let x, y, and z be the numbers. Then

$x + y + z = 1$

and $3z - x = 25$

are equations describing the given statements. We can write this as

$x + y + z = 1$
$-x + 3z = 25$,

and the augmented matrix is

$$\begin{bmatrix} 1 & 1 & 1 & 1 \\ -1 & 0 & 3 & 25 \end{bmatrix}$$

$$\sim \begin{bmatrix} 1 & 1 & 1 & 1 \\ 0 & 1 & 4 & 26 \end{bmatrix} \begin{matrix} \\ r_2' = r_2 + r_1 \end{matrix}$$

$$\sim \begin{bmatrix} 1 & 0 & -3 & -25 \\ 0 & 1 & 4 & 26 \end{bmatrix} \begin{matrix} r_1'' = r_1' - r_2' \\ \end{matrix}.$$

This is as far as we can go using Gaussian reduction. We must solve for x and y in terms of an arbitrary z. We have for z arbitrarily chosen

$x = 3z - 25$

$y = 26 - 4z.$

The solution set is

$\{(3k - 25, 26 - 4k, k),\ k$ any real number$\}$. This can be described in words that if we let z be any arbitrarily chosen real number, say k, then $x = 3k - 25$, $y = 26 - 4k$, and $z = k$ are numbers that satisfy the conditions.

For example, letting k = 1 gives $x = -22$, $y = 22$, and $z = 1$, and these numbers satisfy $x + y + z = 1$ and $3z - x = 25$. Some other solutions are $(-4, -2, 7)$, $(-40, 46, -5)$, and $(3\pi - 25, 26 - 4\pi, \pi)$.

Selected Solutions

1. $\begin{bmatrix} 2 & 3 & | & 11 \\ 1 & 2 & | & 8 \end{bmatrix}$

5. $\begin{bmatrix} 2 & 1 & 1 & | & 3 \\ 3 & -4 & 2 & | & -7 \\ 1 & 1 & 1 & | & 2 \end{bmatrix}$

9. $2x + y = 1$
   $3x - 2y = -9$

13. $3x + 2y + z = 1$
    $2y + 4z = 22$
    $-x - 2y + 3z = 15$

17. $\begin{bmatrix} 1 & 1 & | & -3 \\ 2 & -5 & | & -6 \end{bmatrix} \sim \begin{bmatrix} 1 & 1 & | & -3 \\ 0 & -7 & | & 0 \end{bmatrix}$

Hence, y = 0 and substitution gives x = -3. The solution set is $\{(-3, 0)\}$.

21. The augmented matrix gives

$\begin{bmatrix} 2 & -5 & | & 10 \\ 3 & 1 & | & 15 \end{bmatrix}$

$\sim \begin{bmatrix} 1 & -\frac{5}{2} & | & 5 \\ 3 & 1 & | & 15 \end{bmatrix}\ r_1' = \frac{1}{2}r_1$

$\sim \begin{bmatrix} 1 & -\frac{5}{2} & | & 5 \\ 0 & \frac{17}{2} & | & 0 \end{bmatrix} .\ r_2'' = r_2' - 3r_1'$

Equation 2 gives y = 0. Substitution of y = 0 in equation 1 gives x = 5. The solution set is $\{(5, 0)\}$.

25. $\begin{bmatrix} 1 & 1 & -1 & | & 6 \\ 2 & -1 & 1 & | & -9 \\ 1 & -2 & 3 & | & 1 \end{bmatrix}$

$\sim \begin{bmatrix} 1 & 1 & -1 & | & 6 \\ 0 & -3 & 3 & | & -21 \\ 0 & -3 & 4 & | & -5 \end{bmatrix}\ \begin{matrix} \\ r_2' = r_2 - 2r_1 \\ r_3' = r_2 - r_1 \end{matrix}$

$\sim \begin{bmatrix} 1 & 1 & -1 & | & 6 \\ 0 & 1 & -1 & | & 7 \\ 0 & 0 & 1 & | & 16 \end{bmatrix}\ \begin{matrix} \\ r_2'' = \frac{-1}{3}r_2' \\ r_3'' = r_3' - r_2' \end{matrix}$

$\sim \begin{bmatrix} 1 & 1 & 0 & | & 22 \\ 0 & 1 & 0 & | & 23 \\ 0 & 0 & 1 & | & 16 \end{bmatrix}\ \begin{matrix} r_1''' = r_1'' + r_3'' \\ r_2''' = r_2'' + r_3 \\ \end{matrix}$

$\sim \begin{bmatrix} 1 & 0 & 0 & | & -1 \\ 0 & 1 & 0 & | & 23 \\ 0 & 0 & 1 & | & 16 \end{bmatrix}\ \begin{matrix} r_1^4 = r_1''' - r_2''' \\ \\ \end{matrix}$

This gives the solution x = -1, y = 23, and z = 16. Note that the last two steps are an alternate to the back-substitution method. The solution set is $\{(-1, 23, 16)\}$.

29. $\begin{bmatrix} 2 & -1 & 3 & | & 0 \\ 1 & 2 & -1 & | & 5 \\ 0 & 2 & 1 & | & 1 \end{bmatrix}$

$\sim \begin{bmatrix} 1 & 2 & -1 & | & 5 \\ 2 & -1 & 3 & | & 0 \\ 0 & 2 & 1 & | & 1 \end{bmatrix}\ \begin{matrix} \\ \text{interchange} \\ \text{row 1 and} \\ \text{row 2} \end{matrix}$

$$\sim \begin{bmatrix} 1 & 2 & -1 & | & 5 \\ 0 & -5 & 5 & | & -10 \\ 0 & 2 & 1 & | & 1 \end{bmatrix} \quad r_2' = r_2 - 2r_1$$

$$\sim \begin{bmatrix} 1 & 2 & -1 & | & 5 \\ 0 & 1 & -1 & | & 2 \\ 0 & 0 & 3 & | & -3 \end{bmatrix} \quad \begin{array}{l} r_2'' = -\frac{1}{5}r_2' \\ r_3'' = r_3' + \frac{2}{5}r_2' \end{array}$$

$$\sim \begin{bmatrix} 1 & 2 & 0 & | & 4 \\ 0 & 1 & 0 & | & 1 \\ 0 & 0 & 1 & | & -1 \end{bmatrix} \quad \begin{array}{l} r_1''' = r_1'' + \frac{1}{3}r_3'' \\ r_2''' = r_2'' + \frac{1}{3}r_3'' \\ \text{Divide by 3} \end{array}$$

Adding to the first row -2 times the second row, we arrive at

$$\sim \begin{bmatrix} 1 & 0 & 0 & | & 2 \\ 0 & 1 & 0 & | & 1 \\ 0 & 0 & 1 & | & -1 \end{bmatrix}.$$

The solution is $x = 2$, $y = 1$, $z = -1$.

33. $\begin{bmatrix} 1 & 1 & 1 & | & 6 \\ 2 & -1 & -1 & | & 3 \end{bmatrix}$

$$\sim \begin{bmatrix} 1 & 1 & 1 & | & 6 \\ 0 & -3 & -3 & | & -9 \end{bmatrix}$$

$$\sim \begin{bmatrix} 1 & 1 & 1 & | & 6 \\ 0 & 1 & 1 & | & 3 \end{bmatrix}$$

$$\sim \begin{bmatrix} 1 & 0 & 0 & | & 3 \\ 0 & 1 & 1 & | & 3 \end{bmatrix}.$$

Then $x = 3$ and $y + z = 3$, or $y = 3 - z$, z arbitrary. There are infinetely many solutions, and the solution set can be expressed as $\{(3, 3 - z, z), z \text{ is any real number}\}$.

37. $\begin{bmatrix} 1 & 3 & -1 & | & 0 \\ 0 & 2 & -1 & | & 4 \end{bmatrix}$

$$\sim \begin{bmatrix} 1 & 3 & -1 & | & 0 \\ 0 & 1 & -\frac{1}{2} & | & 2 \end{bmatrix} \quad \text{Multiply by } \frac{1}{2}$$

$$\sim \begin{bmatrix} 1 & 0 & \frac{1}{2} & | & -6 \\ 0 & 1 & -\frac{1}{2} & | & 2 \end{bmatrix} \quad r_1' = r_1 - 3r_2$$

The solutions are

$(-6 - \frac{1}{2}z, \frac{1}{2}z + 2, z)$, z arbitrary.

41. $\begin{bmatrix} 1 & -1 & 2 & 1 & | & 4 \\ 0 & 1 & 1 & 0 & | & 3 \\ 0 & 0 & 1 & -1 & | & 2 \end{bmatrix}$

$$\sim \begin{bmatrix} 1 & 0 & 3 & 1 & | & 7 \\ 0 & 1 & 1 & 0 & | & 3 \\ 0 & 0 & 1 & -1 & | & 2 \end{bmatrix} \quad \begin{array}{l} \text{Add row 2} \\ \text{to row 1} \end{array}$$

$$\sim \begin{bmatrix} 1 & 0 & 0 & 4 & | & 1 \\ 0 & 1 & 0 & 1 & | & 1 \\ 0 & 0 & 1 & -1 & | & 2 \end{bmatrix} \quad \begin{array}{l} r_1' = r_1 - 3r_3 \\ r_2' = r_2 - r_3 \end{array}$$

Then we have $x = 1 - 4w$, $y = 1 - w$, and $z = 2 + w$, w any arbitrary real number. The solution set is $\{(1 - 4w, 1 - w, 2 + w, w)$ w is any real number$\}$.

45. Using a calculator and the method of Gaussian reduction, we have

$$\begin{bmatrix} 9.1 & 2.3 & -1 & | & -3.06 \\ 4.7 & 1 & -3.8 & | & -21.15 \\ 0 & 5.1 & -4.7 & | & -31.77 \end{bmatrix}$$

$$\sim \begin{bmatrix} 9.1 & 2.3 & -1 & | & -3.06 \\ 0 & -.1879 & -3.2835 & | & -19.56956 \\ 0 & 5.1 & -4.7 & | & -31.77 \end{bmatrix}$$

$$\sim \begin{bmatrix} 9.1 & 2.3 & -1 & | & -3.06 \\ 0 & .1879 & 3.2835 & | & 19.56956 \\ 0 & 0 & -93.8211 & | & -562.928 \end{bmatrix}$$

$$\sim \begin{bmatrix} 9.1 & 2.3 & -1 & | & -3.06 \\ 0 & .1879 & 3.2835 & | & 19.56956 \\ 0 & 0 & 1 & | & 6 \end{bmatrix}.$$

Thus, $z = 6$, and substitution gives $y = -.7$ and $x = .5$.

47. Let w = number of days wife worked, and let h = number of days husband worked. Then

$w + h = 72$, and
$32w + 28h = 2176$.

$$\begin{bmatrix} 1 & 1 & | & 72 \\ 32 & 28 & | & 2176 \end{bmatrix} \sim \begin{bmatrix} 1 & 1 & | & 72 \\ 0 & -4 & | & -128 \end{bmatrix}$$

$$\sim \begin{bmatrix} 1 & 1 & | & 72 \\ 0 & 1 & | & 32 \end{bmatrix}$$

$$\sim \begin{bmatrix} 1 & 0 & | & 40 \\ 0 & 1 & | & 32 \end{bmatrix}$$

Thus, $w = 40$ days and $h = 32$ days.

49.   Let x = number of model 201 made
             in one day,

    and let y = number of model 301 made
             in one day.

    Then we have

    $2x + 3y = 34$

    $25x + 30y = 365.$

    $$\begin{bmatrix} 2 & 3 & 45 \\ 25 & 30 & 365 \end{bmatrix} \sim \begin{bmatrix} 2 & 3 & 34 \\ 0 & -7.5 & -60 \end{bmatrix}$$

    $$\sim \begin{bmatrix} 2 & 3 & 34 \\ 0 & 1 & 8 \end{bmatrix} \sim \begin{bmatrix} 2 & 0 & 10 \\ 0 & 1 & 8 \end{bmatrix}$$

    The answer is

    5 model 201 and 8 model 301.

51. Let x = amount at 8%,

         y = amount at 10%,

    and z = amount at 9%.

    Then we have

    $$y = \frac{1}{2}x + 2000,$$

    $$x + y + z = 25000, \text{ and}$$

    $.08x + .10y + .09z = 2220.$

    $$\begin{bmatrix} 1 & 1 & 1 & 25000 \\ -\frac{1}{2} & 1 & 0 & 2000 \\ .08 & .10 & .09 & 2220 \end{bmatrix}$$

    $$\sim \begin{bmatrix} 1 & 1 & 1 & 25000 \\ -1 & 2 & 0 & 4000 \\ 8 & 10 & 9 & 222000 \end{bmatrix}$$

    $$\sim \begin{bmatrix} 1 & 1 & 1 & 25000 \\ 0 & 3 & 1 & 29000 \\ 0 & 2 & 1 & 22000 \end{bmatrix}$$

    $$\sim \begin{bmatrix} 1 & 1 & 1 & 25000 \\ 0 & 1 & 0 & 7000 \\ 0 & 2 & 1 & 22000 \end{bmatrix}$$

    $$\sim \begin{bmatrix} 1 & 1 & 1 & 25000 \\ 0 & 1 & 0 & 7000 \\ 0 & 0 & 1 & 8000 \end{bmatrix}$$

    The answer is:

    $8000 at 9%, $7000 at 10%, and
    $10,000 at 8%.

52. The equation for intersection

    D is $x_3 + x_4 = 400 + 200$, or

         $x_3 + x_4 = 600.$

53. The augmented matrix is

    $$\begin{array}{cccc} x_1 & x_2 & x_3 & x_4 \\ \end{array}$$

    $$\begin{bmatrix} 1 & 0 & 0 & 1 & 1000 \\ 1 & 1 & 0 & 0 & 1100 \\ 0 & 1 & 1 & 0 & 700 \\ 0 & 0 & 1 & 1 & 600 \end{bmatrix}$$

    $$\sim \begin{bmatrix} 1 & 0 & 0 & 1 & 1000 \\ 0 & 1 & 0 & -1 & 100 \\ 0 & 1 & 1 & 0 & 700 \\ 0 & 0 & 1 & 1 & 600 \end{bmatrix} \quad r_2' = r_2 - r_1$$

    $$\sim \begin{bmatrix} 1 & 0 & 0 & 1 & 1000 \\ 0 & 1 & 0 & -1 & 100 \\ 0 & 0 & 1 & 1 & 600 \\ 0 & 0 & 1 & 1 & 600 \end{bmatrix} \quad r_3'' = r_3' - r_2'$$

    $$\sim \begin{bmatrix} 1 & 0 & 0 & 1 & 1000 \\ 0 & 1 & 0 & -1 & 100 \\ 0 & 0 & 1 & 1 & 600 \\ 0 & 0 & 0 & 0 & 0 \end{bmatrix}.$$

    We can let x_4 be arbitrarily chosen,
    and then $x_1 = 100 - x_4$, $x_2 = 100 + x_4$,
    and $x_3 = 600 - x_4$.

57. Since $x_3 = 600 - x_4$ and $x_4 = 600 - x_3$,
    the largest values of x_3 and x_4 so
    that neither variable is negative
    are $x_3 = 600$ and $x_4 = 600$.

59.   Let s = cost of a small box,
    and let ℓ = cost of a large box.
    Then $3s + 8\ell = 13.30$

           $6s + 16\ell = 27.20$

    $$\begin{bmatrix} 3 & 8 & 13.30 \\ 6 & 16 & 27.20 \end{bmatrix} \sim \begin{bmatrix} 3 & 8 & 13.30 \\ 0 & 0 & .60 \end{bmatrix}$$

    No solution, inconsistent.

61. $x + y + z = -10$

         $y + 2z = 5$

    $$\begin{bmatrix} 1 & 1 & 1 & -10 \\ 0 & 1 & 2 & 5 \end{bmatrix} \sim \begin{bmatrix} 1 & 0 & -1 & -15 \\ 0 & 1 & 2 & 5 \end{bmatrix}$$

There are infinitely many solutions. For any number z, $(z - 15, 5 - 2z, z)$ is a solution.

65. We have

$$\frac{A}{m} + \frac{B}{m - 1} + \frac{C}{(m - 1)^2}$$

$$= \frac{A(m - 1)^2 + Bm(m - 1) + Cm}{m(m - 1)^2}.$$

Hence, $A(m - 1)^2 + Bm(m - 1) + Cm$
$= 2m^2 - 3m + 3$ for all real numbers
m. This gives
$A(m^2 - 2m + 1) + B(m^2 - m) + Cm$
$= 2m^2 - 3m + 3$
$(A + B)m^2 + (-2A - B + C)m + A$
$= 2m^2 - 3m + 3.$
Thus, equating coefficients, we have

$$A + B = 2$$
$$-2A - B + C = -3$$
$$A = 3.$$

Substituting $A = 3$ in $A + B = 2$
gives $B = -1$. Then equation two
gives
$$-2(3) - (-1) + C = -3$$
$$C = 2.$$
The constants are $A = 3$, $B = -1$,
and $C = 2$.

Section 9.3   Properties of Matrices

Additional Examples

Example 1   Find the product

$$\begin{bmatrix} 2 & 1 & 3 \\ 1 & 0 & 2 \\ 2 & -1 & 1 \\ -2 & 3 & 1 \end{bmatrix} \begin{bmatrix} 1 & -1 \\ 2 & 3 \\ 2 & 1 \end{bmatrix}.$$

Solution   We have the product of a
4 x 3 matrix and a 3 x 2 matrix.
The result will be a 4 x 2 matrix.
We have

$$\begin{bmatrix} 2 & 1 & 3 \\ 1 & 0 & 2 \\ 2 & -1 & 1 \\ -2 & 3 & 1 \end{bmatrix} \begin{bmatrix} 1 & -1 \\ 2 & 3 \\ 2 & 1 \end{bmatrix}$$

$$= \begin{bmatrix} 2\cdot 1 + 1\cdot 2 + 3\cdot 2 & 2(-1) + 1\cdot 3 + 3\cdot 1 \\ 1\cdot 1 + 0\cdot 2 + 2\cdot 2 & 1(-1) + 0\cdot 3 + 2\cdot 1 \\ 2\cdot 1 + (-1)\cdot 2 + 1\cdot 2 & 2(-1) + (-1)\cdot 3 + 1\cdot 1 \\ -2\cdot 1 + 3\cdot 2 + 1\cdot 2 & -2(-1) + 3\cdot 3 + 1\cdot 1 \end{bmatrix},$$

$$= \begin{bmatrix} 10 & 4 \\ 5 & 1 \\ 2 & -4 \\ 6 & 12 \end{bmatrix}.$$

Example 2   Find numbers x, y, and z
such that

$$\begin{bmatrix} 1 & 2 & -1 \\ 2 & 3 & 1 \\ -1 & 2 & 3 \end{bmatrix} \begin{bmatrix} x \\ y \\ z \end{bmatrix} = \begin{bmatrix} 3 \\ 8 \\ 3 \end{bmatrix}.$$

Solution   Multiplying the matrices on
the left-hand side gives

$$\begin{bmatrix} 1 & 2 & -1 \\ 2 & 3 & 1 \\ -1 & 2 & 3 \end{bmatrix} \begin{bmatrix} x \\ y \\ z \end{bmatrix} = \begin{bmatrix} x + 2y - z \\ 2x + 3y + z \\ -x + 2y + 3z \end{bmatrix},$$

a one-row, one-column matrix. We
then equate this matrix with

$$\begin{bmatrix} 3 \\ 8 \\ 3 \end{bmatrix}.$$

We can conclude that the numbers
x, y, and z must be solutions to
the system
$$x + 2y + z = 3$$
$$2x + 3y + z = 8$$
$$-x + 2y + 3z = 3.$$
Solving by Gaussian reduction gives

$$\begin{bmatrix} 1 & 2 & -1 & 3 \\ 2 & 3 & 1 & 8 \\ -1 & 2 & 3 & 3 \end{bmatrix}$$

$$\sim \begin{bmatrix} 1 & 2 & -1 & 3 \\ 0 & -1 & 3 & 2 \\ 0 & 4 & 2 & 6 \end{bmatrix} \begin{matrix} \\ r_2' = r_2 - 2r_1 \\ r_3' = r_3 + r_1 \end{matrix}$$

$$\sim \begin{bmatrix} 1 & 2 & -1 & 3 \\ 0 & 1 & -3 & -2 \\ 0 & 0 & 14 & 14 \end{bmatrix} \begin{matrix} \\ r_2'' = -r_2' \\ r_3'' = r_3' + 4r_2' \end{matrix}$$

$$\sim \begin{bmatrix} 1 & 2 & -1 & 3 \\ 0 & 1 & -3 & -2 \\ 0 & 0 & 1 & 1 \end{bmatrix}$$

$$\sim \begin{bmatrix} 1 & 2 & 0 & 4 \\ 0 & 1 & 0 & 1 \\ 0 & 0 & 1 & 1 \end{bmatrix} \begin{array}{l} 4_1''' = r_1'' + r_3'' \\ .4_2''' = r_2'' + r_3'' \end{array}$$

Now we can easily see that z = 1, y = 1, and we can solve x + 2y = 4 with y = 1 to arrive at x = 2. The solution is

$$\begin{bmatrix} x \\ y \\ z \end{bmatrix} = \begin{bmatrix} 2 \\ 1 \\ 1 \end{bmatrix} .$$

Selected Solutions

1. If $\begin{bmatrix} 2 & 1 \\ 4 & 8 \end{bmatrix} = \begin{bmatrix} x & 1 \\ y & z \end{bmatrix}$, we must have

x = 2, y = 4, and z = 8.

5. $\begin{bmatrix} -7 + z & 4r & 8s \\ 6p & 2 & 5 \end{bmatrix} = \begin{bmatrix} -9 & 8r & 3 \\ 2 & 5 & 4 \end{bmatrix}$ is

$\begin{bmatrix} -16 + z & 12r & 85 + 3 \\ 6p + 2 & 7 & 8 \end{bmatrix}$, and if

this matrix is equal to

$\begin{bmatrix} 2 & 36 & 27 \\ 20 & 7 & 12a \end{bmatrix}$, then we must have

-16 + z = 2, or z = 18; 12r = 36, or r = 3; 8s + 3 = 27, or s = 3; 6p + 2 = 20, or p = 3; and

12a = 9, or a = $\frac{3}{4}$.

9. $\begin{bmatrix} -6 & 8 \\ 0 & 0 \end{bmatrix} - \begin{bmatrix} 0 & 0 \\ -4 & -2 \end{bmatrix} = \begin{bmatrix} -6 - 0 & 8 - 0 \\ 0 + 4 & 0 + 2 \end{bmatrix}$

$$= \begin{bmatrix} -6 & 8 \\ 4 & 2 \end{bmatrix}$$

13. $\begin{bmatrix} -4x + 2y & -3x + y \\ 6x - 3y & 2x - 5y \end{bmatrix} +$

$\begin{bmatrix} -8x + 6y & 2x \\ 3y - 5x & 6x + 4y \end{bmatrix}$

$$= \begin{bmatrix} -12x + 8y & -x + y \\ x & 8x - y \end{bmatrix}$$

15. Written as a 3 x 2 matrix:

$$\begin{array}{c} \quad\;\; F \quad R \\ \begin{array}{c} L \\ M \\ S \end{array} \begin{bmatrix} 7 & 2 \\ 9 & 0 \\ 8 & 6 \end{bmatrix} , \end{array}$$

and written as a 2 x 3 matrix, we have

$$\begin{bmatrix} 7 & 9 & 8 \\ 2 & 0 & 6 \end{bmatrix} .$$

17. If A = $\begin{bmatrix} -2 & 4 \\ 0 & 3 \end{bmatrix}$, then 2A = $\begin{bmatrix} -4 & 8 \\ 0 & 6 \end{bmatrix}$.

21. -A = $\begin{bmatrix} 2 & -4 \\ 0 & -3 \end{bmatrix}$ and $\frac{1}{2}$B = $\begin{bmatrix} -3 & 1 \\ 2 & 0 \end{bmatrix}$,

so that

-A + $\frac{1}{2}$B = $\begin{bmatrix} 2 & -4 \\ 0 & -3 \end{bmatrix} + \begin{bmatrix} -3 & 1 \\ 2 & 0 \end{bmatrix}$

$$= \begin{bmatrix} -1 & -3 \\ 2 & -3 \end{bmatrix} .$$

25. $\begin{bmatrix} -1 & 2 & 0 \\ 0 & 3 & 2 \\ 0 & 1 & 4 \end{bmatrix} \begin{bmatrix} 2 & -1 & 2 \\ 0 & 2 & 1 \\ 3 & 0 & -1 \end{bmatrix}$

$$= \begin{bmatrix} -2 + 0 + 0 & 1 + 4 + 0 & -2 + 2 + 0 \\ 0 + 0 + 6 & 0 + 6 + 0 & 0 + 3 - 2 \\ 0 + 0 + 12 & 0 + 2 + 0 & 0 + 1 - 4 \end{bmatrix}$$

$$= \begin{bmatrix} -2 & 5 & 0 \\ 6 & 6 & 1 \\ 12 & 2 & -3 \end{bmatrix}$$

29. This multiplication is not possible since the first matrix is 2 x 4 and the second is 2 x 2.

33. $\begin{bmatrix} 3 \\ -2 \\ 1 \end{bmatrix} \begin{bmatrix} -2 & 4 & 6 \end{bmatrix} = \begin{bmatrix} -6 & 12 & 18 \\ 4 & -8 & -12 \\ -2 & 4 & 6 \end{bmatrix}$

37. $\begin{bmatrix} -.6 & .93 \\ .8 & .47 \end{bmatrix} \begin{bmatrix} .9 & .4 \\ .6 & -.8 \end{bmatrix}$

$= \begin{bmatrix} -.54 + (.93)(.6) & -.24 + (.93)(-.8) \\ .72 + (.47)(.6) & .32 + (.47)(-.8) \end{bmatrix}$

$= \begin{bmatrix} 0.18 & -.984 \\ 1.002 & -.056 \end{bmatrix}$

41. Let $A = \begin{bmatrix} a_{11} & a_{12} \\ a_{21} & a_{22} \end{bmatrix}$ and

$B = \begin{bmatrix} b_{11} & b_{12} \\ b_{21} & b_{22} \end{bmatrix}$. Then

$A + B = \begin{bmatrix} a_{11} + b_{11} & a_{12} + b_{12} \\ a_{21} + b_{21} & a_{22} + b_{22} \end{bmatrix}$

$= \begin{bmatrix} b_{11} + a_{11} & b_{12} + b_{22} \\ b_{21} + a_{21} & a_{22} + b_{22} \end{bmatrix}$

$= B + A.$

45. If $A = \begin{bmatrix} a_{11} & a_{12} \\ a_{21} & a_{22} \end{bmatrix}$, then

$-A = \begin{bmatrix} -a_{11} & -a_{12} \\ -a_{21} & -a_{22} \end{bmatrix}$

and

$A + (-A) = \begin{bmatrix} a_{11} & a_{12} \\ a_{21} & a_{22} \end{bmatrix} + \begin{bmatrix} -a_{11} & -a_{12} \\ -a_{21} & -a_{22} \end{bmatrix}$

$= \begin{bmatrix} 0 & 0 \\ 0 & 0 \end{bmatrix} = 0,$ and

$-A + A = \begin{bmatrix} -a_{11} & -a_{12} \\ -a_{21} & -a_{22} \end{bmatrix} + \begin{bmatrix} a_{11} & a_{12} \\ a_{21} & a_{22} \end{bmatrix}$

$= \begin{bmatrix} 0 & 0 \\ 0 & 0 \end{bmatrix} = 0.$

49. We have

$A + B = \begin{bmatrix} a_{11} + b_{11} & a_{12} + b_{12} \\ a_{21} + b_{21} & a_{22} + b_{22} \end{bmatrix},$

so that

$c(A + B) = \begin{bmatrix} c(a_{11} + b_{11}) & c(a_{12} + b_{12}) \\ c(a_{21} + b_{21}) & c(a_{22} + b_{22}) \end{bmatrix}$

$c(A + B) = \begin{bmatrix} ca_{11} + cb_{11} & ca_{12} + cb_{12} \\ ca_{21} + cb_{21} & ca_{22} + cb_{22} \end{bmatrix}$

$= \begin{bmatrix} ca_{11} & ca_{12} \\ ca_{21} & ca_{22} \end{bmatrix} + \begin{bmatrix} cb_{11} & cb_{12} \\ cb_{21} & cb_{22} \end{bmatrix}$

$= cA + cB.$

53. If we let $A = \begin{bmatrix} 1 & 1 \\ 0 & 0 \end{bmatrix}$ and $B = \begin{bmatrix} 1 & 0 \\ 1 & 0 \end{bmatrix}$,

then $A + B = \begin{bmatrix} 2 & 1 \\ 1 & 0 \end{bmatrix}$, $A - B = \begin{bmatrix} 0 & 1 \\ -1 & 0 \end{bmatrix}$,

so that

$(A + B)(A - B) = \begin{bmatrix} 2 & 1 \\ 1 & 0 \end{bmatrix} \begin{bmatrix} 0 & 1 \\ -1 & 0 \end{bmatrix}$

$= \begin{bmatrix} 0 - 1 & 2 + 0 \\ 0 + 0 & 1 + 0 \end{bmatrix}$

$= \begin{bmatrix} -1 & 2 \\ 0 & 1 \end{bmatrix}.$

Also, $A^2 = \begin{bmatrix} 1 & 1 \\ 0 & 0 \end{bmatrix} \begin{bmatrix} 1 & 1 \\ 0 & 0 \end{bmatrix}$

$= \begin{bmatrix} 1 & 1 \\ 0 & 0 \end{bmatrix}$ and

$B^2 = \begin{bmatrix} 1 & 0 \\ 1 & 0 \end{bmatrix} \begin{bmatrix} 1 & 0 \\ 1 & 0 \end{bmatrix}$

$= \begin{bmatrix} 1 & 0 \\ 1 & 0 \end{bmatrix},$ so that

$A^2 - B^2 = \begin{bmatrix} 1 & 0 \\ 0 & 0 \end{bmatrix} - \begin{bmatrix} 1 & 0 \\ 1 & 0 \end{bmatrix}$

$= \begin{bmatrix} 0 & 1 \\ -1 & 0 \end{bmatrix}.$

Hence, $(A + B)(A - B) \neq A^2 - B^2.$

57. We have $A = \begin{bmatrix} a & b \\ c & d \end{bmatrix}$, $A^T = \begin{bmatrix} a & c \\ b & d \end{bmatrix}$,

$B = \begin{bmatrix} m & n \\ p & q \end{bmatrix}$, and $B^T = \begin{bmatrix} m & p \\ m & q \end{bmatrix}.$

Hence,

$$AB = \begin{bmatrix} am + bp & an + bg \\ cm + dp & cn + dg \end{bmatrix}, \text{ and}$$

$$(AB)^T = \begin{bmatrix} am + bp & cm + dp \\ an + bq & cn + dg \end{bmatrix}.$$

also,

$$B^T A^T = \begin{bmatrix} m & p \\ n & q \end{bmatrix} \begin{bmatrix} a & c \\ b & d \end{bmatrix}$$

$$= \begin{bmatrix} ma + pb & mc + pd \\ na + qb & nc + qd \end{bmatrix}$$

$$= \begin{bmatrix} am + bp & cm + dp \\ an + bq & cn + dq \end{bmatrix}$$

$$= (AB)^T.$$

Section 9.4   Matrix Inverses

Additional Examples

Example 1   Find A^{-1} if

$$A = \begin{bmatrix} 1 & -2 & 3 \\ 3 & 1 & 2 \\ 2 & 2 & 1 \end{bmatrix}.$$

Solution   We have the following:

$$\begin{bmatrix} 1 & -2 & 3 & | & 1 & 0 & 0 \\ 3 & 1 & 2 & | & 0 & 1 & 0 \\ 2 & 2 & 1 & | & 0 & 0 & 1 \end{bmatrix}$$

$$\sim \begin{bmatrix} 1 & -2 & 3 & | & 1 & 0 & 0 \\ 0 & 7 & -7 & | & -3 & 1 & 0 \\ 0 & 6 & -5 & | & -2 & 0 & 1 \end{bmatrix} \begin{matrix} \\ r_2' = r_2 - 3r_1 \\ r_3' = r_3 - 2r_1 \end{matrix}$$

$$\sim \begin{bmatrix} 1 & -2 & 3 & | & 1 & 0 & 0 \\ 0 & 1 & -2 & | & -1 & 1 & -1 \\ 0 & 6 & -5 & | & -2 & 0 & 1 \end{bmatrix} \begin{matrix} \\ r_2'' = r_2' - r_3' \\ \end{matrix}$$

$$\sim \begin{bmatrix} 1 & 0 & -1 & | & -1 & 2 & -2 \\ 0 & 1 & -2 & | & -1 & 1 & -1 \\ 0 & 0 & 7 & | & 4 & -6 & 7 \end{bmatrix} \begin{matrix} r_1''' = r_1'' + 2r_2'' \\ \text{no change} \\ r_3''' = r_3'' - 6r_2 \end{matrix}$$

$$\sim \begin{bmatrix} 1 & 0 & -1 & | & -1 & 2 & -2 \\ 0 & 1 & -2 & | & -1 & 1 & -1 \\ 0 & 0 & 1 & | & \frac{4}{7} & -\frac{6}{7} & 1 \end{bmatrix} \begin{matrix} \\ \\ r_3^{(4)} = \frac{1}{7} r_3''' \end{matrix}$$

$$\sim \begin{bmatrix} 1 & 0 & 0 & | & -\frac{3}{7} & \frac{8}{7} & -1 \\ 0 & 1 & 0 & | & \frac{1}{7} & -\frac{5}{7} & 1 \\ 0 & 0 & 1 & | & \frac{4}{7} & -\frac{6}{7} & 1 \end{bmatrix} \begin{matrix} r_1^{(5)} = r_1^{(4)} + r_3^{(4)} \\ r_2^{(5)} = r_2^{(4)} + 2r_3^{(4)} \\ \\ \end{matrix}.$$

Hence,

$$A^{-1} = \begin{bmatrix} -\frac{3}{7} & \frac{8}{7} & -1 \\ \frac{1}{7} & -\frac{5}{7} & 1 \\ \frac{4}{7} & -\frac{6}{7} & 1 \end{bmatrix}.$$

The result can be checked by showing $AA^{-1} = I = A^{-1}A$.

Example 2   Solve the system of equations by finding the inverse of the coefficient matrix.

$$2x - 3y + z = 11$$
$$-x + 2y - 2z = -9$$
$$3x + y + 2z = 12$$

Solution   We can write the system as

$$\begin{bmatrix} 2 & -3 & 1 \\ -1 & 2 & -2 \\ 3 & 1 & 2 \end{bmatrix} \begin{bmatrix} x \\ y \\ z \end{bmatrix} = \begin{bmatrix} 11 \\ -9 \\ 12 \end{bmatrix}, \text{ or } AX = B.$$

To find the inverse of the coefficient matrix we have

$$\begin{bmatrix} 2 & -3 & 1 & | & 1 & 0 & 0 \\ -1 & 2 & -2 & | & 0 & 1 & 0 \\ 3 & 1 & 2 & | & 0 & 0 & 1 \end{bmatrix}$$

$$\sim \begin{bmatrix} 1 & -1 & -1 & | & 1 & 1 & 0 \\ -1 & 2 & -2 & | & 0 & 1 & 0 \\ 3 & 1 & 2 & | & 0 & 0 & 1 \end{bmatrix} \begin{matrix} r_1' = r_1 + r_2 \\ \\ \end{matrix}$$

$$\sim \begin{bmatrix} 1 & -1 & -1 & | & 1 & 1 & 0 \\ 0 & 1 & -3 & | & 1 & 2 & 0 \\ 0 & 4 & 5 & | & -3 & -3 & 1 \end{bmatrix} \begin{matrix} \\ r_2'' = r_2' + r_1' \\ r_3'' = r_3' - r_1' \end{matrix}$$

$$\sim \begin{bmatrix} 1 & 0 & -4 & | & 2 & 3 & 0 \\ 0 & 1 & -3 & | & 1 & 2 & 0 \\ 0 & 0 & 17 & | & -7 & -11 & 1 \end{bmatrix} \begin{matrix} r_1''' = r_1'' + r_2'' \\ \\ r_3''' = r_3'' - 4r_2'' \end{matrix}$$

$$\sim \begin{bmatrix} 1 & 0 & -4 & | & 2 & 3 & 0 \\ 0 & 1 & -3 & | & 1 & 2 & 0 \\ 0 & 0 & 1 & | & \frac{-7}{17} & \frac{-11}{17} & \frac{1}{17} \end{bmatrix} \begin{matrix} \\ \\ r_3^{(4)} = \frac{1}{17} r_3''' \end{matrix}$$

$$\sim \begin{bmatrix} 1 & 0 & 0 \\ 0 & 1 & 0 \\ 0 & 0 & 1 \end{bmatrix} \left.\begin{matrix} \frac{6}{17} & \frac{7}{17} & \frac{4}{17} \\ \frac{-4}{17} & \frac{1}{17} & \frac{3}{17} \\ \frac{-7}{17} & \frac{-11}{17} & \frac{1}{17} \end{matrix}\right] \quad \begin{matrix} r_1^{(5)}=r_1^{(4)}+4r_3^{(4)} \\ r_2^{(5)}=r_2^{(4)}+3r_3^{(4)} \end{matrix}$$

Hence,

$$A^{-1} = \begin{bmatrix} \frac{6}{17} & \frac{7}{17} & \frac{4}{17} \\ \frac{-4}{17} & \frac{1}{17} & \frac{3}{17} \\ \frac{-7}{17} & \frac{-11}{17} & \frac{1}{17} \end{bmatrix}, \text{ so that}$$

$$\begin{bmatrix} x \\ y \\ z \end{bmatrix} = \begin{bmatrix} \frac{6}{17} & \frac{7}{17} & \frac{4}{17} \\ \frac{-4}{17} & \frac{1}{17} & \frac{3}{17} \\ \frac{-7}{17} & \frac{-11}{17} & \frac{1}{17} \end{bmatrix} \begin{bmatrix} 11 \\ -9 \\ 12 \end{bmatrix}$$

$$= \begin{bmatrix} \frac{66}{17} - \frac{63}{17} + \frac{48}{17} \\ \frac{44}{17} - \frac{9}{17} + \frac{36}{17} \\ -\frac{77}{17} + \frac{99}{17} + \frac{12}{17} \end{bmatrix}$$

$$= \begin{bmatrix} \frac{51}{17} \\ \frac{-17}{17} \\ \frac{34}{17} \end{bmatrix} = \begin{bmatrix} 3 \\ -1 \\ 2 \end{bmatrix}.$$

Selected Solutions

1. Multiplying the matrices gives
$$\begin{bmatrix} 2 & 3 \\ 1 & 1 \end{bmatrix}\begin{bmatrix} -1 & 3 \\ 1 & -2 \end{bmatrix} = \begin{bmatrix} -2+3 & 6-6 \\ -1+1 & 3-2 \end{bmatrix}$$
$$= \begin{bmatrix} 1 & 0 \\ 0 & 1 \end{bmatrix}.$$
Hence, these matrices are inverses.

5. $$\begin{bmatrix} 1 & 2 & 0 \\ 0 & 1 & 0 \\ 0 & 1 & 0 \end{bmatrix}\begin{bmatrix} 1 & -2 & 0 \\ 0 & 1 & 0 \\ 0 & -1 & 1 \end{bmatrix} = \begin{bmatrix} 1 & 0 & 0 \\ 1 & 1 & 0 \\ 1 & 1 & 0 \end{bmatrix}$$
This product is not the identity. These matrices are not inverses of each other.

9. Using the Gaussian reduction method we have
$$\begin{bmatrix} 1 & -1 & 1 & 0 \\ 2 & 0 & 0 & 1 \end{bmatrix} \sim \begin{bmatrix} 1 & -1 & 1 & 0 \\ 0 & 2 & -2 & 1 \end{bmatrix} \quad r_2''=r_2-2r_1$$

$$\sim \sim \begin{bmatrix} 1 & -1 & 1 & 0 \\ 0 & 1 & -1 & \frac{1}{2} \end{bmatrix} \quad \begin{matrix}\text{Multiply} \\ \text{by } 1/2\end{matrix}$$

$$\sim \begin{bmatrix} 1 & 0 & 0 & \frac{1}{2} \\ 0 & 1 & -1 & \frac{1}{2} \end{bmatrix} \quad r_1''=r_1'+r_2'$$

Then, if $A = \begin{bmatrix} 1 & -1 \\ 2 & 0 \end{bmatrix}$, we have
$$A^{-1} = \begin{bmatrix} 0 & \frac{1}{2} \\ -1 & \frac{1}{2} \end{bmatrix}.$$

13. When we attempt Gaussian reduction,
$$\begin{bmatrix} -6 & 4 & 1 & 0 \\ -3 & 2 & 0 & 1 \end{bmatrix} \sim \begin{bmatrix} 1 & -\frac{2}{3} & -\frac{1}{6} & 0 \\ -3 & 2 & 0 & 1 \end{bmatrix} \quad \div \text{ by } -6$$

$$\sim \begin{bmatrix} 1 & -\frac{2}{3} & -\frac{1}{6} & 0 \\ 0 & 0 & -\frac{1}{2} & 1 \end{bmatrix} r_2'=r_2+3r_1$$

we cannot possibly arrive at the identity matrix on the left since we have zeros for the bottom row entries. This means that the matrix $A = \begin{bmatrix} -6 & 4 \\ -3 & 2 \end{bmatrix}$ has no inverse.

17. Using Gaussian reduction
$$\begin{bmatrix} -1 & -1 & -1 & 1 & 1 & 0 \\ 4 & 5 & 0 & 0 & 1 & 0 \\ 0 & 1 & -3 & 0 & 0 & 1 \end{bmatrix}$$

$$\sim \begin{bmatrix} 1 & 1 & 1 & -1 & 0 & 0 \\ 0 & 1 & -4 & 4 & 1 & 0 \\ 0 & 1 & -3 & 0 & 0 & 1 \end{bmatrix} \quad \begin{matrix}\text{Multiply } (-1) \\ r_2' = r_2 + 4r_1\end{matrix}$$

$$\sim \begin{bmatrix} 1 & 1 & 1 & -1 & 0 & 0 \\ 0 & 1 & -4 & 4 & 1 & 0 \\ 0 & 0 & 1 & -4 & -1 & 1 \end{bmatrix} \quad r_3'' = r_3 - r_2$$

$$\sim \begin{bmatrix} 1 & 1 & 0 & | & 3 & 1 & -1 \\ 0 & 1 & 0 & | & -12 & -3 & 4 \\ 0 & 0 & 1 & | & -4 & -1 & 1 \end{bmatrix} \begin{matrix} r_1'''=r_1''-r_3'' \\ r_2'''=r_2''+4r_3'' \\ \ \end{matrix}$$

$$\sim \begin{bmatrix} 1 & 0 & 0 & | & 15 & 4 & -5 \\ 0 & 1 & 0 & | & -12 & -3 & 4 \\ 0 & 0 & 1 & | & -4 & -1 & 1 \end{bmatrix}.$$

The inverse is $\begin{bmatrix} 15 & 4 & -5 \\ -12 & -3 & 4 \\ -4 & -1 & 1 \end{bmatrix}.$

21. $\begin{bmatrix} 2 & 4 & 6 & | & 1 & 0 & 0 \\ -1 & -4 & -3 & | & 0 & 1 & 0 \\ 0 & 1 & -1 & | & 0 & 0 & 1 \end{bmatrix}$

$$\sim \begin{bmatrix} 1 & 4 & 3 & | & 0 & -1 & 0 \\ 0 & -4 & 0 & | & 1 & 2 & 0 \\ 0 & 1 & -1 & | & 0 & 0 & 1 \end{bmatrix} \begin{matrix} r_1'=-r_2 \\ r_2'=r_1+2r_2 \\ \ \end{matrix}$$

$$\sim \begin{bmatrix} 1 & 4 & 3 & | & 0 & -1 & 0 \\ 0 & 1 & -1 & | & 0 & 0 & 1 \\ 0 & 0 & -4 & | & 1 & 2 & 4 \end{bmatrix} \begin{matrix} \ \\ r_2''=r_3' \\ r_3''=r_2'+4r_3' \end{matrix}$$

$$\sim \begin{bmatrix} 1 & 4 & 3 & | & 0 & -1 & 0 \\ 0 & 1 & -1 & | & 0 & 0 & 1 \\ 0 & 0 & 0 & | & -\frac{1}{4} & -\frac{1}{2} & -1 \end{bmatrix} \begin{matrix} \ \\ \ \\ \div (-4) \end{matrix}$$

$$\sim \begin{bmatrix} 1 & 4 & 0 & | & \frac{3}{4} & \frac{1}{2} & 3 \\ 0 & 1 & 0 & | & -\frac{1}{4} & -\frac{1}{2} & 0 \\ 0 & 0 & 1 & | & -\frac{1}{4} & -\frac{1}{2} & -1 \end{bmatrix} \begin{matrix} r_1'''=r_1''-3r_3'' \\ r_2'''=r_2''+r_3'' \\ \ \end{matrix}$$

$$\sim \begin{bmatrix} 1 & 0 & 0 & | & \frac{7}{4} & \frac{5}{2} & 3 \\ 0 & 1 & 0 & | & -\frac{1}{4} & -\frac{1}{2} & 0 \\ 0 & 0 & 1 & | & -\frac{1}{4} & -\frac{1}{2} & -1 \end{bmatrix} \begin{matrix} r_1^4=r_1'''-4r_2''' \\ \ \\ \ \end{matrix}$$

The inverse is $\begin{bmatrix} \frac{7}{4} & \frac{5}{2} & 3 \\ -\frac{1}{4} & -\frac{1}{2} & 0 \\ -\frac{1}{4} & -\frac{1}{2} & -1 \end{bmatrix}.$

25. The system can be written as $AX = B$. We have

$$\begin{bmatrix} 2 & 3 \\ 1 & -1 \end{bmatrix} \begin{bmatrix} x \\ y \end{bmatrix} = \begin{bmatrix} 10 \\ -5 \end{bmatrix}.$$

To find A^{-1} we write

$$\begin{bmatrix} 2 & 3 & | & 1 & 0 \\ 1 & -1 & | & 0 & 1 \end{bmatrix} \sim \begin{bmatrix} 1 & -1 & | & 0 & 1 \\ 2 & 3 & | & 1 & 0 \end{bmatrix}$$

$$\sim \begin{bmatrix} 1 & -1 & | & 0 & 1 \\ 0 & 5 & | & 1 & -2 \end{bmatrix} r_2'=r_2-2r_1$$

$$\sim \begin{bmatrix} 1 & -1 & | & 0 & 1 \\ 0 & 1 & | & \frac{1}{5} & -\frac{2}{5} \end{bmatrix} \div \text{ by } 5$$

$$\sim \begin{bmatrix} 1 & 0 & | & \frac{1}{5} & \frac{3}{5} \\ 0 & 1 & | & \frac{1}{5} & -\frac{2}{5} \end{bmatrix} r_1''=r_1'+r_2.$$

Thus, $A^{-1} = \begin{bmatrix} \frac{1}{5} & \frac{3}{5} \\ \frac{1}{5} & -\frac{2}{5} \end{bmatrix}$, and we have

$X = A^{-1}B$

$$X = \begin{bmatrix} \frac{1}{5} & \frac{3}{5} \\ \frac{1}{5} & -\frac{2}{5} \end{bmatrix} \begin{bmatrix} 10 \\ -5 \end{bmatrix} = \begin{bmatrix} 2-3 \\ 2+2 \end{bmatrix} = \begin{bmatrix} -1 \\ 4 \end{bmatrix}.$$

Hence, $x = -1$ and $y = 4$.

29. The system is $\begin{bmatrix} -1 & 1 \\ 2 & -1 \end{bmatrix} \begin{bmatrix} x \\ y \end{bmatrix} = \begin{bmatrix} 1 \\ 1 \end{bmatrix}$

We find the inverse by Gaussian reduction:

$$\begin{bmatrix} -1 & 1 & | & 1 & 0 \\ 2 & -1 & | & 0 & 1 \end{bmatrix} \sim \begin{bmatrix} 1 & -1 & | & -1 & 0 \\ 0 & 1 & | & 2 & 1 \end{bmatrix} r_1'=-r_1$$

$$\sim \begin{bmatrix} 1 & 0 & | & 1 & 1 \\ 0 & 1 & | & 2 & 1 \end{bmatrix}.$$

The inverse is $\begin{bmatrix} 1 & 1 \\ 2 & 1 \end{bmatrix}$. Then we have

$$\begin{bmatrix} x \\ y \end{bmatrix} = \begin{bmatrix} 1 & 1 \\ 2 & 1 \end{bmatrix} \begin{bmatrix} 1 \\ 1 \end{bmatrix} = \begin{bmatrix} 1+1 \\ 2+1 \end{bmatrix} = \begin{bmatrix} 2 \\ 3 \end{bmatrix}.$$

The solution is $x = 2$, $y = 3$.

33. We have $AX = B$, with

$$A = \begin{bmatrix} -1 & -1 & -1 \\ 4 & 5 & 0 \\ 0 & 1 & -3 \end{bmatrix}, \ X = \begin{bmatrix} x \\ y \\ z \end{bmatrix}, \text{ and } B = \begin{bmatrix} 1 \\ -2 \\ 3 \end{bmatrix}.$$

we found in exercise 17 that

$$A^{-1} = \begin{bmatrix} 15 & 4 & 5 \\ -12 & -3 & 4 \\ -4 & -1 & 1 \end{bmatrix},$$

and hence we can find the solution by

$$\begin{bmatrix} x \\ y \\ z \end{bmatrix} = A^{-1}B = \begin{bmatrix} 15 & 4 & -5 \\ -12 & -3 & 4 \\ -4 & -1 & 1 \end{bmatrix} \begin{bmatrix} 1 \\ -2 \\ 3 \end{bmatrix}$$

$$\begin{bmatrix} x \\ y \\ z \end{bmatrix} = \begin{bmatrix} 15 - 8 - 15 \\ -12 + 6 + 12 \\ -4 + 2 + 3 \end{bmatrix} = \begin{bmatrix} -8 \\ 6 \\ 1 \end{bmatrix}.$$

The solution set is $\{(-8, 6, 1)\}$.

37. The system can be written as $AX = B$, with

$$A = \begin{bmatrix} 1 & 2 & 3 \\ 2 & 3 & 2 \\ -1 & -2 & -4 \end{bmatrix}, \quad X = \begin{bmatrix} x \\ y \\ z \end{bmatrix} \quad \text{and} \quad B = \begin{bmatrix} 5 \\ 2 \\ -1 \end{bmatrix}.$$

We find A^{-1} by Gaussian reduction:

$$\begin{bmatrix} 1 & 2 & 3 & | & 1 & 0 & 0 \\ 2 & 3 & 2 & | & 0 & 1 & 0 \\ -1 & -2 & -4 & | & 0 & 0 & 1 \end{bmatrix}$$

$$\sim \begin{bmatrix} 1 & 2 & 3 & | & 1 & 0 & 0 \\ 0 & -1 & -4 & | & -2 & 1 & 0 \\ 0 & 0 & -1 & | & 1 & 0 & 1 \end{bmatrix} \begin{matrix} \\ r_2' = r_2 - 2r_1 \\ r_3' = r_3 + r_1 \end{matrix}$$

$$\sim \begin{bmatrix} 1 & 2 & 3 & | & 1 & 0 & 0 \\ 0 & 1 & 4 & | & 2 & -1 & 0 \\ 0 & 0 & 1 & | & -1 & 0 & -1 \end{bmatrix}$$

$$\sim \begin{bmatrix} 1 & 2 & 0 & | & 4 & 0 & 3 \\ 0 & 1 & 0 & | & 6 & -1 & 4 \\ 0 & 0 & 1 & | & -1 & 0 & -1 \end{bmatrix} \begin{matrix} r_1'' = r_1' - 3r_3' \\ r_2'' = r_2' - 4r_3' \\ \\ \end{matrix}$$

$$\sim \begin{bmatrix} 1 & 0 & 0 & | & -8 & 2 & -5 \\ 0 & 1 & 0 & | & 6 & -1 & 4 \\ 0 & 0 & 1 & | & -1 & 0 & -1 \end{bmatrix} \begin{matrix} r_1''' = r_1'' - 2r_2'' \\ \\ \\ \end{matrix}.$$

Then we have

$$X = A^{-1}B$$

$$\begin{bmatrix} x \\ y \\ z \end{bmatrix} = \begin{bmatrix} -8 & 2 & -5 \\ 6 & -1 & 4 \\ -1 & 0 & -1 \end{bmatrix} \begin{bmatrix} 5 \\ 2 \\ -1 \end{bmatrix}$$

$$= \begin{bmatrix} -40 + 4 + 5 \\ 30 - 2 - 4 \\ -5 + 0 + 1 \end{bmatrix} = \begin{bmatrix} -31 \\ 24 \\ -4 \end{bmatrix}.$$

The solution set is $\{(-31, 24, -4)\}$.

41. We can write the system as

$$\begin{bmatrix} 1 & -2 & 3 & 0 \\ 0 & 1 & -1 & 1 \\ -2 & 2 & -2 & 4 \\ 0 & 2 & -3 & 1 \end{bmatrix} \begin{bmatrix} x \\ y \\ z \\ w \end{bmatrix} = \begin{bmatrix} 4 \\ -8 \\ 12 \\ -4 \end{bmatrix}.$$

The inverse to the coefficient matrix was to be found in exercise 23. The inverse is

$$\begin{bmatrix} \frac{1}{2} & \frac{1}{2} & \frac{-1}{4} & \frac{1}{2} \\ -1 & 4 & \frac{-1}{2} & -2 \\ \frac{-1}{2} & \frac{5}{2} & \frac{-1}{4} & \frac{-3}{2} \\ \frac{1}{2} & \frac{-1}{2} & \frac{1}{4} & \frac{1}{2} \end{bmatrix},$$

and hence the solution is

$$\begin{bmatrix} x \\ y \\ z \\ w \end{bmatrix} = \begin{bmatrix} \frac{1}{2} & \frac{1}{2} & \frac{-1}{4} & \frac{1}{2} \\ -1 & 4 & \frac{-1}{2} & -2 \\ \frac{-1}{2} & \frac{5}{2} & \frac{-1}{4} & \frac{-3}{2} \\ \frac{1}{2} & \frac{-1}{2} & \frac{1}{4} & \frac{1}{2} \end{bmatrix} \begin{bmatrix} 4 \\ -8 \\ -12 \\ -4 \end{bmatrix}$$

$$= \begin{bmatrix} 2 - 4 - 3 - 2 \\ -4 - 32 - 6 + 8 \\ -2 - 20 - 3 + 6 \\ 2 + 4 + 3 - 2 \end{bmatrix} = \begin{bmatrix} -7 \\ -34 \\ -19 \\ 7 \end{bmatrix}.$$

The solution set is $\{(-7, -34, -19, 7)\}$.

45. If $A = \begin{bmatrix} a & b \\ c & d \end{bmatrix}$, we find A^{-1} as follows:

$$\begin{bmatrix} a & b & | & 1 & 0 \\ c & d & | & 0 & 1 \end{bmatrix} \sim \begin{bmatrix} 1 & \frac{b}{a} & | & \frac{1}{a} & 0 \\ c & d & | & 0 & 1 \end{bmatrix}$$

$$\sim \begin{bmatrix} 1 & \frac{b}{a} & | & \frac{1}{a} & 0 \\ 0 & \frac{ad-bc}{a} & | & \frac{-c}{a} & 1 \end{bmatrix} \begin{matrix} \\ r_2' = r_2 - cr_1 \end{matrix}$$

$$\sim \begin{bmatrix} 1 & \frac{b}{a} & | & \frac{1}{a} & 0 \\ 0 & 1 & | & \frac{-c}{ad-bc} & \frac{a}{ad-bc} \end{bmatrix} \times \left(\frac{a}{ad-bc}\right)$$

$$\sim \begin{bmatrix} 1 & 0 & \dfrac{d}{ad-bc} & \dfrac{-b}{ad-bc} \\ 0 & 1 & \dfrac{-c}{ad-bc} & \dfrac{a}{ad-bc} \end{bmatrix} \quad r_1'' = r_1' - \dfrac{b}{a}r_2'$$

Thus, $A^{-1} = \dfrac{1}{ad-bc}\begin{bmatrix} d & -b \\ -c & a \end{bmatrix}$.

If we multiply we have

$$A^{-1}A = \dfrac{1}{ad-bc}\begin{bmatrix} d & -b \\ -c & a \end{bmatrix}\begin{bmatrix} a & b \\ c & d \end{bmatrix}$$

$$= \dfrac{1}{ad-bc}\begin{bmatrix} ad-bc & db-bd \\ -ac+ac & -bc+ad \end{bmatrix}$$

$$= \dfrac{1}{ad-bc}\begin{bmatrix} ad-bc & 0 \\ 0 & ad-bc \end{bmatrix}$$

$$= \begin{bmatrix} 1 & 0 \\ 0 & 1 \end{bmatrix}.$$

49. We will give matrices A and B such that $(AB)^{-1} \neq A^{-1}B^{-1}$. Let

$$A = \begin{bmatrix} 1 & 1 \\ 1 & 0 \end{bmatrix} \text{ and } B = \begin{bmatrix} 2 & 1 \\ 4 & 3 \end{bmatrix}.$$

If $A = \begin{bmatrix} 1 & 1 \\ 1 & 0 \end{bmatrix}$, then $A^{-1} = \begin{bmatrix} 0 & 1 \\ 1 & -1 \end{bmatrix}$,

and if $B = \begin{bmatrix} 2 & 1 \\ 4 & 3 \end{bmatrix}$, then $B^{-1} = \begin{bmatrix} \frac{3}{2} & -\frac{1}{2} \\ -2 & 1 \end{bmatrix}$.

$$AB = \begin{bmatrix} 6 & 4 \\ 2 & 1 \end{bmatrix} \text{ and } (AB)^{-1} = \begin{bmatrix} -\frac{1}{2} & 2 \\ 1 & -3 \end{bmatrix}$$

$$A^{-1}B^{-1} = \begin{bmatrix} 0 & 1 \\ 1 & -1 \end{bmatrix}\begin{bmatrix} \frac{3}{2} & -\frac{1}{2} \\ -2 & 1 \end{bmatrix}$$

$$= \begin{bmatrix} -2 & 1 \\ \frac{7}{2} & -\frac{3}{2} \end{bmatrix}.$$

Note that $(AB)^{-1} \neq A^{-1}B^{-1}$.

53. Using Gaussian reduction, we have

$$\left[\begin{array}{ccc|ccc} a & 0 & 0 & 1 & 0 & 0 \\ 0 & b & 0 & 0 & 1 & 0 \\ 0 & 0 & c & 0 & 0 & 1 \end{array}\right]$$

$$\sim \left[\begin{array}{ccc|ccc} 1 & 0 & 0 & \frac{1}{a} & 0 & 0 \\ 0 & 1 & 0 & 0 & \frac{1}{b} & 0 \\ 0 & 0 & 1 & 0 & 0 & \frac{1}{c} \end{array}\right].$$

$$A^{-1} = \begin{bmatrix} \frac{1}{a} & 0 & 0 \\ 0 & \frac{1}{b} & 0 \\ 0 & 0 & \frac{1}{c} \end{bmatrix}.$$

Section 9.5   Determinants

Additional Examples

Example 1   Evaluate the determinant

$$\begin{vmatrix} 0 & 0 & c & 0 \\ 0 & 0 & 0 & d \\ 0 & b & 0 & 0 \\ a & 0 & 0 & 0 \end{vmatrix}.$$

Solution   Using cofactor expansion about the first column we have

Value of determinant

$$= 0 \cdot A_{11} + 0 \cdot A_{21} + 0 \cdot A_{31} + a \cdot A_{41}$$

$$= a \cdot A_{41}.$$

We do not need to evaluate A_{11}, A_{21}, or A_{31} since they are multiplied by zero. We have

$$A_{41} = (-1)^{4+1}M_{41}$$

$$= -\begin{vmatrix} 0 & c & 0 \\ 0 & 0 & d \\ b & 0 & 0 \end{vmatrix}.$$

To evaluate this 3 x 3 determinant, we use cofactor expansion about the first column. This gives

$$\begin{vmatrix} 0 & c & 0 \\ 0 & 0 & d \\ b & 0 & 0 \end{vmatrix} = 0 \cdot A_{11}' + 0 \cdot A_{12}' + b \cdot A_{13}',$$

and $A_{13}' = (-1)^{3+1}\begin{vmatrix} c & 0 \\ 0 & d \end{vmatrix}$

$$= cd - 0$$

$$= cd.$$

Hence, the value of the determinant is

$$a \cdot A_{41} = a(-bA_{13}') = -ab(cd)$$

$$= -abcd.$$

Example 2   Evaluate the determinant

$$\begin{vmatrix} 2 & -2 & 3 & 3 \\ 0 & 2 & 0 & 1 \\ 3 & 4 & -1 & 2 \\ 1 & -3 & 2 & 1 \end{vmatrix}.$$

Solution   A theorem in the text states that we can use the operation of adding to any row a constant times another row and the determinant of the result is the same. Thus, we can use an operation we are familiar with. Hence, if we let D be the value of the determinent,

$$D = \begin{vmatrix} 2 & -2 & 3 & 3 \\ 0 & 2 & 0 & 1 \\ 3 & 4 & -1 & 2 \\ 1 & 3 & 2 & 1 \end{vmatrix}$$

$$= \begin{vmatrix} 0 & -8 & -1 & 1 \\ 0 & 2 & 0 & 1 \\ 0 & -5 & -7 & -1 \\ 1 & 3 & 2 & 1 \end{vmatrix} \begin{matrix} r_1' = r_1 - 2r_4 \\ \\ r_3' = r_3 - 3r_4 \\ \\ \end{matrix}.$$

Using cofactor expansion about the first column, we have

$$D = 0 + 0 + 0 - 1 \begin{vmatrix} -8 & -1 & 1 \\ 2 & 0 & 1 \\ -5 & -7 & -1 \end{vmatrix}.$$

We do not need to write the co-factors A_{11}, A_{21}, and A_{31} since they are multiplied by zero. In the same fashion

$$D = - \begin{vmatrix} -8 & -1 & 1 \\ 2 & 0 & 1 \\ -5 & -7 & -1 \end{vmatrix}$$

$$= - \begin{vmatrix} -8 & -1 & 1 \\ 10 & 1 & 0 \\ -13 & -8 & 0 \end{vmatrix} \begin{matrix} r_2' = r_2 - r_1 \\ r_3' = r_3 + r_1, \end{matrix}$$

and using cofactor expansion about column 3 we have

$$D = - (1) \begin{vmatrix} 10 & 1 \\ -13 & -8 \end{vmatrix} + 0 + 0$$

$$D = - (-80 + 13) = 67.$$

Selected Solutions

1. Using the definition of a 2 x 2 determinant that $\begin{vmatrix} a & b \\ c & d \end{vmatrix} = ad - bc$, we have $\begin{vmatrix} 3 & 4 \\ 5 & -2 \end{vmatrix} = -6 - 20 = -26.$

5. By definition, $\begin{vmatrix} y & 2 \\ 8 & y \end{vmatrix} = y^2 - 16.$

9. For the determinant $\begin{vmatrix} -2 & 0 & 1 \\ 3 & 2 & -1 \\ 1 & 0 & 2 \end{vmatrix}$, the cofactor of each element in the second row is given by

$$A_{21} = (-1)^3 \begin{vmatrix} 0 & 1 \\ 0 & 2 \end{vmatrix} = - (0 - 0) = 0,$$

$$A_{22} = (-1)^4 \begin{vmatrix} -2 & 1 \\ 1 & 2 \end{vmatrix} = -4 - 1 = -5, \text{ and}$$

$$A_{23} = (-1)^5 \begin{vmatrix} -2 & 0 \\ 1 & 0 \end{vmatrix} = - (0 - 0) = 0.$$

13. Using cofactor expansion about the first row gives

$$\begin{vmatrix} 1 & 0 & 0 \\ 0 & -1 & 0 \\ 1 & 0 & 1 \end{vmatrix} = 1 \cdot A_{11} + 0 \cdot A_{12} + 0 \cdot A_{13}$$

$$= (-1)^2 \begin{vmatrix} -1 & 0 \\ 0 & 1 \end{vmatrix} = -1.$$

17. Using the property of adding to a certain row a constant multiple of another row, we have

$$D = \begin{vmatrix} 3 & 3 & -1 \\ 2 & 6 & 0 \\ -6 & -6 & 2 \end{vmatrix} = \begin{vmatrix} 3 & 3 & -1 \\ 2 & 6 & 0 \\ 0 & 0 & 0 \end{vmatrix} \begin{matrix} \\ \\ r_3' = r_3 + 2r, \end{matrix}.$$

thus, $D = 0$, since any determinant having a row or column of zeros has value zero.

21. Using cofactor expansion about the first row gives

$$\begin{vmatrix} i & j & k \\ -1 & 2 & 4 \\ 3 & 0 & 5 \end{vmatrix}$$

$$= i \begin{vmatrix} 2 & 4 \\ 0 & 5 \end{vmatrix} - j \begin{vmatrix} -1 & 4 \\ 3 & 5 \end{vmatrix} + k \begin{vmatrix} -1 & 2 \\ 3 & 0 \end{vmatrix}$$

$$= 10i - j(-5 - 12) + k(0 - 6)$$

$$= 10i + 17j - 6k.$$

25. Using properties of determinants to simplify the work, we have

$$D = \begin{vmatrix} 0.4 & -0.8 & 0.6 \\ 0.3 & 0.9 & 0.7 \\ 3.1 & 4.1 & -2.8 \end{vmatrix} = \frac{1}{10^3} \begin{vmatrix} 4 & -8 & 6 \\ 3 & 9 & 7 \\ 31 & 41 & -28 \end{vmatrix}.$$

We multiply each row by 10 and compensate by bringing $\frac{1}{10}$ out front.

Another way of thinking is that we __factor__ a $\frac{1}{10}$ out of each row. Then,

$$D = \frac{1}{1000} \begin{vmatrix} 4 & -8 & 6 \\ 3 & 9 & 7 \\ 31 & 41 & -28 \end{vmatrix}$$

$$D = \frac{1}{1000} \begin{vmatrix} 1 & -17 & -1 \\ 3 & 9 & 7 \\ 1 & -49 & -98 \end{vmatrix} \quad \begin{array}{l} r_1' = r_1 - r_2 \\ \\ r_3' = r_3 - 10r_2 \end{array}$$

$$D = \frac{1}{1000} \begin{vmatrix} 1 & -17 & -1 \\ 0 & 60 & 10 \\ 0 & -32 & -97 \end{vmatrix} \quad \begin{array}{l} r_2'' = r_2' - 3r_1' \\ \\ r_3'' = r_3' - r_1' \end{array}$$

$$D = \frac{1}{1000} \begin{vmatrix} 60 & 10 \\ -32 & -97 \end{vmatrix}$$

by using a cofactor expansion about the first column,

$$D = \frac{1}{100} \begin{vmatrix} 6 & 1 \\ -32 & -97 \end{vmatrix},$$

factoring out a 10 from the first row,

$$D = \frac{1}{100} [6(-97) - 1(-32)]$$

$$D = \frac{-550}{100} = -5.5.$$

29. The determinant $\begin{vmatrix} 2 & 0 \\ 3 & 0 \end{vmatrix}$ has value zero since every element in column two is a zero.

33. If we use column operations, we have

$$\begin{vmatrix} m & 2 & 2m \\ 3n & 1 & 6n \\ 5p & 6 & 10p \end{vmatrix} = 2 \begin{vmatrix} m & 2 & m \\ 3n & 1 & 3n \\ 5p & 6 & 5p \end{vmatrix},$$

factoring a 2 from column two,

$$= 2(0) = 0,$$

since the second determinant has two identical columns.

37. We see that

$$\begin{vmatrix} 2 & 6 \\ 3 & 5 \end{vmatrix} = - \begin{vmatrix} 3 & 5 \\ 2 & 6 \end{vmatrix},$$

since we have interchanged the two rows in the first determinant to arrive at $\begin{vmatrix} 3 & 5 \\ 2 & 6 \end{vmatrix}$.

41. If we change row 2 by adding row 1 to row 2, we have

$$\begin{vmatrix} 3 & -4 \\ 2 & 5 \end{vmatrix} = \begin{vmatrix} 3 & -4 \\ 5 & 1 \end{vmatrix} \quad r_2' = r_2 + r_1.$$

45. If we change column 2 by adding -2 times column 1, we have

$$\begin{vmatrix} 2 & 4 \\ 3 & 6 \end{vmatrix} = \begin{vmatrix} 2 & 0 \\ 3 & 0 \end{vmatrix}; \quad c_2' = c_2 - 2c_1.$$

Thus, $\begin{vmatrix} 2 & 4 \\ 3 & 6 \end{vmatrix} = 0.$

49. We have

$$D = \begin{vmatrix} 3 & 1 & 2 \\ 2 & 0 & 1 \\ 1 & 0 & 2 \end{vmatrix} = \begin{vmatrix} 0 & 1 & 0 \\ 2 & 0 & 1 \\ 1 & 0 & 2 \end{vmatrix}; \quad \begin{array}{l} c_1' = c_1 - 3c_2 \\ \\ c_3' = c_3 - 2c_2, \end{array}$$

$$D = \begin{vmatrix} 0 & 1 & 0 \\ 0 & 0 & -3 \\ 1 & 0 & 2 \end{vmatrix} \quad r_2'' = r_2 - 2r_3$$

$$D = \begin{vmatrix} 1 & 0 & 2 \\ 0 & 1 & 0 \\ 0 & 0 & -3 \end{vmatrix} \quad \text{since}$$

interchanging rows 1 and 3, then interchanging rows 2 and 3; gives factor $(-1)^2$,

then, we add to row 1, $\frac{2}{3}$ of row 3. This gives

$$D = \begin{vmatrix} 1 & 0 & 0 \\ 0 & 1 & 0 \\ 0 & 0 & -3 \end{vmatrix} = -3.$$

53.
$$D = \begin{vmatrix} 1 & 0 & 2 & 2 \\ 2 & 4 & 1 & -1 \\ 1 & -3 & 1 & 0 \\ 1 & 1 & 0 & 1 \end{vmatrix}$$

$$= \begin{vmatrix} 1 & 0 & 2 & 2 \\ 0 & 4 & -3 & -5 \\ 0 & -3 & -1 & -2 \\ 0 & 1 & -2 & -1 \end{vmatrix} \begin{matrix} \\ r_2' = r_2 - r_1 \\ r_3' = r_3 - r_1 \\ r_4' = r_4 - r_1 \end{matrix}$$

$$= \begin{vmatrix} 1 & 0 & 2 & 2 \\ 0 & 0 & 5 & -1 \\ 0 & 0 & -7 & -5 \\ 0 & 1 & -2 & -1 \end{vmatrix} \begin{matrix} \\ r_2'' = r_2' - r_4' \\ r_3'' = r_3' + 3r_4' \\ \end{matrix}$$

$$= - \begin{vmatrix} 1 & 0 & 2 & 2 \\ 0 & 1 & -2 & -1 \\ 0 & 0 & -7 & -5 \\ 0 & 0 & 5 & -1 \end{vmatrix} \begin{matrix} \\ \text{interchange} \\ \text{rows 2 and 4} \end{matrix}$$

$$= - \begin{vmatrix} 1 & 0 & 2 & 2 \\ 0 & 1 & -1 & -1 \\ 0 & 0 & -7 & -5 \\ 0 & 0 & 0 & -\frac{32}{7} \end{vmatrix} \begin{matrix} \\ \\ \\ r_4''' = r_4'' + \frac{5}{7}r_3'' \end{matrix}$$

$$= -32.$$

57. If $A = \begin{bmatrix} a_{11} & a_{12} & a_{13} \\ a_{21} & a_{22} & a_{23} \\ a_{31} & a_{32} & a_{33} \end{bmatrix}$,

then exchanging columns 1 and 3 gives

$$B = \begin{bmatrix} a_{12} & a_{12} & a_{11} \\ a_{23} & a_{22} & a_{21} \\ a_{33} & a_{32} & a_{31} \end{bmatrix}.$$

If we expand each determinant by the second column, we have

$$|A| = -a_{12} \begin{vmatrix} a_{21} & a_{23} \\ a_{31} & a_{33} \end{vmatrix} + a_{22} \begin{vmatrix} a_{11} & a_{13} \\ a_{31} & a_{33} \end{vmatrix}$$

$$-a_{32} \begin{vmatrix} a_{11} & a_{13} \\ a_{21} & a_{23} \end{vmatrix}$$

$$|A| = -a_{12}(a_{21}a_{33} - a_{23}a_{31})$$
$$+a_{22}(a_{11}a_{33} - a_{13}a_{31})$$
$$-a_{32}(a_{11}a_{23} - a_{13}a_{21}),$$

and $|B| = -a_{12} \begin{vmatrix} a_{23} & a_{21} \\ a_{33} & a_{31} \end{vmatrix} + a_{22} \begin{vmatrix} a_{13} & a_{11} \\ a_{33} & a_{31} \end{vmatrix}$

$$-a_{32} \begin{vmatrix} a_{13} & a_{11} \\ a_{23} & a_{21} \end{vmatrix}$$

$$|B| = -a_{12}(a_{23}a_{31} - a_{21}a_{33})$$
$$+a_{22}(a_{13}a_{31} - a_{11}a_{33})$$
$$-a_{32}(a_{13}a_{21} - a_{11}a_{23}).$$

Obviously, by inspecting the formulas for $|A|$ and $|B|$, we see that $|B| = -|A|$.

61. If $A = \begin{bmatrix} a_{11} & a_{12} \\ a_{21} & a_{22} \end{bmatrix}$ and $B = \begin{bmatrix} b_{11} & b_{12} \\ b_{21} & b_{22} \end{bmatrix}$

then
$$|A|\cdot|B| = (a_{11}a_{22}-a_{21}a_{12})(b_{11}b_{22}-b_{21}b_{12})$$
$$|A|\cdot|B| = a_{11}a_{22}b_{11}b_{22}-a_{11}a_{22}b_{21}b_{12}$$
$$- a_{21}a_{12}b_{11}b_{22}+a_{21}a_{12}b_{21}b_{22}.$$

Also,
$$|AB| = \begin{vmatrix} a_{11}b_{11}+a_{12}b_{21} & a_{11}b_{12}+a_{12}b_{22} \\ a_{21}b_{11}+a_{22}b_{21} & a_{21}b_{12}+a_{22}b_{22} \end{vmatrix}$$

$$|AB| = (a_{11}b_{11}+a_{12}b_{21})(a_{21}b_{21}+a_{11}b_{22})$$
$$-(a_{21}b_{11}+a_{22}b_{21})(a_{11}b_{12}+a_{12}b_{22})$$

$$|AB| = a_{11}b_{11}a_{22}b_{22} - a_{11}a_{22}b_{21}b_{12}$$
$$-a_{21}a_{12}b_{11}b_{22}+ a_{21}a_{12}b_{21}b_{22}.$$

This shows $|A|\cdot|B| = |AB|$.

65. Given the points $P(0, 1)$, $Q(2, 0)$, and $R(1, 3)$, the area of triangle PQR is

$$A = \frac{1}{2} \begin{vmatrix} 0 & 1 & 1 \\ 2 & 0 & 1 \\ 1 & 3 & 1 \end{vmatrix}$$

$$= \frac{1}{2} \begin{vmatrix} 1 & 3 & 1 \\ 0 & 1 & 1 \\ 2 & 0 & 1 \end{vmatrix} \quad \begin{matrix} \text{two changes:} \\ r_1 \leftrightarrow r_3, \quad \text{then} \\ r_2' \leftrightarrow r_3' \end{matrix}$$

$$A = \frac{1}{2} \begin{vmatrix} 1 & 3 & 1 \\ 0 & 1 & 1 \\ 0 & -6 & -1 \end{vmatrix} \quad r_3' = r_3 - 2r_1$$

$$A = \frac{1}{2} \begin{vmatrix} 1 & 1 \\ -6 & -1 \end{vmatrix} = \frac{1}{2}(-1 + 6) = \frac{5}{2}.$$

Note: The points P,Q,R are taken counterclockwise.

69. Given the points $P(3, 8)$, $Q(-1, 4)$, and $R(0, 1)$, which form a triangle PQR in counterclockwise order, the area of triangle PQR is

$$A = \frac{1}{2} \begin{vmatrix} 3 & 8 & 1 \\ -1 & 4 & 1 \\ 0 & 1 & 1 \end{vmatrix} = \frac{+1}{2} \begin{vmatrix} -1 & 4 & 1 \\ 0 & 1 & 1 \\ 3 & 8 & 1 \end{vmatrix} \quad \begin{matrix} \text{(2 row} \\ \text{changes)} \end{matrix}$$

$$A = \frac{1}{2} \begin{vmatrix} -1 & 4 & 1 \\ 0 & 1 & 1 \\ 0 & 20 & 4 \end{vmatrix} = \frac{-1}{2} \begin{vmatrix} 1 & 1 \\ 20 & 4 \end{vmatrix}$$

$$A = -\frac{1}{2}(4 - 20) = 8.$$

73. The line $a_1 x + b_1 y = c_1$ can be written as $y = \frac{-a_1}{b_1}x + \frac{c_1}{b_1}$. Hence, this line has slope $m_1 = \frac{-a_1}{b_1}$.

Similarly, the line $a_2 x + b_2 y = c_2$ can be written as $y = \frac{-a_2}{b_2}x + \frac{c_2}{b_2}$.

The slope of this line is $m_2 = \frac{-a_2}{b_2}$.

The two lines are parallel if $m_1 = m_2$, or

$$\frac{-a_1}{b_1} = \frac{-a_2}{b_2}$$

$$a_1 b_2 = a_2 b_1$$

$$a_1 b_2 - a_2 b_1 = 0.$$

Since $\begin{vmatrix} a_1 & b_1 \\ a_2 & b_2 \end{vmatrix} = a_1 b_2 - a_2 b_1$, we note that the two lines are parallel if $\begin{vmatrix} a_1 & b_1 \\ a_2 & b_2 \end{vmatrix} = 0$.

74. $\begin{vmatrix} 1 & 1 & 1 \\ a & b & c \\ a^2 & b^2 & c^2 \end{vmatrix} = \begin{vmatrix} 1 & 1 & 1 \\ 0 & b-a & c-a \\ 0 & b^2-a^2 & c^2-a^2 \end{vmatrix} \begin{matrix} r_2'=r_2- ar_1 \\ r_3'=r_3- a^2 r_1 \end{matrix}$

$$= \begin{vmatrix} b-a & c-a \\ b^2-a^2 & c^2-a^2 \end{vmatrix} \begin{matrix} \text{cofactor} \\ \text{expansion} \end{matrix}$$

$$= (b-a)(c^2-a^2) - (c-a)(b^2-a^2)$$
$$= (b-a)(c-a)(c+a) - (c-a)(b-a)(b+a)$$
$$= (c-a)(b-a)[(c+a)-(b+a)]$$
$$= (c-a)(b-a)(c-b)$$
$$= (a-b)(b-c)(c-a).$$

75. $\begin{vmatrix} a & b & c \\ a & a+b & a+b+c \\ a & 2a+b & 3a+2b+c \end{vmatrix}$

$$= \begin{vmatrix} a & b & c \\ 0 & a & a+b \\ 0 & 2a & 3a+2b \end{vmatrix} \begin{matrix} r_2' = r_2 - r_1 \\ r_3' = r_3 - r_1 \end{matrix}$$

$$(I) = a \begin{vmatrix} a & a+b \\ 2a & 3a+2b \end{vmatrix} \begin{matrix} \text{cofactor} \\ \text{expansion} \end{matrix}$$

$$= a[a(3a+2b) - 2a(a+b)]$$
$$= a[3a^2 + 2ab - 2a^2 - 2ab]$$
$$= a(a^2) = a^3$$

Note that we could have reduced at line (I) to arrive at

$$(I) = a \begin{vmatrix} a & a+b \\ 2a & 3a+2b \end{vmatrix}$$

$$= a \begin{vmatrix} a & a+b \\ 0 & a \end{vmatrix} \quad r_2' = r_2 - 2r_1$$

$$= a(a^2 - 0) = a^3.$$

Section 9.6   Cramer's Rule

Additional Examples

Example 1   Use Cramer's rule to solve the system of equations

$x + 2y - z = 1$
$2x - y + 3z = 12$
$2x + 3y - 4z = -5.$

Solution   Evaluating the determinants D, D_x, D_y, and D_z gives

$$D = \begin{vmatrix} 1 & 2 & -1 \\ 2 & -1 & 3 \\ 2 & 3 & -4 \end{vmatrix}$$

$$= \begin{vmatrix} 1 & 2 & -1 \\ 0 & -5 & 5 \\ 0 & -1 & -2 \end{vmatrix} \quad \begin{matrix} r_2' = r_2 - 2r_1 \\ r_3' = r_3 - 2r_1 \end{matrix}$$

$$= \begin{vmatrix} -5 & 5 \\ -1 & -2 \end{vmatrix} = +10 + 5 = 15,$$

$$D_x = \begin{vmatrix} 1 & 2 & -1 \\ 12 & -1 & 3 \\ -5 & 3 & -4 \end{vmatrix}$$

$$= \begin{vmatrix} 1 & 2 & -1 \\ 0 & -25 & 15 \\ 0 & 13 & -9 \end{vmatrix} \quad \begin{matrix} r_2' = r_2 - 12r_1 \\ r_3' + r_3 + 5r_1 \end{matrix}$$

$$= \begin{vmatrix} -25 & 15 \\ 13 & -9 \end{vmatrix} = 225 - 195 = 30,$$

$$D_y = \begin{vmatrix} 1 & 1 & -1 \\ 2 & 12 & 3 \\ 2 & -5 & -4 \end{vmatrix}$$

$$= \begin{vmatrix} 1 & 1 & -1 \\ 0 & 10 & 5 \\ 0 & -7 & -2 \end{vmatrix} \quad \begin{matrix} r_2' = r_2 - 2r_1 \\ r_3' = r_3 - 2r_1 \end{matrix}$$

$$= \begin{vmatrix} 10 & 5 \\ -7 & -2 \end{vmatrix} = -20 + 35 = 15,$$

$$D_z = \begin{vmatrix} 1 & 2 & 1 \\ 2 & -1 & 12 \\ 2 & 3 & -5 \end{vmatrix}$$

$$= \begin{vmatrix} 1 & 2 & 1 \\ 0 & -5 & 10 \\ 0 & -1 & -7 \end{vmatrix} \quad \begin{matrix} r_2' = r_2 - 2r_1 \\ r_3' = r_3 - 2r_1 \end{matrix}$$

$$= \begin{vmatrix} -5 & 10 \\ -1 & -7 \end{vmatrix} = +35 + 10 = 45.$$

Hence,

$$x = \frac{D_x}{D} = \frac{30}{15} = 2, \quad y = \frac{D_y}{D} = \frac{15}{15} = 1,$$

and $z = \frac{D_z}{D} = \frac{45}{15} = 3.$

Example 2   Suppose that 13 pounds of a mixture of three different types of nuts is made. One of the kinds costs $2.80 per pound, the second costs $2.60 per pound, and the third costs $3.00 per pound. Assume the total cost of the 13-pound mixture is $35.80 and that the mixture contains twice as much of the $2.60 nuts as it does the $3.00 nuts. How many pounds of each kind of nut is in the mixture?

Solution   Let x be the number of pounds of the $2.80 nuts, let y be the number of pounds of $2.60 nuts, and let z be the number of pounds of the $3.00 nuts. The system of equations described is

$x + y + z = 13$
$2.80x + 2.60y + 3.00z = 35.80$
$2z = y$

or

$x + y + z = 13$
$28x + 26y + 30z = 358$
$-y + 2z = 0.$

Solving by Cramer's rule, we have

$$D = \begin{vmatrix} 1 & 1 & 1 \\ 28 & 26 & 30 \\ 0 & -1 & 2 \end{vmatrix} = -2,$$

$$D_x = \begin{vmatrix} 13 & 1 & 1 \\ 358 & 26 & 30 \\ 0 & -1 & 2 \end{vmatrix} = -8,$$

$$D_y = \begin{vmatrix} 1 & 13 & 1 \\ 28 & 358 & 30 \\ 0 & 0 & 2 \end{vmatrix} = -12,$$

and $D_z = \begin{vmatrix} 1 & 1 & 13 \\ 28 & 26 & 358 \\ 0 & -1 & 0 \end{vmatrix} = -6.$

This implies

$$x = \frac{D_x}{D} = \frac{-8}{-2} = 4, \quad y = \frac{D_y}{D} = \frac{-12}{-2} = 6,$$

and $z = \frac{D_z}{D} = \frac{-6}{-2} = 3.$

There are 4 pounds of $2.80 nuts, 6 pounds of $2.60 nuts, and 3 pounds of $3.00 nuts.

Selected Solutions

1. For the system

$$x + y = 4$$
$$2x - y = 2$$

we have

$$D = \begin{vmatrix} 1 & 1 \\ 2 & -1 \end{vmatrix} = -3,$$

$$D_x = \begin{vmatrix} 4 & 1 \\ 2 & -1 \end{vmatrix} = -6, \text{ and}$$

$$D_y = \begin{vmatrix} 1 & 4 \\ 2 & 2 \end{vmatrix} = -6.$$

$x = 2$, $y = 2$ is the solution.
The solution set is $\{(2, 2)\}$.

5. For the system

$$2x - 3y = -5$$
$$x + 5y = 17$$

we have

$$D = \begin{vmatrix} 2 & -3 \\ 1 & 5 \end{vmatrix} = 10 + 3 = 13,$$

$$D_x = \begin{vmatrix} -5 & -3 \\ 17 & 5 \end{vmatrix} = -25 + 51 = 26,$$

$$D_y = \begin{vmatrix} 2 & -5 \\ 1 & 17 \end{vmatrix} = 34 + 5 = 39.$$

Hence, $x = \frac{26}{13} = 2$ and $y = \frac{39}{13} = 3$.
The solution set is $\{(2, 3)\}$.

9. For the system

$$10x - 8y = 1$$
$$-15x + 12y = 4$$

we have

$$D = \begin{vmatrix} 10 & -8 \\ -15 & 12 \end{vmatrix} = 0;$$

Cramer's rule does not apply.

13.

$$D = \begin{vmatrix} 2 & -1 & 4 \\ 3 & 2 & -1 \\ 1 & 4 & 2 \end{vmatrix} = \begin{vmatrix} 2 & -1 & 4 \\ 7 & 0 & 7 \\ 9 & 0 & 18 \end{vmatrix} = 63$$

$$D_x = \begin{vmatrix} -2 & -1 & 4 \\ -3 & 2 & -1 \\ 17 & 4 & 2 \end{vmatrix} = \begin{vmatrix} -2 & -1 & 4 \\ -7 & 0 & 7 \\ 9 & 0 & 18 \end{vmatrix} = -189$$

$$D_y = \begin{vmatrix} 2 & -2 & 4 \\ 3 & -3 & -1 \\ 1 & 17 & 2 \end{vmatrix} = \begin{vmatrix} 2 & 0 & 4 \\ 3 & 0 & -1 \\ 1 & 18 & 2 \end{vmatrix} = 252$$

$$D_z = \begin{vmatrix} 2 & -1 & -2 \\ 3 & 2 & -3 \\ 1 & 4 & 17 \end{vmatrix} = \begin{vmatrix} 2 & -1 & 0 \\ 3 & 2 & 0 \\ 1 & 4 & 18 \end{vmatrix} = 126$$

Hence, $x = -3$, $y = 4$, $z = 2$.
The solution set is $\{(-3, 4, 2)\}$.

17.

$$D = \begin{vmatrix} 1 & 2 & 3 \\ 4 & 3 & 2 \\ -1 & -2 & -3 \end{vmatrix} = 0 \text{ since } r_3 + r_1 \text{ gives a row of zeros}$$

Cramer's rule does not apply.

21.

$$D = \begin{vmatrix} 2 & 3 & 0 \\ 0 & 2 & -1 \\ 1 & 0 & 2 \end{vmatrix} = \begin{vmatrix} 0 & 3 & -4 \\ 0 & 2 & -1 \\ 1 & 0 & 2 \end{vmatrix} = 5$$

$$D_x = \begin{vmatrix} 13 & 3 & 0 \\ 5 & 2 & -1 \\ 4 & 0 & 2 \end{vmatrix} = \begin{vmatrix} 13 & 3 & 0 \\ 5 & 2 & -1 \\ 14 & 4 & 0 \end{vmatrix} = 10$$

$$D_y = \begin{vmatrix} 2 & 13 & 0 \\ 0 & 5 & -1 \\ 1 & 4 & 2 \end{vmatrix} = \begin{vmatrix} 2 & 13 & 0 \\ 0 & 5 & -1 \\ 1 & 14 & 0 \end{vmatrix} = 15$$

$$D_z = \begin{vmatrix} 2 & 3 & 13 \\ 0 & 2 & 5 \\ 1 & 0 & 4 \end{vmatrix} = \begin{vmatrix} 0 & 3 & 5 \\ 0 & 2 & 5 \\ 1 & 0 & 4 \end{vmatrix} = 5$$

Hence, $x = 2$, $y = 3$, and $z = 1$.
The solution set is $\{(2, 3, 1)\}$.

25.
$$D = \begin{vmatrix} 1 & 2 & 0 \\ 3 & 0 & 4 \\ 0 & -1 & -1 \end{vmatrix} = \begin{vmatrix} 1 & 2 & 0 \\ 0 & 6 & -4 \\ 0 & 1 & 1 \end{vmatrix} = 10$$

$$D_x = \begin{vmatrix} 10 & 2 & 0 \\ 7 & 0 & 4 \\ 1 & -1 & -1 \end{vmatrix} = \begin{vmatrix} 10 & 12 & 10 \\ 7 & 7 & 11 \\ 1 & 0 & 0 \end{vmatrix} = 62$$

$$D_y = \begin{vmatrix} 1 & 10 & 0 \\ 3 & 7 & 4 \\ 0 & 1 & -1 \end{vmatrix} = \begin{vmatrix} 1 & 10 & 0 \\ 3 & 11 & 4 \\ 0 & 0 & -1 \end{vmatrix} = 19$$

$$D_z = \begin{vmatrix} 1 & 2 & 10 \\ 3 & 0 & 7 \\ 0 & -1 & 1 \end{vmatrix} = \begin{vmatrix} 1 & 12 & 10 \\ 3 & 7 & 7 \\ 0 & 0 & 1 \end{vmatrix} = -29$$

The solution set is $\{(6.2, 1.9, -2.9)\}$.

29.
$$D = \begin{vmatrix} .4 & -.6 \\ .3 & .2 \end{vmatrix} = .08 + .18 = .26$$

$$D_x = \begin{vmatrix} .4 & -.6 \\ -.22 & .2 \end{vmatrix} = .08 - .132 = -.052$$

$$D_y = \begin{vmatrix} .4 & .4 \\ .3 & -.22 \end{vmatrix} = .-088 - .12 = -.208$$

The solution set is $\{(-2, -.8)\}$.

33. Let s be the cost of a shirt and let p be the cost of a pair of pants. We have

$$5s + 2p = 96$$
$$s + 3p = 66.$$

Then, using Cramer's rule,

$$D = \begin{vmatrix} 5 & 2 \\ 1 & 3 \end{vmatrix} = 15 - 2 = 13,$$

$$D_s = \begin{vmatrix} 96 & 2 \\ 66 & 3 \end{vmatrix} = 288 - 132 = 156,$$

$$D_p = \begin{vmatrix} 5 & 96 \\ 1 & 66 \end{vmatrix} = 330 - 96 = 234.$$

Thus, $s = \frac{156}{13} = \$12$ and $p = \frac{234}{13} = \$18$.

37. Let x be the number of pounds of tea worth \$4.60 a pound. Consider the following table:

lbs	price per lb	cost
x	4.60	4.60x
8-x	6.50	6.50(8-x)
Mixture		
8	5.20	41.60

Setting the costs equal gives

$$41.60 = 4.60x + 6.50(8-x)$$
$$41.60 = 4.60x + 52.00 - 6.50x$$
$$1.9x = 10.4$$
$$x = \frac{10.4}{1.9} = \frac{104}{19}$$

The answer is $\frac{104}{19}$ pounds.

41. For the system
$$a_1 x + b_1 y = c_1$$
$$a_2 x + b_2 y = c_2$$
we are given that

(I) $D_x = \begin{vmatrix} c_1 & b_1 \\ c_2 & b_2 \end{vmatrix} = c_1 b_2 - c_2 b_1 = 0,$

and

(II) $D_y = \begin{vmatrix} a_1 & c_1 \\ a_2 & c_2 \end{vmatrix} = a_1 c_2 - a_2 c_1 = 0.$

In (I) we arrive at $c_1 b_2 = c_2 b_1$

or $\frac{c_1}{c_2} = \frac{b_1}{b_2}.$

In (II) we arrive at $a_1 c_2 = a_2 c_1$

or $\frac{a_1}{a_2} = \frac{c_1}{c_2}.$

If $c_1 c_2 \neq 0$, then $c_1 \neq 0$ and $c_2 \neq 0$ and $\frac{c_1}{c_2}$ is defined. Thus, we can conclude that

$$\frac{a_1}{a_2} = \frac{b_1}{b_2}$$
$$a_1 b_2 = b_1 a_2$$
$$a_1 b_2 - b_1 a_2 = 0,$$

and hence

$$D = \begin{vmatrix} a_1 & b_1 \\ a_2 & b_2 \end{vmatrix} = a_1 b_2 - b_1 a_2 = 0.$$

$D = D_x = D_y = 0$ implies that the equations are dependent.

45. For the system of equations

$$\frac{1}{2}x - \frac{1}{b}y = 1$$

$$2x + by = 4b$$

we have

$$D = \begin{vmatrix} \frac{1}{2} & -\frac{1}{b} \\ 2 & b \end{vmatrix} = \frac{b}{2} + \frac{2}{b} = \frac{b^2 + 4}{2b},$$

$$D_x = \begin{vmatrix} 1 & -\frac{1}{b} \\ 4b & b \end{vmatrix} = b + 4, \text{ and}$$

$$D_y = \begin{vmatrix} \frac{1}{2} & 1 \\ 2 & 4b \end{vmatrix} = 2b - 2.$$

Thus,

$$x = \frac{b + 4}{\frac{b^2 + 4}{2b}} = \frac{2b(b + 4)}{b^2 + 4} \quad \text{and}$$

$$y = \frac{2(b - 1)}{\frac{b^2 + 4}{2b}} = \frac{4b(b - 1)}{b^2 + 4}.$$

Section 9.7   Nonlinear Systems

Additional Examples

Example 1   Find all points (x, y) that satisfy the system

$$x^2 + y^2 = 9$$

$$3x^2 - 2y^2 = -8.$$

Solution   We are aksed to find the points of intersection of the circle $x^2 + y^2 = 9$ and the hyperbola $3x^2 - 2y^2 = -8$. Considering $x^2 + y^2 = 9$, we have $y^2 = 9 - x^2$. Substituting this into the second equation gives

$$3x^2 - 2(9 - x^2) = -8$$

$$3x^2 - 18 + 2x^2 = -8$$

$$5x^2 = 10,$$

or

$$x^2 = 2.$$

Hence, $x = \pm\sqrt{2}$. Substituting this into the equation $x^2 + y^2 = 9$, we have $2 + y^2 = 9$, or $y^2 = 7$. Thus, $y = \pm\sqrt{7}$. The points that satisfy

the system are the four points $(-\sqrt{2}, -\sqrt{7})$, $(-\sqrt{2}, \sqrt{7})$, $(\sqrt{2}, -\sqrt{7})$, and $(\sqrt{2}, \sqrt{7})$.

Example 2   Solve the system

$$x^2 + y^2 = 36$$

$$x^2 + y - 16 = 0.$$

Solution   The solutions will be the points of intersection of the circle $x^2 + y^2 = 36$ and the parabola $y = 16 - x^2$. To solve the system we can write

(1) $x^2 + y^2 = 36$

(2) $x^2 + y = 16.$

Subtracting (2) from (1) gives $y^2 - y = 20$, or $y^2 - y - 20 = 0$. Solving, we have $(y - 5)(y + 4) = 0$, so that either $y = 5$ or $y = -4$. This leads to the following, using equation (2):

(i)   If $y = -4$, then $x^2 - 4 = 16$, or $x^2 = 20$, so that $x = \pm2\sqrt{5}$. Hence, $(2\sqrt{5}, -4)$ and $(-2\sqrt{5}, -4)$ are solutions.

(ii)   If $y = 5$, then $x^2 + 5 = 16$, or $x^2 = 11$, so that $x = \pm\sqrt{11}$. Hence, $(-\sqrt{11}, 5)$ and $(+\sqrt{11}, 5)$ are solutions. The solution set is $\{(-\sqrt{11}, 5), (\sqrt{11}, 5), (2\sqrt{5}, -4), (-2\sqrt{5}, -4)\}$.

Example 3   Solve the system of equations

$$\log (4x + 7) - \log y = 1$$

$$6x - 3y = 2.$$

Solution   Solving equation 2 for y gives

$$6x = 3y + 2$$

$$y = \frac{6x - 2}{3}.$$

Substituting this into equation 1 gives

$$\log (4x + y) - \log \left(\frac{6x - 2}{3}\right) = 1$$

$$\log \left(\frac{4x + 7}{\frac{6x - 2}{3}}\right) = 1$$

$$\log \left(\frac{12x + 21}{6x - 2}\right) = 1.$$

From the definition of the logarithm, $\log a = b$ if and only if $a = 10^b$, we have

$$\frac{12x + 21}{6x - 2} = 10'$$

$$12x + 21 = 10(6x - 2) \quad \text{if } 6x \neq 2,$$

$$12x - 60x = -20 - 21$$

$$-48x = -41,$$

or $\quad x = \frac{41}{48}.$

Substituting $x = \frac{41}{48}$ into the equation $6x - 3y = 2$ gives

$$y = \frac{6x - 2}{3}$$

$$y = \frac{6(\frac{41}{48}) - 2}{3}$$

$$y = \frac{\frac{41}{8} - \frac{16}{8}}{3}$$

$$y = \frac{25}{24}.$$

The solution is $x = \frac{41}{48}$, $y = \frac{25}{24}$.

Selected Solutions

1. Given the system

$$2x^2 = 3y + 23$$
$$y = 2x - 5,$$

we substitute for y in the first equation and arrive at

$$2x^2 = 3(2x - 5) + 23$$
$$2x^2 = 6x + 8$$
$$2x^2 - 6x - 8 = 0$$
$$(2x + 2)(x - 4) = 0,$$

so that $\quad x = -1$ or $x = 4.$
If $x = -1$, then $y = 2(-1) - 5 = -7$, and if $x = 4$, then $y = 2(4) - 5 = 3$. The solution set is $\{(-1, -7), (4, 3)\}.$

5. Given the system

$$x^2 - y = -1$$
$$3x = y - 11,$$

the second equation can be written as $y = 3x + 11$. Substituting this into the first equation gives

$$x^2 - (3x + 11) = -1$$
$$x^2 - 3x - 10 = 0$$
$$(x + 2)(x - 5) = 0$$

so that $\quad x = -2$ or $x = 5.$
If $x = -2$, then $y = 3(-2) + 11 = 5$, and if $x = 5$, then $y = 3(5) + 11 = 26$. The solution set is $\{(-2, 5), (5, 26)\}.$

9. For the given system

$$y = x^2 - 2x + 1$$
$$x - 3y = -1,$$

we substitute the first equation for y into equation 2 and arrive at

$$x - 3(x^2 - 2x + 1) = -1$$
$$3x^2 - 7x + 2 = 0$$
$$(3x - 1)(x - 2) = 0,$$

so that $\quad x = 2$ or $x = \frac{1}{3}.$
If $x = 2$, then $y = 4 - 4 + 1 = 1$, and if $x = \frac{1}{3}$, then $y = \frac{1}{9} - \frac{2}{3} + 1 = \frac{4}{9}.$

The solution set is $\{(2, 1), (\frac{1}{3}, \frac{4}{9})\}.$

13. We have

$$x^2 + y^2 = 8$$
$$\underline{x^2 - y^2 = 0}$$
$$2x^2 \qquad = 8,$$
$$x^2 = 4,$$

so that $x = -2$ or $x = 2$. If $x = -2$, then $4 - y^2 = 0$; $y^2 = 4$; or $y = \pm 2$. If $x = 2$, then $4 - y^2 = 0$, or $y = \pm 2$. The solution set is $\{(-2, -2), (-2, 2), (2, -2), (2, 2)\}.$

17. $\qquad 2x^2 + 3y^2 = 5 \qquad (1)$
$\qquad 3x^2 - 4y^2 = -1 \qquad (2)$

$\qquad 8x^2 + 12y^2 = 20$ Multiply (1) by 4
$\qquad \underline{9x^2 - 12y^2 = -3}$ Multiply (2) by 3
$\qquad 17x^2 \qquad = 17$ Add

Hence, we have $x = \pm 1$. The solutions are $(1, 1)$, $(1, -1)$, $(-1, 1)$, $(-1, -1)$, since equation 1 gives the result that if $x = \pm 1$, $2 + 3y^2 = 5$, or $y^2 = 1$, or $y = \pm 1$.

21. Given the system of equations

$$xy = 6$$
$$x + y = 5,$$

we solve the second equation, arrive at $y = 5 - x$, and substitute into the first equation. This gives

$$x(5 - x) = 6$$
$$5x - x^2 = 6$$
$$x^2 - 5x + 6 = 0$$
$$(x - 2)(x - 3) = 0,$$

so that $x = 2$ or $x = 3$. If $x = 2$, then $y = 3$, and if $x = 3$, then $y = 2$. The solution set is $\{(2, 3), (3, 2)\}$.

25. Given the system of equations

$$2xy + 1 = 0 \qquad (1)$$
$$x + 16y = 2, \qquad (2)$$

equation (2) gives $x = 2 - 16y$. Substitution into (1) gives

$$2(2 - 16y)y + 1 = 0$$
$$4y - 32y^2 + 1 = 0$$
$$32y^2 - 4y - 1 = 0$$
$$(8y + 1)(4y - 1) = 0,$$

so that $y = \dfrac{-1}{8}$ or $y = \dfrac{1}{4}$.

Using (2) we see that if $y = \dfrac{-1}{8}$, then $x = 4$, and if $y = \dfrac{1}{4}$, then $x = -2$. The solution set is

$$\left\{(4, \tfrac{-1}{8}), (-2, \tfrac{1}{4})\right\}.$$

29. Given the system

$$x^2 + 2xy - y^2 = 14 \qquad (1)$$
$$x^2 \qquad\quad - y^2 = -16 \qquad (2)$$

$$\overline{\qquad 2xy \qquad\quad = 30,} \text{ (Subtract)}$$

or

$$y = \frac{15}{x}.$$

Substitute this into (2) to arrive at

$$x^2 - \frac{225}{x^2} = -16$$
$$x^4 + 16x^2 - 225 = 0$$
$$(x^2 + 25)(x^2 - 9) = 0,$$

so that $x^2 - 9 = 0$, or $x = \pm 3$. Note that $x^2 + 25$ can never equal zero.

Since $y = \dfrac{15}{x}$ we have that if $x = 3$, $y = 5$, and if $x = -3$, $y = -5$. The solution set is $\{(-3, -5), (3, 5)\}$.

33.
$$x^2 + 2xy - y^2 + y = 1 \qquad (1)$$
$$3x + y = 6 \qquad (2)$$
$$\text{or} \quad y = 6 - 3x \qquad (2)$$

$$x^2 + 2x(6 - 3x) - (6 - 3x)^2 + (6 - 3x) = 1$$
$$14x^2 - 45x + 31 = 0$$
$$(14x - 31)(x - 1) = 0$$

Hence, $x = 1$ or $x = \dfrac{31}{14}$. We find that $(1, 3)$, $(\dfrac{31}{14}, \dfrac{-9}{14})$ are the solutions.

37.
$$y = \log (x - 2) \qquad (1)$$
$$y = -1 + \log (8x + 4) \qquad (2)$$

$$\log (x - 2) = -1 + \log (8x + 4)$$

since $\quad -1 = \log \dfrac{1}{10}$

$$\log (x - 2) = \log \frac{8x + 4}{10}$$
$$x - 2 = \frac{4x + 2}{5}$$

$5x - 10 = 4x + 2$, so that $x = 12$. Substituting $x = 12$ into equation (1) gives $y = \log (12 - 2) = \log 10$. Hence, $y = 1$. The solution set is $\{(12, 1)\}$.

39. Let x and y be the two numbers. Then we have

$$x + y = 12 \qquad (1)$$
$$xy = 36. \qquad (2)$$

Solving (1) for y gives $y = 12 - x$. Substituting in (2) gives

$$x(12 - x) = 36$$
$$12x - x^2 = 36$$
$$0 = x^2 - 12x + 36$$
$$(x - 6)(x - 6) = 0.$$

$x = 6$ is the solution. Then $y = 6$. The two numbers are 6 and 6.

41. Let x and y be the two numbers;
     then the system of equations is

     $$\frac{x}{y} = \frac{5}{3} \qquad (1)$$

     $$xy = 135. \qquad (2)$$

     From (1), $3x = 5y$ so that $y = (\frac{3}{5})x$.
     Substituting in (2) gives

     $$x(\frac{3}{5}x) = 135$$

     $$\frac{3}{5}x^2 = 135$$

     $$x^2 = 135(\frac{5}{3})$$

     $$x^2 = 225$$

     $$x = \pm 15,$$

     so $y = \frac{3}{5}(\pm 15) = \pm 9$.

     There are two sets of numbers that
     work, $-15, -9$ or $15, 9$.

43. If x = short side,

     $$x^2 + (x + 7)^2 = 13^2$$
     $$2x^2 + 14x + 49 = 169$$
     $$x^2 + 7x - 60 = 0$$
     $$(x + 12)(x - 5) = 0$$

     The number $x = -12$ is ridiculous,
     so the only solution is $x = 5$. The
     sides have length $x = 5$ m and
     $x + 7 = 12$ m.

45. If $y = x^2 + 4$ is substituted into
     the ellipse

     $$2x^2 + y^2 - 4x - 4y = 0$$

     we get
     $$2x^2 + (x^2+4)^2 - 4x - 4(x^2 + 4) = 0$$
     $$x^4 + 6x^2 - 4x = 0$$
     $$x(x^3 + 6x - 4) = 0.$$

     Thus, $x = 0$ is a solution. The
     equation $x^3 + 6x - 4 = 0$ is diffi-
     cult to consider. However, if $x = 0$,
     $y = 0^2 + 4 = 4$, and we see that the
     point $P(0, 4)$ is a common point.

49. $$y = -\sqrt{1 + x}$$
     $$(x - 3)^2 + y^2 = 16.$$
     Replace y in the second equation
     with $-\sqrt{1 + x}$.

$$(x - 3)^2 + (-\sqrt{1 + x})^2 = 16$$
$$x^2 - 6x + 9 + 1 + x = 16$$
$$x^2 - 2x - 6 = 0$$
$$(x - 6)(x + 1) = 0$$
$$x - 6 = 0 \quad \text{or} \quad x + 1 = 0$$
$$x = 0 \quad \text{or} \qquad x = -1.$$

Now find y, using $y = -\sqrt{1 + x}$.

If $x = 6$,   If $x = -1$,
  $y = -\sqrt{1 + 6}$ $y = -\sqrt{1 + (-1)}$
  $y = -\sqrt{7}$ $y = 0$

The solution set is
$\{(6, -7), (-1, 0)\}$.

53. Given the system
     $$x^3 - y^3 = a^3 \qquad (1)$$
     $$x - y = 6, \qquad (2)$$
     equation (2) is $y = x - 6$, and we
     can substitute this into (1) to
     arrive at
     $$x^3 - (x - 6)^2 = a^3$$
     $$x^3 - (x^3 - 18x^2 + 108x - 216) = a^3$$
     $$18x^2 - 108x + (216 - a^3) = 0,$$
     or $9x^2 - 54x + (108 - \frac{1}{2}a^3) = 0$.
     Using the quadratic formula we have

     $$x = \frac{54 \pm \sqrt{54^2 - 4(9)(108 - \frac{1}{2}a^3)}}{18}$$

     $$x = \frac{54 \pm \sqrt{2916 - (36)(108) + 18a^3}}{18}$$

     $$x = \frac{3(18) \pm \sqrt{18a^3 - 972}}{18}$$

     $$x = \frac{18 \pm \sqrt{2a^3 - 108}}{6}.$$

     Using $y = x - 6$, we have

     $$y = \frac{18 \pm \sqrt{2a^3 - 108}}{6} - \frac{36}{6}$$

     $$y = \frac{-18 \pm \sqrt{2a^3 - 108}}{6}.$$

     The solution set is

     $$\left\{ \left(\frac{18 - \sqrt{2a^3 - 108}}{6}, \frac{-18 - \sqrt{2a^3 - 108}}{6} \right), \right.$$
     $$\left. \left(\frac{18 + \sqrt{2a^3 - 108}}{6}, \frac{-18 + \sqrt{2a^3 - 108}}{6} \right) \right\}.$$

Section 9.8   Systems of Inequalities

Additional Examples

Example 1   Graph the solution of the
   system
   $x^2 + y^2 < 25$
   $y - x^2 > -1.$

Solution   We graph the circle $x^2 + y^2$
   $= 25$ as a dotted line since we are
   only interested in $x^2 + y^2 < 25.$
   We can test points to see what
   region satisfies the inequality.
   Since the origin gives $0^2 + 0^2 < 25,$
   we see that the inequality $x^2 + y^2$
   < 25 is satisfied by all points
   interior to the circle.

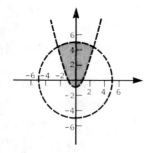

The inequality $y - x^2 > -1$ is
$y > x^2 - 1,$ so we graph the parabola $y = x^2 - 1$ as a dotted line.
Note that the origin also satisfies
this inequality, since $0 > 0^2 - 1.$
Thus, we are interested in the
region above the parabola.

   Shading the region common to
both solution sets gives the graph
in the figure. We could solve for
the points of intersection if
needed.

Example 2   Graph the solution set of
   the system
   $\dfrac{x^2}{4} - \dfrac{y^2}{9} \geq 1$
   $\dfrac{x^2}{9} + \dfrac{y^2}{25} < 1.$

Solution   We must graph the hyperbola
   $\dfrac{x^2}{4} - \dfrac{y^2}{9} = 1$ (solid) and the ellispe
   $\dfrac{x^2}{9} + \dfrac{y^2}{25} = 1$ (dotted). The ellipse

has x-intercepts at $x = \pm 3,$ and
y-intercepts at $y = \pm 5.$

   The hyperbola $\dfrac{x^2}{4} - \dfrac{y^2}{9} = 1$ has
x-intercepts at $x = \pm 2.$ The asymp-
tote lines are found as
$$\dfrac{x^2}{4} - \dfrac{y^2}{9} = 0$$
$$\dfrac{y^2}{9} = \dfrac{x^2}{4},$$
or $y = \pm\dfrac{3}{2}x.$

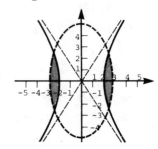

The solution set is interior to the
ellipse and must satisfy $\dfrac{x^2}{4} \geq 1 + \dfrac{y^2}{9}.$
The points $(-3, 0)$ and $(3, 0)$ satisfy
this inequality, so the solution set
is the shaded region in the given
figure.

Selected Solutions

1. $x + y \leq 4$ (1)
    $x - 2y \geq 6$ (2)
    To solve this system we sketch each
    line, $x + y = 4$ and $x - 2y = 6.$

$x + y = 4$				$x - 2y = 6$	
x	0	4		x	0	6
y	4	0		y	-3	0

The solution is the region that lies
simultaneously on and below both
lines. We note that the origin
$(0, 0)$ satisfies equation (1) but
does not satisfy equation (2). See
the graph in the answer section of
the text.

5. $x + 2y \leq 4$

       $y \geq x^2 - 1$

Sketch the line $x + 2y = 4$ (solid) and the parabola $y = x^2 - 1$ (solid).

$x + 2y = 4$				$y = x^2 - 1$		
x	0	4	-2	x	0	1	2
y	2	0	3	y	-1	0	3

The solution is the shaded area below the line <u>and</u> above the parabola, including the boundary. See the graph in the textbook.

9. $x^2 - y^2 < 1$

    $-1 < y < 1$

Sketch the lines $y = -1$ and $y = 1$ (dotted), and sketch the hyperbola $x^2 - y^2 = 1$ (dotted). The hyperbola intersects the x-axis at ± 1 and has asymptote lines $y = \pm x$. To determine the region, note that $(0, 0)$ satisfies both inequalities, so the desired region is the shaded region in the figure. See graph in textbook.

13. $\frac{x^2}{16} + \frac{y^2}{9} \leq 1$

    $\frac{x^2}{4} - \frac{y^2}{16} \geq 1$

Sketch the ellipse $\frac{x^2}{16} + \frac{y^2}{9} = 1$ (solid) and the hyperbola $\frac{x^2}{4} - \frac{y^2}{16} = 1$ (solid). The hyperbola has intercepts $x = \pm 2$ and asymptote lines $y = \pm 2x$. The region is inside or on the ellipse, and outside the hyperbola, since $\frac{x^2}{4} \geq 1 + \frac{y^2}{16}$.

Note: $(0, 0)$ does not satisfy the hyperbola inequality. The solution is the shaded region, including the boundary. See the graph in the textbook.

17. $-2 < x < 3$

    $-1 \leq y \leq 5$

    $2x + y < 6$

$2x + y = 6$		
x	0	3
y	6	0

Draw $2x + y = 6$ (dotted). The region is in the box, below the line $2x + y = 6$. See the graph in the textbook.

21. $\frac{x^2}{4} + \frac{y^2}{9} > 1$

    $x^2 - y^2 \geq 1$

    $-4 \leq x \leq 4$

Sketch the ellipse $\frac{x^2}{4} + \frac{y^2}{9} = 1$ (dotted), the hyperbola $x^2 - y^2 = 1$ (solid), and the lines $x = -4$ and $x = 4$ (solid). The hyperbola has intercepts at $x = \pm 1$ and asymptote lines $y = \pm x$. The solution is the shaded region. See the graph in the textbook.

25. $|x| \geq 2$

    $|y| \geq 4$

    $y < x^2$

The inequality $|x| \geq 2$ is satisfied if $x \in (-\infty, -2)$ or if $x \in (2, \infty)$, the inequality $|y| \geq 4$ is satisfied if $y \in (-\infty, -4)$ or if $y \in (4, \infty)$. The graph $y = x^2$ is a parabola passing through $(0, 0)$ with horns upward, and the graph is dotted since points with $y = x^2$ are not solutions. The solution set consists of all points <u>below</u> the parabola that lie <u>outside</u> or on the rectangular box determined by the lines $x = -2$, $x = 2$, $y = -4$, and $y = 4$. See the graph in the text.

27. $y \leq |x + 2|$

   $\frac{x^2}{16} - \frac{y^2}{9} \leq 1$

Sketch the "vee" curve $y = |x + 2|$ (solid) and the hyperbola $\frac{x^2}{16} - \frac{y^2}{9} = 1$ (solid). The hyperbola has intercepts $x = \pm 4$ and asymptote lines $y = (\pm\frac{3}{4})x$. Note: the V graph, $y = |x + 2|$, will not intersect the hyperbola. To see this, substitute $y = |x + 2|$ into $\frac{x^2}{16} - \frac{y^2}{9} = 1$ and get $\frac{x^2}{16} - \frac{(x+2)^2}{9} = 1$.

$$9x^2 - 16(x^2 + 4x + 4) = 144, \quad \text{or}$$
$$7x^2 + 64x + 208 = 0$$
$$b^2 - 4ac = 64^2 - 4(7)(208)$$
$$= 4096 - 5824$$
$$b^2 - 4ac < 0$$

so no real number solutions. The solution is the shaded area shown in the textbook.

29. $y \geq |4 - x|$
    $y \geq |x|$

    The graph of $y = |4 - x|$ is a "vee" graph with vertex at P(4, 0), and the graph of $y = |x|$ is a "vee" graph with vertex at Q(0, 0). The graphs intersect when $|4 - x| = |x|$, or when $x = 2$. The point of intersection is I(2, 2). The solution set is the region on and above both graphs at I. See the graph in the text.

31. Let b = number of basic pizzas
        p = number of plain pizzas
          $b \geq 3$, $p \geq 2$
    $5b + 4p \leq 50$
    $2b + p \leq 16$
    See the graph in the textbook.

33. Let x = number of red pills
        y = number of green pills
    $8x + 2y \geq 16$
     $x + y \geq 5$
    $2x + 7y \geq 20$
          $x \geq 0$, $y \geq 0$
    See the graph in the textbook. We graph each line (solid). The solution set is the set of points

in the first quadrant ($x \geq 0$, $y \geq 0$) that lies above each line simultaneously. See the graph in the text.

Section 9.9   Linear Programming

Additional Examples

Example 1   Find $x \geq 0$ and $y \geq 0$ such that

$$-x + 2y \leq 8 \qquad (1)$$
$$x + 2y \leq 12 \qquad (2)$$
$$2x + y \leq 16 \qquad (3)$$

and $3x + 4y$ is maximized.

Solution   We need to graph each line, and we need the points of intersection of these lines.

$-x + 2y = 8$		$x + 2y = 12$		$2x + y = 16$	
x	y	x	y	x	y
0	4	0	6	0	16
-8	0	12	0	8	0
2	5	2	5		

$-x + 2y = 8$	(1)	$x + 2y = 12$	(2)
$x + 2y = 12$	(2)	$4x + 2y = 32$	(3)

$$4y = 20 \qquad\qquad 3x = 20$$
$$y = 5 \qquad\qquad x = \frac{20}{3}$$
$$x = 2 \qquad\qquad y = \frac{8}{3}$$

we will not locate the intersection of $-x + 2y = 8$ and $2x + y = 16$ because we will see that this point is not in the solution set of the system of inequalities.

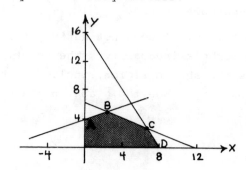

The feasible region is shaded, and the four points A(0, 4), B(2, 5), $C(\frac{20}{3}, \frac{8}{3})$, and D(8, 0) are the vertices to be tested.

A: $3x + 4y = 3(0) + 4(4) = 16$

B: $3x + 4y = 3(2) + 4(5) = 26$

C: $3x + 4y = 3(\frac{20}{3}) + 4(\frac{8}{3}) = \frac{92}{3}$

D: $3x + 4y = 3(8) + 4(0) = 24$

The maximum value of $\frac{92}{3}$ occurs at the point $C(\frac{20}{3}, \frac{8}{3})$.

Selected Solutions

1. We test $3x + 5y$ at each of the vertices A(1, 1), B(6, 3), C(5, 10), and D(2, 7).
   This gives
   A: $3x + 5y = 3(1) + 5(1) = 8$
   B: $3x + 5y = 3(6) + 5(3) = 33$
   C: $3x + 5y = 3(5) + 5(10) = 65$
   D: $3x + 5y = 3(2) + 5(7) = 41$.
   The maximum value of 65 occurs at C and the minimum value of 8 occurs at A.

5. The feasible solutions are in the region described by $x \geq 0$, $y \geq 0$,
   $2x + 3y \leq 6$
   $4x + y \leq 6$.

$2x + 3y = 6$	
x	y
0	2
3	0

$4x + y = 6$	
x	y
0	6
$\frac{3}{2}$	0

   The point of intersection of this pair of lines can be found by
   $$\begin{bmatrix} 2 & 3 & \overline{6} \\ 4 & 1 & \overline{6} \end{bmatrix} \sim \begin{bmatrix} 2 & 3 & \overline{6} \\ 0 & -5 & \overline{-6} \end{bmatrix}$$
   so that $y = \frac{6}{5}$ and then $2x + 3(\frac{6}{5})$
   $= 6$, or $x = \frac{6}{5}$. Hence, there is a

vertex at $P(\frac{6}{5}, \frac{6}{5})$. We can observe (even without graphing the region) that the points we should test are the vertices A(0, 2), $B(\frac{3}{2}, 0)$, and P. We do not test the origin (0, 0) since it obviously gives $5x + 2y$ the value 0. We test these vertices on $5x + 2y$:

A: $5x + 2y = 5(0) + 2(2) = 4$

B: $5x + 2y = 5(\frac{3}{2}) + 2(0) = \frac{15}{2} = 7.5$

P: $5x + 2y = 5(\frac{6}{5}) + 2(\frac{6}{5}) = \frac{42}{5} = 8.4$.

Hence, the maximum value is $\frac{42}{5}$, and this occurs at $P(\frac{6}{5}, \frac{6}{5})$.

9. To find $x \geq 0$, $y \geq 0$ such that
   $$x - y \leq 10$$
   $$5x + 3y \leq 75$$
   and $4x + 2y$ is maximized, we consider the lines $x - y = 10$ and $5x + 3y = 75$.

$x - y = 10$	
x	y
0	-10
10	0

$5x + 3y = 75$	
x	y
0	25
15	0

   The graphs intersect when
   $$\begin{aligned} 5x + 3y &= 75 \\ 3x - 3y &= 30 \\ \hline 8x &= 105 \\ x &= \frac{105}{8}, \end{aligned}$$
   and $y = x - 10 = \frac{105}{8} - \frac{80}{8} = \frac{25}{8}$.
   Without graphing we can see that we must test the vertices A(10, 0) and $B(\frac{105}{8}, \frac{25}{8})$. C(15, 0) does not satisfy $x - y \leq 10$. Testing points A and B gives

   A: $4x + 2y = 4(10) + 2(0) = 40$

   B: $4x + 2y = 4(\frac{105}{8}) + 2(\frac{25}{8}) = \frac{235}{4}$.

   The maximum occurs at $B(\frac{105}{8}, \frac{25}{8})$.

13. Let x = number of pigs and
        y = number of geese.
     The conditions on x and y are
     x + y ≤ 16, y ≤ 12, and 5x + 2y ≤ 50.
     Obviously, we must have x ≥ 0 and
     y ≥ 0.

x + y = 16			5x + 2y = 50	
x	y		x	y
0	16		0	25
16	0		10	0

     x + y = 16 and y = 12 intersect at
     point A(4, 12). 5x + 2y = 50 and
     y = 12 intersect at point B($\frac{26}{5}$, 12).

     x + y = 16 and 5x + 2y = 50 inter-
     sect at C(6, 10)

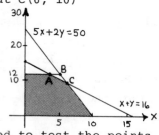

     We need to test the points (0, 12),
     A(4, 12), C(6, 10), and (10, 0).

     Note that point B($\frac{26}{5}$, 12) does not

     satisfy the condition x + y ≤ 16.
     Testing the profit function
     P = 4x + 8y, we have
(0, 12): 4x + 8y = 4(0) + 8(12) = $96
    A: 4x + 8y = 4(4) + 8(12) = $112
    C: 4x + 8y + 4(6) + 8(10) = $104
(10, 0): 4x + 8y = 4(10) + 8(0) = $40.
     The maximum profit is $112 raising
     4 pigs and 12 geese.

17. Let x = number of barrels of gaso-
     line and y = number of barrels of
     oil. Then the conditions on x and
     y are
     x ≥ 2y,
     y ≥ 3,000,000,
     x ≤ 6,400,000, and we wish to maxi-
     mize the revenue R = 1.90x + 1.50y.

The condition x ≥ 2y gives x - 2y ≥ 0,
or y ≤ $\frac{1}{2}$x. Sketching the region
shows the feasible region.

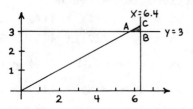

The tiny shaded triangle ABC is the
feasible region. We test the points
A(6, 3), B(6.4, 3), and C(6.4, 3.2),
where each unit represents a million.
Obviously, the maximum revenue
R = 1.90x + 1.50y occurs when
x = 6.4 million and y = 3.2 million
barrels. This maximum revenue is
$16,960,000.

21. Let x = number of type 1 bolts and
     let y = number of type 2 bolts. We
     must obviously have x ≥ 0 and y ≥ 0.
     We will treat the revenue function
     in cents, so that we wish to maximize
     R = 10x + 12y. Our machines operate
     independent of one another so we
     consider each machine separately.
         For group I we have
     .4x + .3y ≤ 1200, or
      4x + 3y ≤ 12,000.
     The intercepts are at A(0, 4) and
     B(3, 0), considering our units
     measured in thousands. Testing
     these vertices, we have
     A: 10x + 12y = 10(0) + 12(4) = 48 ($480)
     B: 10x + 2y = 10(3) + 12(0) = 30.
     The maximum profit from machine
     group I comes from x = 0 and
     y = 4000 bolts.
         Using a similar study for the
     group II machines, we have
     5x + 2y ≤ 12 (12,000),
     and the intercepts are A($\frac{12}{5}$, 0)
     and B(0, 6). Testing the revenue

we have,

A: $10x + 12y = 10(\frac{12}{5}) + 12(0) = 24$

B: $10x + 12y = 10(0) + 12(6) = 72$ ($720).

The maximum profit comes from $x = 0$

and $\underline{y = 6000}$ bolts.

Using the group III machine we
have $2x + 4y \le 12$ (12,000), so the
intercepts are $A(0, 3)$ and $B(6, 0)$.
Testing the revenue, we have

A: $10x + 12y = 10(0) + 12(3) = 36$

B: $10x + 12y = 10(6) + 12(0) = 60$ ($600).

The maximum revenue comes from
$x = \underline{6000\ bolts}$ and $y = 0$.
Hence, in order to maximize the
total revenue, the company will
produce 6000 type 1 bolts and
10,000 type 2 bolts. The revenue
is $R = \$480 + \$720 + \$600 = \$1800$.

Chapter 9   Review Exercises
Selected Solutions

1. $3x - 5y = -18$ $21x - 35x = -126$

$2x + 7y = 19$ $\underline{10x + 35y = 95}$

$\qquad\qquad\qquad 31x \qquad = -31$

$\qquad\qquad\qquad\qquad x = -1$

If $x = -1$, then $-2 + 7y = 19$, or
$y = 3$. The solution set is
$\{(-1, 3)\}$.

5. $\frac{1}{x} + \frac{1}{y} = \frac{7}{10}$ $\frac{5}{x} + \frac{5}{y} = \frac{7}{2}$

$\frac{3}{x} - \frac{5}{y} = \frac{1}{2}$ $\dfrac{\frac{3}{x} - \frac{5}{y} = \frac{1}{2}}{\frac{8}{x} = \frac{8}{2}}$ Add

Then $x = 2$ and $y = 5$. The solution
set is $\{(2, 5)\}$.

9. Let x = number of 25¢ bars, and
y = number of 50¢ bars.
Then $x + y = 22$ and
$.25x + .50y = 8.50$. The last equation can be written as $x + 2y = 34$.
Solving gives $x = 10$, $y = 12$.

13. $\begin{bmatrix} 3 & -4 & 1 & | & 2 \\ 2 & 1 & -4 & | & 1 \end{bmatrix}$

$\sim \begin{bmatrix} 1 & -5 & 5 & | & 1 \\ 2 & 1 & -4 & | & 1 \end{bmatrix}$ $r_1' = r_1 - r_2$

$\sim \begin{bmatrix} 1 & -5 & 5 & | & 1 \\ 0 & 11 & -14 & | & -1 \end{bmatrix}$ $r_2'' = r_2 - 2r_1$

$\sim \begin{bmatrix} 1 & -5 & 5 & | & 1 \\ 0 & 1 & \frac{-14}{11} & | & \frac{-1}{11} \end{bmatrix}$

$\sim \begin{bmatrix} 1 & 0 & -\frac{15}{11} & | & \frac{6}{11} \\ 0 & 1 & \frac{-14}{11} & | & \frac{-1}{11} \end{bmatrix}$

Thus, $x = \frac{15z + 6}{11}$ and $y = \frac{14z - 1}{11}$
for any arbitrary real number z.

17. $x^2 + 2xy + y^2 = 4$ (1)

$\qquad\quad x = 3y - 2$ (2)

Substituting $3y - 2$ for x in
equation (1) gives

$(3y - 2)^2 + 2(3y - 2)y + y^2 = 4$

$9y^2 - 12y + 4 + 6y^2 - 4y + y^2 = 4$

$16y^2 - 16y = 0$

$16y(y - 1) = 0$

$y = 0$, $y = 1$. $y = 0$ gives $x = -2$.
$y = 1$ gives $x = 1$. The solution set
is $\{(-2, 0), (1, 1)\}$.

21. $a = 5$, $y = 0$, $z = 9$, $x = \frac{3}{2}$

25. We cannot subract these matrices
because they do not have the same
size.

29. Solving $2x + 3y = 10$

$\qquad\quad -3x + y = 18$

by Gaussian reduction, we have

$\begin{bmatrix} 2 & 3 & | & 10 \\ -3 & 1 & | & 18 \end{bmatrix} \sim \begin{bmatrix} -1 & 4 & | & 28 \\ -3 & 1 & | & 18 \end{bmatrix}$

$\sim \begin{bmatrix} 1 & -4 & | & -28 \\ 0 & -11 & | & -66 \end{bmatrix} \sim \begin{bmatrix} 1 & -4 & | & -28 \\ 0 & 1 & | & 6 \end{bmatrix}$

$\sim \begin{bmatrix} 1 & 0 & | & -4 \\ 0 & 1 & | & 6 \end{bmatrix}$.

The solution is $x = -4$, $y = 6$.

33. We find the inverse as follows.

$$\left[\begin{array}{cc|cc} 2 & 1 & 1 & 0 \\ 5 & 3 & 0 & 1 \end{array}\right] \sim \left[\begin{array}{cc|cc} 1 & \frac{1}{2} & \frac{1}{2} & 0 \\ 5 & 3 & 0 & 1 \end{array}\right]$$

$$\sim \left[\begin{array}{cc|cc} 1 & \frac{1}{2} & \frac{1}{2} & 0 \\ 0 & \frac{1}{2} & \frac{-5}{2} & 1 \end{array}\right] \quad r_2' = r_2 - 5r_1$$

$$\left[\begin{array}{cc|cc} 1 & \frac{1}{2} & \frac{1}{2} & 0 \\ 0 & 1 & -5 & 2 \end{array}\right]$$

$$\left[\begin{array}{cc|cc} 1 & 0 & 3 & -1 \\ 0 & 1 & -5 & 2 \end{array}\right] \quad r_1'' = r_1' - \frac{1}{2}r_2'$$

The inverse is $\left[\begin{array}{cc} 3 & -1 \\ -5 & 2 \end{array}\right]$.

37. The inverse of $\left[\begin{array}{cc} 2 & 1 \\ 3 & -2 \end{array}\right]$ is found by

$$\left[\begin{array}{cc|cc} 2 & 1 & 1 & 0 \\ 3 & -2 & 0 & 1 \end{array}\right] \sim \left[\begin{array}{cc|cc} 2 & 1 & 1 & 0 \\ 1 & -3 & -1 & 1 \end{array}\right]$$

$$\sim \left[\begin{array}{cc|cc} 1 & -3 & -1 & 1 \\ 2 & 1 & 1 & 0 \end{array}\right] \sim \left[\begin{array}{cc|cc} 1 & -3 & -1 & 1 \\ 0 & 7 & 3 & -2 \end{array}\right]$$

$$\sim \left[\begin{array}{cc|cc} 1 & -3 & -1 & 1 \\ 0 & 1 & \frac{3}{7} & -\frac{2}{7} \end{array}\right] \sim \left[\begin{array}{cc|cc} 1 & 0 & \frac{2}{7} & \frac{1}{7} \\ 0 & 1 & \frac{3}{7} & -\frac{2}{7} \end{array}\right]$$

Hence the solution is found as follows:

$$\left[\begin{array}{cc} 2 & 1 \\ 3 & -2 \end{array}\right]\left[\begin{array}{c} x \\ y \end{array}\right] = \left[\begin{array}{c} 5 \\ 4 \end{array}\right]$$

$$\left[\begin{array}{c} x \\ y \end{array}\right] = \left[\begin{array}{cc} \frac{2}{7} & \frac{1}{7} \\ \frac{3}{7} & -\frac{2}{7} \end{array}\right]\left[\begin{array}{c} 5 \\ 4 \end{array}\right] = \left[\begin{array}{c} 2 \\ 1 \end{array}\right].$$

41. $\begin{vmatrix} -1 & 8 \\ 2 & 9 \end{vmatrix} = -9 - 16 = -25$

45. $\begin{vmatrix} -1 & 0 & 2 & -3 \\ 0 & 4 & 4 & -1 \\ -6 & 0 & 3 & -5 \\ 0 & -2 & 1 & 0 \end{vmatrix} = \begin{vmatrix} -1 & 0 & 2 & -3 \\ 0 & 4 & 4 & -1 \\ 0 & 0 & -9 & 13 \\ 0 & -2 & 1 & 0 \end{vmatrix}$

$$= -1\begin{vmatrix} 4 & 4 & -1 \\ 0 & -9 & 13 \\ -2 & 1 & 0 \end{vmatrix} = -\begin{vmatrix} 0 & 6 & -1 \\ 0 & -9 & 13 \\ -2 & 1 & 0 \end{vmatrix}$$

$$= 2\begin{vmatrix} 6 & -1 \\ -9 & 13 \end{vmatrix}$$
$$= 2(78-9)$$
$$= 2(69) = 138$$

49. The determinant is zero because row 1 and row 3 are the same.

53. Given the system

$$3x + 7y = 2$$
$$5x - y = -22,$$

we have

$$D = \begin{vmatrix} 3 & 7 \\ 5 & -1 \end{vmatrix} = -3 - 35 = -38,$$

$$D_x = \begin{vmatrix} 2 & 7 \\ -22 & -1 \end{vmatrix} = -2 + 154 = 152,$$

$$D_y = \begin{vmatrix} 3 & 2 \\ 5 & -22 \end{vmatrix} = -66 - 10 = -76.$$

Thus,

$$x = \frac{152}{-38} = -4 \text{ and } y = \frac{-76}{-38} = 2.$$

The solution set is $\{(-4, 2)\}$.

57. For the system

$$x - 3y \geq 6$$
$$y^2 \leq 16 - x^2,$$

We graph the line $x - 3y = 6$ and the circle $x^2 + y^2 = 16$ (both solid). The inequality $x - 3y \geq 6$ is equivalent to $-3y \geq -x + 6$, or $3y \leq x - 6$. Hence, the solution set is the set of all points that lie simultaneously below or on the line $x - 3y = 6$ and are interior to or on the circle $x^2 + y^2 = 16$. See the graph in the text.

59. (We need this exercise to work number 65.)
     Let x = number of batches of cakes and let y = number of batches of cookies. We have

$$2x + \frac{3}{2}y \leq 16 \qquad \text{(oven)}$$
$$3x + \frac{2}{3}y \leq 12. \qquad \text{(decorating)}$$

Obviously, we must have $x \geq 0$ and
$y \geq 0$. We graph the lines

$2x + \dfrac{3}{2}y = 16$ and $3x + \dfrac{2}{3}y = 12$

$4x + 3y = 32$ $9x + 2y = 36.$

x	y
0	$\dfrac{32}{3}$
8	0

x	y
0	18
4	0

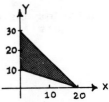

61. We wish to maximize $5x + 7y$ subject
to
$2x + 4y \geq 40$ (1)
$3x + 2y \leq 60,$ (2)
with $x \geq 0$ and $y \geq 0$. We graph
the lines $2x + 4y = 40$ and
$3x + 2y = 60.$

x	y
0	10
20	0

x	y
0	30
20	0

We note that the lines intersect
at the point $A(20, 0)$.

We test $5x + 7y$ at the three
vertices:
$(0, 10)$: $5x + 7y = 5(0) + 7(10) = 70$
$(20, 0)$: $5x + 7y = 5(20) + 7(0) = 100$
$(0, 30)$: $5x + 7y = 5(0) + 7(30) = 210.$
The point $(0, 30)$ gives $5x + 7y$ the
maximum value of 210.

65. We wish to maximize the profit,
which is $30x + 20y$. In exercise
59 we see that we must consider

the points $A(4, 0)$, $B(0, \dfrac{32}{3})$, and
and $P(\dfrac{44}{19}, \dfrac{144}{10})$. The point P is not
a "lattice" point. That is, the
point P does not have integer coordinates. The nearest point to
having integer coordinates <u>and</u> in
the feasible region is $Q(2, 7)$.
Also, rather than B, we test $R(0, 10)$.
A: $30x + 20y = 30(4) = \$120$
R: $30x + 20y = 20(10) = \$200$
Q: $30x + 20y = 30(2) + 20(7) = \$200$
The solution could be either R or Q.
Note that the idea of considering Q
was not presented in the text and is
given here only as a note for the
student. The text will not give Q
as an answer.

Chapter 9 - Test

1. Solve $\begin{array}{l} x + 2y = 5 \\ 2x - 3y = -4 \end{array}$ by elimination.   2. Solve $\begin{array}{l} 3x - 4y = -5 \\ 2x + 2y = 4 \end{array}$ by elimination.

3. Determine all solutions to the system $\begin{array}{l} 2x - 3y = 5 \\ -4x + 6y = -10 \end{array}$.

4. Determine all solutions to the system $\begin{array}{l} -x + 3y = 7 \\ 2x - 6y = 24 \end{array}$.

5. Solve. $\begin{array}{l} \dfrac{3}{x} + \dfrac{2}{y} = \dfrac{29}{30} \\[2mm] \dfrac{4}{x} - \dfrac{3}{y} = -\dfrac{6}{10} \end{array}$

6. Solve. $\begin{array}{l} x + 2y - z = -1 \\ 2x - y + 2z = 7 \\ -x + 3y + z = -4 \end{array}$

7. Solve. $\begin{array}{l} 2x - y + z = 6 \\ x + 2y - 3z = 9 \end{array}$

8. Solve. $\begin{array}{l} 3x + y + 2z = 5 \\ 2y = 3x \end{array}$

9. The sum of two number is 22. If one is multiplied by 8 and the other by 9, the sum of the products is 189. Find the two numbers.

10. A man invested $60,000 in certificates. A certain amount was invested in a 9% certificate, 3/4 that amount in a 10% certificate, and $5000 more than was invested at 9% is invested at 12%. The annual interest was $6300. How much was invested at each rate?

11. Write the augmented matrix of the system $\begin{array}{l} 3x + 2y - 7z = 14 \\ x - 3y + 2z = 9 \\ 2x + y - 3z = -2 \end{array}$.

    Do not solve.

12. Use Gaussian reduction to solve $\begin{array}{l} 2x + y = 8 \\ x - 4y = -5 \end{array}$.

13. Use Gaussian reduction to solve the system $\begin{array}{l} x - 2y + z = 1 \\ 3x + 3y - 2z = 2 \\ -2x + y + 3z = 5 \end{array}$.

14. The sum of three numbers is 29. One number is 3 more than another. Find all solutions to this system.

15. Evaluate the determinant
$$\begin{vmatrix} 3 & -6 \\ -7 & -9 \end{vmatrix}.$$

16. Use a cofactor expansion about row 2 to evaluate
$$\begin{vmatrix} 3 & 2 & 1 \\ -2 & 0 & 3 \\ 1 & 2 & -1 \end{vmatrix}.$$

17. Use any means to evaluate $\begin{vmatrix} 2 & 2 & 3 \\ 1 & 4 & 2 \\ 3 & 1 & 2 \end{vmatrix}$.

18. If $A = \begin{bmatrix} 2 & 1 \\ -3 & 4 \end{bmatrix}$ and $B = \begin{bmatrix} 1 & 1 \\ 2 & 3 \end{bmatrix}$, find (a) $A + 2B$, and (b) $3A - B$.

19. For $A = \begin{bmatrix} 2 & 1 \\ -3 & 4 \end{bmatrix}$ and $B = \begin{bmatrix} 1 & 1 \\ 2 & 3 \end{bmatrix}$, find (a) AB, and (b) BA.

20. Find the product $\begin{bmatrix} 2 & 1 \\ 1 & 2 \\ 3 & -1 \end{bmatrix} \cdot \begin{bmatrix} 1 & 2 \\ 3 & 1 \end{bmatrix}$.

21. Find A^{-1} if $A = \begin{bmatrix} 3 & -1 \\ 2 & -4 \end{bmatrix}$.

22. Find A^{-1} if $A = \begin{bmatrix} 1 & 2 & 1 \\ 2 & 5 & 2 \\ 2 & 7 & 4 \end{bmatrix}$.

23.   Use the method of matrix inverses to solve $\begin{array}{l} 3x - 4y = 5 \\ 2x + 5y = 11 \end{array}$.

24.   Use Cramer's rule to solve $\begin{array}{l} 4x + 3y = 17 \\ 5x + 2y = 16 \end{array}$.

25.   Solve the system of equations in question 11 by Cramer's rule.

26.   Solve. $\begin{array}{l} x^2 + y^2 = 25 \\ x + y = 7 \end{array}$ 27.   Solve. $\begin{array}{l} y^2 - x = 4 \\ x + y = 2 \end{array}$

28.   Solve the system $\begin{array}{l} 2x^2 + 2xy - y^2 = -16 \\ 2x^2 - xy + y^2 = 16 \end{array}$.

29.   Find two numbers whose sum is 22 and whose product is 112.

30.   Graph the solution of the system $\begin{array}{l} 9x^2 + 25y^2 \le 225 \\ x^2 + y > 1 \end{array}$.

31.   Solve for $x \ge 0$ and $y \ge 0$ with

$$3x + 4y \le 24$$
$$6x + 2y \le 30$$

such that $25x + 3y$ is maximized.

(Answers for this test are on page 364.)

32.   Solve for $x \ge 0$ and $y \ge 0$ with

$$2x - 3y \ge 2$$
$$12x + 5y \le 15$$

such that $80x + 150y$ is maximized.

CHAPTER 10   Zeros of Polynomials

Section 10.1   Polynomial Division

Additional Examples

Example 1   Use synthetic division to determine whether or not $x = -2$ is a zero of $f(x) = x^3 - 2x^2 - 3x + 10$, and if so determine all zeros of f.

Solution   Using synthetic division shows that -2 is a zero of f and that

$$f(x) = (x + 2)(x^2 - 4x + 5).$$

$$\begin{array}{r|rrrr} -2 & 1 & -2 & -3 & 10 \\ & & -2 & 8 & -10 \\ \hline & 1 & -4 & 5 & 0 \end{array}$$

The easiest method to find the other zeros is to solve $x^2 - 4x + 5 = 0$ by using the quadratic formula. In this case we have

$$x = \frac{4 \pm \sqrt{16 - 4(1)(5)}}{2}$$

$$x = \frac{4 \pm \sqrt{-4}}{2}$$

$$x = 2 \pm i.$$

The zeros of f are -2, $2 + i$, and $2 - i$.

Example 2   Let $f(x) = x^3 + x^2 - 7x + 2$, and determine $f(2.1)$ by the remainder theorem.

Solution   We can use synthetic division and divide by 2.1. This gives the following.

$$\begin{array}{r|rrrr} 2.1 & 1 & 1 & -7 & 2 \\ & & 2.1 & 6.51 & -1.029 \\ \hline & 1 & 3.1 & -.49 & -.971 \end{array}$$

The remainder is $-.971$. The remainder theorem gives the result that

$$f(2.1) = -.971.$$

Example 3   Let $f(x) = 2x^3 - x^2 - 3x + 4$, and determine $f(2 - i)$ and $f(2 + i)$ by use of the remainder theorem.

Solution   Using synthetic division, we have the following.

$$\begin{array}{r|rrrr} 2 - i & 2 & -1 & -3 & 4 \\ & & 4 - 2i & 4 - 7i & -5 - 15i \\ \hline & 2 & 3 - 2i & 1 - 7i & -1 + 15i. \end{array}$$

Since the remainder of the division is $-1 - 15i$, then $f(2 - i) = -1 - 15i$. Similarly,

$$\begin{array}{r|rrrr} 2 + i & 2 & -1 & -3 & 4 \\ & & 4 + 2i & 4 + 7i & -5 + 15i \\ \hline & 2 & 3 + 2i & 1 + 7i & -1 + 15i. \end{array}$$

Thus, $f(2 + i) = -1 + 15i$. Note that $f(2 - i)$ is the conjugate of $f(2 + i)$.

Selected Solutions

1. Using synthetic division gives

$$\begin{array}{r|rrrr} -5 & 1 & 2 & -17 & -10 \\ & & -5 & 15 & 10 \\ \hline & 1 & -3 & -2 & 0 \end{array}.$$

The quotient is $x^2 - 3x - 2$, and the remainder is 0.

5. Synthetic division gives

$$\begin{array}{r|rrrr} 5 & 3 & -11 & -20 & 3 \\ & & 15 & 20 & 0 \\ \hline & 3 & 4 & 0 & 3. \end{array}$$

The quotient is $3x^2 + 4x$, and the remainder is 3. Hence, we can write

$$\frac{3x^3 - 11x^2 - 20x + 3}{x - 5} = 3x^2 + 4x + \frac{3}{x - 5}.$$

9. Synthetic division gives

$$\begin{array}{r|rrrrrr} -2 & 1 & 3 & 2 & 2 & 3 & 1 \\ & & -2 & -2 & 0 & -4 & 2 \\ \hline & 1 & 1 & 0 & 2 & -1 & 3. \end{array}$$

The quotient is $x^4 + x^3 + 2x - 1$, and the remainder is 3. The division means we can write the answer as

$$x^4 + x^3 + 2x - 1 + \frac{3}{x + 2}.$$

13. The synthetic division gives

$$2 \overline{\smash{\big)}\ 9 \quad -8 \quad 7 \quad -2}$$
$$\underline{\quad 18 \quad 20 \quad 54}$$
$$9 \quad 10 \quad 27 \quad 52.$$

Hence, we have

$$\frac{9z^3 - 8z^2 + 7z - 2}{z - 2} = 9z^2 + 10z + 27 + \frac{52}{z - 2}.$$

17. Placing 0 in for missing coefficients, we have

$$1 \overline{\smash{\big)}\ 1 \quad 0 \quad 0 \quad 0 \quad -1}$$
$$\underline{\quad 1 \quad 1 \quad 1 \quad 1}$$
$$1 \quad 1 \quad 1 \quad 1 \quad 0.$$

Hence,

$$\frac{x^4 - 1}{x - 1} = x^3 + x^2 + x + 1.$$

21. Dividing $f(x) = x^3 + 2x^2 + 4$ by $(x - k) = (x + 2)$, we have

$$-2 \overline{\smash{\big)}\ -1 \quad 2 \quad 0 \quad 4}$$
$$\underline{\quad 2 \quad -8 \quad 16}$$
$$-1 \quad 4 \quad -8 \quad 20.$$

Hence,

$$f(x) = (x + 2)(-x^2 + 4x - 8) + 20.$$

25. Dividing $f(x) = 3x^4 + 4x^3 - 10x^2 + 15$ by $(x - k) = (x + 1)$, we have

$$-1 \overline{\smash{\big)}\ 3 \quad 4 \quad -10 \quad 0 \quad 15}$$
$$\underline{\quad -3 \quad -1 \quad 11 \quad -11}$$
$$3 \quad 1 \quad -11 \quad 11 \quad 4.$$

Hence,

$$f(x) = (x + 1)(3x^3 + x^2 - 11x + 11) + 4.$$

29. For $f(x) = x^2 - 4x + 5$, $f(3)$ is the remainder when we perform the synthetic division by 3.

$$3 \overline{\smash{\big)}\ 1 \quad -4 \quad 5}$$
$$\underline{\quad 3 \quad -3}$$
$$1 \quad -1 \quad \boxed{2}$$

Hence, $f(3) = 2$. Also, we can observe this result by

$$f(3) = 3^2 - 4(3) + 5 = 2.$$

33. Using synthetic divison by $2 + i$ for $f(x) = x^2 - 5x + 1$, we have

$$2 + i \overline{\smash{\big)}\ 1 \quad -5 \quad 1}$$
$$\underline{\quad 2 + i \quad -7 - i}$$
$$1 \quad -3 + i \quad -6 - i,$$

since $(2 + i)(-3 + i)$
$$= -6 - 1 - 3i + 2i = -7 - i.$$
Hence, $f(2 + i) = -6 - i$.

37. Dividing $f(x) = x^2 + 2x - 8$ by $x - 2$ gives

$$2 \overline{\smash{\big)}\ 1 \quad 2 \quad -8}$$
$$\underline{\quad 2 \quad 8}$$
$$1 \quad 4 \quad 0.$$

Since the remainder is zero, then $f(2) = 0$. Thus, $x = 2$ is a zero of f.

41. Dividing $f(r) = 2r^2 - 6r^2 - 9r + 4$ by $r - 4$ gives

$$4 \overline{\smash{\big)}\ 2 \quad -6 \quad -9 \quad 4}$$
$$\underline{\quad 8 \quad 8 \quad -4}$$
$$2 \quad 2 \quad -1 \quad 0.$$

The remainder theorem gives $f(4) = 0$, so that $r = 4$ is a zero of f.

45. Dividing $f(m) = 2m^4 + 3m^3 - 8m^2 - 2m + 15$ by $m + \frac{3}{2}$ gives

$$-\frac{3}{2} \overline{\smash{\big)}\ 2 \quad 3 \quad -8 \quad -2 \quad 15}$$
$$\underline{\quad -3 \quad 0 \quad 12 \quad -15}$$
$$2 \quad 0 \quad -8 \quad 10 \quad 0.$$

The remainder theorem gives $f(-\frac{3}{2}) = 0$, so that $m = \frac{-3}{2}$ is a zero of f.

49. Dividing $f(y) = y^2 - 2y + 2$ by $z - (1 - i)$ gives

$$1 - i \overline{\smash{\big)}\ 1 \quad -2 \quad 2}$$
$$\underline{\quad 1 - i \quad -2}$$
$$1 \quad -1 - i \quad 0,$$

since $(1 - i)(-1 - i) = -2$. The

remainder theorem gives
$f(1 - i) = 0$, so that $1 - i$ is a zero of f.

53. Using synthetic division, we have

$$i \overline{)\begin{array}{cccc} 1 & 2i & 2 & i \end{array}}$$
$$\begin{array}{cccc} & i & -3 & -i \\ \hline 1 & 3i & -1 & 0. \end{array}$$

This shows that $f(i) = 0$.

57. If $x - k$ is a factor of
$f(x) = 2x^4 + 4x^2 + 1$, then $f(k) = 0$,
or $x = k$ is a zero of f. However,
using the quadratic formula to solve
$2x^4 + 4x^2 + 1 = 0$ for x^2, we have

$$x^2 = \frac{-4 \pm \sqrt{16 - 8}}{2} = -2 \pm \sqrt{2}.$$

Note that $-2 - \sqrt{2}$ and $-2 + \sqrt{2}$ are both negative numbers, and it is impossible to find any real number x for which $x^2 < 0$. Since f can have no real zeros, then $f(x)$ has no factors $(x - k)$ with k real.

59. Let $f(x) = x^n - c^n$, where n is a positive integer. We have the fact that $x - c$ is a factor of $f(x)$ if and only if $f(c) = 0$. We have
$$f(c) = c^n - c^n = 0,$$
so that $x - c$ is a factor of $x^n - c^n$.

61. We write $f(x) = (x - a)g(x) + r$, where $g(x)$ and r are the quotient and remainder when $f(x)$ is divided by $x - a$. If c is a zero of f, then $f(c) = 0$. We see that $f(a) = r$ and we consider the line
$y = (x - a)g(a) + f(a)$.
If a is "close" to c, then $f(c)$ is "close" to $f(a)$ and the line has $y = f(a)$ when $x = a$. This line crosses the x-axis $(y = 0)$ near c.

we find the number x where the line crosses the x-axis as follows: setting $y = 0$ gives

$$\frac{-f(a)}{g(a)} = x - a, \text{ or}$$

$$x = a - \frac{f(a)}{g(a)}.$$

Hence,

$$c \simeq a - \frac{f(a)}{g(a)}.$$

Note this would imply the statement that $|a - c| \simeq \left| \frac{f(a)}{g(a)} \right|$, and if $\left| \frac{f(a)}{g(a)} \right|$ is "very close to zero," then a is very close to c. We use this idea for exercises 62 - 65.

64. Let $f(x) = 2x^3 + 3x^2 - 22x - 33$ and $a = 3.2$. Dividing $f(x)$ by $(x - 3.2)$, we get the coefficients of $g(x)$ and $f(3.2)$.

$$3.2 \overline{)\begin{array}{cccc} 2 & 3 & -22 & -33 \end{array}}$$

coefficients of $g(x)$
$$\begin{array}{cccc} & 6.4 & 30.08 & 25.855 \\ \hline 2 & 9.4 & 8.08 & -7.144 \end{array}$$

second synthetic division
$$\begin{array}{ccc} & 6.4 & 50.56 \\ \hline 2 & 15.8 & 58.64 \end{array}$$

Thus, $\to f(3.2) = -7.144$

and $g(3.2) = 58.64$

Hence, the root $c \simeq a - \frac{f(a)}{g(a)}$

$$= 3.2 - \frac{(-7.144)}{58.64}$$
$$= 3.2 + (0.1218)$$
$$= 3.3218.$$

Using this new approximation as a new "a" we use the same procedure, dividing $f(x)$ by $(x - 3.3218)$.

$$3.3218 \overline{)\begin{array}{cccc} 2 & 3 & -22 & -33 \end{array}}$$

$$\begin{array}{cccc} & 6.6436 & 32.03411 & 33.331308 \\ \hline 2 & 9.6436 & 10.03411 & .331308 \end{array}$$

$$\begin{array}{ccc} & 6.6436 & 54.10282 \\ \hline 2 & 16.2872 & 64.13693 \end{array}$$

coefficient of g

second division

$f(3.3218) \simeq .331308$

$g(3.3218) \simeq 64.13693$

The new approximation is

$$c \simeq (3.3218) - \frac{.331308}{64.13693}$$

$$= 3.3218 - .005166 = 3.3166.$$

An approximation correct to the nearest hundredth is 3.32. We make this statement in light of the discussion in exercise 61.

65. We let $f(x) = 2x^3 - 7x^2 + 2x + 6$, and use $a = -0.7$. A reason to use $a = -0.7$ is to note that $f(-\frac{1}{2}) = 3$ and $f(-1) = -5$. Using the same procedure as in exercise 64, we use synthetic division on f with $a = -.07$, finding $f(-.7)$ and $g(x)$. Then we perform the second division finding $g(-.7)$.

```
       -.7 | 2   -7       2        6
           |     -1.4    5.88    -5.516
coefficients 2   -8.4    7.88     0.484
of g(x)    |     -1.4    6.86      └→ = f(-.7)
             2   -9.8   14.74
                          └→ = g(-.7)
```

The approximation to the zero c is

$$c \simeq (-0.7) - \frac{0.484}{14.77}$$

$$c \simeq (-0.7) - 0.032836, \text{ or}$$

$$c \simeq -0.7328.$$

Performing the operation again with $f(x)$ and $a = -0.7328$, we have the following.

```
  -.7328 | 2   -7        2        6
         |     -1.4656   6.2036  -6.0116
           2   -8.4656   8.2036  -.0116
         |     -1.4656   7.2776      ↑
           2   -9.9312  15.4812   f(-.7328)
                          └→ g(-.7328)
```

The next approximation to the zero c of $f(x)$ is

$$c \simeq -.7328 - (\frac{-.0116}{15.4812})$$

$$c \simeq -.7328 + .000749, \text{ or}$$

$$c \simeq -.73205.$$

The term $\frac{f(a)}{g(a)}$ gives an approximation to the difference between c and a. We would be sure that the zero to f is $c = -.73$, correct to the nearest hundreth.

Section 10.2   Complex Zeros of Polynomials

Additional Examples

Example 1   Determine a third-degree polynomial with real coefficients having zeros at 2 and $3 - 2i$.

Solution   By the conjugate zeros theorem, since $3 - 2i$ is a zero, $3 + 2i$ must also be a zero. Let $r_1 = 3 - 2i$ and $r_2 = 3 + 2i$. Then $(x - r_1)$ $(x - r_2)$ is a quadratic factor, and $(x - r_1)(x - r_2) = x_2 - 6x + 13$ since $-(r_1 + r_2) = -6$, and

$$r_1 r_2 = (3 - 2i)(3 + 2i)$$

$$= 9 + 4$$

$$= 13.$$

Thus, $(x - 2)(x^2 - 6x + 13)$

$$= x^3 - 6x^2 + 13x - 2x^2 + 12x - 26,$$

or $P(x) = x^3 - 8x^2 + 25x - 26,$ is a polynomial of degree three having zeros at 2 and $3 - 2i$.

Example 2   Determine the polynomial $P(x)$ of lowest degree having zeros at 2 and $2 - i$, and such that $P(1) = 8$

Solution   If $2 - i$ is a zero, then $2 + i$ must also be a zero. Hence, the polynomial must have $(x - 2)$, $(x - 2 - i)$, and $(x - 2 + i)$ as factors. We can write

$$P(x) = c(x - 2)(x - 2 - i)(x - 2 + i)$$

$$= c(x - 2)(x^2 - 4x + 5)$$

$$= c(x^3 - 6x^2 + 13x - 10).$$

Since $P(1) = 8$, then

$$8 = c(1 - 6 + 13 - 10),$$

or $8 = -2c$, which implies $c = -4$.

Hence, $P(x) = -4x^3 + 24x^2 - 52x + 40$.

Example 3   If we are given that $x = -1 + 2i$ is a zero of the polynomial $f(x) = x^4 + 2x^3 + x^2 - 8x - 20$, determine all the remaining zeros.

Solution   Since $-1 + 2i$ is a zero of f, then $-1 - 2i$ is also a zero. This implies that $(x + 1 - 2i)(x + 1 + 2i)$ is a factor of f. We have that

$$(x + 1 - 2i)(x + 1 + 2i)$$

$$= x^2 + 2x + 5.$$

Using polynomial division of $f(x)$ by $x^2 + 2x + 5$ gives the following.

$$
\begin{array}{r}
x^2 \qquad\qquad - 4 \\
x^2 + 2x + 5 \overline{\smash{\big)}\ x^4 + 2x^3 + x^2 - 8x - 20} \\
\underline{x^4 + 2x^3 + 5x} \\
-4x^2 - 8x - 20 \\
\underline{-4x^2 - 8x - 20} \\
0
\end{array}
$$

Hence, $f(x) = (x^2 + 2x + 5)(x^2 - 4)$

$$= (x^2 + 2x + 5)(x - 2)(x + 2).$$

The zeros of f are -2, 2, $-1 + 2i$, and $-1 - 2i$.

Selected Solutions

1.   The factor theorem states that $(x - k)$ is a factor of $f(x)$ if and only if $f(k) = 0$.   For $f(x) = 4x^2 + 2x + 42$, we have $f(3) = 36 + 6 + 42 = 84 \neq 0$.

Hence, $(x - 3)$ is <u>not</u> a factor of $4x^2 + 2x + 42$.

5.   Using synthetic division, we have

$$
\begin{array}{r|rrrr}
5 & 3 & -12 & -11 & -20 \\
  &   & 15 & 15 & 20 \\
\hline
  & 3 & 3   & 4   & 0
\end{array}
$$

Since $f(5) = 0$, we have $(x - 5)$ is a factor of $f(x) = 3x^3 - 12x^2 - 11x - 20$.

9.   Start with

$$[x - (-3)][x - (-1)](x - 4)$$

$$= (x + 3)(x + 1)(x - 4)$$

$$= (x^2 + 4x + 3)(x - 4)$$

$$= x^3 - 13x - 12.$$

We want $f(2) = 5$, so replace x with 2, which gives

$$2^3 - 13 \cdot 2 - 12 = 8 - 26 - 12 = -30.$$

We have $f(x) = c(x^3 - 13x - 12)$ and that $f(2) = 5 = c(-30)$.   This gives $c = \dfrac{-1}{6}$.   Hence, $f(x) = \dfrac{-1}{6}x^3 + \dfrac{13}{6}x + 2$.

13. Start with $(x - 3)(x - i)[x - (-i)]$, since f is a polynomial with real coefficients so that if i is a root, then $-i$ is also a root.   We have

$$f(x) = a(x - 3)(x - i)(x + i)$$

$$f(x) = a(x - 3)(x^2 + 1)$$

$$f(x) = a(x^3 - 3x^2 + x - 3).$$

Since $f(2) = 50$,

$$50 = a(8 - 12 + 2 - 3)$$

$$50 = -5a,$$

so $a = -10$.

Hence, we have

$$f(x) = -10(x^3 - 3x^2 + x - 3), \text{ or}$$

$$f(x) = -10x^3 + 30x^2 - 10x + 30.$$

17. $f(x) = (x - 2)(x - 1 - i)(x - 1 + i)$

$$= (x - 2)[(x - 1)^2 - i^2]$$

$$= (x - 2)[(x^2 - 2x + 1) + 1]$$

$$= (x - 2)(x^2 - 2x + 2)$$

$$= x^3 - 4x^2 + 6x - 4$$

21. We have

$$f(x) = (x - 2 - i)(x - 2 + i)(x - 3)$$
$$(x + 1)$$

$$= (x^2 - 4x + 5)(x^2 - 2x - 3)$$

$$= x^4 - 6x^3 + 2x^2 + 2x - 15.$$

25. If a function has real coefficients and zeros at $1 \pm \sqrt{2}$ and $1 - i$, then it must also have a zero at $1 + i$, since complex zeros occur in conjugate pairs. Such a polynomial is

$$f(x) = (x - 1 + \sqrt{2})(x - 1 - \sqrt{2})$$
$$(x - 1 + i)(x - 1 - i)$$

$$= (x^2 - 2x - 1)(x^2 - 2x + 2),$$

or

$$f(x) = x^4 - 4x^3 + 5x^2 - 2x - 2.$$

29. If $1 - 2i$ and $3 + 4i$ are zeros of a polynomial with real coefficients, then $1 + 2i$ and $3 - 4i$ are zeros. For the zeros $1 \pm 2i$, their sum is 2 and their product is 5. Hence, $x^2 - 2x + 5$ is a polynomial having these zeros. Similarly, for $3 \pm 4i$, the sum is 6 and the product is 25. Hence, $x^2 - 6x + 25$ has these zeros. Then, a polynomial with real coefficients having zeros at 4, $1 - 2i$, and $3 + 4i$ is

$$f(x) = (x - 4)(x^2 - 2x + 5)$$
$$(x^2 - 6x + 25)$$

$$f(x) = x^5 - 12x^4 + 74x^3 - 248x^2 + 445x - 500.$$

33. Divide $x^3 - x^2 - 4x - 6$ by $x - 3$,

$$3 \overline{)\begin{array}{cccc} 1 & -1 & -4 & -6 \\ & 3 & 6 & 6 \\ \hline 1 & 2 & 2 & 0 \end{array}},$$

and use the quadratic formula to solve the reduced equation

$$x^2 + 2x + 2 = 0.$$

The solutions are $-1 \pm i$. The solution set is $\{3, -1 - i, -1 + i\}$.

37. If we divide $2x^3 - 2x^2 - x - 6$ by $x - 2$, we have

$$2 \overline{)\begin{array}{cccc} 2 & -2 & -1 & -6 \\ & 4 & 4 & 6 \\ \hline 2 & 2 & 3 & 0 \end{array}}.$$

Then we use the quadratic formula to solve the equation

$$2x^2 + 2x + 3 = 0. \text{ This gives}$$

$$x = \frac{-2 \pm \sqrt{2^2 - 4(2)(3)}}{4}$$

$$= \frac{-2 \pm \sqrt{4 - 24}}{4}$$

$$= \frac{-2 \pm 2i\sqrt{5}}{4}, \text{ or}$$

$$x = \frac{-1 \pm i\sqrt{5}}{2}.$$

43. If we divide $x^4 - 6x^3 + 15x^2 - 18x + 10$ by $x - (2 + i)$, we have

$$2 + i \overline{)\begin{array}{cccc} 1 \;\; -6 & 15 & -18 & 10 \\ \;\;\; 2 + i & -9 - 2i & 14 + 2i & -10 \\ \hline 1 \; -4 + i & 6 - 2i & -4 + 2i & 0 \end{array}}.$$

Since $2 + i$ is a zero, $2 - i$ will be also. Hence, we have

$$2 - i \overline{)\begin{array}{cccc} 1 \;\; -4 + i & 6 - 2i & -4 + 2i \\ \;\;\;\; 2 - i & -4 + 2i & 4 - 2i \\ \hline 1 \;\; -2 & 2 & 0 \end{array}},$$

Use the quadratic formula to solve $x^2 - 2x + 2 = 0$, which gives $1 + i$ and $1 - i$.

45. Given that $x = 2$ is a zero of $f(x) = 2x^3 - 3x^2 - 17x + 30$, we use synthetic division to arrive at

$$2 \overline{) \begin{array}{rrrr} 2 & -3 & -17 & 30 \\ & 4 & 2 & -30 \\ \hline 2 & 1 & -15 & 0 \end{array}}.$$

Hence,
$f(x) = (x - 2)(2x^2 + x - 15)$,
$f(x) = (x - 2)(2x - 5)(x + 3)$.

49. Given that $x = 3i$ is a zero of
$f(x) = x^3 + (7 - 3i)x^2 + (12 - 21i)x - 36i$,
we use synthetic division to arrive at

$$3i \overline{) \begin{array}{rrrr} 1 & 7 - 3i & 12 - 21i & -36i \\ & 3i & & 21i & 36i \\ \hline 1 & 7 & 12 & 0 \end{array}}.$$

Hence, we have
$f(x) = (x - 3i)(x^2 + 7x + 12)$, or
$f(x) = (x - 3i)(x + 4)(x + 3)$.

53. Using synthetic division twice, with $f(x) = x^4 + 2x^3 - 7x^2 - 20x - 12$ and $x = -2$, we have

$$-2 \overline{) \begin{array}{rrrr|r} 1 & 2 & -7 & -20 & -12 \\ & -2 & 0 & 14 & 12 \\ \hline 1 & 0 & -7 & -6 & 0 \\ & -2 & 4 & 6 \\ \hline 1 & -2 & -3 & 0 \end{array}}.$$

Hence, $f(x) = (x + 2)^2(x^2 - 2x - 3)$
$f(x) = (x + 2)^2(x + 1)(x - 3)$.
The zeros are $-2, -2, -1, 3$.

57. If $1 + i$ is a zero of a polynomial having real coefficients, then $1 - i$ must also be a zero. This would imply that the polynomial has four zeros and hence must have degree at least four.

61. Let $f(x)$ and $q(x)$ each have c as a zero. Then, $f(c) = 0$ and $q(c) = 0$. This implies that $f(x)$ has $(x - c)$ as a factor and that $q(x)$ has $(x - c)$ as a factor. Thus, $f(x) = (x - c)P_1(x)$ and $q(x) = (x - c)P_2(x)$, where P_1 and P_2 are polynomials. When $f(x)$ is divided by $q(x)$ we get $f(x) = q(x) h(x) + r(x)$, where h is the quotient and r is the remainder. Then,
$r(x) = f(x) - q(x)h(x)$
$= (x - c) P_1(x) - (x - c)P_2(x)h(x)$
$= (x - c) [P_1(x) - P_2(x)h(x)]$
$= (x - c)[\text{a polynomial in } x]$.
Hence, $(x - c)$ is a factor of the remainder $R(x)$ unless $R(x) \equiv 0$. A shorter alternative is to note that when we divide f by q we have a quotient $h(x)$ and a remainder $r(x)$. Then $f(x) = h(x)q(x) + r(x)$. Letting $x = c$ gives
$f(c) = h(c)q(c) + r(c)$,
but $x = c$ is a zero of f and q so that $0 = 0 + r(c)$, or $r(c) = 0$. Hence $x - c$ is a factor of $r(x)$ unless $r(x) \equiv 0$.

65. Let $c = a + bi$. Then $\overline{c} = a - bi$, $c^2 = a^2 - b^2 + 2abi$, and $\overline{(c^2)} = a^2 - b^2 - 2abi$, while $(\overline{c})^2 = (a - bi)^2 = a^2 - b^2 - 2abi$. Hence, $(\overline{c})^2 = \overline{(c^2)}$.
In exercise 63 it was proved that $\overline{cd} = \overline{c}\,\overline{d}$. Thus,
$\overline{c^3} = \overline{c^2 c} = \overline{c^2} \cdot \overline{c} = (\overline{c})^2 \overline{c} = (\overline{c})^3$.
Continuing, we see that for any natural number n, $\overline{c^n} = (\overline{c})^n$.

Section 10.3 Rational Zeros of Polynomials

Additional Examples

Example 1   Determine all rational zeros of the polynomial

$$f(x) = x^3 + \frac{17}{6}x^2 - \frac{4}{6}x - \frac{1}{2}.$$

Solution   To apply the rational zeros theorem, first multiply by 6 to clear fractional coefficients. We have

$$6f(x) = 6x^3 + 17x^2 - 4x - 3.$$

The zeros of this polynomial are also the zeros of f. The rational zeros of this polynomial have the form a/b, where a is a divisor of -3 and b is a divisor of 6. That is, a must be ±1 of ±3, while b must be ±1, ±2, ±3, or ±6. This implies that the only possible rational zeros are ±1, ±1/2, ±1/3, ±1/6. ±3, ±3/2. Using synthetic division and trial and error with the possible rational zeros, some of the trials are shown below.

```
-1⌐6   17   -4   -3      1⌐6   17   -4   -3
       -6  -11   15              6   23   19
    6   11  -15   12          6  23   19   16
```

```
            1/2⌐6   17   -4   -3
                     3   10   +3
                  6  20    6    0 ←
```

We could continue with synthetic division, but we can note that the remaining zeros are zeros of the factor

$$6x^2 + 20x + 6.$$

Factoring gives

$$2(3x^2 + 10x + 3) = 2(3x + 1)(x + 3).$$

Hence, the zeros of f are 1/2, -1/3, and -3.

Example 2   Determine the number of rational zeros of the polynomial

$$f(x) = x^2 - 7.$$

Can we use this to show that $\sqrt{7}$ is irrational?

Solution   If we consider $f(x) = x^2 - 7$, then any rational zero a/b has the property that a is a divisor of 7 (±1 or ±7) and b is a divisor of 1 (±1). This implies that the only possible rational zeros of f are ±1 or ±7. Using synthetic division we have the following.

```
-1⌐1   0   -7        +1⌐1   0   -7
      -1    1              +1    1
    1  -1   -6          1  +1   -6
```

```
-7⌐1   0   -7         7⌐1   0   -7
      -7   49              7   49
    1  -7   42         1  7   42
```

This shows that $f(x) = x^2 - 7$ has no rational zeros.

It is readily seen, however, that $\sqrt{7}$ is a zero of f since $f(\sqrt{7})$

$= (\sqrt{7})^2 - 7 = 7 - 7 = 0.$ Since there are no rational zeros, $\sqrt{7}$ must be irrational.

Selected Solutions

1. The possible rational zeros of

$$f(x) = 6x^3 + 17x^2 - 31x - 1$$ have the form a/b, where a is a divisor of -1(±1) and b is a divisor of 6(±1, ±2, ±3, ±6). The possible rational zeros are ±1, $\pm\frac{1}{2}$, $\pm\frac{1}{3}$, and $\pm\frac{1}{6}$.

5.   The possible rational zeros of

$$f(x) = 2x^3 + 7x^2 + 12x - 8$$ have the form a/b, where b is a divisor of 2(±1, ±2) and a is a divisor of

$-8(\pm 1, \pm 2, \pm 4, \pm 8)$. Hence, the possible rational zeros are $\pm 1, \pm\frac{1}{2}, \pm 2, \pm 4, \pm 8$.

9. For $f(x) = x^3 - 2x^2 - 13x - 10$, the only possible zeros are $\pm 1, \pm 2, \pm 5, \pm 10$, since these divide -10. By synthetic division. -1 is a root and we have $(x^3 - 2x^2 - 13x - 10)$ $= (x + 1)(x^2 - 3x - 10)$. The other roots are 5 and -2.

13. For $f(x) = x^3 + 9x^2 - 14x - 24$, finding rational zeros, the only choices are $\pm 1, \pm 2, \pm 3, \pm 4, \pm 6, \pm 8, \pm 12, \pm 24$. By trial, it can be seen that there are no rational roots.

17. For $f(x) = 6x^3 + 17x^2 - 31x - 12$, the rational zero choices are $\pm 1, \pm 2, \pm 3, \pm 4, \pm 6, \pm 12,$ $\pm\frac{1}{2}, \pm\frac{3}{2}, \pm\frac{1}{3}, \pm\frac{2}{3}, \pm\frac{4}{3}, \pm\frac{1}{6}$. Using synthetic division we see that -4 works, so
$$f(x) = (x + 4)(6x^2 - 7x - 3)$$
$$= (x + 4)(3x + 1)(2x - 3).$$
Hence, $-4, -\frac{1}{3}$ and $\frac{3}{2}$ are the rational roots.

21. For $f(x) = 2x^3 + 7x^2 + 12x - 8$, the rational zero choices are $\pm 1, \pm 2, \pm 4, \pm 8, \pm\frac{1}{2}$. Trial and error shows that $x = \frac{1}{2}$ is the only one that works.

25. For $f(x) = x^4 + 2x^3 - 13x^2 - 38x - 24$, the rational zero choices are $\pm 1, \pm 2, \pm 3, \pm 4, \pm 6, \pm 8, \pm 12, \pm 24$. Synthetic division shows that $x = -1, -3, -2, 4$ are zeros.

29. For $f(x) = x^5 + 3x^4 - 5x^3 - 11x^2 + 12$, the choices are $\pm 1, \pm 2, \pm 3, \pm 4, \pm 6, \pm 12$. We see that $x = 1$ is the only rational root.

33. For $f(x) = x^4 + \frac{1}{4}x^3 + \frac{11}{4}x^2 + x - 5$, we consider $4f(x) = 4x^4 + x^3 + 11x^2 + 4x - 20$. The rational zero choices are $\pm 1, \pm 2, \pm 4, \pm 5, \pm 10, \pm 20,$ $\pm\frac{1}{2}, \pm\frac{5}{2}, \pm\frac{1}{4}, \pm\frac{5}{4}$. Synthetic division shows that $x = 1, -\frac{5}{4}$ are the only rational roots.

37. We see that $f(x) = x^2 - 2$ can have only $\pm 1, \pm 2$ as rational roots. However,
$f(1) = -1$, $f(-1) = -1$,
$f(2) = 2$, $f(-2) = 2$.
So f has no rational roots. If we solve $x^2 - 2 = 0$, we have
$$x^2 = 2$$
$$x = \pm\sqrt{2}.$$
Since $\sqrt{2}$ is a zero, it cannot be rational since f has no rational zeros. Hence $\sqrt{2}$ is irrational.

39. $f(x) = x^4 + 5x^2 + 4 = (x^2 + 4)(x^2 + 1)$, and hence, f has no rational roots.

41. Let $f(x) = a_n x^n + \ldots + a_1 x + a_0$ be a polynomial function. f can be factored into $f(x) = a_n(x - c_1)(x - c_2) \ldots (x - c_n)$, where each c_i is a complex number. Also, each c_i is a zero of f and the product $a_n \cdot c_1 \cdot c_2 \ldots c_n = a_0$. Then each c_i is a complex factor of a_0. That is, c_i divides evenly into a_0. In the case that c_i is an integer, then c_i is a factor of the constant term a_0.

Section 10.4 Approximate Zeros of
            Polynomials

Additional Examples

Example 1   For the polynomial function

$f(x) = x^3 - 3x - 4,$

(a) determine the number of positive
and negative real zeros,

(b) approximate, if possible, each
zero to the nearest tenth, and

(c) sketch a graph of f.

Solution   (a) For the function

$f(x) = x^3 - 3x - 4,$

we can use Descartes' rule of signs
to conclude that since there is
only one variation of sign in the
coefficients 1, -3, -4 of f, then
there is only one positive zero.
Then,

$f(-x) = (-x)^3 - 3(-x) - 4$

$= -x^3 + 3x - 4$

has two variations of sign
(-, +, -), so there are either two
negative zeros, or no negative zeros.
Using synthetic division, we
arrive at the results below.

```
 1│1   0   -3   -4      2│1   0   -3   -4
   │    1    1   -2       │    2    4    2
   └─1   1   -2   -6      └─1   2    1   -2

 3│1   0   -3   -4     -1│1   0   -3   -4
   │    3    9   18       │   -1    1    2
   └─1   3    6   14      └─1  -1   -2   -2

-2│1   0   -3   -4
   │   -2    4   -2
   └─1  -2    1   -6

 -.5│1    0    -3      -4
    │    -.5   .25    1.375
    └──1  -.5  -2.75  -2.625

-1.5│1    0     -3      -4
    │    -1.5   2.25   1.125
    └──1  -1.5   -.75  -2.875
```

We can see that since f(2) = -2
and f(3) = 14, the positive zero
of f is in the interval (2, 3).
Also, we should have noted in the
division using -2 that the numbers
in the bottom row alternate in
sign. Accordingly, -2 is less than
any zero of f. We conclude that
any negative real zero of f is in
the interval (-2, 0).

(b) Since f(0) = -4, f(-1) = -2,
and f(-2) = -6, we cannot determine
without further calculations whether
or not any negative zeros exist.
Note that finding f(-.5) and f(-1.5)
gave no conclusion. We will <u>suppose</u>
that there are no negative zeros
and proceed to approximate the
positive zero. We have

```
2.1│1   0     -3     -4
   │    2.1   4.41   2.961
   └─1  2.1   1.41  -1.039

2.2│1   0     -3     -4
   │    2.2   4.84   4.048
   └─1  2.2   1.84    .048.
```

Thus, f(2.1) = -1.039 and
      f(2.2) = .048.

A close approximation to the
positive zero is 2.2.

(c) Using the points already
calculated gives the following
graph.

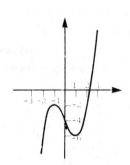

Example 2   Determine the number of positive and negative zeros, find an upper and lower bound for the zeros, and approximate each positive zero to the nearest hundredth for

$$f(x) = x^4 - 2x^3 - 3x^2 - 2x - 4.$$

Solution   The signs of the coefficients of f are +, -, -, -, -. Thus, there is one positive zero. Since

$$f(-x) = (-x)^4 - 2(-x)^3 - 3(-x)^2 - x(-x) - 4$$
$$= x^4 + 2x^3 - 3x^2 + 2x - 4,$$

there are three variations of signs. This implies that there are either three or one negative zero.

Using synthetic division gives the information below.

```
3 | 1   -2   -3   -2   -4
  |      3    3    0   -6
  --------------------------
    1    1    0   -2  -10

4 | 1   -2   -3   -2   -4
  |      4    8   20   72
  --------------------------
    1    2    5   18   68

-2| 1   -2   -3   -1   -4
  |     -2    8  -10   24
  --------------------------
    1   -4    5  -12   20
```

We can conclude that 4 is an upper bound of the zeros of f and -2 is a lower bound. That is, all real zeros of f are between -2 and 4. Also, since f(3) = -10 and f(4) = 68, the positive zero is between 3 and 4.

To approximate the positive zero we use successive synthetic divisions.

```
3.2 | 1   -2     -3     -2      -4
    |     3.2   3.84  2.688   2.2016
    ----------------------------------
      1   1.2    .84    .688  -1.1984

3.3 | 1   -2     -3     -2      -4
    |     3.3   4.29  4.257   7.4481
    ----------------------------------
      1   1.3   1.29  2.257   3.4481
```

Thus, we can conclude that this zero is between 3.2 and 3.3. To approximate this zero to the nearest hundredth, we could use synthetic division again, using 3.21, 3.22, ..., 3.29, 3.3.

Selected Solutions

1. Given $f(x) = 3x^2 - 2x - 6$, we have f(1) = 3 - 2 - 6 = -5 and f(2) = 12 - 4 - 6 = 2. The intermediate value theorem then can be used to conclude that there is a number c with 1 < c < 2 such that f(c) = 0.

5. We use synthetic division with $f(x) = 2x^4 - 4x^2 + 3x - 6$ to find f(2) and f(1.5). This gives the information below.

```
2 | 2   0   -4    3   -6
  |     4    8    8   22          f(2) = 16
  ------------------------
    2   4    4   11   16
```

$$\frac{3}{2} | \quad 2 \quad 0 \quad -4 \quad 3 \quad -6$$

```
3/2 | 2   0    -4     3     -6
    |     3    9/2   3/4   45/8       f(1.5) = -3/8
    ----------------------------
      2   3   1/2   15/4  -3/8
```

Hence, there is a number c with 1.5 < c < 2 such that f(c) = 0.

9. Using synthetic division, we have

```
2 | 1   -1   3   -8    8
  |      2   2   10    4
  ------------------------
    1    1   5    2   12.
```

Since every term is positive in the last line, x = 2 is an upper bound for the zeros of f.

13. Synthetic division gives

$$1 \overline{) \begin{array}{ccccc} 3 & 2 & -4 & 1 & -1 \\ & 3 & 5 & 1 & 2 \\ \hline 3 & 5 & 1 & 2 & 1. \end{array}}$$

Since every term is positive in the last line, $x = 1$ is an upper bound for the zeros of f.

17. For $f(x) = x^3 + 3x^2 - 2x - 6$, we see that

(a) f has one variation of sign, so there is one positive root. Also,

$f(-x) = -x^3 + 3x^2 + 2x - 6$, which has two variations of sign. There are either 2, or no, negative roots.

(b) Consider the given table and use the intermediate value theorem to see that there is a zero at -3, a zero between 1 and 2, and a zero between -2 and -1.

x	f(x)
0	-6
1	-4
2	10
-1	-2
-2	2
-3	0

$$-3 \overline{) \begin{array}{cccc} 1 & 3 & -2 & -6 \\ & -3 & 0 & 6 \\ \hline 1 & 0 & -2 & \boxed{0} \end{array}}$$

Synthetic division shows
$f(x) = (x + 3)(x^2 - 2)$.
The zeros are -3, $-\sqrt{2}$, and $+\sqrt{2}$.
To approximate the zero $\sqrt{2}$ as a decimal, use the synthetic division technique. We have

$$1 \overline{) \begin{array}{cccc} 1 & 3 & -2 & -6 \\ & 1 & 4 & 2 \\ \hline 1 & 4 & 2 & \boxed{-4} \end{array}}$$

$$1.5 \overline{) \begin{array}{cccc} 1 & 3 & -2 & -6 \\ & 1.5 & 6.75 & 7.125 \\ \hline 1 & 4.5 & 4.75 & \boxed{1.125} \end{array}}$$

f(1) < 0 and f(1.5) > 0 implies a zero between 1 and 1.5. Try 1.4. This gives

$$1.4 \overline{) \begin{array}{cccc} 1 & 3 & -2 & -6 \\ & 1.4 & 6.16 & 5.824 \\ \hline 1 & 4.4 & 4.16 & \boxed{-0.176} \end{array}}.$$

f(1.4) < 0 and f(1.5) > 0 implies the zero is between 1.4 and 1.5. An approximation to this zero (which is $\sqrt{2}$) accurate to the nearest tenth is 1.4, since f(1.4) appears to be closer to zero than f(1.5).

21. For $f(x) = x^3 + 6x - 13$, we see that

(a) f has one sign variation so there is one positive zero. We also have

$f(-x) = -x^3 - 6x - 13$; no sign variations, no negative zeros.

(b) Using the table and the intermediate value theorem, there is a zero between 1 and 2. To approximate the zero use the synthetic division technique.

x	f(x)
0	-13
1	-7
2	7

$$1 \overline{) \begin{array}{cccc} 1 & 0 & 6 & -13 \\ & 1 & 1 & 7 \\ \hline 1 & 1 & 7 & \boxed{-6} \end{array}}$$

$$1.5 \overline{) \begin{array}{cccc} 1 & 0 & 6 & -13 \\ & 1.5 & 2.25 & 12.375 \\ \hline 1 & 1.5 & 8.25 & \boxed{-0.625} \end{array}}$$

$$1.6 \overline{) \begin{array}{cccc} 1 & 0 & 6 & -13 \\ & 1.6 & 2.56 & 13.696 \\ \hline 1 & 1.6 & 8.56 & \boxed{0.696} \end{array}}$$

Since f(1.5) < 0 and f(1.6) > 0, the zero is between 1.5 and 1.6. Approximating this zero as a decimal to the nearest tenth, we would use 1.5.

25. For $f(x) = -x^4 + 2x^3 + 3x^2 + 6$, there is

(a) one variation of sign, so f has 1 positive zero. We have

$f(-x) = -x^4 - 2x^3 + 3x^2 + 6$,

which has one variation. Hence, f has one negative zero.

(b) We locate the zeros using synthetic division. After some trial and error. we see that

```
3⌋-1   2   3   0   6        4⌋-1   2   3    0    6
      -3  -3   0   0              -4  -8  -20  -80
   -1  -1   0   0   6         -1  -2  -5  -20  -74
```

```
-1⌋-1   2   3   0   6       -2⌋-1   2   3   0    6
        1  -3   0   0              2  -8  10  -20
   -1   3   0   0   6        -1   4  -5  10  -14.
```

Hence, the positive zero is between the 3 and 4, seemingly closer to 3 than 4, and the negative zero is between -2 and -1.

Once again, by some trial and error we note that

```
3.1⌋-1   2     3      0      6
        -3.1  -3.41  -1.271  -3.9401
    -1  -1.1  -.41   -1.271   2.0599
```

```
3.2⌋-1   2     3      0      6
        -3.2  -3.84  -2.688  -8.6015
    -1  -1.2  -.84   -2.688  -2.6016
```

Hence, correct to the first decimal, the positive zero is 3.1.

Also, using synthetic division,

```
-1.5⌋-1   2     3      0      6
          1.5  -5.25  3.375  -5.0625
     -1   3.5  -2.25  3.375   .9375
```

```
-1.6⌋-1   2     3      0      6
          1.6  -5.76  4.416  -7.0656
     -1   3.6  -2.76  4.416  -1.0656.
```

Hence, we conclude that the negative zero is approximately -1.5.

29. We are given that the function

$f(x) = x^4 - 4x^3 - 20x^2 + 32x + 12$

has zeros in [-4, -3], [-1, 0], [1, 2], and [6. 7].

(a) Trial and error gives

```
-3.6⌋1   -4     -20      32        12
         -3.6  +27.36  -26.496  -19.8144
     1   -7.6   7.36    5.504    -7.8144
```

```
-3.7⌋1   -4     -20      32        12
         -3.7   28.49  -31.413   -2.1719
     1   -7.7   8.49    0.587    18.8281.
```

Hence, this zero is in [-3.7, -3.6]. Also,

```
-3.65⌋1   -4      -20        32          12
          -3.65   27.9225  -28.91713  -11.2525
      1   -7.65   7.9225    3.08287     0.7475
```

```
-3.64⌋1   -4      -20        32          12
          -3.64   27.8096  -28.42694  -13.0059
      1   -7.64   7.8096    3.57306    -1.0059.
```

Hence, we conclude that zero in the interval [-4, -3] is approximately -3.65.

(b) Again, using trial and error to find that the zero in the interval [-1, 0] lies between -.4 and -.3, we then can show

```
-.32⌋1   -4      -20       32         12
         -.32   1.3824   5.95763  -12.14644
     1  -4.32  -18.6176  37.95763  -0.14644
```

```
-.31⌋1   -4      -20       32         12
         -.31   1.3361   5.78581  -11.7136
     1  -4.31  -18.6639  37.78581   0.2864.
```

We conclude that the zero is $\approx$ -.32.

(c) In the interval [1, 2], we use trial and error to conclude that the zero is between 1.6 and 1.7. Then, trying the hundredths intervals, we have

```
1.65⌋1   -4      -20        32        12
         1.65  -3.8775  -39.39787  -12.2065
     1  -2.35  -23.8775  -7.39787   -.2065
```

$$1.64 \overline{) \begin{array}{ccccc} 1 & -4 & -20 & 32 & 12 \\ & 1.64 & -3.8704 & -39.14746 & -11.7218 \\ \hline 1 & -2.36 & -23.8704 & -7.14746 & \boxed{0.2782} \end{array}}$$

We conclude that this zero is
≈ 1.65.

(d) As before, we use trial and error to show that the zero from the interval [6, 7] lies between 6.3 and 6.4. Then, trying the hundredths intervals we finally show that

$$6.32 \overline{) \begin{array}{ccccc} 1 & -4 & -20 & 32 & 12 \\ & 6.32 & 14.6624 & -33.73363 & -10.95655 \\ \hline 1 & 2.32 & -5.3376 & -1.73363 & \boxed{1.04345} \end{array}}$$

$$6.31 \overline{) \begin{array}{ccccc} 1 & -4 & -20 & 32 & 12 \\ & 6.31 & 14.5761 & -34.22481 & -14.03855 \\ \hline 1 & 2.31 & -5.4239 & -2.22481 & \boxed{-2.03855} \end{array}}$$

We conclude that this zero is
≈ 6.32.

33. We note that
$f(x) = x^4 - 5x^2 + 6 = (x^2 - 2)(x^2 - 3)$
Hence, the graph crosses the x-axis at $\pm\sqrt{2}$ and $\pm\sqrt{3}$. We note that
$f(\pm 3) = 42$, $f(\pm 2) = 16 - 20 + 6 = 2$,
$f(\pm 1) = 2$, $f(0) = 6$. These are points on the graph and
$f(\pm\sqrt{2}) = 0 = f(\pm\sqrt{3})$. Since
$\sqrt{2} \approx 1.414$ and $\sqrt{3} \sim 1.732$ and since $f(-1.6) = f(1.6)$, we use synthetic division to conclude

$$1.6 \overline{) \begin{array}{ccccc} 1 & 0 & -5 & 0 & 6 \\ & 1.6 & 2.56 & -3.904 & -6.2464 \\ \hline 1 & 1.6 & -2.44 & -3.904 & \boxed{-.2464} \end{array}}$$

That is, $f(\pm 1.6) = -.2464$. See the graph in the answer section of the text.

37. Let $f(x) = x^3 + 6x^2 - x - 14$. We see that

$$2 \overline{) \begin{array}{cccc} -1 & 6 & -1 & -14 \\ & -2 & 8 & 14 \\ \hline -1 & 4 & 7 & 0 \end{array}}$$

Hence, $f(x) = (x - 2)(-x^2 + 4x + 7)$.
Solving $-x^2 + 4x + 7 = 0$ by the quadratic formula we have
$$x = \frac{-4 \pm \sqrt{16 + 28}}{-2} = \frac{-4 \pm 2\sqrt{11}}{-2}$$
$$= 2 \pm \sqrt{11}.$$
The graph crosses the x-axis at $x = 2 - \sqrt{11}$, 2, $2 + \sqrt{11}$. We have $f(0) = -14$ and we can use synthetic division to locate other points.
We have

$$-2 \overline{) \begin{array}{cccc} -1 & 6 & -1 & -14 \\ & 2 & -16 & 34 \\ \hline -1 & 8 & -17 & \boxed{20} \end{array}} \qquad -1 \overline{) \begin{array}{cccc} -1 & 6 & -1 & -14 \\ & 1 & -7 & 8 \\ \hline -1 & 7 & -8 & \boxed{-6} \end{array}}$$

$$1 \overline{) \begin{array}{cccc} -1 & 6 & -1 & -14 \\ & -1 & 5 & 4 \\ \hline -1 & 5 & 4 & \boxed{-10} \end{array}} \qquad 3 \overline{) \begin{array}{cccc} -1 & 6 & -1 & -14 \\ & -3 & 9 & 24 \\ \hline -1 & 3 & 8 & \boxed{10} \end{array}}$$

$$5 \overline{) \begin{array}{cccc} -1 & 6 & -1 & -14 \\ & -5 & 5 & 20 \\ \hline -1 & 1 & 4 & \boxed{6} \end{array}} \qquad 6 \overline{) \begin{array}{cccc} -1 & 6 & -1 & -14 \\ & -6 & 0 & -6 \\ \hline -1 & 0 & -1 & \boxed{-20} \end{array}}$$

Using these points, we arrive at a fairly accurate graph. See the graph in the text.

41. In order to solve $x^4 - 18x^2 + 5 \geq 0$ let $f(x) = x^4 - 18x^2 + 5$, and we can use the quadratic formula to conclude that $f(x) = 0$ if
$$x^2 = \frac{18 \pm \sqrt{324 - 20}}{2}$$
$$x^2 = \frac{18 \pm \sqrt{304}}{2}$$
$$x^2 \approx 9 \pm 8.7178,$$
$$x^2 \approx 17.7178 \text{ or } x^2 \approx 0.2822.$$
Hence,
$$x \approx \pm 4.2093 \text{ or } x \approx \pm .5312.$$
We test the intervals
$I_1 = (-\infty, -4.2093]$,
$I_2 = [-4.2093, -.5312]$,
$I_3 = [-.5312, .5312]$,
$I_4 = [.5312, 4.2093]$, and
$I_5 = [4.2093, \infty)$.

We see that

$$-6\overline{\big|1\quad 0\quad -18\quad 0\quad 5} \qquad -3\overline{\big|1\quad 0\quad -18\quad 0\quad 5}$$
$$\underline{\quad -6\quad 36\quad -108\quad 648} \qquad \underline{\quad -3\quad 9\quad 27\quad -81}$$
$$1\quad -6\quad 18\quad -108\quad \boxed{653} \qquad 1\ -3\ -9\ 27\ \boxed{-76}.$$

Hence, $f(\pm 6) = 653$, $f(\pm 3) = -76$, and $f(0) = 5$. We conclude that $f(x) = x^4 - 18x^2 + 5 \geq 0$ for $x \in I_1 \cup I_3 \cup I_5$.

44. Let $f(x) = x^n + a_{n-1}x^{n-1} +$

$$a_{n-2}x^{n-2} + \ldots +$$

$$a_1 x + a_0.$$

Let m = largest of $\left|a_{n-1}\right|$, $\left|a_{n-2}\right|$,

$\ldots$, $\left|a_0\right|$.

Suppose $f(\alpha) = 0$, prove that $|\alpha| < m + 1$.

Proof: $f(\alpha) = 0$ means that

$$a^n = -(a_{n-1}\alpha^{n-1} + a_{n-2}\alpha^{n-2} +$$

$$\ldots + a_1\alpha + a_0)$$

$$|\alpha|^n \leq \left|a_{n-1}\right|\left|\alpha\right|^{n-1} + \left|a_{n-2}\right|\left|\alpha\right|^{n-2}$$

$$+ \ldots + \left|a_1\right|\left|\alpha\right| + \left|a_0\right|$$

$$\leq m(\left|\alpha\right|^{n-1} + \left|\alpha\right|^{n-2} + \ldots +$$

$$\left|\alpha\right| + 1)$$

$$= m\left(\frac{\left|\alpha\right|^n - 1}{\left|\alpha\right| - 1}\right)$$

$$|\alpha| - 1 \leq m(1 - \frac{1}{\left|\alpha\right|^n}) < m,$$

Hence, $|\alpha| < m + 1$.

Section 10.5   Partial Fractions

Additional Examples

Example 1   Find the partial fraction decomposition of

$$f(x) = \frac{2x + 24}{x^3 + x^2 - 6x}.$$

Solution   Factoring the denominator of f gives

$$f(x) = \frac{2x + 24}{x(x + 3)(x - 2)}$$

$$= \frac{A}{x} + \frac{B}{x + 3} + \frac{C}{x - 2}$$

$$= \frac{A(x + 3)(x - 2) + Bx(x - 2) + Cx(x + 3)}{x(x + 3)(x - 2)}.$$

This implies that

$$2x + 24 = A(x^2 + x - 6) +$$

$$B(x^2 - 2x) + C(x^2 + 3x)$$

or

$$2x + 24 = (A + B + C)x^2 +$$

$$(A - 2B + 3C)x - 6A.$$

Equating coefficients gives

(1) $A + B + C = 0$,

(2) $A - 2B + 3C = 2$,

(3) $-6A = 24$,

Thus, $A = -4$.   Substituting in (1) and (2) gives

$$B + C = +4 \quad \text{or} \quad 2B + 2C = 8$$
$$-2B + 3C = 6 \qquad\qquad \underline{-2B + 3C = 6}$$
$$\text{(adding)}\ 5C = 14$$
$$C = \frac{14}{5}$$
$$B = \frac{6}{5}.$$

We then have

$$f(x) = \frac{2x + 24}{x^3 + x^2 - 6x}$$

$$= \frac{-4}{x} + \frac{6}{5(x + 3)} + \frac{14}{5(x - 2)}.$$

Example 2   Find the partial fraction decomposition of

$$f(x) = \frac{8x^3}{(x^2 + 2)^2}$$

Solution   The decomposition will be

$$\frac{8x^3}{(x^2 + 2)^2} = \frac{Ax + B}{x^2 + 2} + \frac{Cx + D}{(x^2 + 2)^2}$$

$$= \frac{(Ax + B)(x^2 + 2) + (Cx + D)}{(x^2 + 2)^2}.$$

Hence,

$$8x^3 = (Ax + B)(x^2 + 2) + (Cx + D)$$

$$= Ax^3 + bx^2 + 2Ax + 2B + Cx + D$$

$$= Ax^3 + Bx^2 + (2A + C)x + (2B + D).$$

Equating coefficients gives
$A = 8$, $B = 0$, $2A + C = 0$, and
$2B + D = 0$.
Thus,
$C = -2A = -16$, and $D = -2B = 0$.
The decomposition is

$$\frac{8x^3}{(x^2 + 2)^2} = \frac{8x}{x^2 + 2} - \frac{16x}{(x^2 + 2)^2}.$$

Example 3   Find the partial fraction decomposition of

$$f(x) = \frac{x}{x^3 - 1}.$$

Solution   Since $x^3 - 1 = (x - 1)(x^2 + x + 1)$ is an irreducible factorization of $x^3 - 1$ over the real numbers, we have

$$\frac{x}{x^3 - 1} = \frac{x}{(x - 1)(x^2 + x + 1)}$$

$$= \frac{A}{x - 1} + \frac{Bx + C}{x^2 + x + 1},$$

or

$$\frac{x}{x^3 - 1}$$

$$= \frac{A(x^2 + x + 1) + (Bx + C)(x - 1)}{(x - 1)(x^2 + x + 1)}.$$

This implies that

$$x = A(x^2 + x + 1) + (Bx + C)(x - 1)$$

$$x = Ax^2 + Ax + A + Bx^2 - Bx + Cx - C,$$

or $x = (A + B)x^2 + (A - B + C)x + A - C.$

Equating coefficients gives the system of equations

(1) $A + B \quad = 0$, or $A = -B$,

(2) $A - B + C = 1$, or $A - B + C = 1$,

(3) $A \quad - C = 0$, or $A = C$.

Substituting the value of $-B$ in (1) and C in (3) into (2) we have,

(2)' $A + A + A = 1$ or $3A = 1$.

Thus, $A = 1/3$, and this implies
$B = -1/3$ and $C = 1/3$. The decomposition is

$$\frac{x}{x^3 - 1} = \frac{\frac{1}{3}}{x - 1} + \frac{-\frac{1}{3}x + \frac{1}{3}}{x^2 + x + 1},$$

or

$$\frac{x}{x^3 - 1} = \frac{1}{3(x - 1)} - \frac{x - 1}{3(x^2 + x + 1)}.$$

Selected Solutions

1. $\dfrac{3x - 1}{x(x + 1)} = \dfrac{A}{x} + \dfrac{B}{x + 1}$

$$= \frac{A(x + 1) + Bx}{x(x + 1)}$$

Hence, $A(x + 1) + Bx = 3x - 1$

$$(A + B)x + A = 3x - 1,$$

Thus,

$A + B = 3$

$\underline{A \qquad = -1}$

$\quad B = 4.$ Subtract

The solution is

$$\frac{3x - 1}{x(x + 1)} = \frac{-1}{x} + \frac{4}{x + 1}.$$

5. We have

$$\frac{x + 2}{(x + 1)(x - 1)} = \frac{A}{x + 1} + \frac{B}{x - 1}$$

$$= \frac{A(x - 1) + B(x + 1)}{(x + 1)(x - 1)}.$$

Hence, $x + 2 = (A + B)x + (-A + B)$.
This gives $A + B = 1$

$$\underline{-A + B = 2}$$

$2B = 3$, or $B = \dfrac{3}{2}$,

and $A = 1 - B = 1 - \dfrac{3}{2} = -\dfrac{1}{2}$. Thus

$$\frac{x + 2}{(x + 1)(x - 1)} = \frac{-1}{2(x + 1)} + \frac{3}{2(x - 1)}.$$

9. We have

$$\frac{2}{x^2(x+3)} = \frac{A}{x} + \frac{B}{x^2} + \frac{C}{x+3},$$

$$= \frac{Ax(x+3) + B(x+3) + Cx^2}{x^2(x+3)}$$

Then, we have

$$2 = A(x^2 + 3x) + B(x+3) + Cx^2$$

$$2 = (A+C)x^2 + (3A+B)x + 3B.$$

Thus $A + \quad C = 0$

$\quad\quad 3A + \quad B \quad\quad = 0$

$\quad\quad\quad\quad 3B \quad\quad = 2.$

This gives $B = \frac{2}{3}$, $3A = \frac{-2}{3}$, or

$A = \frac{-2}{9}$, and $C = -A = \frac{2}{9}$. The

solution is

$$\frac{2}{x^2(x+3)} = \frac{-2}{9x} + \frac{2}{3x^2} + \frac{2}{9(x+3)}.$$

13. We have

$$\frac{2x+1}{(x+2)^3} = \frac{A}{x+2} + \frac{B}{(x+2)^2} + \frac{C}{(x+2)^3}$$

$$= \frac{A(x+2)^2 + B(x+2) + C}{(x+2)^3}.$$

Hence,

$$2x + 1 = A(x^2 + 4x + 4) + B(x+2) + C$$

$$2x + 1 = Ax^2 + (4A+B)x + (4A+2B+C).$$

This gives $A = 0$, $4A + B = 2$, or

$B = 2$, and $4A + 2B + C = 1$, or

$C = 1 - 4 = -3$. Hence,

$$\frac{2x+1}{(x+2)^3} = \frac{2}{(x+2)^2} - \frac{3}{(x+2)^3}.$$

17. We have

$$\frac{x}{2x^2 + 5x + 2} = \frac{x}{(2x+1)(x+2)} = \frac{A}{2x+1} = \frac{B}{x+2}$$

$$= \frac{A(x+2) + B(2x+1)}{2x^2 + 5x + 2}.$$

Thus, $x = (A + 2B)x + (2A + B)$, so that

$A + 2B = 1 \quad\quad\quad A + 2B = 1$

$2A + \quad B = 0 \quad$ or $\quad \dfrac{-4A - 2B = 0}{-3A \quad\quad\quad = 1}$

$\quad\quad\quad\quad\quad\quad\quad\quad\quad A = -\frac{1}{3}.$

Then $2A + B = 0$ gives

$B = -2A = \frac{2}{3}.$

The solution is

$$\frac{x}{2x^2 + 5x + 2} = \frac{-1}{3(2x+1)} + \frac{2}{3(x+2)}.$$

21. We have

$$\frac{5}{x(x^2+3)} = \frac{A}{x} + \frac{Bx+C}{x^2+3}$$

$$= \frac{A(x^2+3) + (Bx+C)x}{x(x^2+3)}.$$

Equating the numerators gives

$$5 = (A+B)x^2 + Cx + 3A,$$

so that $3A = 5$, or $A = \frac{5}{3}$, $c = 0$,

and $A + B = 0$, which implies that

$B = -A = -\frac{5}{3}$. Hence,

$$\frac{5}{x(x^2+3)} = \frac{5}{3x} - \frac{5x}{3(x^2+3)}.$$

25. We have

$$\frac{3}{x(x+1)(x^2+1)} = \frac{A}{x} + \frac{B}{x+1} + \frac{Cx+d}{x^2+1}$$

$$= \frac{A(x+1)(x^2+1) + Bx(x^2+1) + (Cx+d)x(x+1)}{x(x+1)(x^2+1)}$$

This gives

$$3 = A(x+1)(x^2+1) + Bx(x^2+1) + (cx+d)x(x+1).$$

Rather than a system of equations at this point, let $x = 0$. This gives

$3 = A(1)(1) + B\cdot 0 + 0$, or $\underline{A = 3}$.

If we let $x = -1$, we have

$3 = A(0) + B(-1)(2) + 0$, or $\underline{B = -\frac{3}{2}}$.

If $x = 1$, we have

$3 = A(2)(2) + B(1)(2) + (c+d)(1)(2)$

$3 = 12 - 3 + 2(c+d)$, or

$\underline{c + d = -3}.$

If $x = 2$, then we have

$3 = A(3)(5) + B(2)(5) + (2c+d)(2)(3)$

$3 = 45 - 15 + 12c + 6d$, or

$12c + 6d = -27$, or $\underline{4c + 2d = -9}.$

Then we have

$$4c + 2d = -9$$
$$\underline{-2c - 2d = 6}$$
$$2c = -3$$

$$c = -\frac{3}{2}, \text{ and } d = \frac{-3}{2}.$$

The solution is

$$\frac{3}{x(x + 1)(x^2 + 1)} = \frac{3}{x} - \frac{3}{2(x + 1)} - \frac{3(x + 1)}{2(x^2 + 1)}$$

29. We have

$$\frac{3x^4 + x^3 + 5x^2 - x + 4}{(x - 1)(x^2 + 1)^2}$$

$$= \frac{A}{x - 1} + \frac{Bx + C}{x^2 + 1} + \frac{Dx + E}{(x^2 + 1)^2}.$$

Multiplying by $(x - 1)(x^2 + 1)^2$ gives

$$3x^4 + x^3 + 5x^2 - x + 4$$

$$= A(x^2+1)^2 + (Bx+c)(x-1)(x^2+1) + (DX+E)(x-1).$$

If we substitute $x = 1$, we arrive at $12 = 4A + 0 + 0$, or $A = 3$. This was convenient to find A. However, we now multiply to arrive at

$$3x^4 + x^3 + 5x^2 - x + 4$$

$$= A(x^4 + 2x^2 + 1) + (Bx + C)$$
$$(x^3 - x^2 + x - 1) + Dx^2 - Dx +$$
$$Ex - E,$$

$$= Ax^4 + 2Ax^2 + A + Bx^4 - Bx^3 + Bx^2 -$$
$$Bx + cx^3 - cx^2 + cx - c + Dx^2 -$$
$$Dx + Ex - E$$

$$= (A + B)x^4 + (-B + C)x^3 +$$
$$(2A + B - C + D)x^2 +$$
$$(-B + C - D + E)x + (A - C - E).$$

We have found that $A = 3$. Equating coefficients we have

x^4: $A + B = 3$, so that $B = 3 - A$ or $B = 0$.

x^3: $-B + C = 1$, so that $C = 1 + B$, or $C = 1$.

x^2: $2A + B - C + D = 5$, or $D = 5 - 5 = 0$.

x: $-B + C - D + E = -1$, or $E = -1 - 1 = -2$.

const: $A - C - E = 4$, or $3 - 1 + 2 = 4$, or $4 = 4$.

The solution is

$$\frac{3}{x - 1} + \frac{1}{x^2 + 1} - \frac{2}{(x^2 + 1)^2}.$$

33. Since $x^4 - 1 = (x - 1)(x + 1)(x^2 + 1)$, we have

$$\frac{x^2}{x^4 - 1} = \frac{A}{x - 1} + \frac{B}{x + 1} + \frac{Cx + D}{x^2 + 1}.$$

Multiplying by $x^4 - 1$ gives

$$x^2 = A(x + 1)(x^2 + 1) +$$
$$B(x - 1)(x^2 + 1) +$$
$$(Cx + D)(x^2 - 1).$$

Note that if $x = -1$, we have

$$(-1)^2 = A(0) + B(-2)(2) + 0,$$

$$1 = -4B, \text{ or } B = -\frac{1}{4}.$$

Also, if $x = 1$, we have

$$1 = A(2)(2) + B(0) + 0, \text{ or } A = \frac{1}{4}.$$

If $x = 0$, we have

$$0 = A(1)(1) + B(-1)(1) + D(-1)$$

$$D = A - B = \frac{1}{4} + \frac{1}{4} = \frac{1}{2}, \text{ or } D = \frac{1}{2}.$$

If $x = 2$, we have

$$4 = A(3)(5) + B(1)(5) + (2C + D)(3)$$

$$4 = 15(\frac{1}{4}) + 5(-\frac{1}{4}) + 6C + 3(\frac{1}{2})$$

$$4 = 4 + 6C, \text{ or } C = 0.$$

The solution is

$$\frac{1}{4(x - 1)} - \frac{1}{4(x + 1)} + \frac{1}{2(x^2 + 1)}.$$

37. If we multiply both sides by $x(x^2 - x - 4)$, we have

$$x - 1 = a(x^2 - x - 4) + x(bx + c)$$

$$x - 1 = (a + b)x^2 + (-a + c)x - 4a.$$

Starting with the constant terms, we have $-1 = -4a$, or $a = \frac{1}{4}$. Then

$$-a + c = 1, \text{ or } c = 1 + a = 1 + \frac{1}{4} = \frac{5}{4}.$$

Also, $a + b = 0$, or $b = -a = \frac{-1}{4}$.

We have $a = \frac{1}{4}$, $b = \frac{-1}{4}$ and $c = \frac{5}{4}$.

Chapter 10   Review Exercises

Selected Solutions

1. Using long division, we have

$$
\begin{array}{r}
2x^2 \qquad\quad + \frac{3}{2} \\
2x - 1\ \overline{\big)\ 4x^3 - 2x^2 + 3x + 5} \\
\underline{4x^3 - 2x^2} \qquad\qquad \\
3x + 5 \\
\underline{3x - \frac{3}{2}} \\
\frac{13}{2}.
\end{array}
$$

Hence, $q(x) = 2x^2 + \frac{3}{2}$ and $r(x) = \frac{13}{2}$.

5. Using synthetic division, we have

$$
\begin{array}{r|rrrr}
1 & 2 & 3 & -4 & 1 \\
  &   & 2 & 5 & 1 \\
\hline
  & 2 & 5 & 1 & \boxed{2}
\end{array}
$$

The quotient is $q(x) = 2x^2 + 5x + 1$ and the remainder is $r = 2$.

9. Using synthetic division to find $f(2)$ for $f(x) = x^3 + 3x^2 - 5x + 1$, we have

$$
\begin{array}{r|rrrr}
2 & 1 & 3 & -5 & 1 \\
  &   & 2 & 10 & 10 \\
\hline
  & 1 & 5 & 5 & 11.
\end{array}
$$

Hence, $f(2) = 11$.

13. A polynomial having zeros at -1, 4, and 7 is

$$
\begin{aligned}
f(x) &= (x + 1)(x - 4)(x - 7) \\
&= (x + 1)(x^2 - 11x + 28) \\
&= x^3 - 11x^2 + 28x + x^2 - 11x + 28,
\end{aligned}
$$

or $f(x) = x^3 - 10x^2 + 17x + 28$.

17. Using synthetic division with

$$f(x) = 2x^4 + x^3 - 4x^2 + 3x + 1,$$

we have

$$
\begin{array}{r|rrrrr}
-1 & 2 & 1 & -4 & 3 & 1 \\
   &   & -2 & 1 & 3 & -6 \\
\hline
   & 2 & -1 & -3 & 6 & -5.
\end{array}
$$

This gives $f(-1) = -5$. Hence, -1 is not a zero of f.

21. Every polynomial of degree three with zeros at -2, 1, and 4 has the form

$$f(x) = c(x + 2)(x - 1)(x - 4).$$

If $f(2) = 16$, then

$$
\begin{aligned}
16 &= c(2 + 2)(2 - 1)(2 - 4) \\
16 &= -8c \\
c &= -2.
\end{aligned}
$$

Hence,

$$
\begin{aligned}
f(x) &= -2(x + 2)(x - 1)(x - 4) \\
&= -2(x + 2)(x^2 - 5x + 4) \\
&= -2(x^3 - 3x^2 - 6x + 8),
\end{aligned}
$$

or $f(x) = -2x^3 + 6x^2 + 12x - 16$.

25. If the polynomial has real coefficients and has $1 - i$ as a zero, then $1 + i$ is a zero. Hence, a polynomial of smallest degree is

$$
\begin{aligned}
f(x) &= (x + 3)(x - 1 - i)(x - 1 + i) \\
&= (x + 3)[(x - 1)^2 + 1] \\
&= (x + 3)(x^2 - 2x + 2), \text{ or}
\end{aligned}
$$

$$f(x) = x^3 + x^2 - 4x + 6.$$

29. The only possible rational roots of $f(x) = 2x^3 = 9x^2 - 6x + 5$ have the form a/b, where a is a divisor of $2(\pm 1, \pm 2)$ and b is a divisor of $5(\pm 1, \pm 5)$. Hence, the only possible rational roots are ± 1, ± 2, $\pm\frac{1}{5}$, $\pm\frac{2}{5}$. Using trial and error, we finally arrive at

$$-1 \overline{\smash{)}\begin{array}{rrrr} 2 & -9 & -6 & 5 \\ & -2 & 11 & -5 \\ \hline 2 & -11 & 5 & 0. \end{array}}$$

Hence, $f(x) = (x + 1)(2x^2 - 11x + 5)$,

or $\qquad f(x) = (x + 1)(2x - 1)(x - 5)$.

The zeros of f are -1, $\frac{1}{2}$, 5.

33. The only possible rational zeros of

$\qquad f(x) = -x^4 + 2x^3 - 3x^2 + 11x - 7$

are ± 1 and ± 7. Synthetic division

gives

$$1 \overline{\smash{)}\begin{array}{rrrrr} -1 & 2 & -3 & 11 & -7 \\ & -1 & 1 & -2 & 9 \\ \hline -1 & 1 & -2 & 9 & 2 \end{array}} \qquad -1 \overline{\smash{)}\begin{array}{rrrrr} -1 & 2 & -3 & 11 & -7 \\ & 1 & -3 & 6 & -17 \\ \hline -1 & 3 & -6 & 17 & -24 \end{array}}$$

$$7 \overline{\smash{)}\begin{array}{rrrrr} -1 & 2 & -3 & 11 & -7 \\ & -7 & -35 & -266 & -1785 \\ \hline -1 & -5 & -38 & -255 & -1792 \end{array}} \qquad -7 \overline{\smash{)}\begin{array}{rrrrr} -1 & 2 & -3 & 11 & -7 \\ & 7 & -63 & 462 & -3311 \\ \hline -1 & 9 & -66 & 473 & -3318. \end{array}}$$

Hence, f has no rational zeros.

35. Consider $f(x) = x^2 - 11$. We know

that $f(x) = 0$ implies $x^2 - 11 = 0$,

or $x^2 = 11$, and that $x = \sqrt{11}$ is a

solution. Using the rational

zeros theorem we see that the only

possible rational roots are ± 1 and

± 11. However, $f(\pm 1) = -10$ and

$f(\pm 11) = 110$. Thus, the zero $\sqrt{11}$

is not rational.

37. Using synthetic division on

$\qquad f(x) = 3x^3 - 8x^2 + x + 2$ we find

$$-1 \overline{\smash{)}\begin{array}{rrrr} 3 & -8 & 1 & 2 \\ & -3 & 11 & -12 \\ \hline 3 & -11 & 12 & \boxed{-10} \end{array}} \qquad 0 \overline{\smash{)}\begin{array}{rrrr} 3 & -8 & 1 & 2 \\ & 0 & 0 & 0 \\ \hline 3 & -8 & 1 & \boxed{2} \end{array}}.$$

Since $f(-1) = -10$ and $f(0) = 2$,

there is a zero of f between -1 and

0. Also,

$$2 \overline{\smash{)}\begin{array}{rrrr} 3 & -8 & 1 & 2 \\ & 6 & -4 & -6 \\ \hline 3 & -2 & -3 & \boxed{-4} \end{array}} \qquad 3 \overline{\smash{)}\begin{array}{rrrr} 3 & -8 & 1 & 2 \\ & 9 & 3 & 12 \\ \hline 3 & 1 & 4 & \boxed{14} \end{array}}.$$

Since $f(x) = -4$ and $f(3) = 14$,

there is a zero of f between 2 and 3.

41. Using synthetic division we have

$$1 \overline{\smash{)}\begin{array}{rrrrr} 6 & 13 & -11 & -3 & 5 \\ & 6 & 18 & 7 & 4 \\ \hline 6 & 18 & 7 & 4 & 9 \end{array}} \qquad -3 \overline{\smash{)}\begin{array}{rrrrr} 6 & 13 & -11 & -3 & 5 \\ & -18 & 15 & -12 & 45 \\ \hline 6 & -5 & 4 & -15 & 50. \end{array}}$$

The division by 1 leaves the last

line as all positive numbers.

Hence, there are no zeros $c \geq 1$.

The division by -3 leaves the last

line having alternating signs.

This implies there is no zero $c \leq -3$.

45. We have

$$\frac{5x - 2}{x^2 - 4} = \frac{5x - 2}{(x - 2)(x + 2)} = \frac{A}{x - 2} + \frac{B}{x + 2}.$$

Multiplying by $x^2 - 4$ gives

$5x - 2 = A(x + 2) + B(x - 2)$

$\qquad = (A + B)x + (2A - 2B).$

Hence, $\quad A + B = 5 \rightarrow \quad A + B = 5$

$\qquad 2A - 2B = -2 \rightarrow \quad \underline{A - B = -1}$

$\qquad\qquad\qquad\qquad\qquad\qquad 2A \quad\quad = 4.$

Thus, $A = 2$ and $B = 5 - A = 3$.

The solution is

$$\frac{2}{x - 2} + \frac{3}{x + 2}.$$

49. The partial fraction expansion has

the form

$$\frac{3x^3 - 18x^2 + 29x - 4}{(x + 1)(x - 2)^3}$$

$$= \frac{A}{x + 1} + \frac{B}{x - 2} + \frac{C}{(x - 2)^2} + \frac{D}{(x - 2)^3}.$$

Multiplying both sides by

$(x + 1)(x - 2)^3$ gives

$3x^3 - 18x^2 + 29x - 4$

$\quad = A(x - 2)^3 + B(x + 1)(x - 2)^2 +$

$\qquad c(x + 1)(x - 2) + D(x + 1).$

We can expand and equate the like

terms or we can give certain values

to x to evaluate constants. For

example, if we let $x = -1$, we have

$-3 - 18 - 29 - 4 = A(-3)^3 + 0 + 0 + 0$

$\qquad\qquad -54 = -27A$

$\qquad\qquad \underline{A = 2.}$

If we let x = 2, we have

$$24 - 72 + 58 - 4 = 0 + 0 + 0 + 3D$$

$$6 = 3D$$

$$\underline{D = 2}.$$

If we let x = 0, we have

$$-4 = -8A + 4B - 2C + D$$

$$48 - 2C = -4 + 16 - 2 = 10,$$

or $\underline{2B - C = 5}$.

If we let x = 1, we have

$$10 = -A + 2B - 2C + 2D,$$

or 2B - 2C = 10 + 2 - 4,

or $\underline{B - C = 4}$.

Solving 2B - C = 5

$$\underline{B - C = 4}$$

$$\underline{B - 1},$$

and 1 - C = 4, or $\underline{C = -3}$.

The solution is

$$\frac{2}{x + 1} + \frac{1}{x - 2} - \frac{3}{(x - 2)^2} + \frac{2}{(x - 2)^3}.$$

Chapter 10 Test

1. Determine the quotient q(x) and remainder r for the division $\frac{x^6 - 2}{x - 1}$.

2. Determine the quotient q(x) and remainder r(x) for the division $\frac{8x^3 + 5}{2x + 1}$.

3. Use synthetic division to find q(x) and r for the division $\frac{3x^3 - 2x^2 + 4x - 18}{x - 2}$.

4. Use synthetic division to find q(x) and r for the division $\frac{4x^3 + 5x^2 - 3x + 6}{x + 1}$.

5. For $f(x) = 6x^3 - 7x^2 + 2x - 5$, use synthetic division to determine f(2) and f(-3).

6. Find a polynomial of lowest degree having zeros at 3 and 2 + 3i.

7. Show that 2 is a zero of $f(x) = x^3 - 2x^2 - x + 2$ and determine the remaining zeros.

8. Determine k so that x + 2 is a factor of $f(x) = 2x^3 - x^2 + x + k$.

9. Find a polynomial f of degree two with -1 and 2 as zeros, and f(3) = 12.

10. Find all complex zeros of $f(x) = x^3 + x^2 + x + 1$, given that -1 is a zero.

11. Find all zeros of $f(x) = x^3 - 3x^2 + 4x - 2$, given that 1 - i is a zero.

12. Find all rational zeros of $f(x) = x^3 - x^2 - 4x + 4$.

13. Find all rational zeros of $f(x) = x^4 + x^3 - x^2 + x - 2$.

14. Find all rational zeros of $f(x) = 2x^4 + 5x^3 - 9x^2 - 15x + 9$.

15. Find all rational zeros of $f(x) = 3x^3 + x^2 + 9x + 3$.

16. Show that $f(x) = x^2 - 17$ has no rational zeros. Use this result to prove that $\sqrt{17}$ is irrational.

17. Show that $f(x) = x^4 + x^3 - 2x^2 - 3x - 3$ has no rational zeros.

18. Show that the polynomial $f(x) = x^4 + x^3 - 2x^2 - 3x - 3$ has a zero in [1, 2].

19. Find the smallest integer that is an upper bound to the zeros of the polynomial $f(x) = x^3 - 4x^2 + 3x - 13$.

20. Use Descartes' rule of signs to determine the number of positive and negative zeros of $f(x) = 2x^3 + 11x^2 + 4x - 2$.

21. Determine the possible number of negative zeros of $f(x) = 2x^3 - 9x^2 - 6x + 7$, and find the largest integer that is a lower bound for the negative zeros.

22. The positive zero of $f(x) = 2x^3 - x^2 - x - 3$ lies between two consecutive integers from the set $\{0, 1, 2, 3, 4\}$. Determine these two consecutive integers.

23. Given that $f(x) = x^3 + 2x^2 - 3x - 6$ has a zero in the interval $[1.5, 1.9]$, approximate this zero to the nearest tenth.

24. Show that $f(x) = x^4 + 5x^2 + 4$ has no rational zeros. Factor f as $(ax^2 + b)(cx^2 + d)$, and show that f has no real zeros.

25. Find the partial fraction decomposition of $f(x) = \dfrac{2x + 4}{x^3 - x}$.

26. Find the partial fraction decomposition of $f(x) = \dfrac{2x^2 + 2x + 1}{x^3 + x}$.

(Answers for this test are on page 365.)

CHAPTER 11   Further Topics in Algebra

Section 11.1   Mathematical Induction

Additional Examples

Example 1   Prove that
$$4 + 4^2 + 4^3 \ldots + 4^n = \frac{4}{3}(4^n - 1).$$

Solution   Let S_n denote the given statement. That is, let
$$S_n: 4 + 4^2 + 4^3 + \ldots + 4^n = \frac{4}{3}(4^n - 1).$$

We wish to show that S_1 is true and that whenever S_n is true for k, it must also be true for k + 1.

The statement S_1 says that $4 = (4/3)(4^1 - 1)$. This is true since $\frac{4}{3}(4 - 1) = \frac{4}{3}(3) = 4$.

Hence, S_1 is true.

Suppose S_k is true. That is,
$$4 + 4^2 + 4^3 + \ldots + 4^k = \frac{4}{3}(4^k - 1).$$

Consider the statement
$$S_{k+1}: 4 + 4^2 + 4^3 + \ldots + 4^{k+1}$$
$$= \frac{4}{3}(4^{k+1} - 1).$$

We wish to use S_k being true to prove S_{k+1} is true. Considering the left-hand side of the equality, S_{k+1}, we have
$$4 + 4^2 + 4^3 + \ldots + 4^{k+1}$$
$$= 4 + 4^2 + 4^3 + \ldots + 4^k + 4^{k+1},$$
since the term before 4^{k+1} is 4^k,
$$= (4 + 4^2 + 4^3 + \ldots + 4^k) + 4^{k+1},$$

grouping terms,
$$= \frac{4}{3}(4^k - 1) + 4^{k+1} \qquad \text{since } S_k \text{ is true}$$
$$= \frac{4}{3} \cdot 4^k - \frac{4}{3} + 4^{k+1}$$
$$= \frac{1}{3}4^{k+1} - \frac{4}{3} + 4^{k+1}$$
$$= (\frac{1}{3} + 1)4^{k+1} - \frac{4}{3}$$
$$= \frac{4}{3} \cdot 4^{k+1} - \frac{4}{3},$$

or $4 + 4^2 + 4^3 + \ldots + 4^k$
$$= \frac{4}{3}(4^{k+1} - 1).$$

This proves S_{k+1} is true. Thus, we have shown that $\underline{if}$ S_k is true, then we can use this fact to prove S_{k+1} is true.

By the principle of mathematical induction S_n is true for all natural numbers n.

Example 2   Use mathematical induction to prove that for every natural number n, $2^{3n} - 1$ is divisible by 7.

Solution   We will use the following definition of the statement "If a and b are natural numbers, then b is divisible by a."

Definition: If a and b are natural numbers, then b is divisible by a if and only if there is some natural number m such that b = am. For example, 72 is divisible by 18 since $72 = 18 \cdot 4$.

Let S_n be the statement $S_n: 2^{3n} - 1$ is divisible by 7. We can see that S_1 is true since
$$2^{3(1)} - 1 = 2^3 - 1 = 8 - 1 = 7$$
is divisible by 7.

Suppose S_n is true for some natural number k. This implies that $S_k: 2^{3k} - 1$ is divisible by 7 is true. Hence, there is some natural number m such that $2^{3k} - 1 = 7m$, or $2^{3k} = 7m + 1$.

We wish to show that if S_k is true, then S_{k+1} is also true.

Consider $2^{3(k+1)} - 1$.

We have
$$2^{3(k+1)} - 1 = 2^{3k+3} - 1$$
$$= 2^3 \cdot 2^{3k} - 1$$
$$= 8 \cdot 2^{3k} - 1$$
$$= 8(7m + 1) - 1 \quad \text{since } 2^{3k}$$
$$= 7m + 1$$
$$= 8 \cdot 7m + 7$$
$$= 7(8m + 1).$$

Since $8m + 1$ is a natural number, $2^{3(k + 1)} - 1$ is divisible by 7 since $2^{3k} - 1$ is divisible by 7. Thus, if S_k is true, then S_{k+} is true.

We have proved that S_n is true for all natural numbers n.

Selected Solutions

1. S_n: $2 + 4 + 6 + \ldots + 2n = n(n + 1)$
    S_1: $2 = 1(1 + 1)$
    S_2: $2 + 4 = 6$
    $2(2 + 1) = 6$
    S_3: $2 + 4 + 6 = 12$
    $3(3 + 1) = 12$
    S_4: $2 + 4 + 6 + 8 = 20$
    $4(4 + 1) = 20$
    S_5: $2 + 4 + 6 + 8 + 10 = 30$
    $5(5 + 1) = 30$

    Proof: True for $n = 1$.

    Suppose S_n is true for $n = k$, that is
    S_k: $2 + 4 + 6 + \ldots + 2k = k(k + 1)$.
    Then consider S_{k+1}.

    S_{k+1}: $(2 + 4 + 6 + \ldots + 2k) + 2(k + 1)$
    $= k(k + 1) + 2(k + 1)$
    $= (k + 1)(k + 2)$
    $= (k + 1)((k + 1) + 1)$

    Since the statement is true for $k + 1$ whenever it is true for k, then it is true for all natural numbers.

5. Let $S(n)$: $1^3 + 2^3 + 3^3 + \ldots + n^3$
    $= \dfrac{n^2(n + 1)^2}{4}$.

    Proof: Let $n = 1$.
    $1^3 = 1$, $\dfrac{1^2(1 + 1)^2}{4} = 1$.

    So the equation is true for $n = 1$. Suppose true for some natural number k. Then,

    $1^3 + 2^3 + \ldots + k^3 = \dfrac{k^2(k + 1)^2}{4}$.

Then, we have for S_{k+1}

$1^3 + 2^3 + \ldots + k^3 + (k + 1)^3$

$= \dfrac{k^2(k + 1)^2}{4} + (k + 1)^3$

$= (k + 1)^2 \left[\dfrac{k^2}{4} + (k + 1)\right]$

$= (k + 1)^2 \left(\dfrac{k^2 + 4k + 4}{4}\right)$

$= \dfrac{(k + 1)^2(k + 2)^2}{4}$

$= \dfrac{(k + 1)^2((k + 1) + 1)^2}{4}$.

Therefore S_{k+1} is true when S_k is true. This proves the formula is true for every natural number.

9. Let $S(n)$: $\dfrac{1}{1 \cdot 4} + \dfrac{1}{4 \cdot 7} + \dfrac{1}{7 \cdot 10} + \ldots +$

    $\dfrac{1}{(3n - 2)(3n + 1)}$

    $= \dfrac{n}{3n + 1}$.

    Proof: Let $n = 1$.
    $\dfrac{1}{1 \cdot 4} = \dfrac{1}{4}$ and $\dfrac{1}{3 \cdot 1 + 1} = \dfrac{1}{4}$,

    so equation is true for $n = 1$. Suppose that the statement is true for some natural number k:

    $\dfrac{1}{1 \cdot 4} + \dfrac{1}{4 \cdot 7} + \ldots + \dfrac{1}{(3k - 2)(3k + 1)}$

    $= \dfrac{k}{3k + 1}$.

    Then, we have for S_{k+1}

    $\dfrac{1}{1 \cdot 4} + \dfrac{1}{4 \cdot 7} + \ldots + \dfrac{1}{(3k - 2)(3k + 1)} +$

    $\dfrac{1}{(3k + 1)(3k + 4)}$

    $= \dfrac{k}{3k + 1} + \dfrac{1}{(3k + 1)(3k + 4)}$

    $= \dfrac{k(3k + 4) + 1}{(3k + 1)(3k + 4)}$

    $= \dfrac{3k^2 + 4k + 1}{(3k + 1)(3k + 4)}$

    $= \dfrac{(3k + 1)(k + 1)}{(3k + 1)(3k + 4)}$

    $= \dfrac{k + 1}{3k + 4}$

    $= \dfrac{k + 1}{3(k + 1) + 1}$.

Hence, it is true for k + 1 _if_ it is true for k. This shows the statement is true for all natural numbers.

13. Let $S(n)$: $x^{2n} + x^{2n-1}y + \ldots +$

$$xy^{2n-1} + y^{2n}$$

$$= \frac{x^{2n+1} - y^{2n+1}}{x - y}.$$

Proof: Let $n = 1$. Then

$x^3 - y^3 = (x - y)(x^2 + xy + y^2)$.

Thus, $x^2 + xy + y^2 = \dfrac{x^3 - y^3}{x - y}$.

Suppose true for some natural number k:

$x^{2k} + x^{2k-1}y + \ldots + xy^{k-1} + y^{2k}$

$$= \frac{x^{2k+1} - y^{2k+1}}{x - y}.$$

Then, we have for S_{k+1}

$$\frac{x^{2k+3} - y^{2k+3}}{x - y}$$

$$= \frac{x^{2k+3} - x^{2k+1}y^2 + x^{2k+1}y^2 - y^{2k+3}}{x - y}$$

$$= \frac{x^{2k+1}(x^2 - y^2)}{x - y} + \frac{y^2(x^{2k+1} - y^{2k+1})}{x - y}$$

$$= x^{2k+2} + yx^{2k+1} + y^2(x^{2k} + x^{2k-1}y + \ldots$$

$$+ xy^{2k-1} + y^{2k},$$

$$= x^{2k+2} + x^{2k+1}y + x^{2k}y^2 + x^{2k-1}y^2 +$$

$$\ldots + xy^{2k+1} + y^{2k+2}.$$

17. Let $S(n)$: $2^n > 2n$ if $n \geq 3$.
Proof: Suppose $n = 3$.

$$2^3 = 8 \text{ and } 2 \cdot 3 = 6$$

Suppose true for some natural number k:

$2^k > 2k$. Then, considering S_{k+1},

$2^{k+1} = 2^k \cdot 2 > 2k \cdot 2 > 2(k + 1)$.
Hence, $S(k + 1)$ is true whenever $S(k)$ is true.

21. Let $S(n)$: $3^{2n} - 1$ is divisible by 8.
Proof: $n = 1$ gives $3^2 - 1 = 8$ divisible by 8.

Suppose $3^{2k} - 1$ is divisible by 8. Then there is a positive integer m so that $3^{2k} - 1 = 8m$.

$3^{2k+2} - 1$

$= 3^{2k} \cdot 3^2 - 1$

$= 3^{2k} \cdot 3^2 - 3^2 + 3^2 - 1$

$= 9(3^{2k} - 1) + 8$

$= 9(8m) + 8 = 8(9m + 1)$,

since $3^{2k} - 1$ is divisible by 8.
Hence S_{k+1} is valid if S_k if true.

25. $2^n > n^2$ is valid for $n \geq 5$.
Proof: Note that:

$n = 1$, $2^1 > 1^2$

$n = 2$, $2^2 = 4 = 2^2$

$n = 3$, $2^3 = 8$, $3^2 = 9$ false!

$n = 4$, $2^4 = 16$, $4^2 = 16$ false; 2^4 is not $> 4^2$

$n = 5$, $2^5 = 32$, $5^2 = 25$ true

We will proved true for $n \geq 5$.
We see it is true for $n = 5$;
suppose it is true for some natural number k:
that is, $2^k > k^2$. Then we have

$$2^{k+1} = 2^k \cdot 2 > 2k^2 > (k + 1)^2,$$

since $2k^2 > k^2 + 2k + 1$, or

$k^2 > 2k + 1$ for $k \geq 5$.
Thus, S_{k+1} is valid if S_k is valid.

29. The proof is not valid because the beginning assumption, that "for some natural number k, k + k + 1," is not a correct statement, since it was not shown to be true for $n = 1$.

31. Given n lines, no two parallel and no three pass through the same point. The total number of points of intersection of the lines can be found by labeling the lines $\ell_1, \ell_2, \ldots, \ell_n$. ℓ_1 intersects with the remaining $n-1$ lines and gives $n-1$ points of intersection. ℓ_2 intersects with the remaining $n-1$ lines, but its intersection with ℓ_1 has already been counted. Thus, we have an additional $n-2$ points of intersection. Similarly, ℓ_3 contributes $n-3$ additional points, and so on, until, finally ℓ_{n-1} contributes one additional point. Line ℓ_n intersects the other lines but all these points have been counted.

The total number of points is $1 + 2 + \ldots + (n-3) + (n-2) + (n-1)$. It has previously been shown that
$$1 + 2 + 3 + \ldots + (n-1) + n = \frac{n(n+1)}{2}.$$
Replacing n by $n-1$, we have
$$1 + 2 + \ldots + (n-2) + (n-1) = \frac{(n-1)n}{2}$$
$$= \frac{n^2 - n}{2}.$$

32. Let a_n = number of sides of the nth figure.

$a_1 = 3$

$a_2 = 3 \cdot 4$,   since each side will develop into 4 sides.

$a_3 = 3 \cdot 4 \cdot 4$,   since each side of a_2 will develop into 4 sides

Thus, $a_n = 3(4)^{n-1}$.

33. Let P_n = perimeter and a_n = number of sides of the nth figure. Refer to Exercise 32.

$P_1 = 3$, since each side has length 1.

$P_2 = \frac{1}{3}a_2 = 4$, since each side has length 1/3.

$P_3 = \frac{1}{9}a_3 = \frac{16}{3}$, since each side has length $1/9 = 1/3^2$.

$P_4 = \frac{1}{27}a_4 = \frac{3(4)^3}{3^3} + \frac{4^3}{9} = \frac{64}{9}$, since each side has length $1/27 = 1/3^3$.

$P_n = \frac{1}{3^{n-1}}a_n = \frac{3(4)^{n-1}}{3^{n-1}} = \frac{4^{n-1}}{3^{n-2}}$, since each side has length $1/3^{n-1}$.

Section 11.2   The Binomial Theorem

Additional Examples

Examples 1   Use the binomial formula to evaluate
$(2x^{2/3} - 3x^{-1/3})^5$.

Solution   The binomial expansion formula gives the result
$$(a+b)^n = a^n + \binom{n}{1}a^{n-1}b + \binom{n}{2}a^{n-2}b^2$$
$$+ \ldots + \binom{n}{n-1}ab^{n-1} + \binom{n}{n}b^n.$$

Hence, using $a = 2x^{2/3}$ and $b = -3x^{-1/3}$, we have

$(2x^{2/3} - 3x^{-1/3})^5$

$= (2x^{2/3})^5 + \binom{5}{1}(2x^{2/3})^4(-3x^{-1/3})$

$+ \binom{5}{2}(2x^{2/3})^3(-3x^{-1/3})^2$

$+ \binom{5}{3}(2x^{2/3})^2(-3x^{-1/3})^3$

$+ \binom{5}{4}(2x^{2/3})(-3x^{-1/3})^4$

$+ \binom{5}{5}(-3x^{-1/3})^5$

$= 32x^{10/3} + \frac{5!}{4!1!}(16x^{8/3})(-3x^{-1/3})$

$+ \frac{5!}{3!2!}(9x^{6/3})(9x^{-2/3})$

$+ \frac{5!}{2!3!}(4x^{4/3})(-27x^{-3/3})$

$$= + \frac{5!}{1!4!}(2x^{2/3})(81x^{-4/3})$$

$$+ \frac{5!}{0!5!}(-243x^{-5/3})$$

$$= 32x^{10/3} + 5(-48)x^{7/3} + 10(72)x^{4/3}$$

$$+ 10(-108)x^{1/3} + 5(162)x^{-2/3}$$

$$- 243x^{-5/3}$$

$$= 32x^{10/3} - 240x^{7/3} + 720x^{4/3}$$

$$- 1080x^{1/3} + 810x^{-2/3} - 243x^{-5/3}.$$

Example 2   Find the term involving x^{10} in the expansion of $(2x^2 - \frac{1}{2}y^{1/2})^{12}$.

Solution   The term involving x^{10} will be the term involving $(2x^2)^5$. Letting $n = 12$, this will be the $(n - 7)$th power. Thus, using the binomial expansion formula, the term we are looking for is

$$\binom{n}{n-7}a^{n-7}b^7.$$

Using $n = 12$, $a = 2x^2$, and $b = -\frac{1}{2}y^{1/2}$, the term is

$$\binom{12}{5}(2x^2)^5(-\frac{1}{2}y^{1/2})^7$$

$$= \frac{12!}{7!5!}(32x^{10})(-128y^{7/2})$$

$$= \frac{(12)(11)(10)(9)(8) \cdot 7!}{7!(5)(4)(3)(2)}(-\frac{1}{4}x^{10}y^{7/2})$$

$$= - \frac{(11)(9)(8)}{4}x^{10}y^{7/2}$$

$$= -198x^{10}y^{7/2}.$$

Selected Solutions

1. $(x + y)^6$

$$= x^6 + 6x^5y + \frac{6 \cdot 5}{2}x^4y^2 + \frac{6 \cdot 5 \cdot 4}{3 \cdot 2}x^3y^3$$

$$+ \frac{6 \cdot 5 \cdot 4 \cdot 3}{4 \cdot 3 \cdot 2}x^2y^4 + \frac{6 \cdot 5 \cdot 4 \cdot 3 \cdot 2}{5 \cdot 4 \cdot 3 \cdot 2}xy^5 + y^6$$

$$= x^6 + 6x^5y + 15x^4y^2 + 20x^3y^3 + 15x^2y^4$$

$$+ 6xy^5 + y^6.$$

5. $(r^2 + s)^5$

$$= r^{10} + 5r^8s + 10r^6s^2 + 10r^4s^3$$

$$+5r^2s^4 + s^5.$$

9. $(\frac{m}{2} - 1)^6 = \frac{m^6}{2^6} + \binom{6}{1}(\frac{m}{2})^5(-1)$

$$+ \binom{6}{2}(\frac{m}{2})^4(-1)^2$$

$$+ \binom{6}{3}(\frac{m}{2})^3(-1)^3 + \binom{6}{4}(\frac{m}{2})^2(-1)^4$$

$$+ \binom{6}{5}(\frac{m}{2})(-1)^5 + (-1)^6,$$

and hence,

$$(\frac{m}{2} - 1)^6 = \frac{m^6}{64} - \frac{3m^5}{16} + \frac{15m^4}{16} - \frac{5m^3}{2} + \frac{15m^2}{4}$$

$$- 3m + 1.$$

13. $(m^{-2} + m^2)^4$

$$= (m^{-2})^4 + 4(m^{-2})^3(m^2)$$

$$+ 6(m^{-2})^2(m^2)^2 + 4(m^{-2})(m^2)^3$$

$$+ (m^2)^4$$

$$= m^{-8} + 4m^{-4} + 6 + 4m^2 + m^8$$

17. Find first four terms only:

$(x + 6)^{21}$

$$= x^{21} + \binom{21}{1}x^{20} \cdot 6 + \binom{21}{2}x^{19} \cdot 6^2$$

$$+ \binom{21}{3}x^{18} \cdot 6^3 + \ldots$$

$$= x^{21} + 126x^{20} + 7560x^{19} + 287,280x^{18},$$

since $\binom{21}{3} = \frac{21 \cdot 20 \cdot 19}{3 \cdot 2 \cdot 1} = 190.$

21. The fifth term of $(m - 2p)^{12}$ is

$$\binom{12}{12-4}m^{12-4}(-2p)^4$$

$$= \binom{12}{8}m^8(16p^4)$$

$$= 7920m^8p^4.$$

25. $\binom{20}{4}p^8q^{16} = 4845p^8q^{16}$ is the 17th term.

29. $\binom{8}{4}(3x^7)^4(2y^3)^4 = 90,720x^{28}y^{12}$

33. $(1.99)^8 = (2 - .01)^8$

$\approx 2^8 - 8 \cdot 2^7(.01) +$

$28 \cdot 2^6(.01)^2 - 56(2^5)(.01)^3$

$= 245.937$

Note that the next term in the expansion would be

$+ \binom{8}{4}2^4(.01)^4 = (70)(16)(10^{-8})$

$= .0000112.$

37. $(1 + \frac{5}{625})^{1/4}$

$\approx 1 + \frac{1}{4} \cdot \frac{5}{625} + \frac{\frac{1}{4}(-\frac{3}{4})}{2}(\frac{5}{625})^2$

$+ \frac{\frac{1}{4}(-\frac{3}{4})(-\frac{7}{4})}{6}(\frac{5}{625})^3$

$= 1.002$

$(630)^{1/4} = 5(1 + \frac{5}{625})^{1/4} \approx 5(1.002)$

$= 5.010$

41. $(1 + x)^{-1} = 1 - x + x^2 - x^3 + x^4 - x^5 + \ldots$

45. $n(n - 1)! = n!$

By definition,

$n! = 1 \cdot 2 \cdot 3 \cdots n$, so

$(n - 1)! = 1 \cdot 2 \cdot 3 \cdots (n - 1).$

Hence,

$n(n - 1)! = n[1 \cdot 2 \cdot 3 \cdots (n - 1)]$

$= 1 \cdot 2 \cdot 3 \cdots (n - 1) \cdot n$

$= n!$

47. If $(n + 2)! = 56 \cdot n!$, then

$(n + 2)! = (n + 2)(n + 1) \cdot n! = 56n!$

$(n + 2)(n + 1) = 56$

$n^2 + 3n + 2 = 56$

$n^2 + 3n - 54 = 0$

$(n + 9)(n - 6) = 0.$

Hence,

$n = -9$ or $n = 6$. The only possible solution is $n = 6$.

Section 11.3   Arithmetic Sequences

Additional Examples

Example 1   If we have an arithmetic sequence in which $a_1 = 5$ and $a_{12} = -\frac{5}{7}$, find a_{20} and S_{20}.

Solution   For arithmetic sequences we have the formulas

$a_n = a_1 + (n - 1)d$ and $S_n = \frac{n}{2}(a_1 + a_n)$.

In order to determine a_{20} we need to find d. Using the given information that $a_1 = 5$ and $a_{12} = -5/7$, we have

$a_{12} = a_1 + 11d,$

$-\frac{5}{7} = 5 + 11d,$

$11d = -\frac{5}{7} - 5 = \frac{-40}{7},$

or $d = -\frac{40}{77}.$

Hence,

$a_{20} = a_1 + 19d = 5 + 19(-\frac{40}{77})$

$a_{20} = 5 - \frac{760}{77}$

$a_{20} = \frac{-375}{77},$

and

$S_{20} = \frac{20}{2}(a_1 + a_{20}) = \frac{20}{2}(5 - \frac{375}{77})$

$S_{20} = \frac{20}{2}(\frac{10}{77}) = \frac{190}{77}.$

Example 2   Evaluate

$$\sum_{i=1}^{27}(3i - 2).$$

Solution   The terms of the series are the first 27 terms of the arithmetic sequence $a_1, a_2, a_3, \ldots$, where the i-th term is $a_i = 3i - 2$. Using this formula, $a_1 = 3 \cdot 1 - 2 = 1$ and $a_{27} = 3 \cdot (27) - 2 = 81 - 2 = 79$. The sum $S_{27} = 27/2(1 + 79) = 27/2(80) = 27 \cdot 40 = 1080$. Hence

$$\sum_{i=1}^{27}(3i - 2) = 1080.$$

Example 3   If money is put on each square of an 8-by-8 checkerboard by placing \$2 on the first square, \$4 on the second square, \$6 on the third square, and so on, what is the total sum of money on the checkerboard?

Solution   The answer is the sum of an arithmetic sequence where $a_1 = 2$ and $d = 2$. Since it is an 8-by-8 checkerboard, there are 64 squares, and $a_{64} = a_1 + 63d = 2 + 63(2)$
$$= 2 + 126 = 128.$$

The sum is
$$S_{64} = \frac{64}{2}[a_1 + a_{64}] = 32(2 + 128)$$
$$= 32(130)$$
$$= \$4,160.$$

Example 4   Given an arithmetic sequence with $a_{12} = 60$ and $a_{20} = 92$, find a_1.

Solution   Using the formula
$$a_n = a_1 + (n - 1)d,$$ we have
$$a_{20} = a_1 + 19d, \text{ or } 92 = a_1 + 19d,$$
and $a_{12} = a_1 + 11d$, or $60 = a_1 + 11d$.

We have two equations in two unknowns, and we wish to solve for a_1. Actually, it is easier to first solve for d and use this to find a_1. Subtracting the equations gives $32 = 8d$, or $d = 4$. Then
$$60 = a_1 + 11(4),$$
or $a_1 = 60 - 44 = 16.$

Selected Solutions

1. If $a_n = 6n + 4$, then the first five terms are 10, 16, 22, 28, and 34.

5. If $a_n = \frac{2}{n + 3}$, the first five terms are $\frac{1}{2}$, $\frac{2}{5}$, $\frac{1}{3}$, $\frac{2}{7}$, and $\frac{1}{4}$.

9. If $a_n = \frac{n^2 + 1}{n^2 + 2}$, then the first five terms are $\frac{2}{3}$, $\frac{5}{6}$, $\frac{10}{11}$, $\frac{17}{18}$, and $\frac{26}{27}$.

13. If $a_1 = 4$ and $a_n = a_{n-1} + 5$ for $n > 1$, then
$a_2 = 4 + 5 = 9,$
$a_3 = 9 + 5 = 14,$
$a_4 = 14 + 5 = 19,$
$a_5 = 19 + 5 = 24,$
and we see that $a_6 = 29$, $a_7 = 34$, $a_8 = 39$, $a_9 = 44$, $a_{10} = 49$.

17. If $a_1 = 1$, $a_2 = 1$, and for $n \geq 3$
$a_n = a_{n-1} + a_{n-2}$, then
$a_3 = 1 + 1 = 2,$
$a_4 = 2 + 1 = 3,$
$a_5 = 3 + 2 = 5,$
$a_6 = 5 + 3 = 8,$
$a_7 = 8 + 5 = 13,$
and we see that $a_8 = 21$, $a_9 = 34$, and $a_{10} = 55$.

21. If $a_2 = 9$ and $d = -2$, then we must have $a_1 = 11$ in order for $a_2 = a_1 + d$. Then $a_1 = 11$, $a_2 = 9$, $a_3 = 7$, and $a_4 = 5$.

23. If $a_1 = 4 - \sqrt{5}$ and $a_2 = 4$, then
$d = a_2 - a_1 = 4 - (4 - \sqrt{5}) = \sqrt{5}.$
Hence, $a_1 = 4 - \sqrt{5}$, $a_2 = 4$, $a_3 = 4 + \sqrt{5}$, $a_4 = 4 + 2\sqrt{5}$, and $a_5 = 4 + 3\sqrt{5}$.

25. For the sequence 12, 17, 22, 27, 32, 37, ... , we see that $a_1 = 12$ and d = 5. Hence,
$$a_n = a_1 + (n - 1)d = 12 + (n - 1)5,$$
or $a_n = 7 + 5n$.

29. For the sequence $-6 + \sqrt{2}$, $-6 + 2\sqrt{2}$, $-6 + 3\sqrt{2}$, ... , we see that $a_1 = -6 + \sqrt{2}$ and $d = \sqrt{2}$. Hence,
$$a_n = a_1 + (n - 1)d$$
$$a_n = -6 + \sqrt{2} + (n - 1)\sqrt{2}$$
$$a_n = -6 + \sqrt{2} + n\sqrt{2} - \sqrt{2}$$
$$a_n = -6 + n\sqrt{2}.$$

33. For $2z + m$, $2z$, $2z - m$, $2z - 2m$, ... , we see that $a_1 = 2z + m$ and $d = -m$. Hence,
$$a_n = a_1 + (n - 1)d$$
$$a_n = 2z + m + (n - 1)(-m)$$
$$a_n = 2z + m - nm + m$$
$$a_n = 2z + 2m - nm.$$

37. If $a_3 = 2$ and d = 1, then
$$a_2 = a_3 - d = 2 - 1 = 1 \text{ and}$$
$$a_1 = a_2 - d = 0.$$
Thus, $a_n = a_1 + (n - 1)d$
$$a_n = 0 + (n - 1) \cdot 1$$
$$a_n = n - 1.$$
Also, $a_8 = 8 - 1 = 7$.

41. If $a_1 = 12$ and $a_3 = 6$, then we can find d using the formula
$a_n = a_1 + (n - 1)d$, since for n = 3 we have
$$a_3 = 6 = 12 + (3 - 1)d$$
$$-6 = 2d, \text{ or}$$
$$d = -3.$$
Then, $a_n = 12 + (n - 1)(-3)$

Then, $a_n = 12 + (n - 1)(-3)$
$$a_n = 15 - 3n.$$
Also, $a_8 = 15 - 24 = -9$.

45. If $a_1 = x$ and $a_2 = x + 3$, then
$d = a_2 - a_1 = 3$. Then we have
$$a_n = a_1 + (n - 1)d$$
$$a_n = x + (n - 1)3$$
$$a_n = x + 3(n - 1).$$
Also, $a_8 = x + 21$.

49. If $a_1 = 8$ and d = 3, then we use
$S_n = \frac{n}{2}[2a_1 + (n - 1)d]$ to show
$$S_{10} = 5[16 + (9)(3)]$$
$$S_{10} = 5(43) = 215.$$

53. For the sequence 5, 9, 13, ... , we see that $a_1 = 5$ and d = 4. We use $S_n = \frac{n}{2}[2a_1 + (n - 1)d]$ to arrive at
$$S_{10} = 5[10 + 9(4)]$$
$$S_{10} = 5[46] = 230.$$

57. If $a_4 = 2.556$ and $a_5 = 3.004$, then
$d = a_5 - a_4 = .448$ and thus
$a_1 = a_4 - 3d = 2.556 - 1.344 = 1.212$.
Then, we have
$$S_{10} = \frac{10}{2}[2(1.212) + 9(.448)]$$
$$S_{10} = 32.28.$$

61. Evaluating $\sum\limits_{i=1}^{10} (2i + 3)$ is the same as finding S_{10} for the sequence $a_1, a_2, a_3 ...$, with $a_n = 2n + 3$. Using the formula $S_n = \frac{n}{2}(a_1 + a_n)$, we have

$S_{10} = 5(5 + 23)$

$S_{10} = 5(28) = 140,$

since $a_1 = 2(1) + 3 = 5$ and

$a_{10} = 2(10) + 3 = 23.$

65. Evaluating $\sum\limits_{i=1}^{1000} i$ is the same as

finding S_{1000} for the sequence

$a_1, a_2, a_3, \ldots$, where $a_n = n.$

Using

$S_n = \dfrac{n}{2}(a_1 + a_n),$ we have

$S_{1000} = \dfrac{1000}{2}(1 + 1000)$

$S_{1000} = 500(1001)$

$S_{1000} = 500,500.$

69. In order to evaluate $\sum\limits_{i=7}^{12} (6 - 2i)$

we can find $S_{12} - S_6$ for the sum

using $a_n = 6 - 2n.$ We have $a_1 = 4,$

$a_6 = 6 - 12 = -6,$ and $a_{12} = 6 - 24 = -18.$

Hence, using $S_n = \dfrac{n}{2}(a_1 + a_n)$ we

have

$S_6 = 3[4 + (-6)] = 3(-2) = -6,$

and

$S_{12} = 6[4 + (-18)] = 6(-14) = -84.$

Hence

$\sum\limits_{i=7}^{12} (6 - 2i) = S_{12} - S_6 = -84 - (-6)$

$= -78.$

73. If $a_{15} = 168$ and $a_{16} = 180,$ then

$d = a_{16} - a_{15} = 180 - 168 = 12.$

Then, using the formula

$a_n = a_1 + (n - 1)d,$ we have

$a_{15} = a_1 + 14d$

$168 = a_1 + 14(12)$

$a_1 = 168 - 168 = 0.$

77. If we let $a_1 = 51,$ $a_2 = 52,$ $a_3 = 53,$

... , then $d = 1$ and the number 71

is the 21st term. That is,

$a_{21} = a_1 + 20d = 51 + 20 = 71.$

Then, $S_{21} = 51 + 52 + \ldots + 70 + 71$

$S_{21} = \dfrac{21}{2}(51 + 71)$

$S_{21} = \dfrac{21}{2}(122) = 21(61),$ or

$S_{21} = 1281.$

81. The clock strikes

$(1 + 2 + 3 + \ldots + 11 + 12)$

times <u>twice</u> each day. Hence, in

30 days the clock strikes

$n = 60(1 + 2 + \ldots + 12) = 60[\dfrac{12 \cdot 13}{2}]$

$n = 60(78) = 4680$ times.

85. We have $a_1 = 16,$ $a_2 = 48,$ $a_3 = 80,$

and so on. Thus, $d = 32$ since

$a_3 - a_2 = a_2 - a_1 = 32.$ Hence,

using $a_n = a_1 + (n - 1)d,$ we have

$a_8 = 16 + 7(32)$

$a_8 = 240$ ft.

The total distance traveled in 8

seconds is

$S_8 = \dfrac{8}{2}(a_1 + a_8)$

$S_8 = 4(16 + 240)$

$S_8 = 1024$ ft.

89. We have $a_1 = 2$ and $a_{20} = 15.$ Hence,

the sum of the lengths is $S_{20} =$

$S_{20} = 10(2 + 15) = 170$ m.

93. Since $\log A + \log B = \log AB,$ we

have $a_1 = \log 2,$ $a_2 = \log 2 + \log 2$

$= \log 4,$ $a_3 = \log 4 + \log 2 = \log 8,$

etc. This is an arithmetic sequence

with $d = \log 2.$

97. The statement $\sum\limits_{i=1}^{n} kx_i = k^n \sum\limits_{i=1}^{n} x_i$ is _not_ true. Consider for $k = 2$, $n = 3$,

$$\sum_{i=1}^{3} 2i = 2 + 4 + 6 = 12,$$

while

$$2^3 \cdot \sum_{i=1}^{3} i = 8(1 + 2 + 3) = 48.$$

101. This formula is false. Consider

$$\left[\sum_{i=1}^{3} i\right]^2 = (1 + 2 + 3)^2 = 36,$$

while

$$\sum_{i=1}^{3} i^2 = 1 + 4 + 9 = 14.$$

Section 11.4   Geometric Sequences

Additional Examples

Example 1   Suppose the number of bacteria in a culture doubles each week and there were 1000 bacteria in the culture to begin with. What is the number of bacteria after 6 weeks?

Solution   The number of bacteria present after 6 weeks would be the term a_6 in a geometric series with $a_1 = 1000$ and $r = 2$. Thus,

$$a_6 = a_1 r^5 = 1000(2)^5,$$

or $a_6 = 32,000.$

Example 2   Find the value of

$$\sum_{i=3}^{12} 32\left(\tfrac{3}{4}\right)^i.$$

Solution   To evaluate this sum we note that we are summing the terms of a geometric sequence, where the first term of the sum is $32(3/4)^3$ and the last term is $32(3/4)^{12}$. Also, note that $r = 3/4$. If we

let $a_1 = 32(3/4)^3$ and $r = 3/4$, then the term $32(3/4)^{12}$ is a_{10}, since

$$a_{10} = a_1 r^9 = [32\left(\tfrac{3}{4}\right)^3]\left(\tfrac{3}{4}\right)^9$$

$$= 32\left(\tfrac{3}{4}\right)^{12}.$$

Hence,

$$\sum_{i=3}^{12} 32\left(\tfrac{3}{4}\right)^i = S_{10} = a_1\left(\frac{r^{10} - 1}{r - 1}\right)$$

$$= 32\left(\tfrac{3}{4}\right)^3\left[\frac{\left(\tfrac{3}{4}\right)^{10} - 1}{\left(\tfrac{3}{4}\right) - 1}\right]$$

$$= 32\left(\tfrac{27}{64}\right)\frac{\frac{3^{10}}{4^{10}} - 1}{\left(-\tfrac{1}{4}\right)}$$

$$= \frac{27}{2}\left(\frac{3^{10}}{4^{10}} - 1\right)\left(-\tfrac{4}{1}\right)$$

$$= -54\left(\frac{3^{10} - 4^{10}}{4^{10}}\right)$$

$$= 54\left(\frac{4^{10} - 3^{10}}{4^{10}}\right).$$

We have $4^{10} = 1,048,576$, $3^{10} = 59,049$, and $4^{10} - 3^{10} = 989,527$, so that

$$\sum_{i=3}^{12} 32\left(\tfrac{3}{4}\right)^i \approx 50.959,$$

as a decimal approximation.

Example 3   If money is placed on each square of an 8-by-8 checkerboard by placing 1¢ on the first square, 2¢ on the second square, 4¢ on the third square, and so on (each time doubling the amount placed on the previous square), find the amount of money placed on the 21st square. Determine the total amount of money that would be placed on the board.

Solution   The terms would be the terms of the geometric sequence having $a_1 = 1$ and $r = 2$. Hence, the amount of money needed for the 21st square would be

$a_{21} = a_1 r^{20} = 1(2)^{20}$, or

$a_{21} = 1,048,576$ cents.

That is, \$10,485.76 is needed for the 21st square.

The total amount of money needed to fill the board according to this plan is

$$S_{64} = a_1 \left(\frac{r^{64} - 1}{r - 1} \right)$$

$$S_{64} = 1 \left(\frac{2^{64} - 1}{2 - 1} \right)$$

$$S_{64} = 2^{64} - 1 \text{ cents.}$$

Using a calculator, 2^{64} registers as 1.8447×10^{19}, which would imply

$$S_{64} = \$184,470,000,000,000,000.00.$$

This is quite a handsome sum of money from such a meager start of 1¢.

Selected Solutions

1. $a_2 = 2 \cdot 3 = 6$

 $a_3 = 2 \cdot 3^2 = 18$

 $a_4 = 2 \cdot 3^3 = 54$

5. If $a_3 = 6$, $a_4 = 12$, then $r = \dfrac{a_4}{a_3}$

 $= \dfrac{12}{6} = 2$. Hence, $a_3 = 2a_2$ implies

 $a_2 = 3$, and $a_2 = 2a_1$ implies $a_1 = \dfrac{3}{2}$.

 The first 5 terms are $\dfrac{3}{2}$, 3, 6, 12, 24.

9. If $a_1 = -3$, $r = -5$, then using

 $a_n = a_1 r^{n-1}$, we have

 $a_5 = (-3)(-5)^4 = -3(625) = -1875$,

 and $a_n = -3(-5)^{n-1}$.

13. If $a_4 = 64$, $r = -4$, then

 $a_5 = a_4 r = 64(-4) = -256$, and

 $a_n = a_1 r^{n-1} = a_2 r^{n-2} = a_3 r^{n-3}$

 $a_n = a_4 r^{n-4} = 64(-4)^{n-4}$

 $= -(-4)^{n-1}$.

17. For $\dfrac{3}{4}$, $\dfrac{3}{2}$, 3, 6, 12, ... ,

 since $r = \dfrac{a_k}{a_{k-1}}$ for any k, $r = \dfrac{6}{3} = 2$.

 Then we have

 $a_n = a_1 r^{n-1} = \dfrac{3}{4}(2)^{n-1} = 3(2)^{n-3}$.

21. If $a_3 = -2$, $r = 3$, then since

 $a_3 = a_1 r^2$, we have $-2 = a_1(9)$, or

 $a_1 = -\dfrac{2}{9}$. Then

 $a_n = \left(-\dfrac{2}{9}\right)(3)^{n-1} = -2(3)^{n-3}$.

25. For 12, -6, 3, $-\dfrac{3}{2}$, ... , we

 obviously have $r = -\dfrac{1}{2}$. Using

 $S_n = a_1 \left(\dfrac{1 - r^n}{1 - r} \right)$, we have

 $S_5 = 12 \left[\dfrac{1 - \left(-\frac{1}{2}\right)^5}{1 + \frac{1}{2}} \right] = 12 \left[\dfrac{1 + \frac{1}{32}}{\frac{3}{2}} \right]$

 $S_5 = 12 \left[\dfrac{\frac{33}{32}}{\frac{3}{2}} \right] = 12 \left(\dfrac{33}{32} \right) \left(\dfrac{2}{3} \right) = \dfrac{33}{4}$.

27. If $a_1 = 8.423$ and $r = 2.859$, then

 $a_n = 8.423(2.859)^{n-1}$.

 Thus, the sum of the first five terms is

 $S_5 = \dfrac{5}{2}(a_1 + a_5)$

 $= \dfrac{5}{2}[8.423 + 8.423(2.859)^4]$

 $= \dfrac{5}{2}(8.423)[1 + (2.859)^4]$

 $= \dfrac{5}{2}(8.423)(67.8123306)$

 $S_5 \approx 1,427.958$

 rounded off to 3 decimals.

29. $\sum\limits_{i=1}^{4} 2^i = 2 + 4 + 8 + 16 = 30$

33. $\sum\limits_{i=3}^{6} 2^i = 2^3 + 2^4 + 2^5 + 2^6$
$= 8 + 16 + 32 + 64 = 120$

37. For 10, 100, 1000, 10,000, ... ,
since $r = \dfrac{a_k}{a_{k-1}}$ for any k, we have
$r = \dfrac{100}{10} = 10.$
The sum of the infinite geometric series does not exist since $|r| > 1$.

39. $12, 6, 3, \dfrac{3}{2}, \ldots$
In this sequence, $a_1 = 12$ and $r = \dfrac{1}{2}$.
Thus, $a_n = 12\left(\dfrac{1}{2}\right)^{n-1}$, so that the sum of the infinite sequence is
$\sum\limits_{n=1}^{\infty} 12\left(\dfrac{1}{2}\right)^{n-1} = \dfrac{12}{1 - \dfrac{1}{2}} = \dfrac{12}{\dfrac{1}{2}} = 24.$

41. For $16 + 4 + 1 + \ldots$, we have
$a_1 = 16$ and $r = \dfrac{4}{16} = \dfrac{1}{4}$. Thus,
$a_n = 16\left(\dfrac{1}{4}\right)^{n-1}.$
Then, $\sum\limits_{n=1}^{\infty} a_n = \sum\limits_{n=1}^{\infty} 16\left(\dfrac{1}{4}\right)^{n-1}$
$= \dfrac{16}{1 - \dfrac{1}{4}} = \dfrac{16}{\dfrac{3}{4}} = \dfrac{64}{3}.$

45. For $\dfrac{3}{4} + \dfrac{3}{8} + \dfrac{3}{16} + \ldots$, we have
$a_1 = \dfrac{3}{4}$ and $r = \dfrac{\dfrac{3}{8}}{\dfrac{3}{4}} = \dfrac{1}{2}.$
Hence $a_n = \dfrac{3}{4}\left(\dfrac{1}{2}\right)^{n-1}$, so that
$\sum\limits_{n=1}^{\infty} \dfrac{3}{4}\left(\dfrac{1}{2}\right)^{n-1} = \dfrac{\dfrac{3}{4}}{1 - \dfrac{1}{2}} = \dfrac{3}{4} \cdot 2 = \dfrac{3}{2}.$

47. $\dfrac{1}{3} - \dfrac{2}{9} + \dfrac{4}{27} - \dfrac{8}{81} + \ldots$ is the sum of the terms of a geometric sequence with $a_1 = \dfrac{1}{3}$ and $r = -\dfrac{2}{3}$. Hence, $a_n = \dfrac{1}{3}\left(\dfrac{-2}{3}\right)^{n-1}$, so the sum is
$\sum\limits_{n=1}^{\infty} \dfrac{1}{3}\left(\dfrac{-2}{3}\right)^{n-1} = \dfrac{\dfrac{1}{3}}{1 + \dfrac{2}{3}} = \dfrac{\dfrac{1}{3}}{\dfrac{5}{3}} = \dfrac{1}{5}.$

49. We have
$\sum\limits_{i=1}^{\infty} \left(\dfrac{1}{4}\right)^i = \dfrac{\dfrac{1}{4}}{1 - \dfrac{1}{4}} = \dfrac{1}{4} \cdot \dfrac{4}{3} = \dfrac{1}{3}.$

53. The distance traveled downward by the ball is
$d_1 = 10 + \dfrac{3}{4}(10) + \left(\dfrac{3}{4}\right)^2(10) + \ldots$
$+ \left(\dfrac{3}{4}\right)^{n-1}(10) + \ldots ,$
and the distance traveled upward on the bounces is
$d_2 = \dfrac{3}{4}(10) + \left(\dfrac{3}{4}\right)^2(10) + \ldots$
$+ \left(\dfrac{3}{4}\right)^{n-1}(10) + \ldots .$
$d_1 = \sum\limits_{n=1}^{\infty} 10\left(\dfrac{3}{4}\right)^{n-1}$ and $d_2 = d_1 - 10,$
$d_1 = \dfrac{10}{1 - \dfrac{3}{4}} = 40$ and $d_2 = 30.$
The total distance traveled by the ball is $d_1 + d_2 = 70$ m.

55. We have $a_1 = 400$, $a_2 = 400\left(\dfrac{3}{4}\right) = 300,$
$a_3 = 400\left(\dfrac{3}{4}\right)^2 = 225, \ldots,$
$a_n = 400\left(\dfrac{3}{4}\right)^{n-1}.$
Since it rotates 3/4 as many times as it did the previous minute, we never reach in a finite time a time when the number of revolutions (a_n) is zero. Thus, the answer is
$\sum\limits_{n=1}^{\infty} 400\left(\dfrac{3}{4}\right)^{n-1} = \dfrac{400}{1 - \dfrac{3}{4}} = \dfrac{400}{\dfrac{1}{4}}$
$= 1600$ revolutions.

57. Here $a_1 = 1$ and $r = 2$. Thus, the amount saved during January is

$$S = \sum_{n=1}^{31} a_1 r^{n-1} = \sum_{n=1}^{31} 2^{n-1} = \frac{1 - 2^{31}}{1 - 2}$$

$$S = 2^{31} - 1 = 2,147,483,648 - 1$$

$$S = \$2,147,483,647.$$

The amount saved on January 31 is $2^{30} = \$1,073,741,824.$

59. Let x = amount of fixer present to begin with. After 15 minutes $.98x$ fixer is removed, so $.02x$ fixer remains. After 30 minutes $(.98)(.02)x$ fixer is removed, so $(.02)(.02)x = (.02)^2 x$ fixer remains. Thus, after 1 hour, $(.02)^4 x$ fixer remains. That is, $.00000016x$ fixer remains. That is, $.000016\%$ fixer remains.

61. We have $P_1 = 6$, $P_2 = 3$, $P_3 = \frac{3}{2}$, $\ldots$, $P_n = 6\left(\frac{1}{2}\right)^{n-1}$, $\ldots$. Hence, the sum of the perimeters is

$$S = \sum_{n=1}^{\infty} 6\left(\frac{1}{2}\right)^{n-1} = \frac{6}{1 - \frac{1}{2}} = \frac{6}{\frac{1}{2}} = 12.$$

63. Let a_1 be the strength after the first step. a_1 has a strength of 80% of the initial strength (which was 100% pure).

$$a_1 = .8, \quad a_2 = (.8)(.8) = .64, \quad \ldots,$$

$$a_n = (.8)^n$$

Thus after nine drainings the strength is $(.8)^9 \approx .134 = 13.4\%$ chemical.

64. Suppose the half-life of a substance is 3 years. Let $A(t)$ be the number of molecules present at time t. We are given that initially ($t = 0$) there are 10^{15} molecules present.

That is, $A(0) = 10^{15}$. Then $A(3) = \frac{1}{2} \cdot A(0) = \frac{1}{2} \cdot 10^{15}$, $A(6) = \frac{1}{2} \cdot A(3)$, or $A(6) = \frac{1}{4} \cdot 10^{15}$, $A(9) = \frac{1}{2} \cdot A(6) = \frac{1}{8} \cdot 10^{15}$, $A(12) = \frac{1}{2} \cdot A(9) = \frac{1}{16} \cdot 10^{15}$, and finally $A(15) = \frac{1}{2} \cdot A(12) = \frac{1}{32} \cdot 10^{15}$. Hence, after 15 years there are $\frac{10^{15}}{32}$ molecules present.

We should see that a geometric sequence is formed by $a_1 = A(0)$, $a_2 = A(3)$, $a_3 = A(6)$, $\ldots$, $a_n = A(3(n-1))$, $\ldots$, with $r = \frac{1}{2}$. Thus, $A(15) = a_6 = A(0)\left(\frac{1}{2}\right)^5 = 10^{15}\left(\frac{1}{32}\right) = \frac{10^{15}}{32}$.

65. The value at the end of year 1 is $.80(100,000)$, so the value at the end of 6 years is $(.80)^6(100,000) = \$26,214.40$.

67. After the first fold the thickness is $2(.008)$, so the thickness after 12 such folds is $2^{12}(.008) = 32.768$ inches.

69. A constant sequence has this property. That is, if $a_n = a$ for each n, then $a, a, a, \ldots$, has $d = 0$ or $r = 1$.

73. If $a_2 = 64$ and $a_8 = 1$, then $a_n = a_1 r^{n-1}$, so $64 = a_1 r$ and $1 = a_1 r^7$. Dividing, we have $\frac{1}{64} = r^6$, which implies $r = \frac{\pm 1}{2}$. Then $64 = a_1\left(\pm\frac{1}{2}\right)$, or $a_1 = \pm 128$.

75.   log 6, log 36, log 1296,

log 1,697,616

$a_1 = \log 36 = \log 6^2 = 2 \log 6$

$a_2 = \log 1296 = 4 \log 6$

$a_3 = \log 1,697,616 = 8 \log 6$

Thus, $a_1 = \log 6$ and $a_n = 2^n \log 6$,

$r = 2$.

77.   Prove $a_n = a_1 r^{n-1}$.

Proof: Let $S(n)$ be the statement that for any given natural number n, the nth term in a geometric sequence with ratio r is

$a_n = a_1 r^{n-1}$.

Test $n = 1$: $a_1 = a_1 r^0 = a_1$, true.

Suppose the statement is true for the natural number k. Then $a_k = a_1 r^{k-1}$. Consider the next term a_{k+1}. By definition we have

$a_{k+1} = a_k \cdot r$. However,

$a_k = a_1 r^{k-1}$, which leads to

$a_{k+1} = (a_1 r^{k-1})r = a_1 r^k$

$= a_1 r^{(k+1)-1}$.

This implies that whenver the statement is true for k, it is also true for k + 1. Thus, the formula is true for all natural numbers.

Section 11.5   Series

Additional Examples

Example 1   Let $f(x) = x^2 + 1$ and let $x_1 = 1$, $x_2 = 3$, $x_3 = 5$, and $\Delta x = 2$.

Evaluate $\sum\limits_{i=1}^{3}$ for $f(x_i)\Delta x$.

Solution   We have

$f(x_1) = f(1) = 1^2 + 1 = 2$,

$f(x_2) = f(3) = 9 + 1 = 10$,

$f(x_3) = f(5) = 25 + 1 = 26$,

and hence,

$\sum\limits_{i=1}^{3} f(x_i)\Delta x = 2(2) + 10(2) + 26(2)$

$= 4 + 20 + 52 = 76$.

Example 2   Rewrite the series

$\sum\limits_{i=3}^{10} (3i^2 + i)$ as a series with

the index of summation beginning with i = 0.

Solution   We can accomplish this result if we replace each i by i + 3. This gives

$\sum\limits_{i=3}^{i=10} (3i^2 + i)$

$= \sum\limits_{1+3=3}^{i+3=10} [3(i+3)^2 + (i+3)]$

$= \sum\limits_{i=0}^{i=7} [3(i^2 + 6i + 9) + i + 3]$

$= \sum\limits_{i=0}^{7} (3i^2 + 19i + 30)$.

We can note that writing out the terms of each series, the series are identical.

Selected Solutions

1.   If $x_1 = -1$, $x_2 = 0$, $x_3 = 1$, $x_4 = 2$, and $x_5 = 3$, then

$\sum\limits_{i=1}^{4} (3x_i - 2) = (-5) + (-2) + (1) + (4)$.

5.   We have

$\sum\limits_{i=1}^{5} \dfrac{x_i - 1}{x_i + 3} = \dfrac{-2}{2} + \dfrac{-1}{3} + \dfrac{0}{4} + \dfrac{1}{5} + \dfrac{2}{6}$

$= -1 - \dfrac{1}{3} + 0 + \dfrac{1}{5} + \dfrac{1}{3}$.

9. If $f(x) = x^2 - 1$, $x_1 = 0$, $x_2 = 2$, $x_3 = 4$, $x_4 = 6$, and $\Delta x = .5$, then

$$\sum_{i=i}^{4} f(x_i)\Delta x = f(0)(.5) + f(2)(.5) +$$
$$f(4)(.5) + f(6)(.5)$$
$$= (-1)(.5) + 3(.5) +$$
$$15(.5) + 35(.5).$$

13. The series $8 + 6 + 4 \ldots + (-20)$ is an arithmetic series with $a_1 = 8$ and $d = -2$. Hence,

$$a_n = a_1 + (n-1)d$$
$$a_n = 8 + (n-1)(-2)$$
$$a_n = 10 - 2n.$$

We see that the term -20 occurs when $n = 15$. The summation notation for this series is

$$\sum_{i=1}^{15} (10 - 2i).$$

17. The series $7 + 14 + 28 + \ldots + 1792$ is a geometric series with $a_1 = 7$ and $r = 2$. Thus,

$$a_n = a_1 r^{n-1} = 7(2)^{n-1}.$$

We see that the term 1792 occurs when $7(2)^{n-1} = 1792$

$$2^{n-1} = 256,$$

or when $n = 9$. Hence, the summation notation for this series is

$$\sum_{i=1}^{9} 7(2)^{n-1}.$$

21. The series $4 + 9 + 16 + \ldots + 169$ is a series where $a_1 = 4 = 2^2$, $a_2 = 9 = 3^2$, $a_3 = 16 = 4^2$, or $a_n = (n+1)^2$. The term 169 occurs for $n = 12$. Hence, the summation notation for this series is

$$\sum_{i=1}^{12} (i+1)^2.$$

25. The series $2 + 4 + 8 + \ldots + 64$ is a series where $a_1 = 2$, $a_2 = 4 = 2^2$, $a_3 = 8 = 2^3$, so that $a_n = 2^n$. The term 64 occurs when $n = 6$. Hence, the series can be written as

$$\sum_{i=1}^{6} 2^i.$$

29. The series $\sum_{i=1}^{10} 2(3)^i$ can be written so the index starts with $i = 0$ by replacing each i by $i + 1$. This gives $\sum_{i=1}^{i=10} 2(3)^i = \sum_{i+1=1}^{i+1=10} 2(3)^{i+1}$

$$= \sum_{i=0}^{9} 2(3)^{i+1}.$$

33. Using the properties of series, we have

$$\sum_{i=1}^{5} (5i + 3) = 5 \sum_{i=1}^{5} i + 3 \sum_{i=1}^{5} 1$$
$$= (5)\frac{5(6)}{2} + (3)(5)$$
$$= 75 + 15 = 90.$$

37. We have

$$\sum_{i=1}^{4} (3i^3 + 2i - 4)$$
$$= 3 \sum_{i=1}^{4} i^3 + 2 \sum_{i=1}^{4} i - 4 \sum_{i=1}^{4} 1$$
$$= 3\frac{4^2(5)^2}{4} + 2\frac{4(5)}{2} - 4(4)$$
$$= 3 \cdot 4 \cdot 5^2 + 20 - 16$$
$$= 320 - 16 = 304.$$

41. We have

$$\left(3 + \frac{i}{n}\right)^2 = 9 + \frac{6i}{n} + \frac{i^2}{n^2}, \text{ so that}$$
$$\left(3 + \frac{i}{n}\right)^2 \frac{1}{n} = \frac{9}{n} + \frac{6i}{n^2} + \frac{i^2}{n^3}.$$

Hence,

$$\sum_{i=1}^{n} \left(3 + \frac{i}{n}\right)^2 \frac{1}{n}$$

$$= \frac{9}{n} \sum_{i=1}^{n} 1 + \frac{6}{n^2} \sum_{i=1}^{n} i + \frac{1}{n^3} \sum_{i=1}^{n} i^2$$

$$= \frac{9}{n}(n) + \frac{6}{n^2} \cdot \frac{n(n+1)}{2} +$$

$$\frac{1}{n^3} \frac{n(n+1)(2n+1)}{6}$$

$$= 9 + \frac{3(n+1)}{n} + \frac{(n+1)(2n+1)}{6n^2}.$$

Section 11.6   Counting Problems

Additional Examples

Example 1   A coin is flipped 9 times and each time the result of heads (H) or tails (T) is recorded. How many different sequences of heads and tails are possible?

Solution   There are 9 flips of the coin so there are 9 positions to fill in each sequence. On each flip the result could be either a head or a tail. We use the counting principle to calculate the result. The counting principle states that, "If one event can occur in m different ways and if a second event can occur in n different ways, then both events can occur in mn different ways."

For the event of filling the first term of the sequence, the event can occur in 2 different ways, either H or T. Similarly, the event of filling each of the 8 additional terms of the sequence can occur as either H or T. Thus, applying the counting principal successively, the number of different sequences possible is $2 \cdot 2 \cdot 2 \ldots \cdot 2$, 9 terms; that is, 2^9. We calculate that $2^9 = 512$. This means that there are 512 possible different sequences.

Example 2   How many permutations of the letters a, b, c, d, e, f, and g are there when taken (a) two at a time, (b) three at a time, or (c) four at a time.

Solution   Since we are interested in calculating the number of arrangements in which different ordering of the same letters are counted, we have the following: Since there are seven letters, the answers are

(a) $P(7, 2) = \frac{7!}{5!} = (7)(6) = 42$,

(b) $P(7, 3) = \frac{7!}{4!} = (7)(6)(5) = 210$,

(c) $P(7, 4) = \frac{7!}{3!} = (7)(6)(5)(4)$

$$= 840.$$

Example 3   A box contains 14 buttons, of which 9 are red and 5 are blue. Find the number of ways in which 5 buttons can be chosen so that (a) all 5 are red, (b) 3 are red and 2 are blue, and (c) 1 is red and 4 are blue.

Solution   In this example we note that order does not matter because if we choose 3 red and 2 blue buttons, the order in which they were chosen is not important. Hence, we make the following conclusions:

(a) the number of ways to choose 5 buttons so that all 5 are red is

$$\binom{9}{5} = \frac{9!}{4!5!} = \frac{(9 \cdot 8 \cdot 7 \cdot 6)5!}{(4 \cdot 3 \cdot 2 \cdot 1)5!} = 126,$$

since there are 9 red buttons in the box;

(b) the number of ways to choose 3 red and 2 blue buttons is

$$\binom{9}{3} \cdot \binom{5}{2} = \frac{9!}{6!3!} \cdot \frac{5!}{3!2!}$$

$$= \frac{(9 \cdot 8 \cdot 7)6!}{6!(3 \cdot 2 \cdot 1)} \frac{(5 \cdot 4)3!}{3!(2 \cdot 1)}$$

$$= \frac{9 \cdot 8 \cdot 7 \cdot 5 \cdot 4}{3 \cdot 2 \cdot 1 \cdot 2 \cdot 1}$$

$$= 840;$$

(c) the number of ways to choose 1 red and 4 blue buttons is

$$\binom{9}{1} \cdot \binom{5}{4} = \frac{9!}{8!1!} \cdot \frac{5!}{4!1!} = (9)(5)$$

$$= 45.$$

Example 4   Find all numbers n such that

$$\binom{n+3}{5} = 6\binom{n+1}{5}.$$

Solution   We have

$$\binom{n+3}{5} = \frac{(n+3)!}{(n+3-5)!5!}$$

$$= \frac{(n+3)!}{(n-2)!5!}$$

$$= \frac{(n+3)(n+2)(n+1)n(n-1)[(n-2)!]}{(n-2)!5!}$$

$$= \frac{(n+3)(n+2)(n+1)n(n-1)}{120},$$

and

$$\binom{n+1}{5} = \frac{(n+1)!}{(n+1-5)!5!}$$

$$= \frac{(n+1)!}{(n-4)!5!}$$

$$= \frac{(n+1)n(n-1)(n-2)(n-3)[(n-4)!]}{(n-4)!5!}$$

$$= \frac{(n+1)n(n-1)(n-2)(n-3)}{120}.$$

Hence, the equation $\binom{n+3}{5} = 6\binom{n+1}{5}$ implies that

$$\frac{(n+3)(n+2)(n+1)n(n-1)}{120}$$

$$= 6 \cdot \frac{(n+1)(n)(n-1)(n-2)(n-3)}{120},$$

$(n+3)(n+2) = 6(n-2)(n-3)$, after canceling like terms, so that

$$n^2 + 5n + 6 = 6(n^2 - 5n + 6)$$

$$n^2 + 5n + 6 = 6n^2 - 30n + 36$$

$$0 = 5n^2 - 35n + 30, \text{ or}$$

$$n^2 - 7n + 6 = 0, \qquad \text{dividing by 5}$$

$(n-6)(n-1) = 0,$

so that either n = 6, or n = 1. However, substituting n = 1 leads to the expressions $\binom{4}{5}$ and $\binom{2}{5}$, which are meaningless. Substituting n = 6 gives $\binom{9}{5} = 6\binom{7}{5}$, which is correct since

$$\binom{9}{5} = \frac{9!}{5!4!} = \frac{9 \cdot 8 \cdot 7 \cdot 6}{4 \cdot 3 \cdot 2 \cdot 1} = 126, \text{ and}$$

$$\binom{7}{5} = \frac{7!}{2!5!} = \frac{7 \cdot 6}{2} = 21, \text{ and}$$

$$6(21) = 126.$$

Thus, n = 6 is the only number satisfying the equation.

Selected Solutions

1. $P(7, 7) = \frac{7!}{(7-7)!} = \frac{7!}{0!} = 7! = 5040$

5. $P(10, 2) = \frac{10!}{8!} = \frac{10 \cdot 9 \cdot (8!)}{8!} = 90$

9. $P(7, 1) = \frac{7!}{6!} = \frac{7 \cdot (6!)}{6!} = 7$

13. $\binom{6}{5} = \frac{6!}{(6-5)!5!} = \frac{6!}{1!5!} = \frac{6!}{5!} = 6$

17. $\binom{15}{4} = \frac{15!}{11!4!} = \frac{15 \cdot 14 \cdot 13 \cdot 12(11!)}{4 \cdot 3 \cdot 2 \cdot 1(11!)} = 1365$

21. $\binom{14}{1} = \frac{14!}{13!1!} = 14$

25. $6! = 720$

29. $5 \cdot 3 \cdot 2 = 30$

31. Since order is unimportant, $5! = 120$.

33. $2 \cdot 2 = 4$ Two choices for the order of the modern work and then two choices for the order of the romantic.

37. The letters in Mississippi can be arranged in

$$\frac{11!}{1!4!4!2!} = 34,650 \text{ ways,}$$

since the word has m once, s four times, i four times, and p twice.

41. If there are 4 blue, 3 green, and 2 red books, then the answers are

(a) $9! = 362,880$ ways,

(b) $3! = 6$ ways to arrange the three colors, and

(c) $\dfrac{9!}{4!3!2!} = 1260$ ways.

45. (a) A group of 3 can be selected from a group of 12 in $\binom{12}{3} = 220$ ways.

(b) The group not selected is size 9. The answer is $\binom{12}{9} = 220$ ways.

49. There are $\binom{5}{2} = 10$ different 2-card <u>combinations</u> possible.

53. The answers are

(a) $\binom{9}{3} = \dfrac{9!}{6!3!} = \dfrac{9 \cdot 8 \cdot 7}{3 \cdot 2} = 84$,

(b) $\binom{5}{3} = \dfrac{5!}{2!3!} = \dfrac{5 \cdot 4}{2 \cdot 1} = 10$,

(c) $\binom{5}{2}\binom{4}{1} = 10 \cdot 4 = 40$

(d) In this case we choose 2 members in addition to the mayor from the 8 remaining members. The answer is $\binom{8}{2} = 28$.

55. The number of 5-card hands that are possible from a deck of 52 cards is $\binom{52}{5} = 2,598,960$.

57. There is 1 royal flush in each of 4 suits. The answer is 4.

59. A flush consists of 5 cards from the same suit. From each suit there are $\binom{13}{5}$ possible flushes. There are 4 suits, so the answer is $4\binom{13}{5} = 5148$.

61. The letters in the word TOUGH are all distinct, so the answer is $P(5, 5) = 5! = 120$.

65. Solve $P(n, 3) = 8P(n - 1, 2)$.

We have $P(n, 3) = n!/(n - 3)!$ and

$P(n - 1, 2) = (n - 1)!/(n - 3)!$.

Thus, $P(n, 3) = 8P(n - 1, 2)$ becomes

$n!/(n - 3)! = 8(n - 1)!/(n - 3)!$

$n! = 8(n - 1)!$

$\dfrac{n!}{(n - 1)!} = 8$,

or $n = 8$.

67. Solve $\binom{n + 2}{4} = 15\binom{n}{4}$,

we have $\binom{n + 2}{4} = \dfrac{(n + 2)!}{(n + 2 - 4)!4!} = \dfrac{(n + 2)!}{(n - 2)!4!}$

$= \dfrac{(n+2)(n+1)n(n-1)}{24}$, and

$\binom{n}{4} = \dfrac{n!}{(n-4)!4!} = \dfrac{n(n-1)(n-2)(n-3)}{24}$.

Thus, we have

$\dfrac{(n+2)(n+1)n(n-1)}{24} = 15\dfrac{n(n-1)(n-2)(n-3)}{24}$,

or $(n+2)(n+1) = 15(n-2)(n-3)$

$n^2 + 3n + 2 = 15n^2 - 75n + 90$

$0 = 14n^2 - 78n + 88$,

or $7n^2 - 39n + 44 = 0$

$(7n-11)(n-4) = 0$.

Hence, $n = \dfrac{11}{7}$ or $n = 4$.

The only valid solution is $n = 4$.

69. Prove $P(n, n - 1) = P(n, n)$.

Proof: $P(n, n - 1) = \dfrac{n!}{(n - (n - 1))!} = n!$,

and $P(n, n) = \dfrac{n!}{(n - n)!} = \dfrac{n!}{0!} = n!$.

70. Prove $P(n, 1) = n$.

Proof: $P(n, 1) = \dfrac{n!}{(n - 1)!} = \dfrac{n(n - 1)!}{(n - 1)!}$

$= n$.

71. Prove $P(n, 0) = 1$.

Proof: $P(n, 0) = \dfrac{n!}{(n - 0)!} = \dfrac{n!}{n!} = 1$.

72. Prove $\binom{n}{n} = 1$.

    Proof: $\binom{n}{n} = \frac{n!}{(n-n)!\,n!} = \frac{n!}{0!\,n!} = 1$.

73. Prove $\binom{n}{0} = 1$.

    Proof: $\binom{n}{0} = \frac{n!}{(n-0)!\,0!} = \frac{n!}{n!} = 1$.

74. Prove $\binom{n}{n-1} = n$.

    Proof: $\binom{n}{n-1} = \frac{n!}{[n-(n-1)]!\,(n-1)!}$

    $ = \frac{n!}{1!\,(n-1)!} = n$.

75. Prove $\binom{n}{n-r} = \binom{n}{r}$.

    Proof: $\binom{n}{r} = \frac{n!}{(n-r)!\,r!}$, and

    $\binom{n}{n-r} = \frac{n!}{(n-(n-r))!\,(n-r)!}$

    $\phantom{\binom{n}{n-r}} = \frac{n!}{r!\,(n-r)!}$

77. Prove that for $2 \le r \le n-2$,

    $\binom{n}{r} = \binom{n-2}{r-2} + 2\binom{n-2}{r-1} + \binom{n-2}{r}$.

    Proof: We have

    $\binom{n-2}{r-2} = \frac{(n-2)!}{(n-2-r+2)!\,(r-2)!}$

    $\phantom{\binom{n-2}{r-2}} = \frac{(n-2)!}{(n-r)!\,(r-2)!}$,

    $2\binom{n-2}{r-1} = \frac{2(n-2)!}{(n-r-1)!\,(r-1)!}$, and

    $\binom{n-2}{r} = \frac{(n-2)!}{(n-r-2)!\,r!}$.

    Then, we see that the sum on the right is

    $\frac{(n-2)!}{(n-r)!\,(r-2)!} + \frac{2(n-2)!}{(n-r-1)!\,(r-1)!} +$

    $ + \frac{(n-2)!}{(n-r-2)!\,r!}$

    $= \frac{(n-2)!}{(n-r)!\,r!}[(r-1)r + 2r(n-r) + (n-r-1)(n-r)]$

    $= \frac{(n-2)!}{(n-r)!\,r!}[r^2 - r + 2rn - 2r^2 + n^2 2rn + r^2 - n + r]$

    $= \frac{(n-2)!}{(n-r)!\,r!}[n^2 - n]$

    $= \frac{(n-2)!}{(n-r)!\,r!}(n-1)n = \frac{n!}{(n-r)!\,r!} = \binom{n}{r}$.

79. Prove $\binom{n}{1} + \binom{n}{2} + \ldots + \binom{n}{n} = 2^n + 1$.

    Proof: The binomial theorem gives

    $(a+b)^n = a^n + \binom{n}{1}a^{n-1}b +$

    $ \binom{n}{2}a^{n-2}b^2 + \ldots + \binom{n}{n}b^n$.

    If we let $a = 1$ and $b = 1$, we have

    $2^n = 1 + \binom{n}{1} + \binom{n}{2} + \ldots + \binom{n}{n}$, or

    $2^n - 1 = \binom{n}{1} + \binom{n}{2} + \ldots + \binom{n}{n}$.

Section 11.7   Basics of Probability

Additional Examples

Example 1   Four cards are drawn from a standard deck of 52 cards. Find the probability that (a) all 4 are diamonds, and (b) all 4 are queens.

Solution   (a) The number of ways of drawing 4 cards from a deck of 52 is $\binom{52}{4}$. Since 13 of the cards are diamonds, the number of ways of drawing 4 diamonds is $\binom{13}{4}$. Hence, the probability of drawing 4 diamonds is

$$\frac{\binom{13}{4}}{\binom{52}{4}} = \frac{\frac{13!}{9!\,4!}}{\frac{52}{48!\,4!}} = \frac{\frac{(13)(12)(11)(10)}{(4)(3)(2)(1)}}{\frac{(52)(51)(50)(49)}{(4)(3)(2)(1)}}$$

$$= \frac{(13)(12)(11)(10)}{(52)(51)(50)(49)}$$

$$= \frac{11}{4165}.$$

(b) Since 4 of the 52 cards are queens, the number of ways of drawing 4 queens is $\binom{4}{4} = 1$. Hence, the probability of drawing 4 queens is

$$\frac{1}{\binom{52}{4}} = \frac{1}{\frac{52!}{48!\,4!}} = \frac{4 \cdot 3 \cdot 2 \cdot 1}{52 \cdot 51 \cdot 50 \cdot 49}$$

$$= \frac{1}{13 \cdot 17 \cdot 25 \cdot 49}$$

$$= \frac{1}{270,725}.$$

Example 2   A pair of dice is thrown. Find (a) the probability of a 10 or an 11 being thrown, and (b) the probability of no higher than a 5 being thrown.

Solution   (a)   Let $P(n)$ denote the probability that n results from the throw of the dice. Then we have that the probability of a 10 or an 11 is thrown is $P(10)$ or $P(11)$. Since the faces on dice have the numbers 1, 2, 3, 4, 5, and 6, the sum of the numbers on a pair of dice can be any number 2 through 12. Each outcome is not equally likely, however. For example, a 2 can occur in only one way, that each die has the 1 showing. On the other hand, an 8 can occur in several possible ways: (2, 6), (3, 5), (4, 4), (5, 3), (6, 2), where the ordered pair denotes (die 1, die 2). Perhaps the best method is to construct a table showing the possible outcomes.

Die 1↓ \ Die 2→	1	2	3	4	5	6
1	2	3	4	5	6	7
2	3	4	5	6	7	8
3	4	5	6	7	8	9
4	5	6	7	8	9	10
5	6	7	8	9	10	11
6	7	8	9	10	11	12

We list the possible outcomes 1 to 6 for die 1 in the column on the left and the possible outcomes 1 to 6 for die 2 in the row at the top. Then the table is filled with the sums of the dice. We note that there are 36 total outcomes possible. We can also see from the table that 5 of the possible outcomes are a 10 or an 11. Hence,

the probability of a 10 or an 11 being thrown is

$$\frac{\text{number of successful outcomes}}{\text{total number of outcomes}} = \frac{5}{36}.$$

The fraction $\frac{5}{36}$ as a decimal is $.13888\ldots$, so we can conclude that throwing a pair of dice results in a 10 or an 11 approximately 14% of the time.   (b)   To calculate the probability that no higher than a 5 be thrown, we use the table again to calculate

$$P(2) = \frac{1}{36}, \quad P(3) = \frac{2}{36}, \quad P(4) = \frac{3}{36}, \text{ and}$$

$$P(5) = \frac{4}{36}.$$

Hence, the probability of no higher than a 5 be thrown is

$$\frac{\text{number of successful outcomes}}{\text{total outcomes}} = \frac{1+2+3+4}{36}$$

$$= \frac{10}{36}$$

$$= \frac{5}{18}.$$

We can say that no higher than a 5 is thrown approximately 28% of the time, since $\frac{5}{18} = .27777\ldots$.

Example 3   What is the probability of drawing an ace on each of 3 successive draws from a standard deck of 52 cards if (a) after each draw the card drawn is placed back in the deck and the deck is reshuffled, and (b) the card drawn on each draw is not replaced?

Solution   Since there are 4 aces in the deck of cards, the probability of drawing an ace on the first draw is $\frac{4}{52} = \frac{1}{13}$. Then we have the following:

(a) If the card drawn is replaced, then each time a card is to be drawn, the result is independent of any previous event. Hence, the probability of drawing an ace on 3 successive draws is

$$\left(\frac{4}{52}\right)\left(\frac{4}{52}\right)\left(\frac{4}{52}\right) = \frac{1}{2197}.$$

(b)   If a card is drawn and not replaced, there is a change in the calculation. On the first draw, the probability of drawing an ace is $\frac{4}{52}$. Since the drawn card is not replaced into the deck, and if the drawn card is an ace, then there are 3 aces left in a total of 51 cards. The probability of drawing an ace on the second draw is $\frac{3}{51}$. If the second draw gives an ace, then 2 aces and 50 cards remain. The probability of drawing an ace on the third draw is $\frac{2}{50}$. Hence, the probability of drawing an ace 3 times in succession when the cards drawn are not replaced is

$$\left(\frac{4}{52}\right)\left(\frac{3}{51}\right)\left(\frac{2}{50}\right) = \frac{24}{132,600} = \frac{1}{5525}.$$

Selected Solutions

1. Since both sides of the coin are heads, the sample space has only 1 outcome: $S = \{H\}$.

5. There are 8 possible outcomes.
    {TTT, TTF, TFT, FTT, TFF, FTF, FFT, FFF}

9. In exercise 4, the sample space is {(1, 2), (1, 3), (1, 4), (1, 5), (2, 3), (2, 4), (2, 5), (3, 4), (3, 5), (4, 5)}.
    (a)   There is only one possibility: {(2, 4)}.
    The total number of outcomes from the sample space is
    $\binom{5}{2} = \frac{5!}{3!\,2!} = \frac{5 \cdot 4}{2} = 10$.
    Hence, the probability is $\frac{1}{10}$.
    (b)   The possible outcomes are (1, 3), (1, 5), (3, 5). The probability is $\frac{3}{10}$.

(c)   There is no possibility of drawing the same number twice. The probability is 0.
(d)   The possible outcomes are (1, 2), (1, 4), (2, 3), (2, 5), (3, 4), (4, 5).
The probability is $\frac{6}{10} = \frac{3}{5}$.

11. Box contains 3 yellow, 4 white, and 8 blue.
    (a) $P(\text{yellow}) = \frac{3}{3 + 4 + 8} = \frac{3}{15} = \frac{1}{5}$
    (b) $P(\text{blue}) = \frac{8}{15}$
    (c) $P(\text{black}) = 0$
    (d)   We have, $P(\text{yellow}) = \frac{1}{5}$ and $P(\text{not yellow}) = \frac{4}{5}$, so the odds in favor of drawing a yellow are
    $\frac{1/5}{4/5} = \frac{1}{5} \cdot \frac{5}{4} = \frac{1}{4}$, or 1 to 4.
    (e)   We have $P(\text{blue}) = \frac{8}{15}$ and $P(\text{not blue}) = \frac{7}{15}$, so the odds against drawing a blue marble are
    $\frac{7/15}{8/15} = \frac{7}{15} \cdot \frac{15}{8} = \frac{7}{8}$, or 7 to 8.

13. The possible events are {1, 4}, {2, 3}. The probability of the sum being 5 is $\frac{2}{10} = \frac{1}{5}$. The probability of the sum not being 5 is $\frac{8}{10} = \frac{4}{5}$. Thus, the odds that the sum is 5 are $P(\text{sum } 5)$ to $P(\text{sum not } 5)$
    $= \frac{1/5}{4/5} = \frac{1}{4}$, or 1 to 4.

17. (a) $P(\text{uncle}) = \frac{2}{10}$ and $P(\text{brother}) = \frac{3}{10}$. Then
    $P(\text{uncle}) + P(\text{brother}) = \frac{5}{10} = \frac{1}{2}$.
    (b) $P(\text{cousin}) = \frac{4}{10}$, then
    $P(\text{brother}) + P(\text{cousin}) = \frac{3}{10} + \frac{4}{10} = \frac{7}{10}$.
    (c) $P(\text{mother}) = \frac{1}{10}$, then
    $P(\text{brother}) + P(\text{mother}) = \frac{3}{10} + \frac{1}{10}$
    $= \frac{4}{10} = \frac{2}{5}$.

21. $P(\text{yellow}) = \frac{3}{15} = \frac{1}{5}$, $P(\text{white}) = \frac{4}{15}$,

   $P(\text{blue}) = \frac{8}{15}$

   (a) $P(\text{yellow}) + P(\text{white}) = \frac{7}{15}$

   (b) $P(\text{yellow}) + P(\text{blue}) = \frac{3}{15} + \frac{8}{15} = \frac{11}{15}$

   (c) Since there are no red marbles,

   $P(\text{red}) = 0$. Hence,

   $P(\text{red}) + P(\text{white}) = 0 + \frac{4}{15} = \frac{4}{15}$.

25. The probability of the score being
   in the 90's is $.04 + .02 = .06$.

29. The probability of a score in the
   70's is $S = .28 + .22 = .50$, and
   the probability of a score not in
   the 70's is $1 - .50 = .50$. Hence,
   the odds against a score in the 70's
   is $\frac{.50}{.50} = 1$, or 1 to 1.

33. The probability that it will take
   at least 2 hours is
   $P(2) + P(3) + P(4) + P(5) + P(6)$
   $= .10 + .20 + .40 + .10 + .15$
   $= .95$.

37. The probability that the purchase
   is $20 or more is
   $.11 + .09 + .07 + .08 + .03 = .38$.

41. The probability of no more than 4
   good toes is $1 - P(\text{exactly 5 good}$
   $\text{toes})$, or $1 - .10 = .90$.

43. If $E = \{S_1, S_2, S_5\}$, then
   $P(E) = P(S_1) + P(S_2) + P(S_5)$
   $\qquad = .17 + .03 + .21$
   $\qquad = .41$.

45. We have $E \cap F = \{S_5\}$, so that
   $P(E \cap F) = .21$.

47. We have $E' = \{S_3, S_4, S_6\}$ and
   $F' = \{S_1, S_2, S_3, S_6\}$, so that
   $E' \cup F' = \{S_1, S_2, S_3, S_4, S_6\}$.
   Hence,
   $P(E' \cup F') = 1 - P(S_5)$
   $\qquad\qquad\quad = 1 - .21$
   $\qquad\qquad\quad = .79$.

Chapter 11   Review Exercises

Selected Solutions

1. Let S_n be $1 + 3 + 5 + \ldots +$
   $(2n - 1) = n^2$.
   Proof: $n = 1$ gives $1 = 1^2$.
   Suppose $1 + 3 + 5 + \ldots + (2k - 1) = k^2$
   is true, which is S_k. Adding the
   $(k + 1)$st term to both sides gives
   $1 + 3 + 5 + \ldots + (2k - 1) + (2k + 1)$
   $= k^2 + 2k + 1 = (k + 1)^2$.
   Thus, if the formula is true for
   $n = k$, then it is true for $n = k + 1$.
   This implies the formula is true
   for all natural numbers n.

3. Let S_n be $2^2 + 4^2 + 6^2 + \ldots + (2n)^2$
   $= \frac{2n(n+1)(2n+1)}{3}$.

   Proof: Test $n = 1$.
   $2^2 = 4$ on the left-hand side, and
   $\frac{2 \cdot 1(1+1)(2+1)}{3} = \frac{2(2)(3)}{3} = 4$ for the
   right-hand side. The formula is
   true for $n = 1$.
   Suppose the formula is true for
   some natural number k. Then,
   $2^2 + 4^2 + 6^2 + \ldots + (2k)^2$
   $= \frac{2k(k + 1)(2k + 1)}{3}$.
   Adding the $(k + 1)$st term, $[2(k+1)]^2$,
   to both sides gives
   $2^2 + 4^2 + 6^2 + \ldots + (2k)^2 + [2(k + 1)]^2$
   $= \frac{2k(k + 1)(2k + 1)}{3} + [(2(k + 1)]^2$

$$= (k+1)\left[\frac{2k(2k+1)}{3} + 4(k+1)\right]$$

$$= (k+1)\left[\frac{4k^2 + 2k + 12(k+1)}{3}\right]$$

$$= \frac{(k+1)}{3}(4k^2 + 14k + 12)$$

$$= \frac{k+1}{3}[2(k+2)(2k+3)]$$

$$= \frac{2(k+1)(k+2)(2k+3)}{3}$$

$$= \frac{2(k+1)[(k+1)+1][2(k+1)+1]}{3}.$$

Thus, if the formula is true for k, then it will be true for k + 1. This implies the formula S_n is true for all natural numbers.

5. $S_n = 1 \cdot 4 + 2 \cdot 9 + 3 \cdot 16 + \ldots + n(n+1)^2$

$$= \frac{n(n+1)(n+2)(3n+5)}{12}$$

Proof: For n = 1; $1 \cdot 4 = 4$,

and $\frac{1(2)(3)(8)}{12} = 4.$

The formula is true for n = 1. Suppose $1 \cdot 4 + 2 \cdot 9 + \ldots + k(k+1)^2$

$$= \frac{k(k+1)(k+2)(3k+5)}{12}.$$

That is, suppose the formula is true for k. Then, we have

$1 \cdot 4 + 2 \cdot 9 + \ldots + k(k+1)^2 +$

$\qquad (k+1)(k+2)^2$

$$= \frac{k(k+1)(k+2)(3k+5)}{12} +$$

$\qquad (k+1)(k+2)^2$

$$= (k+1)(k+2)\left\{\frac{k(3k+5) + 12(k+2)}{12}\right\}$$

$$= \frac{(k+1)(k+2)(3k^2 + 17k + 24)}{12}$$

$$= \frac{(k+1)(k+2)(k+3)(3k+8)}{12}$$

$$= \frac{(k+1)(k+2)(k+3)(3(k+1)+5)}{12}.$$

Hence, S_{k+1} is true whenever S_k is true.

9. $\left(3\sqrt{x} - \frac{1}{\sqrt{x}}\right)^5$

$$= (3\sqrt{x})^5 + 5(3\sqrt{x})^4\left(-\frac{1}{\sqrt{x}}\right) +$$

$$10(3\sqrt{x})^3\left(-\frac{1}{\sqrt{x}}\right)^2 + 10(3\sqrt{x})^2\left(-\frac{1}{\sqrt{x}}\right)^3 +$$

$$5(3\sqrt{x})\left(-\frac{1}{\sqrt{x}}\right)^4 + \left(-\frac{1}{\sqrt{x}}\right)^5$$

$$= 243(\sqrt{x})^5 - 405(\sqrt{x})^3 + 270\sqrt{x} -$$

$$\frac{90}{\sqrt{x}} + \frac{15}{(\sqrt{x})^3} - \frac{1}{(\sqrt{x})^5}.$$

13. $3^{16} + \binom{16}{15}3^{15}x + \binom{16}{14}3^{14}x^2 +$

$\qquad \binom{16}{13}3^{13}x^3$

15. If $a_n = 2(n+3)$, then

$a_1 = 2(1+3) = 8$, $a_2 = 2(2+3) = 10$,

$a_3 = 2(3+3) = 12$, $a_4 = 2(4+3) = 14$,

and $a_5 = 2(5+3) = 16.$

17. If $a_1 = 5$, $a_2 = 3$, and for $n \geq 3$

$a_n = a_{n-1} - a_{n-2}$, then

$a_3 = 3 - 5 = -2$, $a_4 = -2 - 3 = -5$,

and $a_5 = -5 - (-2) = -3.$

21. If $a_1 = 3 - \sqrt{5}$ and $a_2 = 4$, then

$d = a_2 - a_1 = 4 - (3 - \sqrt{5}) = 1 + \sqrt{5}.$

Hence,

$a_3 = a_2 + d = 5 + \sqrt{5},$

$a_4 = a_3 + d = 6 + 2\sqrt{5}$, and

$a_5 = a_4 + d = 7 + 3\sqrt{5}.$

25. $a_1 = -3$ and $a_2 \cdot = 4$ in a geometric sequence implies that

$$r = \frac{a_2}{a_1} = -\frac{4}{3}.$$

Hence, $a_3 = 4\left(-\frac{4}{3}\right) = \frac{-16}{3},$

$a_4 = \frac{-16}{3}(-\frac{4}{3}) = \frac{64}{9}$,

$a_5 = \frac{64}{9}(-\frac{4}{3}) = \frac{-256}{27}$.

27. If $a_6 = -4$, $a_{17} = 51$, then using

$a_n = a_1 + (n-1)d$, we have

$a_6 = -4 = a_1 + 5d$, and

$a_{17} = 51 = a_1 + 16d$.

Subtract: $55 = 11d$, so that $d = 5$.
Then, substituting, we have
$-4 = a_1 + 25$, or $a_1 = -29$.
Then

$a_{20} = -29 + 19(5) = -29 + 95$

$= 66$.

29. We have $a_n = a_1 + (n-1)d$, so that

for $a_1 = 6$, $d = 2$, we find that

$a_8 = 6 + 7(2) = 20$.

31. If $a_1 = 6x - 9$ and $a_2 = 5x + 1$, then

$d = a_2 - a_1 = (5x + 1) - (6x - 9)$

$= 10 - x$.

Then

$a_8 = a_1 + 7d = (6x - 9) + 7(10 - x)$

$= 70 - 9 + 6x - 7x = 61 - x$.

33. If $a_1 = 2$ and $d = 3$, then $a_n = a_1 +$

$(n-1)d$, so that

$a_{12} = 2 + 11(3) = 35$.

Hence, using $S_n = \frac{n}{2}(a_1 + a_n)$,

we have

$S_{12} = \frac{12}{2}(2 + 35) = 6(37) = 222$.

37. If $a_2 = 3125$ and $r = \frac{1}{5}$, then

$a_3 = \frac{3125}{5} = 625$, $a_4 = \frac{625}{5} = 125$,

and $a_5 = \frac{125}{5} = 25$.

41. If $a_1 = 1$ and $r = 2$, then using

$a_n = a_1 r^{n-1}$, we have

$S_4 = \sum_{n=1}^{4} a_n = \sum_{n=1}^{4} 2^{n-1}$

$= 1 + 2 + 4 + 8 = 15$.

45. The sum $20 + 15 + \frac{45}{4} + \frac{135}{16} + \ldots$ is

a geometric series with $a_1 = 20$ and

$r = \frac{15}{20} = \frac{3}{4}$. The infinite sum is

$\sum_{n=1}^{\infty} 20(\frac{3}{4})^{n-1} = \frac{20}{1 - \frac{3}{4}} = \frac{20}{\frac{1}{4}} = 80$.

49. $\sum_{i=1}^{4} \frac{2}{i} = \frac{2}{1} + \frac{2}{2} + \frac{2}{3} + \frac{2}{4}$

$= 3 + \frac{2}{3} + \frac{1}{2} = \frac{18 + 4 + 3}{6}$

$= \frac{25}{6}$

53. $\sum_{i=1}^{4} \frac{i+1}{i} = \frac{2}{1} + \frac{3}{2} + \frac{4}{3} + \frac{5}{4}$

$= \frac{24 + 18 + 16 + 15}{12}$

$= \frac{73}{12}$

55. For $\sum_{i=1}^{10,000} i = 1 + 2 + 3 + \ldots + 10,000$,

remember the formula $1 + 2 + 3 + \ldots + n$

$= \frac{n(n+1)}{2}$. Then

$\sum_{i=1}^{10,000} i = 1 + 2 + 3 + \ldots + 10,000$

$= \frac{10,000(10,001)}{2}$

$= (5000)(10,001)$

$= 50,005,000$.

57. $\sum_{i=1}^{4} 8 \cdot 2^i = 8 \sum_{i=1}^{4} 2^i$

$= 8(2 + 4 + 8 + 16)$

$= 8(30)$

$= 240$

59. $\displaystyle\sum_{i=1}^{\infty} -10\left(\frac{5}{2}\right)^i$ does not exist since $r = \frac{5}{2} > 1.$

61. If $x_1 = 0$, $x_2 = 2$, $x_3 = 4$, $x_4 = 6$, and $x_5 = 8$, then $\displaystyle\sum_{i=1}^{5}(x_i^2 - 4)$ $= -4 + 0 + 12 + 32 + 60 = 100.$

65. The series $4 - 1 - 6 - \ldots - 66$ is an arithmetic sum with $a_1 = 4$ and $d = -5$. Since $a_n = a_1 + (n-1)d$, or $a_n = 4 + (n-1)(-5) = 9 - 5n$, the term -66 corresponds to $n = 15$, since $9 - 5(15) = 9 - 75 = -66$. Hence, the summation notation for this sum is

$\displaystyle\sum_{i=1}^{15}(9 - 5i).$

69. If we want the index of the summation to start at -2, we replace each i by $i + 3$. This gives

$\displaystyle\sum_{\substack{i=1 \\ i+3=1}}^{\substack{i=8 \\ i+3=8}}(3 + 2i) = \sum[3 + 2(i+3)]$

$= \displaystyle\sum_{i=-2}^{5}(9 + 2i).$

73. We have

$\displaystyle\sum_{i=1}^{7}(6i + 2) = 6\sum_{i=1}^{7}i + 2\sum_{i=1}^{7}1$

$= (6)\left(\frac{7 \cdot 8}{2}\right) + 2(7)$

$= 6(28) + 14$

$= 182.$

75. We have

$\displaystyle\sum_{i=1}^{4}(i^2 + 2i) = \sum_{i=1}^{4}i^2 + 2\sum_{i=1}^{4}i$

$= \dfrac{4(5)(8+1)}{6} + 2\left(\dfrac{4 \cdot 5}{2}\right)$

$= 30 + 20 = 50.$

77. Since $P(n, r) = \dfrac{n!}{(n-r)!}$, we have

$P(9, 2) = \dfrac{9!}{7!} = 9 \cdot 8 = 72.$

81. Since $\dbinom{n}{r} = \dfrac{n!}{(n-r)!\,r!}$, we have

$\dbinom{10}{5} = \dfrac{10!}{5!\,5!} = \dfrac{10 \cdot 9 \cdot 8 \cdot 7 \cdot 6}{5 \cdot 4 \cdot 3 \cdot 2 \cdot 1}$

$= 2 \cdot 9 \cdot 2 \cdot 7 = 252.$

85. The sample space for the roll of a single die is $S = \{1, 2, 3, 4, 5, 6\}.$

89. If the balls in one urn are labeled 3, 5, 7, 9, and 11, and if the second urn contains 4 red and 2 green balls, then the sample space is $S = \{(3, R), (3, G), (5, R), (5, G), (7, R), (7, G), (9, R), (9, G), (11, R), (11, G)\}.$

91. The event F, that the second ball is green, is $F = \{(3, G), (5, G), (7, G), (9, G), (11, G)\}.$

93. The statement "a customer buys neither" means that the customer does not buy a typewriter and the customer does not buy a copier. The symbol $\cap$ goes with the conjunction "and." Thus, the desired statement is $E' \cap F'.$

97. There are 6 red face cards and 2 additional queens. Hence, if E is the event of drawing a red face card or a queen, we see that there are 8 successes and $52 - 8 = 44$ possible failures. Thus,

$P(E) = \dfrac{8}{52} = \dfrac{2}{13}$ and $P(E') = \dfrac{44}{52} = \dfrac{11}{13}.$

The odds in favor of event E are $\dfrac{P(E)}{P(E')} = \dfrac{2/13}{11/13} = \dfrac{2}{11}.$ We say the odds are 2 to 11.

99. Using the given table, the proba-
    bility of at least 3 defective
    filters is
    $$P(3) + P(4) + P(5) = .12 + .08 + .06$$
    $$= .26.$$

101. There are 12 face cards and 4 aces.
     Hence, if E is the event of drawing
     a face card or an ace, then
     $$P(E) = \frac{16}{52} = \frac{4}{13}.$$

105. There are 13 diamonds, but none of
     them is black. Hence, it is im-
     possible to draw a card that is a
     diamond and black. The probability
     is 0.

Chapter 11   Test

1. Use mathematical induction to prove that for every natural number n

    $1 + 3 + 5 + \ldots + (2n - 1) = n^2$.

2. Use mathematical induction to prove that for every natural number n

    $3 + 3^2 + 3^3 + \ldots + 3^n = \frac{3}{2}(3^n - 1)$.

3. Use mathematical induction to prove that for every natural number n

    $3^{3n} - 1$ is divisible by 13.

4. Use the binomial theorem to expand $(2x - y)^4$.

5. Use the binomial theorem to expand $(\frac{3}{x} + 2x^2)^3$.

6. Find the first three terms of $(\frac{1}{a} - \frac{\sqrt{b}}{2})^{12}$.

7. Find the term involving x^{10} of $(2y + x^2)^{10}$.

8. Write the first five terms of the sequence whose nth term is $a_n = \frac{n^2 + 1}{2n}$.

9. Write the first six terms of the sequence with $a_1 = 2$, $a_2 = 3$, and for all

    $n \geq 3$, $a_n = 2a_{n-1} - a_{n-2}$.

10. Find the 29th term of the arithmetic sequence $-8, -5, -2, 1, \ldots$

11. In an arithmetic sequence $a_5 = 16$ and $a_{14} = 34$. Find a_{20}.

12. Find the sum of the first 40 terms of the arithmetic sequence having $a_4 = 3.6$
    and $a_{10} = 6$.

13. A certain arithmetic sequence has $a_5 = 27$ and $a_{12} = 6$. Find a_{30} and the sum
    of the first 30 terms.

14. Find the 6th term of the geometric sequence $0.09, 0.3, 1, \ldots$

15. In a certain geometric sequence $a_4 = 128$ and $a_7 = 16$. Find a_{15}.

16. Find the sum of the first 7 terms of the geometric sequence having $r = 2/3$
    and $a_6 = 160/243$.

17. Find the sum $\sum\limits_{i=2}^{5} 2i(3i - 1)$.

18. Find the sum of the infinite geometric sequence $5/3, -1, 3/5, -9/25, \ldots$

19. If the sequence $2 - 2\sqrt{2},\ 2 - \sqrt{2},\ 1 - \sqrt{2},\ \ldots$ is a geometric sequence, find
    r and a_9.

20. Evaluate $\sum\limits_{i=1}^{\infty} \frac{2}{3}(\frac{2}{5})^i$.   21. Find the sum $\sum\limits_{i=1}^{1000} (i + 1)$.

22. Find $P(10, 4)$ and $P(4, 4)$.   23. Find $\binom{8}{6}$ and $\binom{9}{3}$.

24. Find all n such that $\binom{n+2}{n} = 8n - 19$.

25.   Find the number of 3-letter arrangements that can be written using the letters a, b, c, d, e, f, g, and h if (a) letters may be repeated, and (b) no letter can be used a second time.

26.   How many different 4-letter arrangements can be made using the letters of the word subjecting?

27.   How many 5-person committees can be formed from a group of 20 people?

28.   A coin is flipped 4 times. What is the probability that the coin comes up heads on each of the 4 flips?

29.   If 5 cards are drawn from a standard deck of 52 cards, find the probability that all of the cards are face cards, that is, jacks, queens, or kings.

30.   A box contains 9 white buttons, 6 green buttons, and 2 red buttons. Find the probability of randomly selecting (a) a red button, and (b) a white button.

(Answers for this test are on page 366.)

Appendix: Rotation of Axes

Selected Solutions

1. For the equation

$$2x^2 + \sqrt{3}xy + y^2 + x = 5,$$

the xy-term is removed by a rotation
of angle θ, $0 < \theta < 90°$, if

$$\cot 2\theta = \frac{A - C}{B} = \frac{2 - 1}{\sqrt{3}}$$

$$\cot 2\theta = \frac{1}{\sqrt{3}}$$

$$2\theta = 60°,$$

or $\theta = 30°$.

5. For the equation

$$x^2 - 4xy + 5y^2 = 18,$$

the xy-term is removed by a rotation of angle θ, where

$$\cot 2\theta = \frac{A - C}{B} = \frac{1 - 5}{-4}$$

$$\cot 2\theta = 1$$

$$2\theta = 45°,$$

or $\theta = 22.5°$.

9. Given the equation

$$8x^2 - 4xy + 5y^2 = 36,$$

and given that $\sin \theta = \frac{2}{\sqrt{5}}$, we can

find $\cos \theta$ by

$$\sin^2 \theta + \cos^2 \theta = 1$$

$$\frac{4}{5} + \cos^2 \theta = 1$$

$$\cos^2 \theta = \frac{1}{5}$$

$$\cos \theta = \frac{1}{\sqrt{5}}.$$

We then let

$$x = x' \cos \theta - y' \sin \theta = \frac{1}{\sqrt{5}}(x' - 2y'),$$

and

$$y = x' \sin \theta + y' \cos \theta = \frac{1}{\sqrt{5}}(2x' + y').$$

Substitution into the equation
gives

$$\frac{8}{5}(x' - 2y')^2 - \frac{4}{5}(x' - 2y')(2x' + y') +$$

$$\frac{5}{5}(2x' + y')^2 = 36$$

$$8(x'^2 - 4x'y' + 4y'^2) -$$

$$4(2x'^2 - 3x'y' - 2y'^2) +$$

$$5(4x'^2 + 4x'y' + y'^2) = 180$$

$$20x'^2 + 45y'^2 = 180,$$

or $\frac{x'^2}{9} + \frac{y'^2}{4} = 1.$

This is an ellipse with center at
the origin having x'-axis intercepts
at $x' = \pm 3$ and y'-axis intercepts
at $y' = \pm 2$. The angle of rotation
is

$$\theta = \sin^{-1}\left(\frac{2}{\sqrt{5}}\right) \approx 63.43°.$$

See the graph in the answer section
of the text.

13. For the given equation

$$x^2 - 4xy + y^2 = -5, \text{ we have}$$

$$\cot 2\theta = \frac{A - C}{B} = \frac{1 - 1}{-4} = 0,$$

and hence, $2\theta = 90°$, or $\theta = 45°$.
Thus, we substitute

$$x = \frac{\sqrt{2}}{2}(x' - y') \text{ and } y = \frac{\sqrt{2}}{2}(x' + y').$$

This gives

$$\frac{1}{2}(x' - y')^2 - \frac{4}{2}(x' - y')(x' + y') +$$

$$\frac{1}{2}(x' + y')^2 = -5$$

$$(x'^2 - 2x'y' + y'^2) - 4(x'^2 - y'^2) +$$

$$(x'^2 + 2x'y' + y'^2) = -10$$

$$-2x'^2 + 6y'^2 = -10,$$

or $x'^2 - 3y'^2 = 5.$

This is a hyperbola. See the final
graph in the text. Note that the
asymptotes are $x' = \pm \sqrt{3} \, y'$.

17. For the equation

$$3x^2 - 2\sqrt{3}xy + y^2 - 2x - 2\sqrt{3}y = 0,$$

we have

$$\cot 2\theta = \frac{A - C}{B} = \frac{3 - 1}{-2\sqrt{3}} = \frac{-1}{\sqrt{3}},$$

or $\tan 2\theta = -\sqrt{3}$. This implies that
$2\theta = 120°$, or $\theta = 60°$. Hence,

$\cos \theta = \frac{1}{2}$ and $\sin \theta = \frac{\sqrt{3}}{2}$.   The substitution is

$x = \frac{1}{2}(x' - \sqrt{3}y')$,

$y = \frac{1}{2}(\sqrt{3}x' + y')$.

The equation becomes

$\frac{3}{4}(x' - \sqrt{3}y')^2 - \frac{2\sqrt{3}}{4}(x' - \sqrt{3}y') \cdot$

$(\sqrt{3}x' + y') + \frac{1}{4}(\sqrt{3}x' + y')^2 -$

$(x' - \sqrt{3}y') - \sqrt{3}(\sqrt{3}x' + y') = 0$

$3(x'^2 - 2\sqrt{3}x'y' + 3y'^2) -$

$2\sqrt{3}(\sqrt{3}x'^2 - 2x'y' - \sqrt{3}y'^2) +$

$(3x'^2 + 2\sqrt{3}x'y' + y'^2) -$

$4x' + 4\sqrt{3}y' - 12x' - 4\sqrt{3}y' = 0$

$(3 - 6 + 3)x'^2 + (9 + 6 + 1)y'^2 -$
$\qquad 16x' = 0$

$16y'^2 - 16x' = 0$

or $y'^2 = x'$.

See the final graph in the answer section of the text.

21.   For the equation

$4x^2 + 4xy + y^2 - 24x + 38y - 19 = 0$,

we have

$\cot 2\theta = \frac{4 - 1}{4} = \frac{3}{4}$.

Hence, we must use the formulas

$\sin \theta = \sqrt{\frac{1 - \cos 2\theta}{2}} = \sqrt{\frac{1 - \frac{3}{5}}{2}}$

$\qquad = \frac{1}{\sqrt{5}}$

and $\cos \theta = \sqrt{\frac{1 + \frac{3}{5}}{2}} = \frac{2}{\sqrt{5}}$.

Then we use the substitution

$x = \frac{1}{\sqrt{5}}(2x' - y')$ and $y = \frac{1}{\sqrt{5}}(x' + 2y')$

to arrive at

$\frac{4}{5}(2x' - y')^2 + \frac{4}{5}(2x' - y') \cdot$

$(x' + 2y') + \frac{1}{5}(x' + 2y')^2 -$

$\qquad \frac{24}{\sqrt{5}}(2x' - y') + \frac{38}{\sqrt{5}}(x' + 2y') = 19$

$4(4x'^2 - 4x'y' + y'^2) +$

$4(2x'^2 + 3x'y' - 2y'^2) +$

$(x'^2 + 4x'y' + 4y'^2) -$

$48\sqrt{5}x' + 24\sqrt{5}y' +$

$38\sqrt{5}x' + 76\sqrt{5}y' = 95$

$25x'^2 + 0 \cdot y'^2 - 10\sqrt{5}x' + 100y' = 95$

$5x'^2 - 2\sqrt{5}x' = 19 - 20y'$

$x'^2 - \frac{2}{\sqrt{5}}x' + \frac{1}{5} = 4 - 4y'$, or

$(x' - \frac{1}{\sqrt{5}})^2 = -4(y' - 1)$.

This is a parabola in the x'y'-plane with the vertex translated to the point $(x', y') = (\frac{1}{\sqrt{5}}, 1)$.   See the graph in the answer section of the text.

ANSWERS TO CHAPTER TESTS

CHAPTER 1   TEST ANSWERS

1. (a) 1 (b) 13   2. $2x^2 + x - 8$ 3. $3x^3 - 7x^2 - 27x - 14$ 4. $8x^3 - 27$

5. $25a^3$ 6. (a) $(2x - 3)(x + 4)$ (b) $(5x - 6)(3x + 7)$ 7. $(9x^2 + 4)(3x + 2) \cdot$

$(3x - 2)$ 8. $(3x + 2y)(9x^2 - 6xy + 4y^2)$ 9. $(x + 2)/(x - 3)$ 10. $7/(15a)$

11. $a^2 + b^2$ 12. $2/[(x + h + 2)(x + 2)]$ 13. $y - x$ 14. $a^{20}/256$ 15. -5

16. $4x^2 - 4xy + y^2 - 6ay + 12ax + 9a^2$ 17. $2tr^2/3$ 18. $5\sqrt{3}/12$ 19. $1/(9a^6)$

20. $4(2 - \sqrt{3})$ or $8 - 4\sqrt{3}$ 21. $1/[\sqrt{x + h} + \sqrt{x}]$ 22. $15x^{29/12}$

23. $(3x + 4)/(x + 2)^{1/2}$ 24. If $x > 0$, then $\sqrt{x}$ is defined, and we have

$$\sqrt{1 + (\tfrac{1}{2}x^{1/2} - \tfrac{1}{2}x^{-1/2})^2} = \sqrt{1 + \tfrac{1}{4}x - \tfrac{2}{4}x^{1/2}x^{-1/2} + \tfrac{1}{4}x^{-1}} = \sqrt{1 + \tfrac{1}{4}x - \tfrac{1}{2} + \tfrac{1}{4x}}$$

$$= \sqrt{\tfrac{1}{4}x + \tfrac{1}{2} + \tfrac{1}{4x}} = \sqrt{\frac{x^2 + 2x + 1}{4x}} = \sqrt{\frac{(x + 1)^2}{4x}} = \frac{|x + 1|}{2\sqrt{x}} = \frac{x + 1}{2\sqrt{x}}$$

since $x > 0$ implies $x + 1 > 0$, so that $|x + 1| = x + 1$.

25. $23 - 14i$ 26. $2 - 3i$ 27. $-46 - 9i$ 28. $1/2 - 5i/2$

29. By definition, $\sqrt{a} = b$ if and only if $a = b^2$. We have

$$(2\sqrt{2} + \sqrt{7})^2 = (2\sqrt{2})^2 + 2(2\sqrt{2})(\sqrt{7}) + (\sqrt{7})^2 = 8 + 4\sqrt{14} + 7 = 15 + 4\sqrt{14}.$$

According to the definition of a square root of a positive number, we have

$$\sqrt{15 + 4\sqrt{14}} = 2\sqrt{2} + \sqrt{7}.$$

30. To show that $2 + 3i$ is a square root of $-5 + 12i$, we show that $(2 + 3i)^2$

$= -5 + 12i$. Work as follows.

$$(2 + 3i)^2 = 4 + 12i + 9i^2 = 4 + 12i + 9(-1) = 4 + 12i - 9 = -5 + 12i$$

Thus, $2 + 3i$ is a square root of $-5 + 12i$. Also,

$$(-2 - 3i)^2 = 4 + 12i + 9i^2 = 4 + 12i - 9 = -5 + 12i.$$

This implies that $-2 - 3i$ is also a square root of $-5 + 12i$.

CHAPTER 2   TEST ANSWERS

1. $\{20\}$ 2. $\{-3/2\}$ 3. $\{7\}$ 4. $y = 6/(4x - 7)$ 5. $r = tx/(x - t)$

6. 370 adult tickets were sold and 130 child tickets   7. 8 liters of acid

8. (a) $\{(-3 \pm 2\sqrt{6})/2\}$ (b) $\{-2 \pm \sqrt[4]{2}\}$ 9. $\{2/3, 3/2\}$ 10. $\{(-3 \pm \sqrt{89})/8\}$

11. $\{(2 \pm i\sqrt{14})/2\}$ 12. $\{-2/3, -1/4\}$ 13. $\{4\}$ 14. $\{4, 12\}$ 15. $\{6\}$

16. $\{0, 9\}$ 17. $k = \pm 4$ 18. 11 feet by 33 feet   19. $(-\infty, 2]$

20. $(-\infty, -2] \cup [3, +\infty)$ 21. $(-9/2, 3/2]$ 22. $(-\infty, -2] \cup (-1/2, 2]$

23. $(-\infty, -3] \cup (1/2, +\infty)$ 24. $(-2, 1) \cup [7, +\infty)$ 25. $\{-1/3, 3\}$

26. $\{-4/5, 0\}$ 27. $(-\infty, -2) \cup (5, +\ )$ 28. $(-1/6, +\infty)$ 29. k is any number

in $(-\infty, -2] \cup [2, +\infty)$ 30. $(2/3, 10)$

CHAPTER 3   TEST ANSWERS

1.

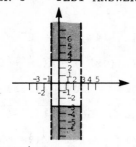

2. (a) $\sqrt{136}$ or $2\sqrt{34}$

   (b) (1, -2)

5. Not a function

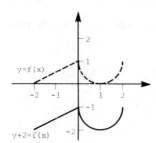

3. Not the vertices of a
   right triangle.

4. x = 6 or x = -2

6. Function

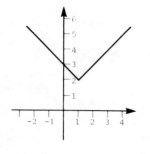

7. $(x + 3)^2 + (y - 4)^2 = 16$

8. The center is the point (-2, 4) and the radius is 3.

9. The graph is symmetric only to the y-axis.

10. The graph of y = |x - 1| + 2 has the same "vee"

shape as y = |x|, but is shifted one unit to the right

because of the x - 1, and is shifted 2 units upward.

See the graph at the left.

10. (graph)

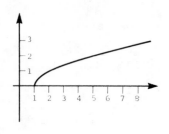

11. [1/2, +∞)   12. (-∞, -3) ∪ [2, +∞)

13. Domain: (-∞, +∞); range: (-∞, 4]   14. -5/[2(x - 2)]

15.

16. Odd function

17. (a) 10   (b) 50/3

18. (-∞, -1) ∪ (-1, 1) ∪

(1, 4]   19. (a) -2/3

(b) -2/5   20. $2x^2 + 2x + 1$

21. $(2x^2 + 5)/(x^2 + 1)$

22. The graph is increasing on the interval (-∞, 0] and decreasing on the interval
[0, +∞).   23. A and B are functions, while the graph shown in C is not a function.

24. Only the graph in Figure B is that of a one-to-one function.

25. Consider the function $y = f(x) = 2x^3 + 1$. If $x_1 \neq x_2$, then it is true that
$x_1^3 \neq x_2^3$, and hence $2x_1^3 + 1 \neq 2x_2^3 + 1$. Thus, $x_1 \neq x_2$ implies that $f(x_1) \neq f(x_2)$.
For this reason, the function is one-to-one.   26. $f^{-1}(x) = (x + 6)/3$

27. $f^{-1}(x) = (x + 3)/(2x)$; domain: (-∞, 0) ∪ (0, +∞)   28. $x = kab^2/\sqrt{c}$, where k

is constant   29. 16/75   30. 800/9, or approximately 89 pounds

CHAPTER 4   TEST ANSWERS

1. 7x + 3y = 27   2. -3/4

3.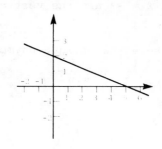

4. 3x - 4y = -5   5. 2x + y = 8   6. 3x + y = 5.

9. The vertex is (5, 2) and the axis is x = 5

11. the function is decreasing on (-∞, 1/2] and increasing on [1/2, +∞).   12. 13 and 13

13. 9/4 and 9/8   14. A hyperbola; asymptotes y = (±5/2)x; e = √29/2

7.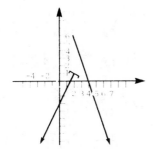

8.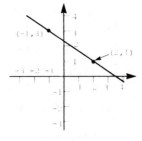

10. Vertex (1, 5); axis x = 1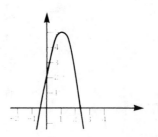

15. Parabola; vertex (1, 2), e = 1   16. Ellipse, major axis is the x-axis with intercepts x = ±3; minor axis is the y-axis; e = √3/3   17. Ellipse; major axis the line x = 3; minor axis the line y = -5; e = √3/2   18. Hyperbola; asymptotes y + 1 = (±1/3)x; e = √10   19. Parabola, vertex (0, 6)   20. y = (±3/4)x

21.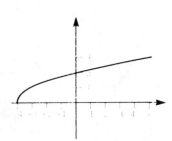

22.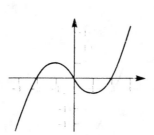

23. 2x + y = -1

24.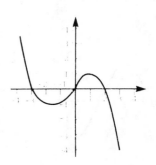

25.

26.

27.

28. y = 3/2 is a horizontal asymptote;   30.
x = 2 and x = -2 are the vertical
asymptotes

29. $y = \frac{2}{3}x$ is the oblique asymptote

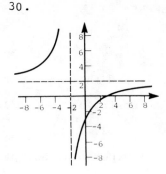

CHAPTER 5   TEST ANSWERS

1.

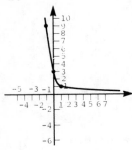

2. {1/2}   3. a = 4   4. (a) $5^{-3} = 1/125$

(b) $\log_2 8 = 3$ 5. $3 \cdot \log_4 x + 2 \cdot \log_4 y + \frac{2}{5} \log_4 n -$
$\frac{3}{5} \log_4 p$ 6. {4/3}   7. {2, 3}   8. 8   9. -1/4

10. 10/3   11. ln $[(2x + 1)^{2/3}(2y)^{4/3}/(x^{1/3})]$

12. 1.8572   13. -.4055   14. {1}   15. {3, 7}

16. $2388 (rounded to the nearest dollar)   17. 3.15

18. 1.43   19. $t = (\ln A_0 - \ln A)/k$

20. {1 + (log 7)/(log 12)} or about {1.783}   21. {(log 5)/(log 3) - 4} or about
{-2.54}   22. Ø   23. Solving 4 (log x) = (log x)^3, the solution set is
$\{\frac{1}{100}, 100, 1\}$.   24. x = ln[2y/(1 - 2y)]   25. about 10.24 years

26. $y = e^{(t \ln 3)/7} = e^{(t/7)\ln 3} = e^{(\ln 3)(t/7)} = 3^{t/7}$ 27. 2870   28. 2.17

CHAPTER 6   TEST ANSWERS

1. ($\sqrt{2}/2$, $-\sqrt{2}/2$)   2. -1, 0   3. $-\sqrt{2}/2$, $-\sqrt{2}/2$ 4. 3/4, 4/3   5. II or III
6. tan t = $-3\sqrt{10}/20$, cot t = $-2\sqrt{10}/3$, sec t = $-7\sqrt{10}/20$, csc t = 7/3   7. 243°
8. 5π/2   9. 132°   10. 240,000°   11. 2374 miles   12. $-\sqrt{2}/2$, $-\sqrt{2}/2$
13. 15/17, 8/17, 15/8, 8/15, 17/8, 17/15   14. 38°10'   15. 1.3320   16. 7.5958
17. .9111   18. .1322   19. 30°30'   20. 55.4 m
21.   22.   23.

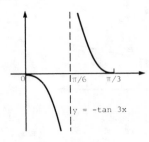

24.

25. $5\pi/6$ 26. π 27. $-83°40'$ 28. $13/12$

29. 0   30. $x = \cos\left(\dfrac{3 + y}{2}\right)$

CHAPTER 7   TEST ANSWERS

1. $-2\sqrt{5}/5$ 2. $\sqrt{55}/8$ 3. $\sin\theta = 2\sqrt{6}/5$, $\tan\theta = 2\sqrt{6}$, $\cot\theta = \sqrt{6}/12$, $\sec\theta = 5$, $\csc\theta = 5\sqrt{6}/12$ 4. $\sin\theta = -\sqrt{17}/17$, $\cos\theta = 4\sqrt{17}/17$, $\cot\theta = -4$, $\sec\theta = \sqrt{17}/4$, $\csc\theta = -\sqrt{17}$ 5. 1   6. $1/(\sin^2\gamma \cos^2\gamma)$ 7. -1 8. $-\cos 2\theta/\sin^4\theta$ or $(\sin^2\theta - \cos^2\theta)/\sin^4\theta$ 9. $\sin s = \pm 1/\sqrt{1 + \cot^2 x}$ 14. $\sin 39°17'$

15. $\tan \pi/4$ 16. $(\sqrt{2} - \sqrt{6})/4$ 17. $(\sqrt{6} - \sqrt{2})/4$ 18. $(\sqrt{2} - \sqrt{6})/4$

19. $56/65$, $16/65$ 20. 0, $240/289$ 21. $-33/65$, $63/16$ 22. 1, $-161/240$

23. $17\sin(x + 118°)$ 24. $5\sin(x + 143°)$ 25. $1/2$ 26. $\sqrt{31 - 8\sqrt{15}}$

27. $(1/2)\sqrt{2 - \sqrt{2}}$ 28. $(-1/2)\sqrt{2 - \sqrt{3}}$ 29. $\sqrt{5}/5$, $2\sqrt{5}/5$, $1/2$, 2, $\sqrt{5}/2$, $\sqrt{5}$

30. $\sqrt{7}/3$, $-\sqrt{2}/3$, $-\sqrt{14}/2$, $-\sqrt{14}/7$, $-3\sqrt{2}/2$, $3\sqrt{7}/7$ 31. $\{\pi/4, 5\pi/4\}$

32. $\{0, \pi, \pi/3, 5\pi/3\}$ 33. $\{\pi/2, 3\pi/2, 2\pi/3, 4\pi/3\}$ 34. $\{\pi/2, 3\pi/2, \pi/4, 7\pi/4, 3\pi/4, 5\pi/4\}$ 35. $\{\pi/2, 3\pi/2, \pi/3, 4\pi/3\}$ 36. $\{\pi, \pi/3, 5\pi/3\}$

37. $\{x \mid x = 36°52' + 360° \cdot n, 143°08' + 360° \cdot n, 199°28' + 360° \cdot n, 340°32' + 360° \cdot n\}$

38. $\{x \mid x = 90° + 360° \cdot n\}$ 39. $\{\pi/6 + 2k\pi, 5\pi/6 + 2k\pi, 3\pi/2 + 2k\pi\}$

40. $\{\pi/2 + 2k\pi\}$

CHAPTER 8   TEST ANSWERS

1. $B = 41°40'$, $a = 88.7$ m, $c = 119$ m   2. $A = 79°50'$, $a = 131$ in, $c = 133$ in

3. 40,600 ft   4. 24,100   5. $B = 37°20'$, $a = 38.6$ ft, $b = 51.3$ ft

6. $a = 49°40'$, $b = 16.1$ cm, $c = 25.8$ cm   7. $78°20'$, $60°20'$, or $101°40'$, $37°00'$

8. $49°20'$, $92°00'$, or $130°40'$, $10°40'$ 9. $B = 53°10'$, $C = 59°30'$, $a = 43.7$ m

10. $A = 5°10'$, $C = 6°40'$, $b = 34.1$ cm   11. $A = 28°30'$, $B = 53°20'$, $C = 98°10'$

12. 10.9 m   13. 42.6 m^2 14. 467 m^2 15. $\langle 12, -25 \rangle$ 16. $\langle -15, 21 \rangle$

17. 13.7, 7.11   18. 39.8, 68.1   19. 2, 330°   20. 12, 315°   21. 5, $-53°10'$

22. 10, 150°   23. 51   24. -8 25. 45°   26. 96°50'   27. 2250 lb

28. 28.5 lb, 55°30' with 47.2 lb force   29. (4, 60°)   30. (2, 315°)

31. $-2 + 2i\sqrt{3}$ 32. $-9i$ 33. $3i$ 34. $5/2 - 5i\sqrt{3}/2$ 35. $-8 - 8i\sqrt{3}$

36. $-500\sqrt{2} - 500i\sqrt{2}$ 37. $1, -1/2 + i\sqrt{3}/2, -1/2 - i\sqrt{3}/2$ 38. $\sqrt[3]{4}$ (cos 20° + i sin 20°)

$\sqrt[3]{4}$ (cos 140° + i sin 140°), $\sqrt[3]{4}$ (cos 260° + i sin 260°)

39.
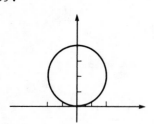

40.
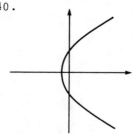

41.
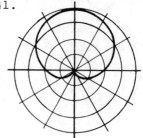

42.
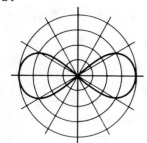

43.
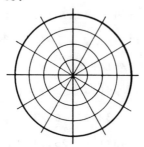

44.
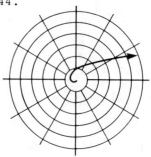

CHAPTER 9   TEST ANSWERS

1. $\{(1, 2)\}$ 2. $\{(3/7, 11/7)\}$ 3. $\{((5 + 3y)/2, y)\}$ 4. $\emptyset$ 5. $\{(10, 3)\}$

6. $\{(2, -1, 1)\}$ 7. $\{((z + 21)/5, (7z + 12)/5, z)\}$ 8. $\{(x, 3x/2, (10 - 9x)/4)\}$

9. 9 and 13   10. \$20,000 at 9%, \$15, 000 at 10% and \$25,000 at 12%

11. $\begin{bmatrix} 3 & 2 & -7 & | & 14 \\ 1 & -3 & 2 & | & 9 \\ 2 & 1 & -3 & | & -2 \end{bmatrix}$ 12. $\{(3, 2)\}$ 13. $\{(1, 1, 2)\}$ 14. Any triple of numbers $(-2z + 26, z + 3, z)$ 15. -69 16. -20

17. -13

18. (a) $\begin{bmatrix} 4 & 3 \\ 1 & 10 \end{bmatrix}$ (b) $\begin{bmatrix} 5 & 2 \\ -11 & 9 \end{bmatrix}$ 19. (a) $\begin{bmatrix} 4 & 5 \\ 5 & 9 \end{bmatrix}$ (b) $\begin{bmatrix} -1 & 5 \\ -5 & 14 \end{bmatrix}$ 20. $\begin{bmatrix} 5 & 5 \\ 7 & 4 \\ 0 & 5 \end{bmatrix}$

21. $\begin{bmatrix} 2/5 & -1/10 \\ 1/5 & -3/10 \end{bmatrix}$ 22. $\begin{bmatrix} 3 & -1/2 & -1/2 \\ -2 & 1 & 0 \\ 2 & -3/2 & 1/2 \end{bmatrix}$ 23. $\{(3, 1)\}$ 24. $\{(2, 3)\}$

25. $\{(2, 3)\}$ 26. $\{(3, 4), (4, 3)\}$

27. $\{(0, 2), (5, -3)\}$ 28. $\{(-2\sqrt{22}/11, 8\sqrt{22}/11), (2\sqrt{22}/11, -8\sqrt{22}/11)\}$ 29. 8 and 14.

30. $9x^2 + 25y^2 = 225$ is an ellipse with x-axis intercepts at ±5 and y-intercepts at ±3. $x^2 + y = 1$ is the parabola $y = -x^2 + 1$ and the parabola has x-intercepts at ±1 and a y-intercept at 1. The solution is the set of points interior to the ellipse and above the parabola.

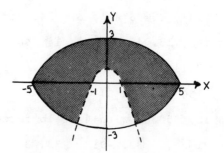

31.

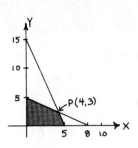

Test A(0, 6), 3(5, 0) and P(4, 3)

Max for 25x + 3y is M = 125;

occurs at B(5, 0)

32.

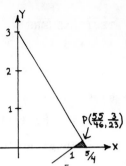

Test A(1, 0), B($\frac{5}{4}$, 0) and P($\frac{3}{23}$, $\frac{55}{46}$)

Max for 80x + 150y is M = $\frac{8730}{46}$;

occurs at P.

CHAPTER 10   TEST ANSWERS

1. $q(x) = x^5 + x^4 + x^3 + x^2 + x + 1$ and $r = -1$ 2. $q(x) = 4x^2 - 2x + 1$ and $r = 4$

3. $q(x) = 3x^2 + 4x + 12$ and $r = 4$ 4. $q(x) = 4x^2 + x - 4$ and $r = 10$

5. $f(2) = 19$ and $f(-3) = -236$ 6. $p(x) = x^3 - 7x^2 + 25x - 39$

7. Given $f(x) = x^3 - 2x^2 - x + 2$, and using synthetic division, we have

$f(x) = (x - 2)(x^2 - 1)$. Hence, $f(x) = (x - 2)(x - 1)(x + 1)$, so that the zeros are 2, 1,

and -1.   8. $k = 22$ 9. $f(x) = 3x^2 - 3x - 6$ 10. -1, ±i   11. 1, 1 - i, 1 + i

12. 1, 2, -2   13. -2, 1   14. 1/2, -3   15. -1/3   16. The only possible

rational zeros of $f(x) = x^2 - 17$ have the form a/b where a is a divisor of 17 and b

is a divisor of 1. Thus, a can be ±1 or ±17 and b can be ±1. Hence, the only possible

rational zeros of $f(x) = x^2 - 17$ are ±1 or ±17. Use synthetic division to show that

none of them are solutions. Thus, $f(x) = x^2 - 17$ has no rational zeros. However,

$f(\sqrt{17}) = (\sqrt{17})^2 - 17 = 17 - 17 = 0$, so that $\sqrt{17}$ is a zero of f. This means $\sqrt{17}$ is

not rational.   17. The only possible rational zeros of $f(x) = x^4 + x^3 - 2x^2 - 3x - 3$

are ±1 or ±3.   Trial and error, with synthetic division, shows that none of these

is a zero.   18. Using synthetic division for $f(x) = x^4 + x^3 - 2x^2 - 3x - 3$ we have

$f(1) = -6$ and $f(2) = 7$. The Intermediate Value Theorem guarantees that f is zero for

some x between 1 and 2.   19. 5   20. One positive zero, either 2 or 0 negative zeros

21. One negative zero, -2   22. 1 and 2   23. 1.7   24. The possible rational

zeros for $f(x) = x^4 + 5x^2 + 4$ would be ±1, ±2, and ±4. By synthetic division or

substitution we find that $f(\pm1) = 10$, $f(\pm2) = 40$, and $f(\pm4) = 340$. Hence, there are

no rational zeros of f. Factor to get $f(x) = (x^2 + 4)(x^2 + 1)$. Setting $x^2 + 4 = 0$

gives $x = \pm2i$, with $x^2 + 1 = 0$ giving $x = \pm i$. These zeros are all imaginary, and

there are no real zeros.   25. $f(x) = -\frac{4}{x} + \frac{3}{x - 1} + \frac{1}{x + 1}$

CHAPTER 11   TEST ANSWERS

1. Let S_n: $1 + 3 + 5 + \ldots + (2n - 1) = n^2$ be the statement we wish to prove. We must show that (i) S_1 is true, and (ii) if S_k is true for some natural number k, then S_{k+1} is also true. S_1 is true since the left hand side is just one term, 1. Substituting n = 1 in the right hand side gives 1^2, and $1^2 = 1$. Assume the statement is true for some natural number k. Thus, S_k is true, so that $1 + 3 + 5 + \ldots + (2k - 1) = k^2$. Consider the effect of adding the next odd number to the sum $1 + 3 + 5 + \ldots + (2k - 1)$. The next number would be 2k + 1. Since S_k is true, we have $[1 + 3 + 5 + \ldots + (2k - 1)] + (2k + 1) = k^2 + (2k+1)$, or $1 + 3 + 5 + \ldots + (2k - 1) + (2k + 1) = k^2 + 2k + 1 = (k + 1)^2$. This is exactly the statement of S_{k+1}. We have thus proved that if S_k is true, then S_{k+1} is also true. Hence, S_n is true for all natural numbers n.

2. Let S_n: $3 + 3^2 + 3^3 + \ldots + 3^n = \frac{3}{2}(3^n - 1)$ be the statement we wish to prove. We must show that (i) S_1 is true and (ii) whenever S_k is true, then S_{k+1} is true. For n = 1 the left hand side is the sum of one term only, the term 3. Substituting n = 1 on the right hand side gives $\frac{3}{2}(3^1 - 1) = \frac{3}{2}(2) = 3$. Hence S_1 is true. Assume now that the statement is true for some natural number k, or S_k: $3 + 3^2 + 3^3 + \ldots + 3^k = \frac{3}{2}(3^k - 1)$ is true. Then consider the sum of the first k + 1 terms. We have

$$
\begin{aligned}
3 + 3^2 + 3^3 + \ldots + 3^{k+1} &= 3 + 3^2 + 3^3 + \ldots + 3^k + 3^{k+1} \\
&= (3 + 3^2 + 3^3 + \ldots + 3^k) + 3^{k+1} \\
&= \frac{3}{2}(3^k - 1) + 3^{k+1} \quad \text{since } S_k \text{ is true} \\
&= \frac{3}{2} \cdot 3^k - \frac{3}{2} + 3^{k+1} \\
&= \frac{3}{2} \cdot 3^k - \frac{3}{2} + 3 \cdot 3^k \\
&= 3^k(\frac{3}{2} + 3) - \frac{3}{2} \\
&= 3^k(\frac{9}{2}) - \frac{3}{2} \\
&= 3^k[3(\frac{3}{2})] - \frac{3}{2} \\
&= 3^{k+1}(\frac{3}{2}) - \frac{3}{2} \\
&= \frac{3}{2}(3^{k+1} - 1).
\end{aligned}
$$

Thus, we have shown that $3 + 3^2 + 3^3 + \ldots + 3^{k+1} = \frac{3}{2}(3^{k+1} - 1)$ the statement S_{k+1}. We have proved that if S_k is true, then S_{k+1} is true. Hence, S_n is true for all natural numbers n.

3. Let S_n: $3^{3n} - 1$ is divisible by 13, be the statement we wish to prove. We use the definition that b is divisible by a, a and b natural numbers, if and only if

there is some natural number M such that b = Ma. We must show (i) S_1 is true, and
(ii) whenever S_k is true, then S_{k+1} is true. When n = 1, $3^{3n} - 1 = 3^3 - 1 = 27 - 1$
= 26 = 2(13). Hence, S_1 is true. Assume the statement is true for some natural
number k. Then $3^{3k} - 1$ is divisible by 13, which implies that there is some natural
number, say M_k, such that $3^{3k} - 1 = 13(M_k)$. Consider $3^{3(k+1)} - 1$.

$$3^{3(k+1)} - 1 = 3^{3k+3} - 1 = 3^3 \cdot 3^{3k} - 1.$$

However, since $3^{3k} - 1 = 13(M_k)$, we have $3^{3k} = 1 + 13(M_k)$. Substituting this into
the previous equation gives

$$3^{3(k+1)} - 1 = 3^3 \cdot 3^{3k} - 1$$
$$= 3^3[1 + 13(M_k)] - 1 \qquad \text{since } S_k \text{ is true}$$
$$= 27[1 + 13(M_k)] - 1$$
$$= 27 + 13(27M_k) - 1$$
$$= 26 + 13(27M_k)$$
$$= 13[2 + 27M_k].$$

Since M_k is a natural number, $2 + 27M_k$ is a natural number, call it M_{k+1}. Hence,
there is a natural number M_{k+1} such that $3^{3(k+1)} - 1 = 13(M_{k+1})$, so that $3^{3(k+1)}$
is divisible by 13. We have now proved that if S_k is true, then S_{k+1} is true.
Hence, S_n is true for all natural numbers n.

4. $16x^4 - 32x^3y + 24x^2y^2 - 8xy^3 + y^4$ 5. $27/x^3 + 54 + 36x^3 + \varepsilon x^6$

6. $1/a^{12} - 6\sqrt{b}/a^{11} + 33b/(2a^{10})$ 7. $8064x^{10}y^5$ 8. 1, 5/4, 5/3, 17/8, 13/5

9. 2, 3, 4, 5, 6, 7   10. 76   11. 46   12. 408   13. $a_{30} = -48$; $S_{30} = -135$

14. 1000/27   15. 1/16   16. $S_7 = 3325/243$ 17. 268   18. 25/24

19. $r = -\sqrt{2}/2$; $a_9 = (1 - \sqrt{2})/8$ 20. 4/9   21. 501,500   22. P(10, 4) = 5040

P(4, 4) = 24   23. $\binom{8}{6} = 28$; $\binom{9}{3} = 84$ 24. n = 5 or n = 8

25. (a) $8 \cdot 8 \cdot 8 = 512$ (b) $8 \cdot 7 \cdot 6 = 336$ 26. 5040   27. 15,504   28. 1/16

29. 33/108,290   30. (a) 2/17   (b) 9/17